2ND EDITION CLIMATE VULNERABILITY MONITOR

A GUIDE TO THE COLD CALCULUS OF A HOT PLANET

DARA and the Climate Vulnerable Forum

Climate Vulnerability Monitor 2nd Edition.
A Guide to the Cold Calculus of a Hot Planet

This book was set in Heroic Condensed, Franklin Gothic and Uni Sans

Graphic Design: wearebold.es

Icons inspired in The Noun Project collection
Photographs: Thinkstock/Getty Images

Includes bibliographical references

ISBN: 978-84-616-0567-5

(paper: offset 120 gr., interior; couché semimate 300 gr., cover)

LD: M-31813-2012

First published 2012

Printed and bound in Spain by Estudios Gráficos Europeos, S.A.

HEADQUARTERS

Felipe IV, 9 - 3 Izquierda
28014 Madrid - Spain
Phone: +34 91 531 03 72
Fax: +34 91 522 0039
cvm@daraint.org
www.daraint.org

GENEVA OFFICE

International Environment House 2/MIE2
7-9 Chemin de Balexert
Châtelaine CH-1219 Geneva - Switzerland
Phone: +41 22 749 40 30
Fax: +41 22 797 40 31

DEDICATED TO THE INNOCENT VICTIMS OF CLIMATE CHANGE

" **A GREAT DEAL** has been written on the influence of the absorption of the atmosphere upon the climate.. Another side of the question that has long attracted the attention of physicists, is this: Is the mean temperature of the ground in any way influenced by the presence of heat-absorbing gases in the atmosphere? (..) If the quantity of carbonic acid [CO_2] decreases from 1 to 0.67, the fall of temperature is nearly the same as the increase in temperature if this quantity augments to 1.5. And to get a new increase of this order of magnitude (3-4°C), it will be necessary to alter the quantity of carbonic acid till it reaches a value nearly midway between 2 and 2.5."

SVANTE AUGUST ARRHENIUS
April 1896
The London, Edinburgh, and Dublin Philosophical Magazine and Journal of Science

" **FEW OF THOSE** familiar with the natural heat exchanges of the atmosphere, which go into the making of our climates and weather, would be prepared to admit that the activities of man could have any influence upon phenomena of so vast a scale.. I hope to show that such influence is not only possible, but it is actually occurring at the present time."

GUY STEWART CALLENDAR
April 1938
Quarterly Journal of the Royal Meteorological Society

" **IF AT THE END** of this century, measurements show that the carbon dioxide content of the atmosphere has risen appreciably and at the same time the temperature has continued to rise throughout the world, it will be firmly established that carbon dioxide is an important factor in causing climatic change."

GILBERT NORMAN PLASS
May 1956
American Journal of Physics

"**THE EARTH'S CLIMATE** system has demonstrably changed on both global and regional scales since the pre-industrial era.. The atmospheric concentrations of key anthropogenic greenhouse gases (i.e., carbon dioxide (CO_2)..) reached their highest recorded levels in the 1990s."

THE INTERGOVERNMENTAL PANEL ON CLIMATE CHANGE
September 2001

"**A HUNDRED YEARS** from now, looking back, the only question that will appear important about the historical moment in which we now live is the question of whether or not we did anything to arrest climate change."

THE ECONOMIST
December 2011

COLLABORATORS

ADVISORY PANEL

MARY CHINERY-HESSE, Member of the Panel of the Wise of the African Union; Chief Advisor to the Former President of Ghana; Former Deputy Director-General of the International Labour Organization (ILO)

HELEN CLARK, Administrator, United Nations Development Programme (UNDP)

JOSÉ MARÍA FIGUERES, Former President of Costa Rica; Chairman of the Carbon War Room

ROBERT GLASSER, Secretary General, CARE International, Geneva

SALEEMUL HUQ, Director, International Institute for Environment and Development (IIED), Independent University, Dhaka

YOLANDA KAKABADSE, International President, WWF

ASHOK KHOSLA, President, International Union for Conservation of Nature (IUCN); Chairman of Development Alternatives, Co-Chair of the UN Resources Panel

RICARDO LAGOS, Former President of Chile; Former President of the Club of Madrid

LOREN LEGARDA, Senator of the Philippines; UN International Strategy for Disaster Reduction (ISDR) Regional Champion for Disaster Risk Reduction and Climate Change Adaptation for Asia and the Pacific

MICHAEL MARMOT, Director, International Institute for Society and Health, University College, London

SIMON MAXWELL, Executive Chair, Climate and Development Knowledge Network (CDKN)

DAVID NABARRO, Special Representative of the UN Secretary-General for Food Security and Nutrition

ATIQ RAHMAN, Executive Director, Bangladesh Centre for Advanced Studies (BCAS), Dhaka

TERESA RIBERA, Former Secretary of State for Climate Change of Spain

JOHAN ROCKSTRÖM, Executive Director, Stockholm Environment Institute (SEI) and Stockholm Resilience Centre

JEFFREY SACHS, Director, The Earth Institute, Columbia University, New York

HANS JOACHIM SCHELLNHUBER, Founding Director of the Potsdam Institute for Climate Impact Research (PIK)

JAVIER SOLANA, President, ESADE Center for Global Economy and Politics; Distinguished Senior Fellow, Brookings Institution; Chairman, Aspen Institute España

ANDREW STEER, President, World Resources Institute, Washington, D.C.

MARGARETA WAHLSTRÖM, United Nations Assistant Secretary-General for Disaster Risk Reduction

MICHAEL ZAMMIT CUTAJAR, Former Executive Secretary, United Nations Framework Convention on Climate Change (UNFCCC)

PEER REVIEW COMMITTEE

YASEMIN AYSAN, Former Under Secretary General, International Federation of Red Cross and Red Crescent Societies (IFRC)

SURUCHI BHADWAL, Associate Director, Earth Sciences and Climate Change Division, The Energy and Resources Institute (TERI), New Delhi

DIARMID CAMPBELL-LENDRUM, Senior Scientist, Public Health and Environment, World Health Organization (WHO)

MANUEL CARBALLO, Executive Director, International Centre for Migration, Health and Development (ICMHD), Geneva

IAN CHRISTOPLOS, Senior Project Researcher, Danish Institute for International Studies (DIIS), Copenhagen

JOSHUA COOPER, Director, Hawaii Institute for Human Rights

MARIANE DIOP KANE, Head of Forecasting, Agence Nationale de la Météorologie du Sénégal (ANAMS)

SEAN DOOLAN, Climate Change & Environmental Governance Advisor, United Kingdom Department for International Development (DfID), Ghana

PIERRE ENCONTRE, Chief, Special Programmes, Division for Africa, Least Developed Countries and Special Programmes, UN Conference on Trade and Investment (UNCTAD)

HANS-MARTIN FÜSSEL, Project Manager for Climate Impacts, Vulnerability, and Adaptation at the European Environment Agency (EEA)

TIM GORE, International Policy Advisor for Climate Change, Oxfam International Advocacy Office, New York

ANNE HAMMILL, Senior Researcher, Climate Change and Energy, International Institute for Sustainable Development (IISD), Geneva

RANDOLPH KENT, Director, Humanitarian Futures Programme, King's College, London

TORD KJELLSTROM, Senior Professor, Department of Public Health and Clinical Medicine, Umea University; Visiting Fellow, Honorary Professor, Australia National University, Canberra, and University College, London

ISABEL KREISLER, Climate Policy Specialist, Environment and Energy Group, Bureau for Development Policy, Bureau for Development Policy, United Nations Development Programme (UNDP)

JUERGEN KROPP, Head, North-South Research Group, Potsdam Institute for Climate Impact Research (PIK)

ALLAN LAVELL, Coordinator, Programme for Disaster Risk Management, Secretary General's Office, Latin America Social Science Faculty (FLASCO), San José

MARC LEVY, Deputy Director, Center for International Earth Science Information Network (CIESIN), Earth Institute at Columbia University, New York

FILIPE LÚCIO, Head of the Global Framework for Climate Services, World Meteorological (WMO)

URS LUTERBACHER, Chairman, Environmental Studies Unit, Graduate Institute of International and Development Studies, Geneva

ANDREW MASKREY, Coordinator, Global Assessment Report (GAR), UN International Strategy for Disaster Reduction (UNISDR)

BENITO MÜLLER, Director Energy and Environment, Oxford Institute for Energy Studies

MICHELE DE NEVERS, Visiting Senior Associate, Center for Global Development, Washington, D.C.

MARTIN PARRY, Fellow, Grantham Institute for Climate Change, Imperial College, London

JAMES ROOP, Climate Change Advisor for Asia and Pacific, Climate Change Branch, AusAID

BEN RAMALINGAM, Visiting Fellow, Institute of Development Studies (IDS) and Research Associate, Overseas Development Institute (ODI), London

CARLO SCARAMELLA, Coordinator, Office for Climate Change, Environment and Disaster Risk Reduction, UN World Food Programme (WFP)

MATTHIAS SCHMALE, Under Secretary General, National Society and Knowledge Development, International Federation of Red Cross and Red Crescent Societies (IFRC)

HANSJOERG STROHMEYER, Chief, Policy Development and Studies Branch, UN Office for the Coordination of Humanitarian Affairs (OCHA)

FARHANA YAMIN, Research Fellow, Institute of Development Studies, Brighton

The Advisory Panel and the Peer Review Committee members serve in their personal capacity, providing input to the Climate Vulnerability Initiative that informs the development of the Climate Vulnerability Monitor. DARA is solely responsible for the final content of this report.

STEERING GROUP

CO-CHAIRS

ROSS MOUNTAIN, Director General, DARA

SUFIUR RAHMAN, Director General, Economic Affairs, Ministry of Foreign Affairs, Bangladesh

MEMBERS

JAVIER DÍAZ CARMONA, Ambassador for Climate Change and Global Environmental Affairs, Costa Rica

SALAHUDDIN NOMAN CHOWDHURY, Director, Economic Affairs, Ministry of Foreign Affairs, Bangladesh

MATTHEW MCKINNON, Head of Climate Vulnerability Initiative, DARA

EDITORIAL AND RESEARCH TEAM

EDITOR
Matthew McKinnon

PROJECT COORDINATOR
Lucía Fernández Suárez

PRINCIPAL PROJECT ADVISOR
Søren Peter Andreasen

LEAD TECHNICAL RESEARCHERS
Beatriz Asensio (Coordination)
Cristian Conteduca (Modeling)
Dominik Hülse (Quantitative)

TECHNICAL ADVISOR
Peter Utzon Berg

SENIOR AID ADVISOR
Magda Ninaber van Eyben

FIELD STUDIES COORDINATOR
Belén Paley

COUNTRY STUDY RESEARCHERS
Nguyen Huong Tra
Nguyen Quang Thanh
Nguyen Thuy Hang
Emmanuel Tachie-Obeng
Tran Chung Chau

RESEARCH ASSISTANTS
Daniel Barnes (Coordination)
Johanna Barth
Rachel Clancy
Ana Chamberlain
Bosco Lliso
Abby Moran
Rachad Nassar
Jenena Oliver
Ana Rodríguez Seco
Emily Schuckert

PUBLICATION MANAGER
Rebecca B. Moy

COMMUNICATIONS AND VISUALS
Fiona Guy (Advisor)
Christina Samson
Nacho Wilhelmi
Begoña Yagüe

GRAPHIC DESIGNERS
Mariano Sarmiento (Lead)
María Lasa
Ruth Otero
Marta San Marín

COPYEDITING
Morwenna Marshall
Tim Morris

PREFACE

THIS REPORT CHALLENGES A CONVENTIONAL VIEW: THAT GLOBAL ACTION ON CLIMATE CHANGE IS A COST TO SOCIETY. INSTEAD, IT ENLIGHTENS OUR UNDERSTANDING OF HOW TACKLING CLIMATE CHANGE THROUGH COORDINATED EFFORTS BETWEEN NATIONS WOULD ACTUALLY PRODUCE MUCH-NEEDED BENEFITS FOR ALL.

Climate change is already with us. It kills. It steals livelihoods. And it takes the most from those who have the least. But the costs are largely hidden from our understanding. Inaction on climate change actually takes from us all. Only together can we plot a different course: one of greater prosperity and well-being.

Technical barriers no longer hold back our transition to a low-carbon world, and technological solutions exist to manage risks. We struggle instead with other barriers.

There are political barriers: while some countries are committed to change and making progress, there is still a lack of conviction among the governments of too many industrialized and developing nations.

Social and cultural barriers also exist: lack of understanding causes popular indifference or even hostility to sensible change.

And financial barriers mean that only a fraction of the resources needed for low-carbon development and to support worst-hit communities are being made available.

To tackle all these barriers, 20 countries highly vulnerable to climate change came together to form the Climate Vulnerable Forum.

Our countries favour action on climate change. We are frustrated with the inadequacy of the global response and a world economy that continues to price carbon irresponsibly. We bear witness to the extremes at the climate frontlines of today. Despite having contributed the least to climate change, we are forced, almost unaided, to take costly measures to protect our people and our economies. We know the world is rapidly becoming more not less vulnerable, and that all our fates are tied.

"Many Forum governments are already embracing the call to action: Bangladesh has committed never to exceed the average per capita emissions of the developing countries. Costa Rica aims to be carbon neutral by 2021. But there are limits to what individual countries can achieve."

Farmers face more hot days as they set to work. Families are sleeping outside in mosquito-infested areas because their homes are unbearable in the heat of the night. Roads and buildings on permanently frozen land in the cooler regions are being damaged as melting sets in. Rivers are drying up, causing transport shocks, while unprecedented floods are devastating other areas. Salt from rising seas harms fertile land and fresh water supplies. Coastlines erode. Land is submerged. Populations fail to make a living. People move.

Pollution also kills. It acidifies lakes and oceans, poisons plants and animal life, corrodes infrastructure and contaminates the air we breathe.

We pay for each of these damages in lives, suffering and dollars. Yet the world has struggled to see how all these concerns are interlinked. That is why this report has sought to tackle our knowledge barriers.

With a better understanding of the full array of issues and the causes behind them, nobody should remain indifferent or inactive.

The Climate Vulnerable Forum commissioned this second Climate Vulnerability Monitor at its Ministerial Meeting at Dhaka in November 2011. The report was again mandated to DARA for independent development and was reviewed by an external Advisory Panel and Peer Review Committee comprised of international authorities on this subject.

Against a struggling world economy, its main findings offer sobering news: climate change is already lowering economic output globally and will increasingly hold back growth – unless strong action is urgently taken. Its pages seek to move us to act by highlighting the human plight of an increasingly hotter and more polluted planet. Severe impacts on livelihoods, health and the world's poorest groups speak of fundamental injustices that simply cannot go unaddressed.

The report relies on the incredible wealth of some of the most recently published research and scientific knowledge, assimilating literally hundreds of studies and bodies of data into a common framework that makes its collective meaning clear. More research is plainly needed and will continuously enrich our understanding, but improving knowledge should not be a premise to refrain from acting when so much is at stake.

In the past, humanity has prevailed against recognized threats to our security and prosperity. Today there are two wars we must win: the continued fight against poverty, and the new challenge of climate change. Both can be tackled simultaneously with the same policy framework that would shift our development path to a low-carbon footing. Taking action, we can lessen the social, economic and environmental damages of a carbon-intensive economy.

We would create jobs, investment opportunities, new possibilities for international cooperation and technological deployment to the benefit of all.

Despite capacity constraints, many Forum governments are already embracing the call to action: Bangladesh has committed never to exceed the average per capita emissions of the developing countries. Costa Rica aims to be carbon neutral by 2021. But there are limits to what individual countries can achieve.

Solving the climate challenge requires broadest international cooperation. And yet countries still argue economic barriers to change. This report argues instead that strong measures on climate change would reap the most monetary benefits for society.

Indeed, building global partnerships where all nations can fully participate in the transition to a low-carbon economy will lessen costs and heighten the social, environmental and economic dividends for all. Just as supporting vulnerable communities will ultimately improve the well-being of society as a whole.

Divided, we face declining prosperity and immense suffering. Together, we have the chance to strengthen global welfare and safeguard the fate of the nations.

SHEIKH HASINA
Prime Minister of Bangladesh
JOSÉ MARÍA FIGUERES
Trustee of DARA, Former President of Costa Rica

ACKNOWLEDGEMENTS

This report was a project that took on a life - almost - of its own. Unrivalled is a word that comes to mind when describing the energy, interest and dedication of our core partners: donors, advisors, researchers, reviewers, the team within DARA, experts at Commons Consultants, or the celebrated graphic designers - wearebold.es - who made the "measles" you generally love (and less often disprove of) as readers.

We set out to "improve" the 2010 report and ended up with something that struggles to bear a passing resemblance to what we thought was a useful contribution back in 2010. Somehow four maps turned into fifty-nine, a methodology note of twenty-five pages became a tome of well over one hundred that we ultimately couldn't print in the book (the reader will find it online: www.daraint.org/cvm2). "Expert" workshops in Accra and Hanoi developed into fully-fledged policy exchanges, while delegates of the Climate Vulnerable Forum crowded Side Event rooms in Durban, Bonn and Rio. We hope you all appreciate the final result and cannot thank you enough for helping us to pull this unusual new work together.

Some much warranted apologies go to our close families and those of the core collaborators on this project. Thanks next to Lucía Fernández Suárez and the whole team and house in DARA, all of whom have helped make this report what it is - included of course are DARA's Board of Trustees, in particular our key benefactor Diego Hidalgo, and our Trustee José María Figueres.

May we also extend our utmost gratitude to friends and colleagues at King's College's Humanitarian Futures Programme at the helm of the FOREWARN project, of which this report is one part: Randolph Kent, Hugh Macleman, Jonathan Paz, Emma Visman and Okey Uzoechina.

We would like to thank the members of our Advisory Panel for their generous insight and contributions to this effort over many, many months: Mary Chinery-Hesse, Helen Clark, José María Figueres, Robert Glasser, Saleemul Huq, Yolanda Kakabadse, Ashok Khosla, Ricardo Lagos, Loren Legarda, Michael Marmot, Simon Maxwell, David Nabarro, Atiq Rahman, Teresa Ribera, Johan Rockström, Jeffrey Sachs, Hans Joachim Schellnhuber, Javier Solana, Andrew Steer, Margareta Wahlström, and Michael Zammit Cutajar. And also to Jan Eliasson, even though you had to take up a new role part way through the endeavour, we were and will continue to be most grateful for your encouragement and support.

The Peer Review Committee continually challenged us and suggested innovations, adjustments and corrections we never would have thought of ourselves. We certainly hope the final report meets your high expectations of it: Yasemin Aysan, Suruchi Bhadwal, Diarmid Campbell-Lendrum, Manuel Carballo, Ian Christoplos, Joshua Cooper, Mariane Diop Kane, Sean Doolan, Pierre Encontre, Hans-Martin Füssel, Tim Gore, Anne Hammil, Randolph Kent, Tord Kjellstrom, Isabel Kreisler, Juergen Kropp, Allan Lavell, Marc Levy, Filipe Lúcio, and Urs Luterbacher.

The Government of Bangladesh as Chair of the Climate Vulnerable Forum has not ceased to drive forward the climate cause with energy and dynamism in a truly international spirit. Thank you for your openness to the research team's fresh ideas on this topic, and your willingness to explore where they might lead. Thanks goes in particular to Dr. Dipu Moni, The Honorable Foreign Minister of Bangladesh; Dr. Hasan Mahmud, The Honorable Minister of Environment and Forests of Bangladesh; Ambassador Mohamed Mijarul Quayes, Foreign Secretary of Bangladesh; Mr. Mesbah ul Alam, Secretary of Ministry of Environment and Forests; Ambassador Abdul Hannan, Permanent Representative to the United Nations Office at Geneva; Dr. S.M. Munjurul Khan, Deputy Secretary of Ministry of Environment and Forests; Deputy Permanent Representative to the United Nations, Mr. Rahman Mustafizur; and Mr Faiyaz Murshid Kazi of the Bangladesh Foreign Ministry. Finally, thanks so much to two of the leading doyens of international macro-economic diplomacy in South Asia: Mr. Md. Sufiur Rahman, Director General and Mr. Salahuddin Noman Chowdhury, Director, each of Economic Affairs Wing of Ministry of Foreign Affairs of Bangaldesh – may you continue to think and lead the way forward.

To our donors at AECID, AusAID and Fundación Biodiversidad: thank you for your many efforts to support this project and your helpful assistance in coordinating and realizing the wide-ranging activities involved. Thank you Juan Ovejero Dohn for looking after the team in Hanoi and Vietnam. To the Australian (and Italian) team in Accra, we hope you also enjoyed the experience of the country study: Sarah Willis and Azzurra Chiarini.

This report would not have been possible without the analytical expertise and dedicated work of Commons Consultants, the main research and production partner of DARA in this effort, a team led by Søren Peter Andreasen as Principal Advisor to the project and Peter Utzon Berg as the primary Technical Advisor to the endeavour. Your honed creativity and technical precision allowed this project to achieve its close to outlandish aims. Mariano Sarmiento, lead designer and his dedicated and talented team are responsible for all of the extremely helpful or too complex graphics in this report, depending on your viewpoint. However, the complexity is all our fault and not Mariano's nor his team's – what you see is much, much better than anything we would have subjected you to without their help. Morwenna Marshall, thanks once again for being there even at the most inconvenient moments, and to Tim Morris, our copy editors who each receive a special vote of thanks.

We particularly owe our thanks to additional scientists and experts who provided strong guidance and assistance with model selection of which there are simply too many to list here. You may have just thought you were just doing our chief modeller, Cristian Conteduca, a favour (you were) but your assistance in helping us to track down the knowledge which forms the foundation of this work was absolutely fundamental to helping this report make what we hope is a meaningful contribution to the debate. Antonia Praetorius, Sebastian Strempel, YiWei Ng, we thank you.

Many thanks also to the governments of Ghana and Vietnam and to the UNDP country offices here, as well as UNDP headquarters in New York, for your most helpful support. In Vietnam, Live&Learn, Hang Nguyen and colleagues were tremendous in supporting our country research, and in Ghana, the Environmental Protection Agency-Ghana with expert support from Emmanuel Tachie-Obeng did a highly effective job of facilitating our trip and national and community activities and for which credit is deserved. Mary Chinery-Hesse, thank you so much for welcoming us and taking part.

Finally, many thanks goes to Christer Elfverson, Magda Ninaber van Eyben, Marc Limon and Erik Keus, all of whom went out of their way to help see this project achieve its objectives. Thanks additionally to John Cuddy, Christiana Figueres, William Hare and Nicholas Stern for your sage advice, and to the Asia Society and friends at TckTckTck for your kind support behind the Monitor launch.

ROSS MOUNTAIN
DARA Director General

MATTHEW MCKINNON
Editor

CONTENTS

INTRODUCTION 14
EXECUTIVE SUMMARY 16
FINDINGS AND OBSERVATIONS 24
RECOMMENDATIONS 28
RESEARCH PROCESS 36

KEY ISSUES 40

A VERY SHORT HISTORY OF CLIMATE SCIENCE 58

THE MONITOR 60

CLIMATE 104
ENVIRONMENTAL DISASTERS 106
HABITAT CHANGE 124
HEALTH IMPACT 154
INDUSTRY STRESS 176

COUNTRY STUDIES 202
GHANA 204
VIETNAM 216

CARBON 228
ENVIRONMENTAL DISASTERS 230
HABITAT CHANGE 240
HEALTH IMPACT 254
INDUSTRY STRESS 272

METHODOLOGY 286

MONITOR DATA TABLES 294
PARTNERS 302
ABBREVIATIONS 303
GLOSSARY 304
BIBLIOGRAPHY 308

A GUIDE TO THE COLD CALCULUS OF A HOT PLANET / INTRO-DUCTION

TWO DECADES OF FAILURE TO ACT DECISIVELY ON CLIMATE CHANGE HAVE MADE THE EARTH HOTTER AND MORE POLLUTED.[1] There is still a window of opportunity, fast closing, to scale back pollution and tame the rising heat. But the world economy is locked onto a different course: fossil fuel consumption is expected to continue its rapid growth in the coming decades.[2]
Major economies not committed to low-carbon development would need to enact policy changes to alter this fact. Current frontline stockpiles of hydrocarbons – of oil, coal, and gas – are multiples of what could possibly be consumed this century if the climate is to be kept under control, despite being valued as if all and more of these will be burnt.[3]
The cold calculus of a hot planet is that millions of people already suffer from the failure of the world economy to embark on a low-carbon transition. This report estimates that 5 million lives are lost each year today as a result of climate change and a carbon-based economy, with detailed explanations for why this is the case found in the relevant chapters that follow. In particular, effects are most severe for the world's poorest groups whose struggle against poverty is worsened.[4] Although no country is spared the impact: a depleted ozone layer for instance – also caused by potent greenhouse gases – has significantly increased the incidence of skin cancer, above all in the wealthiest of countries. The US will lose more than 2% of its GDP by 2030 according to this report's estimates.[5]
On the basis of this report's comprehensive reassessment of the incremental costs and benefits of a hotter, more polluted planet, a second cold calculus can also be made.
Climate change is found to have already set back global development by close to 1% of world GDP.
This impact is felt, but rarely counted, in the bottom lines of companies, industries and major economies, and is already playing a role in determining the wealth or poverty of nations. Inaction on climate change cost Least Developed Countries an average of 11% of their GDP for the year 2010 – with losses that will greatly increase in the years ahead. Indeed, the explosive increase in heat expected over the coming decades will only lead to a corresponding escalation in these costs, increasingly holding back growth as emissions go unabated and efforts to support the worst-affected communities fail to meet the challenges at hand.
The losses incurred already exceed by a significant margin any costs of reducing emissions in line with a low-carbon transition.[6] Action on climate change would therefore already reap monetary benefits for the world, both globally and for major economies like the US, China and India.
So the second cold, bottom-line calculus of a hot planet is that tackling climate change is already sensible in economic terms today. The step will also minimize widespread illness and mortality that inaction causes. And it would bolster the fight against poverty while helping to safeguard a natural world in steep decline.[7]
The findings of this report differ from previous studies that largely understand climate change as a net benefit or minimal cost to society today (or prior to mid-century), and which inform current economic decision-making on climate change, making it easier for governments to avoid serious action.[8]
While the methods of this study resemble previous research, three key distinctions in the approach have led to fundamentally different results.
First, this report draws on the most recent science and research into different climate-related impacts, taking advantage of the incredible growth in understanding on this issue since the 1990s era research that provides the basis of almost all other studies of this kind.[9]
Second, building on freshly available research, a number of new effects are considered here. Chief among these is the impact that increasing heat has on labour productivity, or the fact that workers (especially outdoors) produce less in a given hour when it is very hot. Fractional increases in global temperature can translate into tens of additional hot days with each passing decade.[10]
Labour productivity is estimated to result in the largest cost to the world economy of any effects analysed in this report. Other effects newly considered here include the thawing of permafrost in cold regions and the accelerated depreciation of infrastructure that results as frozen land shifts when it thaws.[11]
Finally, this report also considers a full range of the closely inter-linked costs and benefits of the carbon economy, independent of any climate change impacts. When accounting for the large-scale costs imposed by carbon-intensive hazards to human health, the environment and economic sectors, such as the fisheries industry, the full costs of inaction are laid bare.
Human society and the natural world, it turns out, are fundamentally susceptible to changes in ambient heat. Civilization itself emerged during an age subsequent to the last glacial era that was characterized by a uniquely stable and mild

THE CLIMATE VULNERABLE FORUM

The Climate Vulnerable Forum (CVF) is an international cooperation group for coordination, advocacy and knowledge-building among countries that face significant insecurity due to climate change. The Forum has distinguished itself through a determination to catalyze more effective and broad-based action for tackling the global climate challenge, internationally and nationally. Founded in 2009 by the Maldives, it now includes 20 governments and is a major foreign policy initiative of its current chair, Bangladesh. The Climate Vulnerability Monitor's second edition was commissioned at the November 2011 Ministerial Meeting of the Forum at Dhaka, Bangladesh.

climate. The balance is delicate: a few degrees cooler and much of the northern hemisphere freezes.[12] Several degrees hotter and parts of the planet exceed the thermal maximum at which human beings can exist outdoors.[13]

The world is just one degree Celsius (1.8° F) hotter than prior to industrialization – the principal cause of climate change.[14] But small changes count: Ghana for instance, a focus country in this report, has warmed faster than others. In just 50 years, the number of very hot days in Ghana has increased by 50 in number.[15] Inaction on climate change would see Ghana experience three to five times that increase in heat this century alone.[16]

It goes almost without saying that changes of this proportion have profound effects for human beings, the natural environment and the market economy. Releasing gigatonnes of carbon dioxide and other pollutants and gases into the atmosphere every year is neither a safe, sound nor healthy practice when cleaner, safer and more environmentally sound alternatives so readily exist. Low-carbon energy solutions –such as wind, solar, tidal or geothermal power – involve 10 to 100 times less negative externalities than carbon-intensive alternatives.[17]

Even for the sceptically minded, the argument for switching to safer, less damaging energy sources can be justified on account of the heavy costs of the prevailing carbon-intensive means.

The Climate Vulnerability Monitor (hereafter: "the Monitor") was commissioned by the Climate Vulnerable Forum, an international cooperation group of climate-insecure countries, and mandated to DARA as an independent global study into precisely these effects. As its name indicates, the report serves to monitor the evolution of changes related to the climate as they are already being felt around the world. Its role is to shed light on how society experiences inaction on the climate crisis today in order that the insight might assist in enhancing the contemporary global response to this most serious of societal concerns. The study has benefitted from the input of wide-ranging external advisory bodies and field research undertaken in Ghana and Vietnam.

Governments like those of the Climate Vulnerable Forum are already allocating significant taxpayer funds to deal with the local effects of climate change as they are taking hold. Governments worldwide are weighing macroeconomic energy and environmental policies, from infrastructure incentives to low-carbon regulation, nuclear energy reliance, or the exploitation of hazardous unconventional fuel reserves. In doing so, decisions are being made to allocate highly specific sums of money, human and intellectual capacities, and other resources of all kinds.

The Monitor helps to inform these decisions by presenting a snapshot of what current knowledge on climate change issues in their aggregate can reasonably be assumed to imply for the world. The analysis includes monetary, human and ecological estimations of the ramifications of inaction on climate change. These estimations are the result of this specific research effort and provide a reference of interest when considering what societal benefits might result from different policy strategies. The exercise enables the comparison of costs with benefits in order to judge the overall merits of different endeavours.

The report's structure has three main parts. The front matter of the report provides an executive summary, context to and details of this study, as well as an overview of key findings and a series of detailed recommendations targeted at specific groups. The Monitor itself is then presented, with the results of the assessment provided for every country and each of the different indicators used detailed one-by-one with key information provided each time at the country level, for different groups and overall. Finally, a number of special focus sections are also contained in this report, including independent chapters on the country-based research undertaken in Ghana and Vietnam. It is the hope that this report will spur debate and awareness of the double-sided cold calculus of action versus inaction on climate change with which the world now desperately struggles.

The choice for society is critical but hardly difficult if the externalities of inaction on climate change have indeed been underestimated by the world economy. Business-as-usual impacts would for this century be multiples of any costs associated with a transition to a low-carbon economy and imply unthinkable human suffering.

All but the firmest responses leave the door wide open to catastrophic risks and threats to the planet's ability to support life, none of which even enter into the Monitor's assessment of costs. According to the International Energy Agency, just five years remain for the world's major economies to enact structural economic transformations in order to break out of a dead end business-as-usual trap. If not, planned investments in high-carbon infrastructure would from 2017 rule out keeping the global temperature rise below the internationally agreed on level of 2° Celsius (3.6° F).[18] Technological barriers no longer hold back the transition. Prolonging change only increases costs. Firm, urgent and internationally cooperative action heightens benefits for all. The best way forward is quite obviously clear.

DARA

Founded in 2003, DARA is an independent organisation headquartered in Madrid, Spain, committed to improving the quality and effectiveness of aid for vulnerable populations suffering from conflict, disasters and climate change. DARA was mandated by the Climate Vulnerable Forum as independent developer of the Climate Vulnerability Monitor in its first and second editions.

[1] The UN Framework Convention on Climate Change was signed in 1992 (UNFCCC, 1992)
[2] US EIA, 2011; IEA, 2011
[3] BP, 2011; US EIA, 2011; CTI, 2011
[4] UNDP, 2007
[5] Martens, 1998; UNEP, 2002
[6] For mitigation costs, see: Edenhofer et al., 2010 and IPCC, 2012b
[7] Butchart et al., 2010; Crutzen, 2010
[8] Tol, 2011; Nordhaus, 2011
[9] Tol, 2011; Exceptions include: Nordhaus, 2006; Rehdanz and Maddison, 2005
[10] Kjellstrom et al., 2009
[11] Nelson et al., 2002
[12] Petit et al., 1999
[13] Sherwood and Huber, 2010
[14] IPCC, 2007a
[15] McSweeney et al., 2012: "A 'Hot' day or 'hot' night is defined by the temperature exceeded on 10% of days or nights in the current climate of that region and season."
[16] Ibid
[17] IPCC, 2012a
[18] IAE, 2011

EXECUTIVE SUMMARY

This report provides a reassessment of the human and economic costs of the climate crisis. The reassessment is based on a wealth of the latest research and scientific work on climate change and the carbon economy, research that is assimilated as a part of this report.

THE MAIN FINDING OF THIS REPORT IS THAT CLIMATE CHANGE HAS ALREADY HELD BACK GLOBAL DEVELOPMENT: IT IS ALREADY A SIGNIFICANT COST TO THE WORLD ECONOMY, WHILE INACTION ON CLIMATE CHANGE CAN BE CONSIDERED A LEADING GLOBAL CAUSE OF DEATH.

CLIMATE – TOTAL COSTS

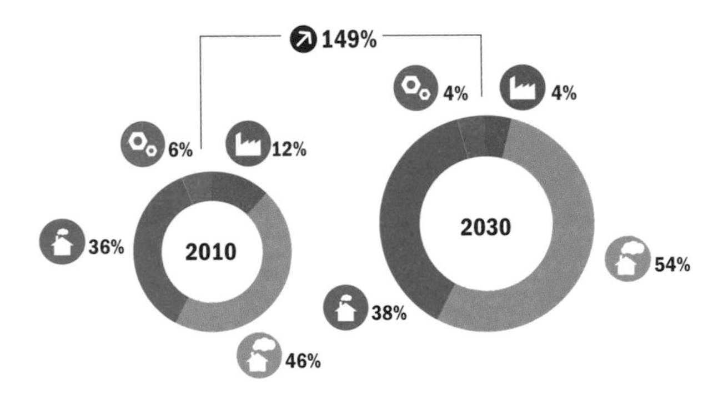

CARBON – TOTAL COSTS

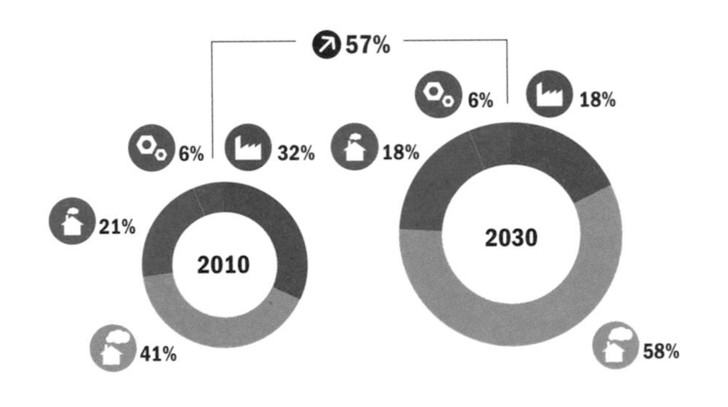

CLIMATE – TOTAL DEATHS

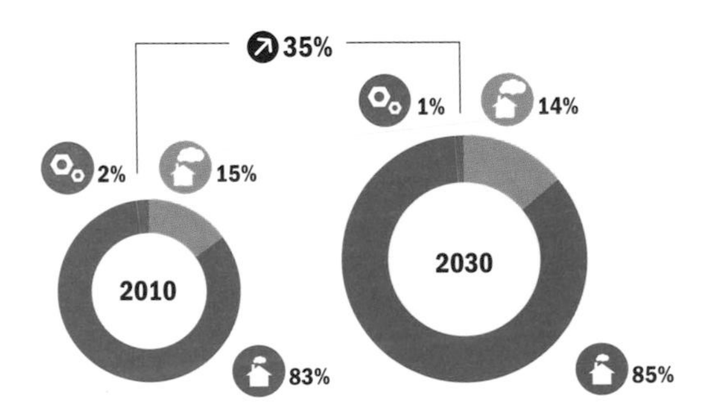

CARBON – TOTAL DEATHS

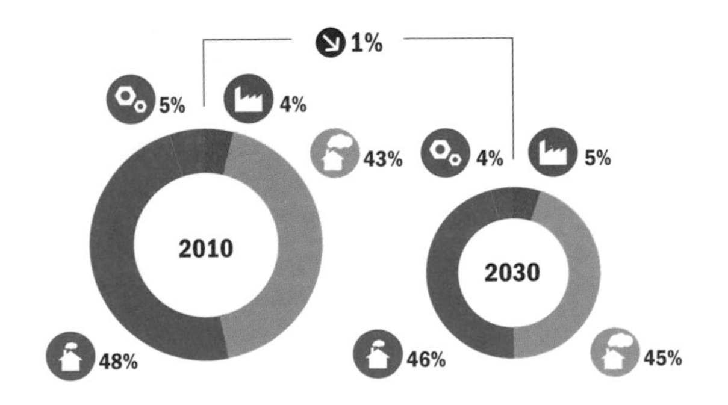

This report estimates that climate change causes 400,000 deaths on average each year today, mainly due to hunger and communicable diseases that affect above all children in developing countries. Our present carbon-intensive energy system and related activities cause an estimated 4.5 million deaths each year linked to air pollution, hazardous occupations and cancer.

the world's oceans, the slow response of the carbon cycle to reduced CO_2 emission and limitations on how fast emissions can actually be reduced.[1]
The world economy therefore faces an increase in pressures that are estimated to lead to more than a doubling in the costs of climate change by 2030 to an estimated 2.5% of global GDP. Carbon economy costs also increase over this same period so that

OVERALL COSTS

	Losses 2010, Bln PPP corrected USD	Losses 2010, % of GDP	Net Losses, % of GDP 2010	Net Losses, % of GDP 2030
Climate	696	0.9%	0.8%	2.1%
Carbon	542	0.7%	0.7%	1.2%
World	**1,238**	**1.7%**	**1.6%**	**3.2%**

Climate change caused economic losses estimated close to 1% of global GDP for the year 2010, or 700 billion dollars (2010 PPP). The carbon-intensive economy cost the world another 0.7% of GDP in that year, independent of any climate change losses. Together, carbon economy- and climate change-related losses amounted to over 1.2 trillion dollars in 2010.
The world is already committed to a substantial increase in global temperatures – at least another 0.5° C (1° F) due to a combination of the inertia of

global GDP in 2030 is estimated to be well over 3% lower than it would have been in the absence of climate change and harmful carbon-intensive energy practices.
Continuing today's patterns of carbon-intensive energy use is estimated, together with climate change, to cause 6 million deaths per year by 2030, close to 700,000 of which would be due to climate change. This implies that a combined climate-carbon crisis is estimated to claim 100 million lives between now and the end of the next decade. A significant

NUMBER OF DEATHS

		2010	2030
Climate	Diarrheal Infections	85,000	150,000
	Heat & Cold Illnesses	35,000	35,000
	Hunger	225,000	380,000
	Malaria & Vector Borne Diseases	20,000	20,000
	Meningitis	30,000	40,000
	Environmental Disasters	5,000	7,000
Carbon	Air Pollution	1,400,000	2,100,000
	Indoor Smoke	3,100,000	3,100,000
	Occupational Hazards	55,000	80,000
	Skin Cancer	20,000	45,000
World		**4,975,000**	**5,957,000**

TECHNICAL SUMMARY

The Monitor presents a new and original analysis, synthesizing the latest research and scientific information on the global impact – including benefits and losses – of climate change and the carbon economy in economic, environmental and health terms. Climate change already causes 400,000 deaths each year on average. The present carbon-intensive economy moreover is linked to 4.5 million deaths worldwide each year. Climate change to date and the present carbon economy are estimated to have already lowered global output by 1.6% of world GDP or by around 1.2 trillion dollars (2010 PPP). Losses are expected to increase rapidly, reaching 6 million deaths and 3.2% of GDP in net average global losses by 2030. If emissions continue to increase unabated in a business-as-usual fashion (similar to the new IPCC RCP8.5 scenario), yearly average global losses to world output could exceed 10% of global GDP before the end of the century, with damages accelerating throughout the century. The costs of climate change and the carbon economy are already significantly higher than the estimated costs of shifting the world economy to a low-carbon footing – around 0.5% of GDP for the current decade, although increasing for subsequent decades.[1]
This report and scientific literature imply adaptation costs

share of the global population would be directly affected by inaction on climate change.
Global figures mask enormous costs that will, in particular, hit developing countries and above all the world's poorest groups. Least Developed Countries (LDCs) faced *on average* in excess of 10% of forgone GDP in 2010 due to climate change and the carbon economy, as all faced inequitable access to energy and sustainable development.
Over 90% of mortality assessed in this report occurs in developing countries only – more than 98% in the case of climate change.
Of all these losses, it is the world's poorest communities within lower and middle-income countries that are most exposed. Losses of income among these groups is already extreme. The world's principal objectives for poverty reduction, the Millennium Development Goals (MDGs), are therefore under comprehensive pressures, in particular as a result of climate change.
The impact for rural and coastal communities in the lowest-income settings implies serious threats for food security and extreme poverty (goal 1 of 8), child health and the ability of children to attend school (goals 2 and 4), maternal health and women's development (goals 3 and 5), the prevalence of infectious diseases (goal 6) and, through water, fisheries and biodiversity impacts, environmental sustainability (goal 7). Furthermore, in a difficult fiscal environment, the advent of climate change has pressured governments to divert Official Development Assistance (ODA) funds from other development commitments and activities in an attempt to provide support for climate change concerns, including to a marginal degree, for helping vulnerable communities adapt to climate change. The Green Climate Fund, agreed upon in incrementally greater detail at the successive international climate talks at Copenhagen, Cancún and Durban, faces an economic environment of declining ODA tied to acute fiscal crises across a host of the world's wealthiest economies (see: climate finance). These developments have ultimately compromised the global partnership for development (goal 8). Lag areas towards MDG achievement also align very closely with the most pronounced vulnerabilities resulting from climate change: sub-Saharan Africa, small island developing states, and South Asia in particular.
Poverty reduction efforts are in peril as the potential temperature increase the world is already committed to has only begun to be realized, and the world's major economies are in no way spared. The United States, China and India in particular are expected to incur enormous losses that in 2030 for these three countries alone will collectively total 2.5 trillion dollars in economic costs and over 3 million deaths per year, or half of all mortality – the majority in India and China.
The whole world is affected by these comprehensive concerns: 250 million people face the pressures of sea-level rise; 30 million people are affected by more extreme weather, especially flooding; 25 million people are affected by permafrost thawing; and 5 million people are pressured by desertification. The pressures that these combined stresses put on affected communities are immense and force or stimulate the movement of populations. As is highlighted in the Ghana country study in this report, they can also fuel violence and an erosion of the social and economic fabric of communities.
The impact of climate change on Labour Productivity is assessed here as the most substantial economic loss facing the world as a result of climate change. A large proportion of the global workforce is exposed to the incessant increase in heat, with the number of very hot days and nights increasing in many places by 10 days a decade.[2] Developing countries, and especially the lowest-income communities, are highly vulnerable to these effects because of geographical location – northern countries like Scandinavia, it is assumed, *benefit* from improved labour productivity due to warmer weather – but also because their labour forces have the highest proportion of non-climate controlled occupational environments.[3]
Global productivity in labour is surging due to technological advances and a shift of emphasis from agricultural activities to an industrial and service sector focus for most developing countries, among other key developments.[4] Climate change, however, holds back the full extent of productivity gains the world would otherwise enjoy.[5] In this way, the

to be at least 150 billion dollars per year today for developing countries, rising to a minimum of more than 1 trillion dollars per year by 2030. These costs are, however, considerably lower than costs of damages to developing countries estimated here, so adapting to climate change is very likely a cost-effective investment in almost all cases and should be central to any climate change policy.
Beyond adaptation, this report also emphasizes the urgency of mitigating key risks: tackling food security, indoor fires/smoke, air pollution and other health issues such as diarrheal illnesses, malaria and meningitis that are all urgent priorities for lessening the extent of the human toll of this crisis.
With costs due both to unabated climate change and the carbon economy expected to rise rapidly over the course of this century, tackling climate change by reducing emissions yields net benefits to the world economy in monetary terms – amounting to around a 1% higher GDP for the entirety of the 21st century (net present value at a 3% discount rate). World net benefits from action on climate change are insensitive to discount rates from 0.1% to 20% (the highest tested).
Even the most ambitious reductions in emissions aimed at holding warming below 2°C (e.g. 400ppm CO_2e/IPCC AR5 RCP2.6 scenario) generates economic benefits for the

costs of climate change are hidden, which helps to explain in part how their full extent may have been missed. Even so, not all have benefitted from fast expanding labour productivity: labour productivity is a core indicator for MDG 1 (on extreme poverty and hunger), for instance, where little progress has been registered in many developing regions of the world, in particular for sub-Saharan Africa and the Pacific.[6] Not one country is *invulnerable* to the combined effects of climate change and the carbon economy. Inaction on climate change penalizes every country in the world, just as all are set to gain from action

MULTI-DIMENSIONAL VULNERABILITY

CLIMATE

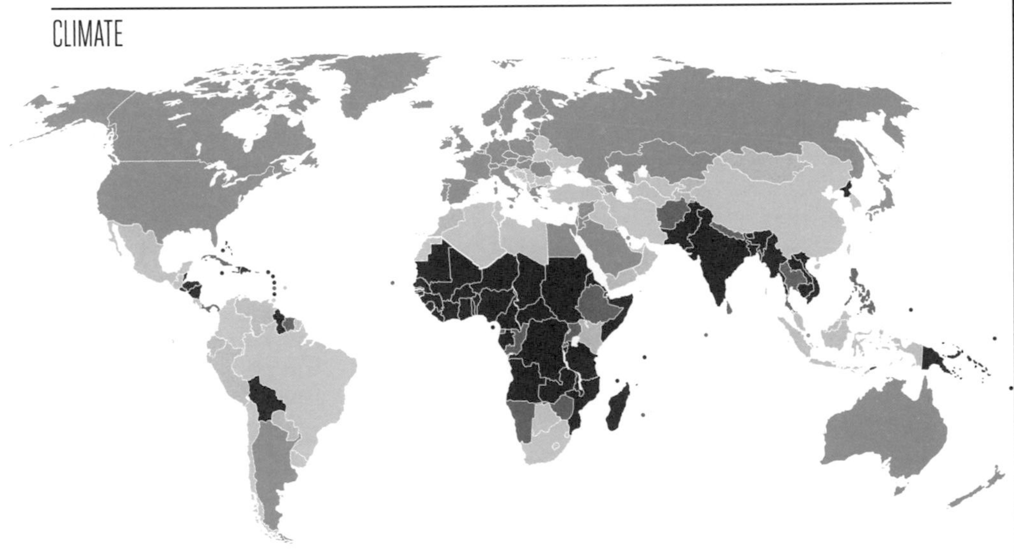

CARBON

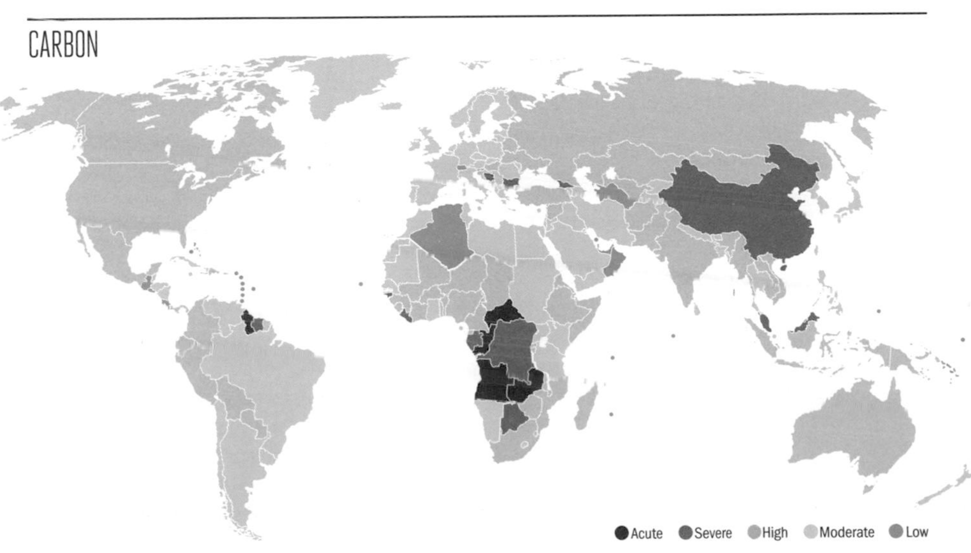

world economy after accounting for the costs of reducing emissions (mitigation costs). Limiting warming to this level would limit human, territorial and ecological damage as well as other concerns, such as climate-induced forced movement of human populations.

Over 98% of all climate change mortality and over 90% of all carbon economy related mortality is in developing countries: between 80% and 90% of all economic costs are projected to fall on developing countries. The most extreme effects of climate change are estimated to be felt by the Least Developed Countries, with average GDP losses of 8% in 2030. With respect to carbon economy effects, inequitable access to sustainable development sees Least Developed Countries again incurring the highest relative losses at over 3% of GDP, while between two thirds and three quarters of all carbon economy costs are borne by developing countries.

When the costs of climate change and the carbon economy estimated here are combined, not one country in the world is left unharmed. In terms of regional incentives to tackle climate change, every region is estimated to experience net economic benefits from action on climate change even for the highest levels of action.

The Monitor only analyses incremental impacts as a result of climate change, or changes in the frequency of well-known stochastic events, such as floods and landslides. Not assessed here in any way are potential catastrophic impacts that could occur due to more rapid climate change fuelled on climate change. Moreover, the vulnerability of the world is shifting with every passing decade. Countries once resilient to marginal weather effects increasingly realize susceptibilities to a changed climate as the increase in heat and associated effects continue to reach new extremes.

Some quite serious damage is now unavoidable, but certain losses can still be reduced in the short term. In particular, human costs can be transferred to economic costs. This can be achieved through programmes aimed at reducing rural poverty – at the origin of hunger deaths and many communicable diseases afflicting the world's poorest groups, with risks that worsen with climate change. Or it can be achieved by ensuring clean air regulations, safer working conditions and modern energy options for people at risk due to carbon-intensive forms of energy. All these measures will save lives but cost money.

Economic losses themselves can also be lessened. A major recent review of humanitarian assistance work noted that Mozambique had requested 3 million dollars from the international community for flood preparations. That sum went unsecured, and 100 million dollars was subsequently spent on emergency flood response.[7] Investment in agriculture might also be cost-effective if the costs of supporting upgraded farming were to generate more benefits (in productivity, output) than the initial outlay.[8]

There are, however, limits to the ability of populations to adapt. The oceans can hardly be refrigerated against marine stresses.[9] Desert encroachment can be prevented but rarely reversed, and if so, generally at great expense.[10] It might be possible to protect a beach, but concrete polders could well be to the detriment of an area's authentic charm and so to the value of properties.

A low-carbon, renewable economy – of hydro, wind, solar, geothermal, tidal and other innovative sources of energy – now competes with the most carbon-intensive forms of power generation in the open market, where they constitute around 10% of the global energy mix today.[11] Shifting the balance in favour of low-carbon energy has been estimated to cost approximately 0.5% or less of GDP for the current decade.[12]

The carbon economy is largely responsible for the incredible growth in overall wealth society has amassed over the last 200 years, although, according to the World Bank, 1.3 billion people continue to remain trapped in dire poverty.[13]

Regardless, an economic system developed to support a global population of 1 or 2 billion people in the 19th century is ill suited to a global population in excess of 7 billion and growing.[14]

The climate challenge runs in parallel to other key global developments: a growing world population, a major propensity to urbanization, and structural

by feedbacks such as a release of Arctic methane deposits, more rapid sea-level rise that could result from the disintegration of the West Antarctic Ice Sheet or large-scale climatic disruptions such as the collapse of ocean circulation mechanisms, all of which are understood to pose significantly larger human, economic and ecological risks than anything portrayed here. The possibilities of these events are by no means ruled out, with risks increasing substantially with warming.[2] Other economists have therefore factored such risks into their economic analysis to a degree.[3]

Only with the deep and sustained emissions reductions spelled out in the lowest of the new IPCC RCP 2.6 scenario is there a reasonable chance (comfortably over 50%) of not exceeding the internationally accepted "safety" temperature threshold of 2°C global mean warming above preindustrial.[4] Given the clear human, ecological and,

REGIONAL COST BENEFIT ANALYSIS, 2010-2100** PERCENTAGE OF GLOBAL GDP (NOMINAL), NET PRESENT VALUE AT 3% DISCOUNT RATE

	Climate + Carbon Costs				Highest Action		High Action		Moderate Action		Net Benefit		
Region	**No Action**	**Highest action (400 ppm)**	**High action (450 ppm)**	**Moderate action (550 ppm)**	**Avoided costs***	**Mitigation costs**	**Avoided costs***	**Mitigation costs**	**Avoided costs***	**Mitigation costs**	**Highest action**	**High Action**	**Moderate action**
USA	3.0%	1.0%	1.0%	1.5%	2.0%	1.5%	2.0%	1.0%	1.5%	0.5%	0.5%	1.0%	1.0%
Japan	0.5%	0.5%	0.5%	0.5%	0.5%	0.5%	0.5%	0.5%	0.5%	0.5%	0.0%	0.0%	0.0%
Russia	4.5%	1.5%	1.5%	2.0%	3.0%	2.0%	3.0%	2.0%	2.5%	2.5%	1.0%	1.0%	0.0%
China	4.5%	2.0%	2.0%	2.5%	2.5%	2.0%	2.5%	1.5%	2.0%	1.0%	0.5%	1.0%	1.0%
India	11.0%	5.0%	5.5%	6.5%	6.0%	3.0%	5.5%	2.0%	4.5%	0.5%	3.0%	3.5%	4.0%
EU27	1.0%	0.5%	0.5%	0.5%	0.5%	1.0%	0.5%	0.5%	0.5%	0.5%	0.0%	0.0%	0.0%
ROW	8.5%	3.5%	3.5%	4.5%	5.5%	2.0%	5.0%	1.0%	4.5%	0.5%	3.5%	4.0%	3.5%
World***	4.0%	1.5%	1.5v	2.0%	2.5%	1.5%	2.0%	1.0%	2.0%	0.5%	1.0%	1.0%	1.0%

*Avoided costs: No action (A1B +8.5) minus reduced ppm scenario (400 ppm C02e: RCP2.6; 450 ppm: RCP2.9; 550 ppm: SRES B1)

** Discounted (3%) sum of costs and GDP – mitigation costs from Edenhofer et al., 2010 (regional: Remind + Poles)

*** Median value of all 5 scenarios (Edenhofer et al., 2010)

ACTION VERSUS INACTION OVER THE 21ST CENTURY

NPV OF GLOBAL CLIMATE/CARBON COSTS AND MITIGATION COSTS RELATIVE TO GDP (NOMINAL 2010-2100, 3% DISCOUNT RATE)

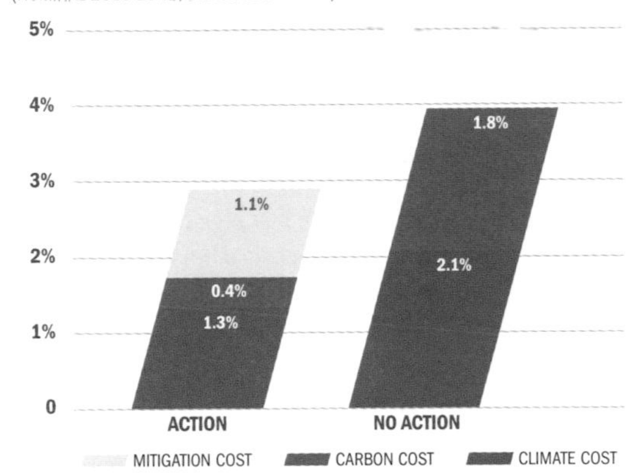

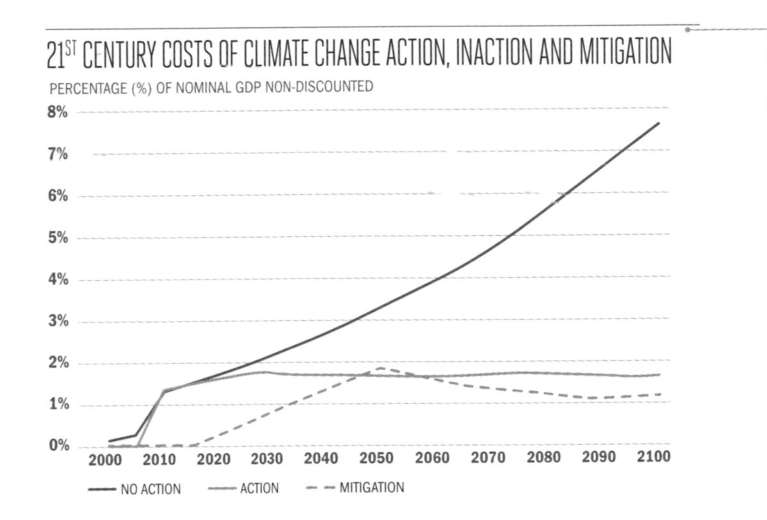

shifts occurring in economies around the world. All of these tendencies - most pronounced in developing countries, in particular the process of industrialization now spreading more and more widely[15] - can worsen or attenuate vulnerabilities to climate change or the carbon economy.

In order to understand the fuller implications of this study and to make its findings comparable with previous works that take on longer-term perspectives, the costs of climate change and the carbon economy were also estimated for the period up until 2100. On this basis, business-as-usual development could see the costs of inaction exceeding 10% of global GDP in losses prior to 2100.

Reducing emissions results in net benefits for society in every case because the costs of a low-carbon transition are more than outweighed by averted losses due to climate change and the carbon economy.

In the global context, the highest level of emission reductions results in similar global benefits to lower levels of action. However, the highest action sees fewer negative impacts on society -from human health to biodiversity and for the world's oceans - but requires slightly greater investments in low-emission forms of energy. Less ambitious action means accepting larger scales of human and ecological impacts.

The regional analysis of costs and benefits differs little in fundamental terms from the global analysis: all regions benefit from climate action in economic terms. Most regions find optimal climate action in the high-action scenario. The highest action to reduce emissions also limits the risks of crossing tipping points leading to large-scale climate disruptions.[16] Less ambitious action on climate change does not: moderate action on climate change has a high chance of exceeding the accepted international temperature goal of holding warming below 2° C (3.6° F) above pre-industrial levels.[17] The most vulnerable countries have called for warming to be limited below 1.5° C above pre-industrial levels as they believe 2° C is far too damaging and a risk to their survival.

Neither should the risks of catastrophic impacts be discarded as heresy: new research has highlighted great risks associated with *heat*, as opposed to ocean-related immersion of countries, with heat risks concerning far greater shares of the world economy and its population. In particular, at certain levels of high-end warming, large areas of the planet would progressively beginning to exceed the thermal maximum at which human beings are able to survive outdoors.[18] The possibilities of very rapid climate change are not implausible or ruled out by climate change models, especially as the planet warms beyond the 2 degrees Celsius temperature threshold

ultimately, economic advantages of aiming for a highest-action scenario, this report's findings imply that the highest action targets would reap the most benefits for the world. Therefore, the highest-action scenario is recommended to policy makers as the preferred target for enhancing and safeguarding global prosperity. Mainstream economic modelling shows that this transition is technologically and economically feasible but that action is needed now to get onto this pathway.[5] *International cooperation will clearly be central to ensuring that the costs of the transition are maintained at the lowest most efficient level and that the transition yields the highest co-benefits.*[6]

[1] See: Edenhofer et al., 2010; IPCC, 2012a
[2] Weitzman, 2007; Hare in Mastny, 2009
[3] For example: Hope, 2006; Stern, 2006
[4] Pope et al., 2010
[5] For an overview of some leading mitigation scenarios, see: Edenhofer et al., 2010; UNEP, 2011; IPCC, 2012a
[6] For example the economic benefits of cross-border emission reduction cooperation: De Cian and Tavoni, 2010

the international community has set for itself.[19] Of particular long-term concern are 1500 gigatonnes of CO_2 ($GtCO_2$) of methane stored in frozen sediments in the East-Siberian Sea at depths of less than 40 to 50 metres.[20] This represents three times the amount of CO_2 that could be released over much of this century if the 2 degrees target is to be kept.[21] As the Arctic sea warms due to climate change, these sediments are thawing and methane is already being visibly released at rates that currently exceed the total amount of methane emitted through natural processes over the entirety of the world's oceans.[22]
While all policy pathways for reducing emissions have similar net benefits in economic terms, the highest-action route would clearly reap the greatest human, societal, economic and environmental benefits, since it would ensure the greatest chances of avoiding climate-triggered catastrophe and would minimize the human, social and environmental impacts of a hotter planet. Therefore, the cold calculus of a hot planet implies the most ambitious action on climate change is the savviest choice both in monetary, humanitarian and environmental terms. The highest-action approach is the pathway that the analysis in this report most supports.
The world risks carbon lock-in due to high-intensity carbon infrastructure plans still moving forward in the near term, so the shift in focus to a low-carbon transition should likely occur prior to 2017 and continue aggressively thereafter.[23] Several major economies will need to adjust and enact important domestic policy and legislative initiatives in order to make this a reality. Whatever the case, action on climate change that seeks out international partnership is most likely to further lessen the costs of a low-carbon transition and expand the benefits of this transition for all concerned. This report documents in part the potential benefits of avoided impacts of climate change in addition to the potential co-benefits of emission reductions that are targeted at key economic, health and environmental concerns.[24]

[1] Hansen et al., 2005
[2] Kjellstrom et al., 2009a; McSweeney et al., 2012
[3] ILO LABORSTA, 2012
[4] Storm and Naastepad, 2009; Wacker et al., 2006; Restuccia, et al., 2004; Storm and Naastepad, 2009; McMillan and Rodrik, 2012
[5] Kjellstrom et al., 2009a-b
[6] UN, 2012
[7] Ashdown et al., 2011
[8] Parry et al., 2009; EACC, 2010
[9] Cheung et al., 2010
[10] Puigdefaabregas, 1998
[11] US EIA, 2011
[12] Edenhofer et al., 2010; IPCC, 2012b
[13] Chen and Ravallion, 2012
[14] World Population Prospects/UN DESA, 2011
[15] OECD, 2012; IMF WEO, 2012; World Population Prospects/UN DESA, 2011
[16] Pope et al., 2010
[17] UNFCCC, 2009
[18] Sherwood and Huber, 2010
[19] Wietzman, 2007
[20] Shakhova et al., 2008
[21] Meinshausen et al., 2009
[22] Shakhova et al., 2008 and 2010
[23] IAE, 2011; UNEP, 2011
[24] De Cian and Tavoni, 2010

CLIMATE+CARBON

2030 54
ACUTE
2010 21

2030 31
SEVERE
2010 27

2030 38
HIGH
2010 59

2030 55
MODERATE
2010 73

2030 6
LOW
2010 4

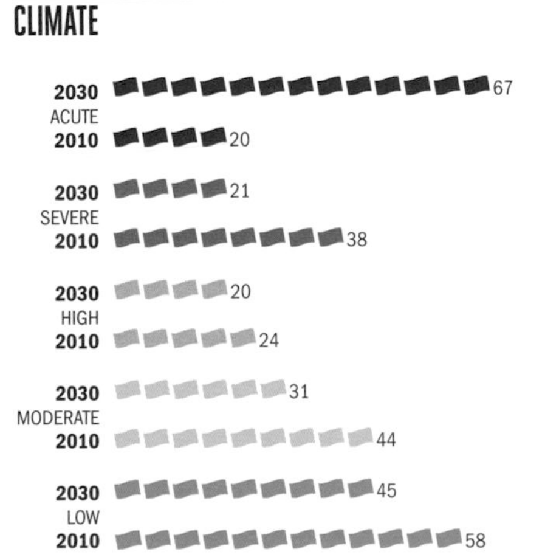

SUMMARY OF ECONOMIC IMPACT

			NET 2030	NET 2010	LOSSES 2010	GAINS 2010	2010 Developing Country Low Emitters	2010 Developing Country High Emitters	2010 Developed	2010 Other Industrialized	2030 Developing Country Low Emitters	2030 Developing Country High Emitters	2030 Developed	2030 Other Industrialized
CLIMATE	Environmental disasters	DROUGHT	18	4	4	*	*	2	1	*	4	11	3	1
		FLOODS & LANDSLIDES	94	10	10	*	2	6	1	*	21	66	5	3
		STORMS	100	15	15	*	2	3	7	*	16	64	20	*
		WILDFIRES	*	*	*	*	*	*	*	*	*	*	*	*
		TOTAL	**213**	**29**	**29**	*****	**5**	**14**	**10**	**1**	**40**	**142**	**28**	**4**
	Habitat change	BIODIVERSITY	389	78	78	*	8	26	36	9	56	299	80	54
		DESERTIFICATION	20	4	5	*	*	*	2	1	5	4	6	6
		HEATING & COOLING	-77	-33	5	-38	1	2	24	-8	30	7	-65	-49
		LABOUR PRODUCTIVITY	2,400	311	314	-3	135	162	16	-1	1,035	1,364	49	-12
		PERMAFROST	153	31	31	*	1	10	3	17	5	68	5	75
		SEA-LEVEL RISE	526	86	86	*	23	42	15	5	166	310	29	22
		WATER	13	14	44	-30	3	-3	13	7	-21	45	39	39
		TOTAL	**3,461**	**491**	**563**	**-71**	**166**	**235**	**60**	**30**	**1,276**	**1,908**	**144**	**135**
	Health impact	**TOTAL**	**106**	**23**	**23**	*****	**17**	**5**	*****	**0.5**	**84**	**21**	*****	**1**
	Industry stress	AGRICULTURE	367	50	51	*	27	17	3	2	208	144	8	10
		FISHERIES	168	13	16	-3	7	7	1	-1	97	80	-3	-6
		FORESTRY	44	6	7	-1	*	4	*	*	9	34	1	1
		HYDRO ENERGY	-24	-4	*	-4	*	-3	*	*	3	-20	-1	*
		TOURISM	*	*	5	-5	2	*	-1	*	19	-16	-2	-1
		TRANSPORT	7	1	1	*	*	*	1	*	*	1	6	*
		TOTAL	**565**	**66**	**80**	**-13**	**37**	**25**	**2**	**2**	**329**	**223**	**8**	**5**
		TOTAL GLOBAL RESULTS	**4,345**	**609**	**695**	**-84**	**225**	**279**	**72**	**33**	**1,730**	**2,294**	**179**	**144**
CARBON	Environmental disasters	OIL SANDS	24	7	7	*	*	*	7	*	2	1	20	0.5
		OIL SPILLS	38	13	13	*	1	6	6	0.5	3	24	9	2
		TOTAL	**61**	**20**	**20**	*****	**1**	**6**	**13**	**0.5**	**5**	**25**	**29**	**3**
	Habitat change	BIODIVERSITY	1,734	291	291	*	32	128	114	17	236	1,034	349	115
		CORROSION	5	1.5	1.5	*	*	0.5	0.5	*	1	4	0.5	0.5
		WATER	10	4	4	*	*	*	3	1	*	2	4	4
		TOTAL	**1,749**	**296**	**296**	*****	**32**	**129**	**117**	**18**	**238**	**1,038**	**353**	**120**
	Health impact	**TOTAL**	**630**	**172**	**172**	*****	**74**	**67**	**21**	**10**	**226**	**341**	**37**	**26**
	Industry stress	AGRICULTURE	-17	15	17	-2	1	2	9	4	-58	-121	4	4
		FISHERIES	77	9	9	*	1	7	0.5	*	5	70	2	0.5
		FORESTRY	83	28	28	*	3	9	14	1	13	48	18	4
		TOTAL	**-11**	**52**	**54**	**-2**	**4**	**18**	**24**	**5**	**-40**	**-3**	**24**	**8**
		TOTAL GLOBAL RESULTS	**2,429**	**540**	**542**	*****	**112**	**220**	**174**	**34**	**429**	**1,401**	**444**	**156**

* Less than one billion dollars

Billions of dollars (2010 PPP) non-discounted. Totals do not correspond exactly due to rounding.

Environmental disasters · Habitat change · Health impact · Industry stress

Developing Country Low Emitters · Developing Country High Emitters · Developed · Other Industrialized

FINDINGS AND OBSERVATIONS

1.

THE MOST AMBITIOUS RESPONSE TO CLIMATE CHANGE IS THE MOST ADVANTAGEOUS POLICY IN HUMAN, ECONOMIC AND ENVIRONMENTAL TERMS

- Tackling climate change reaps significant net benefits for society in monetary terms, with monetary gains resulting from even the strongest action and far outweighing any associated expenses
- Climate change is estimated to have already cost the world close to 1% of GDP, the negative effects of the carbon economy add a further 0.7% of GDP to today's losses
- Both climate change and carbon economy costs grow as emissions expand and are lessened as they are cut
- Combined costs could double by 2030, lowering world GDP by well over 3% in absence of concerted action to reduce emissions and vulnerabilities globally
- This major revision of climate-related costs is based on an original research aggregation exercise of third-party scientific studies and data with more comprehensive and updated analysis than previously available including the full breadth of effects linked to the carbon economy, with overall conclusions notably unaffected by a differing of the discount rate applied
- The analysis excludes the willingness to pay to avoid long-term non-marginal catastrophic risks, often factored in by economists, which would further increase the costs of inaction and raise the benefits of ambitious responses, only strengthening the conclusion drawn here
- All collective actions aimed at stabilizing GHGs in the Earth's atmosphere generate net benefits to society: on the basis of available information the 400ppm CO_2 equivalent (RCP2.6) target results in the least human and environmental damages in addition to its monetary benefits
- Inaction would see a continuing escalation of the costs of the climate crisis and a diminishing ability for any policy action to bring it under control as humanity would be increasingly placed at the most extreme of risks

2.

THE HUMAN TOLL OF INACTION COULD EXCEED 100 MILLION DEATHS BETWEEN NOW AND 2030 ALONE

- Climate change and the carbon economy as estimated here are responsible for 5 million deaths each year today and cause illness in tens of million people globally comparable to the third leading cause of preventable death with a similar societal impact as tobacco use (see: Health Impact Climate/Carbon)
- The carbon economy claims the largest share of this impact, in particular due to toxic air pollution, at over 4.5 million deaths a year today
- Climate change is estimated to be responsible for 400,000 deaths each year, particularly due to hunger and communicable diseases in the lowest-income countries
- By 2030, the annual death toll is estimated to rise to 6 million, including close to 5.5 million deaths due to the carbon economy, and over 600,000 as a result of climate change
- Inaction on climate change could claim well over 100 million lives in the twenty year period to 2030
- Reducing emissions will rapidly diffuse risks to populations due to the carbon economy, although the effect on the burden of disease will persist for decades
- Constraining climate change will have less of a beneficial effect on its near-term health impacts given that an additional half a degree of warming is now virtually inevitable in the decades immediately ahead
- Climate change linked health concerns are therefore an urgent priority for policies aimed at adapting to climate change, since the accelerating rate of change is outpacing the ability of expected large-scale gains in socio-economic development to lessen key health vulnerabilities in lower-income countries

3.

CLIMATE ACTION IS GOOD VALUE, BUT THE COST OF ADAPTING TO CLIMATE CHANGE HAS LIKELY BEEN UNDERESTIMATED

- Tackling the carbon economy alone is in many cases a sound proposition without even consideration of climate change – reducing the scale of future damages due to climate change are an added bonus to what can be a set of financially and environmentally sound policy measures in their own right
- Given the extent of near-future warming that decades of insufficient regulatory action have now unavoidably forced the world to experience, reducing emissions remains just half of the picture: parallel efforts to adapt to climate change are now essential to a safe and prosperous world
- While a full reassessment of the costs of adaptation is beyond the scope of this report, this Monitor's findings imply that it is very unlikely that the adaptation costs currently facing developing countries could be less than 150 billion US dollars per year today – double the highest of previous published estimates of around 75 billion US dollars per year – simply because a number of key climate change impacts assessed here, such as Heating and Cooling, or Water represent quasi adaptation costs by virtue of how they have been calculated – autonomous adaptation at cost (or gain) being assumed
- Moreover, provided the costs of adaptation rise at similar rates as the

costs of climate change, developing countries could be facing a minimum of over 1 trillion dollars of annual adaptation costs a year by 2030 (in 2010 dollars PPP) – an order of magnitude higher than any previous estimate

- While those figures represent minimum amounts, it is unlikely that the margin of error exceeds much more than double the minimums estimated here, whereas the impact of climate change is estimated to incur several times greater losses for developing countries: 500 billion dollars for 2010 and 4 trillion dollars for 2030 (2010 dollars PPP non-discounted)
- On the basis of existing literature on the subject, adaptation costs are therefore very likely to be less than the costs of the impacts of climate change – as a result adaptation represents a cost-effective investment across a broad range of sectors, meaning resources spent on adaptation are almost certain to reap net benefits for affected countries and for society as a whole
- An important qualification to any estimations of the costs of adaptation however is that climate-related uncertainty significantly increases costs, since planning is ideally robust to the full (or nearly) range of potential outcomes which may include opposites, such as more water, and inundation, or less water but drought

4.
CLIMATE INJUSTICE IS EXTREME

- Climate change takes the most from those who have the least: Least Developed Countries faced in excess of 10% GDP losses due to climate change and the carbon economy in 2010
- The Monitor uses four different country groups as broad geopolitical markers covering developed and industrialized countries as well as developing countries split between "high" and "low" emission categories – the latter group consists of 85 countries with less than 4 tons of CO_2e of GHG emissions (in 2005) or well below the safe per capita emissions level necessary for ensuring stabilized climate conditions in the near-term
- Low-emission countries have essentially contributed nothing to climate change –if all countries were polluting only to those levels, climate change would be marginal – although with a global carbon budget now all but exhausted even the lowest emitting countries can contribute or detract from the world's ability to rise to the climate challenge
- Lacking any responsibility for climate change, the low-emission country group nevertheless experiences approximately 40% of all its economic losses, and over 80% of all climate change-related mortality
- In an intergenerational perspective, more than half of all climate change-related deaths are solely among young children in lower or middle income countries who have virtually no responsibility whatsoever for the problem – which adds further insult to the also serious implications of today's inaction for the welfare of future generations

5.
CLIMATE INACTION COMPROMISES GLOBAL DEVELOPMENT AND POVERTY REDUCTION EFFORTS

- With serious ramifications for agricultural and coastal communities in both economic, health and productivity terms, climate change almost surgically targets global poverty reduction efforts, in particular towards the eight internationally agreed Millennium Development Goals (MDGs), directly and manifestly compromising above all the targets for extreme poverty and hunger (goal 1), child health (goal 4) and environmental sustainability (goal 7), but with important repercussions also for gender equality (goal 3), maternal health (goal 5) and infectious disease (goal 6)
- Effects are most extreme for countries understood to have the lowest levels of capacity, where local efforts are less able to be relied upon for making headway in responding to these additional and growing pressures
- Regional lag towards the MDGs, particularly for Least Developed Countries, small island developing states and African countries also corresponds very precisely to those geographic groups worst affected by the impacts of climate change, where the relative scale of losses reach their most extreme values as assessed by the Monitor
- The net impact of climate change doubles as a share of global GDP between 2010 and 2030 with the growth in losses increasing rather than slowing over time regardless of an expected tripling of global wealth during this 20-year period
- So despite an extremely strong link between wealth and a capacity to withstand climate change, impacts still outstrip the ability of economic development to rid developing countries of heightened vulnerabilities to climate change - contrary therefore to the assertions of previous studies, investment in development is not a sufficient response to limit the impacts of climate change and should not be considered a substitute for a dual policy strategy on climate change encompassing early and strong reductions of emissions together with adaptation

6.
INTERNATIONAL CLIMATE FINANCE: A CLEAR DEFAULT ON COPENHAGEN/CANCUN COMMITMENTS

- Two important goals on "new and additional" finance for climate change were agreed in 2009 in Copenhagen at the major UN climate conference there (COP15) and adopted in more official form at subsequent talks a year later in Cancún (COP16): 1) "Fast Start Finance" of 30 billion US dollars balanced between adaptation and mitigation to flow from developed to developing countries between 2010 and 2012; and, 2) a similar collective goal to mobilize 100 billion dollars a year of climate finance in support of developing countries

- Several possible definitions of "new" and "additional" are left open to interpretation, and include: a) resources that are over and above pre-existing (2009) flows of climate change finance; b) resources additional to commitments to deliver foreign aid of 0.7% GNI as Official Development Assistance (ODA) - a commitment widely unmet since it was adopted by the UN in the 1970s; c) additional to commitments or intentions for progressively increasing ODA to meet the 0.7% target as communicated by governments well prior to the new climate finance pledges; and d), additional to 2009 levels of ODA
- Climate change finance fails to meet any of the above criteria except the first: climate change finance has increased significantly, especially finance for mitigation of climate change
- Because the other definitions do not qualify however, it is clear that "Fast Start" climate change finance has been withdrawn from earlier parallel commitments to sustainable development and poverty reduction efforts - the annual new and additional share of climate change finance is actually in the realm of just 2-3 billion US dollars for 2010, and not 10 billion a year, which raises further serious concerns that long-term financial goals could result in still more and greater diversions
- Numerous developed countries did however face in precisely this period the most extreme of financial pressures of the recent historical era, with a number among them facing fiscal collapse as a result of serious domestic and transnational economic and credit crises during the years of 2008-2012
- The recently agreed Green Climate Fund faces a difficult initiation environment as a result, endangering effective and cost-efficient climate action, in particular there is still no clarity on the scale and sources of generation of funding above all for the interim period from 2013-2020
- Given that ODA fell in real terms in 2011 versus 2010, the new and additional proportion of climate finance for the second year of the three year commitment period can only be lower still, meaning around 20 billion dollars of new and additional climate change finance should flow in 2012 if Copenhagen/Cancún commitments are to be met
- The finance provided is also imbalanced: adaptation makes up a mere 14% of the committed 14 billion dollars of overall climate change finance in 2010, or around 2 billion dollars - indications of change since then are unclear due to delayed reporting cycles - the need for enhance Monitoring, Reporting and Verification (MRV) is critical, in particular because there are serious risks of double or inaccurate accounting for resources under current reporting regimes
- Worse still, "Fast Start" finance is very slow: disbursal rates for conventional ODA are much faster than for climate finance - 76% versus 48% - mainly due to the complex array of funding instruments involved, slowing the rate at which climate-related funds reach beneficiaries
- Adaptation finance is not responding to vulnerabilities: with just over 2 billion dollars of adaptation finance flowing annually from developed to developing countries, wholesale gaps remain for even the most severely affected front-line nations - these are often complicated by conditionalities and other barriers that lock-out some of the world's most vulnerable countries from support
- The Clean Development Mechanism - albeit under sever pressure since several developed countries discontinued forward association - is currently leveraging tens of billion dollars of annual investment in low-carbon initiatives in developing countries and has emerged as one of the most meaningful de facto technology transfer instruments currently operational with around half of all projects resulting in a technology transfer of one form or another - coverage however is extremely limited with almost 90% of all investment benefitting either China or India alone

7.
NOBODY IS SPARED THE GLOBAL CLIMATE CRISIS

- In one respect or another, every country is experiencing negative impacts either resulting from the effects of climate change or as brought about by the carbon economy - not one country has Low vulnerability to the combined effects of climate change and the carbon economy, and just seven of the 184 assessed have Moderate vulnerability
- Even the largest and most advanced of the world's economies face serious losses, such as the United States, which is estimated to incur a 2.1% reduction in GDP by 2030
- That many wealthy countries exhibit low general vulnerability to climate change is more an indication of the extremity of effects taking hold on the climate frontlines, than of how inconsequential the effects of climate change are for the affluent
- Wealthy countries may have much lower thresholds of tolerance for climate-related impacts since wealth to a large extent insulates communities from suffering extreme societal risks: for example, the 75,000 additional deaths estimated to have been caused by the 2003 European Heat Wave that leading experts believe would almost certainly not have occurred in the absence of global warming is a major anomaly and point of concern for Europeans
- Advanced economies can also afford to part with much less of their economic growth than their developing counterparts - according to the International Monetary Fund, developing countries are growing more than four times as fast in real terms than advanced economies for whom

any marginal loss will have a disproportionate effect on what has been an average of just 1.5% in collective real economic growth over the last decade

- Furthermore, in the increasingly globalized world economy of the 21st century, the fortunes of all nations are more intimately tied, especially for highly networked developed countries that rely on foreign investments both domestically and abroad to sustain even marginal growth and retain high levels of prosperity - an unrestrained climate crisis can only become a major impediment to that prosperity whether or not its effects are felt locally or elsewhere
- The Monitor examines marginal short-term impacts and the implied evolution of these beyond the 2010-2030 scope of much of this report, but in the longer-term climate change implies rapidly growing risks of non-marginal and truly catastrophic impacts, such as a collapse in ocean circulation or of major ice sheets, or the breaching of thermal tolerance levels for humans - all of which would generate large-scale losses for any income group and none of which are accounted for in the Monitor

8.

OUTDATED ESTIMATES OF THE NEGATIVE EXTERNALITIES OF CLIMATE INACTION GUIDE TODAY'S REGULATORY DECISIONS

- Previous global estimates of the impact of climate change reveal less than 20 original studies developed by a much smaller range of authors, and with the exception of three, all are based on third-party research or data from the 1990s or earlier
- Previous studies routinely include the positive effects of carbon fertilization due to high levels of CO_2 without controlling for negative effects of an expanding carbon economy, such as ground-level ozone toxicity, ocean acidification, acid rain or the health hazards of pollution, among others
- No single study includes the impact of climate change on labour productivity, which the Monitor estimates as the most significant near-term impact of climate change in monetary terms
- Hundreds of estimates of the social cost of carbon are based on just nine studies of the negative externalities of climate change, all grounded in 1990s research and data, and which are actually integrated into and continue to guide the regulatory decisions of major countries
- In many cases these studies feed policy recommendations on emission reductions that would allow the rise in global temperatures to exceed the internationally agreed 2° Celsius (3.6°Fahrenheit) safety limit, since a common conclusion is that the costs of firm mitigation exceed any marginal benefits from reduced damages

RECOMMENDATIONS

FOR *ALL* NATIONAL POLICY MAKERS

Commit firmly to low-carbon prosperity

- Breaking free from the climate crisis will save lives, improve health and extend the lifespan and well-being of entire populations
- Tackling climate change results in net economic benefits and can reduce instability and system-level market volatility, restore domestic energy independence and jobs, while boosting business productivity and enhancing trade balances and economic competitiveness among major economies
- A low-carbon economy *will* reduce the stunning rate of contemporary environmental degradation, deforestation and irreversible biodiversity loss that is crippling the world's ecosystems with serious economic repercussions
- A global commitment to a low-carbon economy could strand half or more of all hydrocarbon reserves, rendering them unmarketable and potentially creating space for regulatory actions with very low costs not yet factored into economic modelling on low-carbon transition costing

Prioritize parallel measures to adapt to climate change

- Adaptation cannot be a stand alone response to the climate challenge: treating only the symptoms but not the cause of the climate crisis would result in spectacular economic losses for the world economy – not all the effects of climate change can be adapted to; some come at a pure sunken cost, while uncertainty in many cases doubles the costs of adaptation since the possibility of random outcomes (e.g. more or less rain) require parallel measures in opposing directions
- Adapting to climate change is expensive, but not doing so is even more costly – on the whole, adaptation is cost effective and, if strategically programmed, may result in productivity boosts that more than compensate for any investment made – governments are accordingly advised to close the adaptation gap
- Not investing in convincing adaptation responses will increasingly hold back country-level business and investor confidence, especially for highly vulnerable countries where climate change is already one of the most significant economic challenges
- Climate change is radically more dangerous and damaging for the world's poorest populations than for any other groups. Not empowering marginalized communities to overcome the daunting new challenges only multiplies economic, social and political risks and instability, and will guarantee a steady erosion of longstanding poverty-reduction investments
- International funding and resources of all kinds need to be anchored both in the best possible understanding of the probable distribution and severity of vulnerabilities and impacts attributable to climate change and the highest co-benefits of supported mitigation actions in terms of human health and the environment

Unite strengths in international partnership

- A new international partnership is called for based not only on essential mutual trust and reassurances but also on pure common interest and shared economic, environmental and social benefits
- The climate crisis has emerged as one of the greatest common challenges of humankind: in a planet at risk, with death and damages in pandemic proportions and humanity and justice tested to the limits, not even half of the world's powers are capable of solving the problem alone
- Working in partnership, any costs associated with a low-carbon transition are minimized as the global comparative advantages of emission reduction and removal are fully leveraged, while the dividends of climate action for sustainable human development can be maximized in greater fulfillment of human rights
- That partnership can build on the significant energy already invested by the international community over the course of nearly two decades and 17 major UN climate conferences dealing with every conceivable technical aspect of the climate problematic in great detail and to the steady improvement of complex but vital institutional instruments such as the Clean Development Mechanism

FOR GOVERNMENT GROUPS

Developed countries

1.1 Support the vulnerable *effectively*: Decades of investment in poverty-reduction efforts largely on the basis of public taxpayer resources have been seriously undermined by climate change and environmentally unsound development. Explosive climate stress and what are often termed its "risk multiplier" ramifications for health, social and political security, migration and global prosperity are also likely to indirectly endanger the already slow growth prospects of many developed countries. Act effectively by ensuring efforts are aligned with an evidence-based prioritization that places vulnerability up front, support promising local government initiatives, and reach for the last mile of impact.

1.2 Deliver fully on Copenhagen/Cancún commitments: Full delivery of climate finance is an essential component for meeting ambitious emission-reduction objectives. The prevailing financial climate is unfavourable, but climate finance has been largely transposed from parallel planned increases in Official Development Assistance committed or announced prior to and separately from international climate change agreements. Current flows are heavily imbalanced, with only marginal support for vulnerable countries to adapt to escalating damages. While mitigation actions can have very substantial benefits for sustainable human development, diverting resources intended for urgent poverty reduction priorities penalizes the world's poorest groups as more than one billion people are still living with hunger on a daily basis. The global response to climate change cannot be taken out of the international community's commitment to eradicate extreme forms of poverty, a project now seriously endangered in large part precisely as a result of climate change. Despite the prevailing macro-economic difficulties, developed countries are urged to convene an extraordinary session of OECD Development Assistance Committee and to subsequently communicate a joint and time-bound action plan for delivering on the full set of collective climate finance and sustainable development commitments, much of which would otherwise go unmet by the end of 2012 and thereafter.

1.3 Rescue the MDGs: The Millennium Development Goals (MDGs) would have had significantly greater chances of being met globally in the absence of the climate crisis. The MDGs may not now be fully attained unless additional resources are devoted to the cause, targeting in particular progress specifically jeopardized by climate change impacts not accounted for when the MDGs were developed. With only a few years remaining before the foreseen conclusion timeframe, substantial emergency resources should be put into efforts to achieve the MDGs on the basis of goal specific, geographic and income-group lag. The evidence for seriously compromising effects for key MDGs and progress in priority regions as a result of climate change underscores the critical importance of mainstreaming climate change considerations into national-, provincial- and even town- or village-level development policies. An MDG rescue fund could constitute an early thematic funding window for the newly established Green Climate Fund set to be established within the framework of the UN Climate Change Convention (UNFCCC). While the international community is now busy designing the successor "Sustainable Development Goals" that will take over from the MDGs after 2015, this important process should nevertheless not detract from the vital importance of first ensuring success by 2015 on the original MDGs.

Developing countries

2.1 Prioritize climate policy with highest co-benefits: Faced with limited capacities and resources, policy makers should deliberately target high-impact actions with multiple societal benefits in human, economic and environmental terms. One example is the promotion of efficient and clean-burning cooking stoves, which addresses indoor smoke-linked disease and deforestation, as well as supporting gender development and labour productivity. Promoting clean-burning stoves also limits potent particulate emissions which could help slow the aggressive short-term increase in temperatures. Dozens of other high-impact policy options abound. Pursuing low-carbon development strategies across the sectors of construction, forestry, water and agriculture in addition to the electricity-generation industry will broaden the possible development dividends yielded.

2.2 Pledge strong national action: Strong leadership can pay dividends. Above all, it is in the firm interests of developing countries to create a domestic environment of predictability as to the direction and intent of national climate change policies. More ambitious climate change policies will reassure foreign investors that climate risks are under control and that steps are being taken to ensure economic competitiveness and risk diversification with respect to energy usage and forward planning. With climate change already firmly embedded in the contemporary economic system, strong national action plans are an assertive starting point for reassuring key stakeholders in the economic and social prospects of an economy in the near term.

2.3 Invest in national risk analysis: Developing countries are overwhelmingly more vulnerable to climate-related impacts than industrialized nations. This is not only due to income inequalities and poverty but is also a product of heightened environmental vulnerabilities since the majority of developing countries are tropical or sub-tropical, where the implications of climate change are most severe. The high carbon intensity of economic activities common to many developing countries is a further disadvantage. As such, climate-related concerns are an important emerging factor for macroeconomic planning and the pursuit of optimal economic competitiveness. Effectively addressing climate-related risks requires sustained investment in local expertise, educational programmes, civil society groups and specialist technical networks. Ideally, reference climate change and emission scenarios, the backbone of climate change response planning, would be updated every 2-3 years and involve wide-ranging stakeholder groups in the development of each new iteration. National governments are best placed to foster the development of the most sophisticated country-specific climate-related analysis possible. Solid reference scenarios and analysis supports more accurate and efficient national policies and solidifies support for its implementation, including among development partners.

Highly vulnerable countries

3.1 Prioritize adaptation: Climate change is already a major determinant of the prosperity of economies most vulnerable to its effects. A highly robust climate change adaptation strategy and implementation plan is an essential safeguard for national development progress and economic growth prospects.

As the knowledge base expands, country risk will increasingly factor in the diverse negative and positive effects of climate change to the economic prospects of nations, with direct financial implications for investor confidence and foreign investment. Vulnerable countries need to learn from each other's successes and reassure the global economy that climate-related risks are well under control. Regional and localized knowledge tools, such as focused climate models, warrant serious investment in order to improve localized analysis as best as possible.

3.2 Boost domestic capacity: Considerable institutional competences are required to manage costly adaptation programmes necessary to limit damages and productivity losses due to climate change. If institutional arrangements are not in place, serious opportunities for participation in the global low-carbon transition may be foregone. Just one example relates to the Clean Development Mechanism (CDM). National authorities responsible for the registration of projects that could enable local environmentally sound energy-related projects to access financial resources from international carbon markets are still absent in a number of highly vulnerable countries. Capacity goes beyond the public sector too: no point in establishing a national CDM authority in the absence of any local entrepreneurial activity for developing low-carbon projects in the first place. Moreover, making the most of vibrant civil society interest on climate change will only add value and legitimacy to the climate change policy development process and is a valuable asset to governments that should be cultivated and strongly promoted.

3.3 Strengthen climate governance: The diffuse nature of climate change means its varied effects cut across the institutional divisions of policy both vertically, from national to provincial and district or municipal levels, as well as horizontally, encompassing government departments ranging from environment agencies to foreign, finance or planning ministries, resource management, civil defence, labour relations, agriculture, forestry, fisheries, commerce, science and education, health and safety, national meteorological services, to name just a few. Implementing meaningful policy requires extraordinary levels of coordination and stewardship. The most successful examples, such as the Philippines, thrive because of a deliberate high-level consolidation of national responsibility on climate issues in legislatively-mandated central authorities backed by direct executive involvement. The success of countries like the Philippines in implementing effective domestic climate change policies shows that improved climate change governance is a more significant determinant of climate policy success than the level of national domestic resources committed to climate policies.

FOR CIVIL SOCIETY AND THE PRIVATE SECTOR

Communicators and the Media

4.1 Question received wisdom: It has often been argued that green policies "curb economic growth", "increase gasoline prices" or "destroy jobs". Taxes on carbon do increase certain costs, namely by putting more of the burden of the negative affects of pollution back onto its sources. For most economies, an ambitious response to climate change would only attenuate dependency on costly and insecure imported fuel supplies in favour of locally developed energy solutions, such as energy efficiency upgrades to buildings. If the US was able to cut its trade deficit in half purely by shifting to domestic solutions for meeting and reducing energy requirements, would that not increase domestic prosperity, rather than curtail it? If half or more of the world's existing stocks of hydrocarbons, such as oil, were rendered obsolete, might not their market price just as well plummet not rise? If climate policy is only another ruse in support of "big" executive government, why in the US are individual states taking the legislative initiative and not the capital? When the local building and automobile industries actively lobby in favour of national legislation on climate change while hydrocarbon businesses with most of their operations offshore do the opposite, to what extent are policy outcomes being determined by vested influences as opposed to domestic economic interests?

4.2 Promote awareness on risks as opportunities: Risks are opportunities. Serious environmental and health impacts of the carbon economy will abate as low carbon development progressively dominates economic activities. The same for climate change impacts. In almost every case, taking measures to limit damages due to the warming the world is already committed to will improve competitiveness and minimize any losses. The Monitor emphasizes that it is no longer credible that mitigation of climate change will lead to reduced economic growth.

Indeed, the benefits of reducing the carbon intensity of growth far outweigh any small and artificial premium in profit margins associated with carbon based development strategies. The dividend of mitigation furthermore is most pronounced in fast-growing, newly industrialized developing countries.

4.3 Take a stand: Time is running out, and the stakes are tremendous, if not incalculable. If a low-carbon transition is not engineered within the decade, the consequences will be dire regardless of the ultimate magnitude, since they involve irreversible damage: the extinction of whole species, and thousands upon thousands of human lives lost. In worst cases, not solving climate change could render large areas of the planet unsuitable for human existence outdoors. The injustices, environmental irresponsibility and inhumanity involved are simply staggering. A nearly unparalleled body of scientific and observational evidence now amassed and plain for all to see with the steady disappearance of Arctic sea ice and glaciers. The dramatic weather-related adjustments and extremes repeated around the world are difficult to ignore. Despite the complexity of the topic, ignorance is no excuse for inaction, and indifference can be tied to complicity. With this report, there is now a comprehensive current-day economic justification for action in addition to the human, ethical, environmental and rights-based arguments already in wide circulation. Civil society groups, communicators and people of all kinds in positions of public influence or authority within their communities, whether in faith-based groups, municipal or educational establishments, should find no further obstacles to taking a stand in tackling climate change.

Investors

5.1 Perform comprehensive risk analysis: Corporations reliant on business models based on carbon assets, such as reserves of oil, are taking a daily gamble that a low-carbon economy will never prevail and those assets will never be stranded unable to reach markets due to regulation. Certainly, the structural features of the global economy and every mainstream energy outlook analysis back the narrative of the low-carbon economy as a pipe dream. But only a very narrow window of legislative action in favour of a firm response to climate change would strand half or more of the world's existing stockpiles of carbon-based fuels as unmarketable. To what extent are investment portfolios exposed or not to that possibly marginal but phenomenal risk? Are those risks worth bearing? How might they be minimized?

5.2 Encourage diversification strategies: Hydrocarbon companies should be capable of presenting comprehensive diversification strategies into low-carbon alternatives. If no convincing diversification strategies have been developed, it is clear that corporate leadership are carrying investor resources along a risky political gamble. Detailed economic modelling by major pension funds has demonstrated that a diversified portfolio should reap more benefits for investors in the case of a low-carbon transition than under business-as-usual conditions. Few companies in the energy sector rival the omnipotence of hydrocarbon businesses, mainly state-owned as they are. Therefore, whether or not the future energy requirements of the planet are met through renewable sources or via point-supplied carbon intensive fuels, the leading global energy corporations of today are still the best equipped to service the world's energy requirements of a low-carbon economy. Not preparing the ground for a potential low-carbon transition only builds up risks that need not exist. Coal businesses, for instance, with strong investments in carbon capture and storage (CCS) and employee and environmental safety research and development, would most likely benefit from a low-carbon transition rather than suffer.

5.3 Foster transition stability: Legislative steps that entail irreversible change to the landscape of the world's energy industry are a systemic risk embedded in global markets, just like climate change is already an inescapable and growing determinant of market prosperity itself. The energy sector constitutes the primary or at least a major share of virtually every major stock exchange. Abrupt policy action that results in a stranding of a majority of carbon assets could cause serious instability. And yet changes are very specifically a contingent necessity to the constraining of climate change, which in spite of current business trends is nevertheless a widely ratified international priority. In a globalized economy, it is a sovereign regulatory concern for any party to the UNFCCC. Equity market regulators across the 194 parties involved should be monitoring and publicly reporting on the extent to which systemic carbon-linked risks might jeopardize national and global prosperity. This would enhance investor visibility to the risk profiles of entire indexes and encourage better carbon risk management. Regardless of the motivations, regulators unwilling to publicize relevant information on such hazards might be suspected of purposely concealing inordinate risks, which may only compound exchange-specific risks and compromise investor confidence here.

Research community

6.1 Encourage attribution research: Imperfect data sets, confounding parallel effects, basic empirical limitations and otherwise, thwart the identification of climate change's role (or lack thereof) in any socio-economic or environmental phenomena. Yet the exercise is highly relevant and significant. Hundreds of billions of dollars of taxpayer resources virtually everywhere are already being diverted each year, consciously or not, to address the sprawling repercussions of a hotter planet. Knowing where these resources should or should not be deployed is of prime concern. Just one example serves to illustrate why. If climate change is assumed solely responsible for localized coastal degradation in a river delta due to a subjective rise in sea levels, a concrete wall along the foreshore might conceivably be built. However, equal or greater blame may well be attributable to upstream damns, hydro stations, irrigation, or localized ground-water pumping that would continue to cause land to sink further behind a prohibitively expensive, infrastructure-heavy coastal fortress aimed at containing sea-level rise. Furthermore, coastal defences in one area often accelerate degradation in adjacent coastal zones by inhibiting the natural dissipation qualities of tidal energy, spreading inadvertent losses further still.

6.2 Expand global analysis: Global estimates and models of the impact of climate change are so complex and subject to such a wide array of assumptions and proxies by the experts or research teams involved in their development as to be almost irreproducible by third parties, even when full transparency is provided on the methodological steps involved. And yet understanding the costs and benefits involved in addressing any serious policy concern is ordinarily an unavoidable imperative. Climate change proposes nonetheless perhaps the most ambitious policy agenda the modern world has had to decide on. The dearth of recent analysis on the question has no doubt lessened confidence in global policies capable of enabling a major macroeconomic restructuring crucial to the initiation of a low-carbon transition. The Monitor's reassessment of the costs of climate change would best be judged through comparison with other similarly updated studies. Where future studies include also carbon economy side effects, such as carbon fertilization, they should also include the full range of carbon economy side effects, including ozone toxicity, acid rain, pollution issues relating to health and other relevant impacts such as those assessed by the Monitor.

6.3 Avoid misrepresentation of risks: The level of confidence and agreement among academic specialists and their models is less important for vulnerable communities than the potential risks implied by science. Understating risks by stressing instead the uncertainties associated with attributional association to climate change is irresponsible because the implication is to displace concern, entailing potentially deadly and economically debilitating ramifications if policy makers fail to act on risks. While many risks cannot be affirmed as stemming from climate change with a high degree of confidence, neither can their causal association to climate change be discounted with any better degree of confidence. Future reference reports should aim to highlight first the range of risks, then the levels of confidence and uncertainty associated with them, and not the other way around. It is safer to risk being over prepared than under.

FOR THE INTERNATIONAL DEVELOPMENT AND HUMANITARIAN COMMUNITY

Development actors

7.1 Focus on economic development, education and environmental governance: Any strategy that boosts economic and human development will almost certainly also reduce climate vulnerability by some degree. This is highlighted by the very low levels of climate impacts assessed for the few high-income tropical countries that share environmental vulnerabilities with lower-income neighbours, such as Brunei, Saudi Arabia or Singapore. Education is also critical so that communities experiencing a growth of income are equally equipped with high degrees of awareness of the risks faced and the means available to mitigate these. Educating children, especially girls, may be the most cost-effective method to spread awareness, since the school system, as well as informal educational avenues, is a sustainable conduit to invest in, and children are more likely to further pass on their knowledge to other groups, namely adults. Environmental governance is equally key, since the unsustainable exploitation of natural resources, above all fisheries, forests and water, might occur regardless of the level of education and may even intensify as incomes rise. But environmental governance should look beyond simple protection towards actually enhancing the public goods natural resources have to offer. This might include the construction of damns to trap water from heavy downpours for irrigation during drier spells, or the expansion of natural reserves or wetlands for pollination, waste water treatment or wind protection.

7.2 Raise the disposable income of farmers and fishermen: Support national efforts to establish appropriate national government policies and investments that yield for the lowest income groups. The groups most consistently and heavily exposed to climate-related impacts are small-scale or subsistence farmers and fishermen, and especially their children. The greatest challenge faced by the lowest income bracket of these groups is to reverse the vicious cycle of decline that climate-related risks are constantly feeding. In order to break out of decline, farmers and fishermen need to expand their incomes and profitability. If not, even the most cost-effective of opportunities to protect against damages may remain out of reach on purely financial grounds, such as higher quality seeds, clean burning stoves, irrigation equipment or crop insurance. Education and rural extension training has a role to play in helping farmers to boost productivity so that more can be achieved with the same resources available. Expanding market access for the raw or finished goods produced by this group is another option of growing interest as the world's markets continue to globalize. Providing financial stimulus and training to local entrepreneurs or cooperatives to establish light agro-fishery industries capable of packaging these goods for admission to global supply chains would allow local producers to appropriate a greater share of the value chain and maximize the commercial value of their goods.

7.3 Integrate climate strategies to revitalize development: Access to carbon markets via the reformed CDM, which allows the pooling of micro-level activities into one larger and therefore collectively financeable project, and the possibility of a global carbon market for forests, represent new sources of long-term income streams that could enable a host of fresh sustainable development initiatives to take hold in developing countries. Simple large-scale energy projects like hydro damns or extensive concrete sea defences may be attractive climate-related initiatives for administrative or other reasons, but energy-efficient cooking stoves and mangrove plantations would likely accomplish the same objectives - reduce emissions, protect against coastal degradation - but bring much higher co-benefits - for health, biodiversity, forests, carbon sinks, or wind protection, to name just some key advantages. Several successes in payment for ecosystem services systems, Costa Rica's scheme being a prime example, also provide templates for governments to regulate and incentivize the protection and growth of valuable environmental assets in an integrated and self-sustaining way. International policy makers should prioritize high co-benefit initiatives and integrated programmes that deal simultaneously with multiple issues in order to maximize the scarce resources available for tackling climate vulnerability while making the most out of the transition to a low-carbon economy in terms of sustainable human development at a global level. With far fewer resources available for adapting to climate change, prioritizing mitigation projects that also boost local adaptive capacity or directly result in adaptation dividends could double or more the possible extent of adaptation efforts. As an example, retrofitting buildings with thermal insulation would reduce cooling energy loads, and therefore emissions, but also safeguard health and labour productivity from rising temperatures.

The humanitarian system

8.1 Brace for change: Change is already underway. That change is also significant: as heat rises, parts of the world will experience climates with no analogue in human history. It is still extremely difficult to confidently attribute a specific extreme weather event in part or entirely to climate change, especially not close to the time of its occurrence. Certain types of events, such as extreme heat leading to drought or flooding triggered by heavy rains, nevertheless carry the classic hallmarks of disasters suspected to have been caused or aggravated by climate change. On the basis of the classical laws of physics, moreover, it is nearly impossible that, for example, more abundant, frequent and concentrated heavy rainfall or severe hot and dry spells would not result in a general increase in flooding or drought. As such, the humanitarian sector needs to be capable not just of preparing for but also responding to weather-related emergencies on larger scales and at more frequent intervals. Likewise, all development and humanitarian partners should increasingly realize the value of building, together, the resilience of communities to avoid simply racing to respond to emergencies and maximize the effectiveness of development investments.

8.2 Establish a thematic funding window for climate-linked emergency response: The damage caused by the general increase in the extremity of certain types of weather already accounts for a significant and growing share of human and economic disaster losses. The concern falls squarely within the competence of the UNFCCC and is a legitimate target for climate change finance, especially for developing countries with marginal capacity that are penalized by current finance flows, which seek out strong "absorptive capacity". Persistent Horn of Africa and Sahel food security crises highlight the extent to which the international humanitarian community is not sufficiently equipped to cope with climate-related disasters. As climate stresses continue to mount, that capability will only be further eroded if action is not taken to ensure it is reinforced. The track record of humanitarian sector resource mobilization makes it unlikely that standard sources of funding will keep pace with costly additional burdens to emergency response. A climate finance-replenished thematic funding window should be established to finance a share of all emergency relief and rehabilitation costs associated with any extreme weather events, especially floods and drought – since such events can neither be attributed nor *dis-attributed* to climate change. The same window could also finance emergency preparedness activities in known high-risk hotspots. The UN's Central Emergency Response Fund (CERF) could establish a dedicated window for this purpose in conjunction (or not) with the Green Climate Fund.

8.3 Evolve thinking and partnerships: Even without today's clear resource constraints, it will take more than just additional financial resources to cope with the increases in risks expected as a result of heavier rain and more extreme heat. Strategic planning should question whether the past is an accurate basis for future situations given the highly dynamic conditions the world now finds itself dealing with as a result of climate change, economic and population growth, globalization, and otherwise. Extreme droughts are breaking new records today, but those records will only be re-broken again and again in the years to come. Organizations and institutional response structures will need to become more accustomed to dealing with highly uncertain and speculative information, find efficient ways to prepare for a range of different possible outcomes, including unprecedented multi-country crises that could be triggered by repeated extremes, such as heavy flooding followed by extreme and prolonged drought, and compounded by additional risks, such as energy price spikes. The interactions between climate change and other wide-ranging crises merits more focused examination: just as climate change outcomes are affected by wide-ranging issues, so too climate change will affect critical determinants of tomorrow's humanitarian crises, if not already, today's. Breaching conventional comfort zones in order to work more widely and effectively with non-traditional humanitarian actors like the private sector or the military, would also help to expand reach and impact.

RESEARCH PROCESS

INCEPTION AND DEVELOPMENT

The first edition of the Monitor was meant to serve as a departure point for discussions to refine understanding of climate vulnerability. As stated in that 2010 report, the goal has been to improve both the methodology and the accuracy of this tool going forward. A number of considerations raised during the development of the first report by external review bodies could not be adequately addressed at that time, but instead have fed into development of the second edition. So while this new report was only formally commissioned in November 2011, the second Monitor nevertheless has its origins well rooted in the first.

The original Monitor approached the problem of climate change in a non-technical but policy-relevant way. It established a conceptual framework that assessed vulnerability at the national level. But it allowed for an understanding of vulnerability as internationally fluid not static, with today's isolated vulnerabilities rapidly becoming tomorrow's shared vulnerabilities. Separating out some of the different components of vulnerability helped to show that nearly every country in the world faces some aspect of the problem to a high degree. Much of the architecture of the original report is retained in this Monitor.

Not unsurprisingly, a number of headline conclusions from the 2010 report still hold, such as an insufficient focus on the human health impacts affecting most vulnerable communities or the highly significant links between a country's level of vulnerability to climate change and its human development status. However, it became evident that not all original country-level results were satisfactory and that certain sections of the original report oversimplified the socio-economic effects of climate change. Nor did the original format provide sufficient granularity for sector-level effects (economic impacts were limited to "land" and "marine") or convey key nuances between different levels of certainty.

Much of the difficulty stemmed from a heavy reliance on third-party global or regional macro models that pooled information at those levels, leading to a certain degree of inaccuracy in the results for some countries, since the information wasn't designed for the Monitor's nation-by-nation analysis. This second edition continued to draw on other studies; however, it still did not solve the challenge of providing accurate national-level outputs.

The difficulties of re-running climate impacts models developed by others is a recognised issue for the field (Nordhaus, 2011).

The second Monitor's now greatly expanded set of indicators is therefore primarily anchored in individual bodies of recent research pertaining to discrete effect areas, such as distinct economic sectors (agriculture, fisheries, forestry, etc.) and specific resource, health or environmental impacts (e.g. water, heat and cold illnesses and biodiversity). DARA has also worked with additional external advisory bodies in order to further the range of inputs. The new Monitor also includes a new thematic pillar.

While the original edition focused on the effect of "Climate", this edition focuses on both "Climate" and "Carbon". The new section on the socio-economic impacts of the carbon economy came from recognition that there is a distinct, symbiotic relationship between climate change concerns and the carbon economy. Viewing climate policy more holistically will help decision makers form parallel or combined responses to both the consequences of global warming and its root causes.

Another major adjustment to the second Monitor is the inclusion of in-depth country-level input, including field research and exchanges with local specialists. This input was viewed as a must for the effective development of an improved Monitor report, and the governments and experts of Ghana and Vietnam fully embraced and engaged with that process.

CONSULTATION & COUNTRY RESEARCH

EXTERNAL ADVISORY BODIES

Two external advisory bodies have provided critical input at various intervals during the course of the Monitor's development. A senior Advisory Panel provides strategic guidance on the Monitor's framing, analysis and recommendations. An open format Peer Review Committee provides specialist and technical input in particular on methodological and theoretical issues.

Participants in these two bodies serve in a non-remunerated personal capacity and represent a broad spectrum of expertise and viewpoints on the topic as well as a variety of stakeholder groups whose perspectives and involvement have helped enrich the Monitor's development, analysis and presentation. The research team responds to every question and critique from these groups and endeavours to reflect all input within the limitations of the overall project.

The expectations for the second Monitor were presented to the report advisory bodies at the beginning of 2012 in the form of an Inception Report to which DARA received a first round of substantive feedback.

The second Monitor then underwent two separate methodological and quantitative reviews by its Peer Review Committee, including a full-day workshop in Geneva in April 2012. A dialogue between Committee members and the Research Team was also organised with representatives of the Climate Vulnerable Forum on that occasion. A draft report was submitted for review to both bodies in August 2012 and adjusted prior to public release Individual members of the advisory bodies comment only on certain aspects of the project, not on its entirety, based on their expertise, availability and other considerations.

While the Monitor benefits from external advisory bodies and open peer review, the system and approach of this project is to be distinguished from academic peer-reviewed scientific literature. This report is designed primarily as a policy and communication tool that strives for technical accuracy in encapsulating the scientific work of third parties together with other forms of qualitative and quantitative information, including field-based research.

COUNTRY STUDIES

Country studies were undertaken in Vietnam and Ghana in March 2012. In each case, a half-day national workshop was convened to present conclusions of desk research conducted by DARA and to seek substantive input from key stakeholders and policy makers across public, private and civil society groups. Two representative territorial units were also identified in each country for field research, and dozens of extended interviews were conducted there with senior representatives of local government, civil society and business groups.

ADDITIONAL CONSULTATIONS

Climate Vulnerable Forum delegates were briefed on the Monitor's progress at an official open session of the group at the UN climate change talks in Bonn, Germany in May 2012 Additionally, some early results from the Monitor project were presented and discussed publicly at an official Climate Vulnerable Forum Side Event to the UN Conference on Sustainable Development (Rio+20) in Rio de Janeiro in June 2012.

RESEARCH PROCESS

10

ACCRA
National Workshop
March 2012

11

BOLGATANGA, GHANA
Field Research
March 2012

12

1ST METHODOLOGICAL/ QUANTITATIVE REVIEW
Monitor 2nd Ed.
April 2012

9

SOUTH-EAST COAST, GHANA
Field Research
March 2012

8

BEN TRE, VIETNAM
Field Research
March 2012

7

HANOI
National Workshop
March 2012

6

YEN BAI, VIETNAM
Field Research
March 2012

5

INCEPTION REPORT
Monitor 2nd Ed.
February 2012

4

DURBAN
UNFCCC COP17 Official Forum Side Event Presentation of the Dhaka Declaration
December 2011

13

GENEVA

Peer Review Committee Workshop
April 2012

14

BONN

UNFCCC Intercessional Negotiations Official Forum Side Event
May 2012

15

RIO DE JANEIRO

UN Conference on Sustainable Development Official Forum Side Event
June 2012

16

2ND METHODOLOGICAL / QUANTITATIVE REVIEW

Monitor 2nd Ed.
July 2012

17

DRAFT REPORT REVIEW

Monitor 2nd Ed.
August 2012

CLIMATE VULNERABILITY MONITOR

18

NEW YORK

Launch of Monitor 2nd Ed.
September 2012

19

WASHINGTON, D.C.

Expert Discussion
October 2012

DHAKA

Climate Vulnerable Forum Ministerial Meeting
November 2011

3

CANCÚN

UNFCCC COP16 Launch of Monitor 1st Ed.
December 2010

2

LONDON

Launch of Monitor 1st Ed.
December 2010

1

20

DOHA

UNFCCC COP18 Official Forum Side Event
November 2012

KEY ISSUES

ADDITIONAL DEATHS

2010 · 2,750
2030 · 3,500

2010 · 20,000
2030 · 45,000

2010 · 2,500
2030 · 3,500

2010 · 55,000
2030 · 80,000

2010 · 85,000
2030 · 150,000

2010 · 3.1 MILLION
2030 · 3.1 MILLION

2010 · 35,000
2030 · 35,000

2010 · 1.4 MILLION
2030 · 2.1 MILLION

2010 · 225,000
2030 · 380,000

2010 · 30,000
2030 · 40,000

2010 · 20,000
2030 · 20,000

Floods & landslides · Storms · Diarrheal infections · Heat & cold illnesses · Hunger · Malaria & vector-borne · Meningitis
Air pollution · Indoor smoke · Occupational hazards · Skin cancer

ADDITIONAL COSTS

2010 · **29**
2030 · **213**

2010 · **20**
2030 · **61**

2010 · **66**
2030 · **565**

2010 · **52**
2030 · **-11**

2010 · **491**
2030 · **3,461**

2010 · **296**
2030 · **1,749**

2010 · **23**
2030 · **106**

2010 · **172**
2030 · **630**

Enviromental disasters | Habitat change | Health | Industry stress | = Billion USD PPP (2010 non-discounted) - negative values show gains

AFFECTED GROUPS

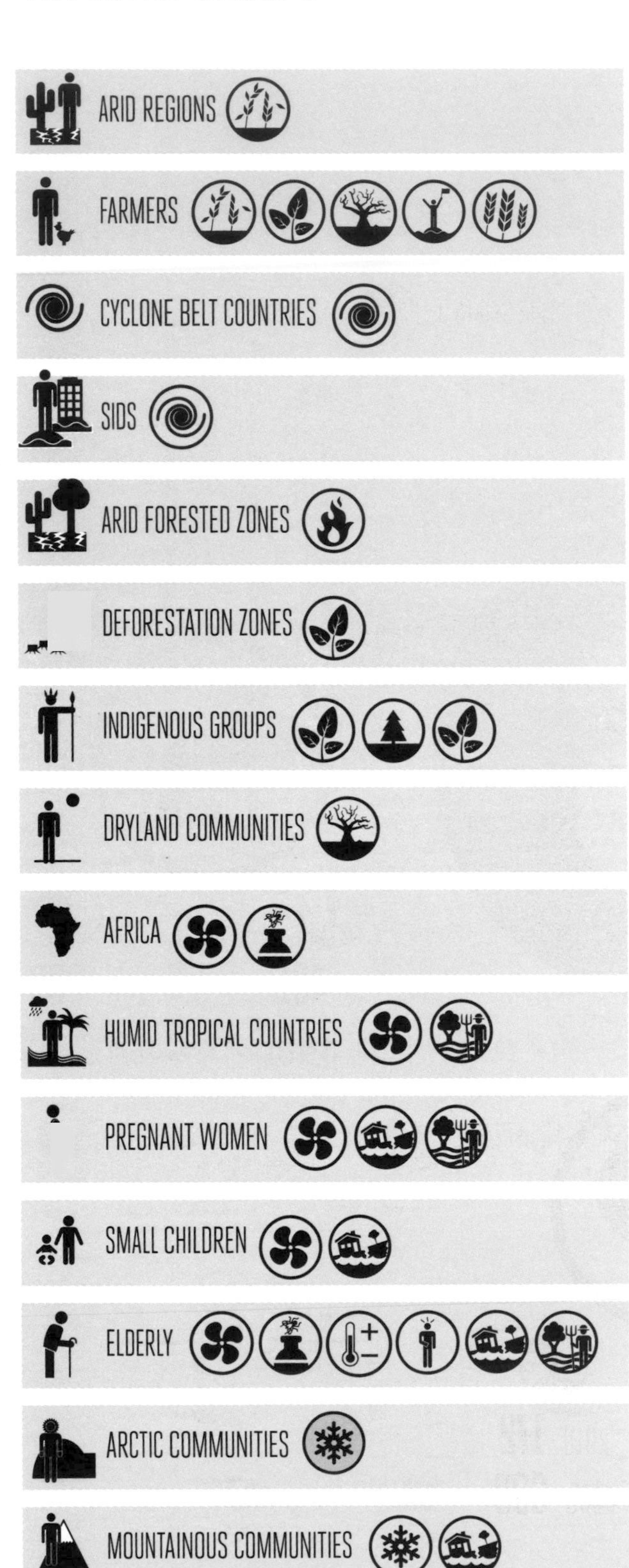

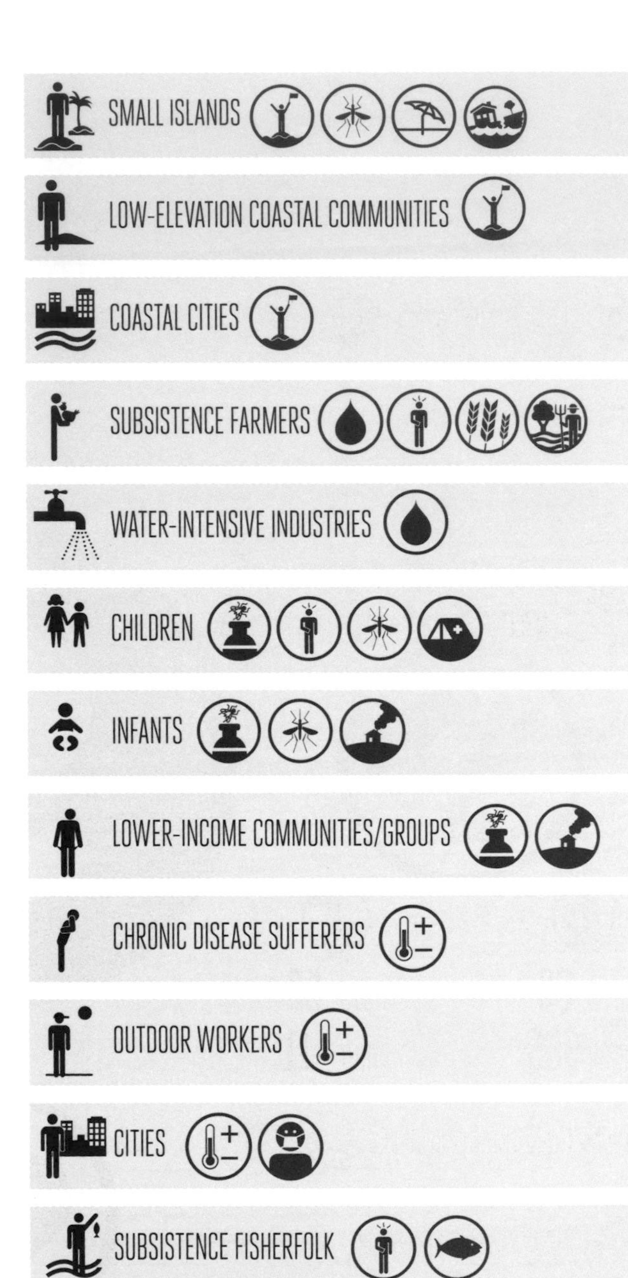

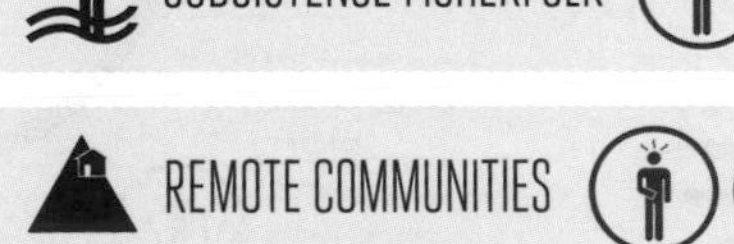

TROPICAL COUNTRIES
LIVELIHOODS DERIVED FROM FISHING
ENERGY COMPANIES
BEACH RESORTS
LOW-ELEVATION WINTER RESORTS
DENSELY POPULATED RIVER WAYS
OIL SAND HOST COMMUNITIES
COASTAL COMMUNITIES
TROPICAL FOREST COMMUNITIES/ZONES
NEWLY-INDUSTRIALIZED COUNTRIES
TRANSITION ECONOMIES
INDUSTRIALIZED COUNTRIES
WOMEN
RURAL POPULATIONS WITH POOR ENERGY ACCESS
COAL MINERS

VEHICLE DRIVERS
COAL AND GAS POWER PLANT WORKERS
FAIR SKINNED
DEVELOPED COUNTRIES
CHINA
RIVER BASINS
OUTDOOR OCCUPATIONS
MIDDLE INCOME COUNTRIES
HEAVILY LABOURING WORKERS
LOWER INCOME COMMUNITIES
FISHERMEN

Drought
Floods & landslides
Storms
Wildfires
Biodiversity
Diarrheal infections
Heat & cold illnesses
Hunger
Malaria & vector-borne
Meningitis
Desertification
Heating and Cooling
Labour productivity
Sea level rise
Agriculture
Fisheries
Tourism
Water
Forestry
Hydro Energy
Transport
Permafrost
Biodiversity
Fisheries
Oil sands
Air pollution
Indoor smoke
OIL Spills
Water
Skin cancer
Agriculture
Forestry
Corrosion
Occupational hazards

GEOPOLITICS

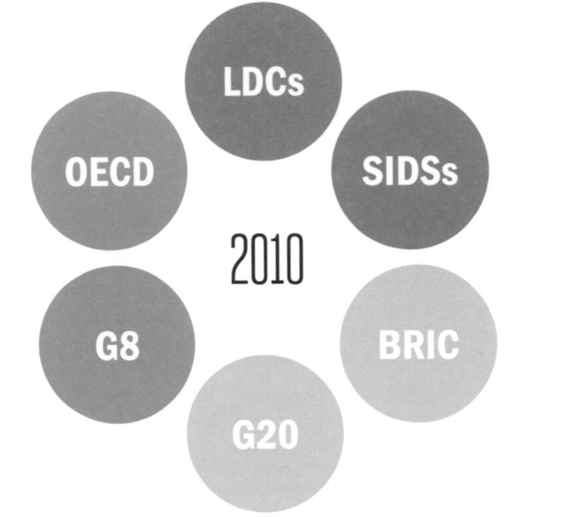

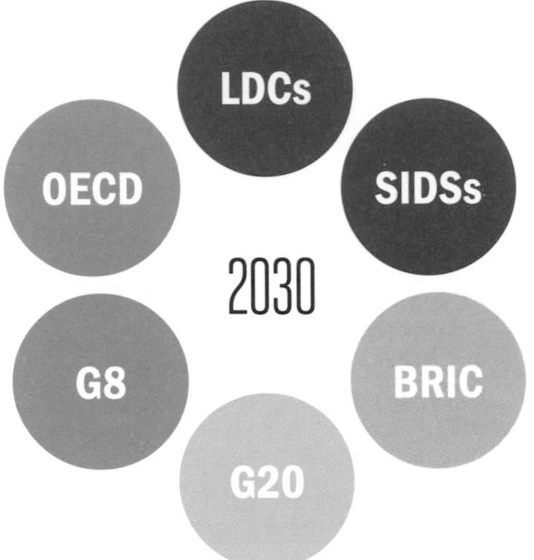

DEATHS DUE TO CLIMATE AND CARBON PER 100,000

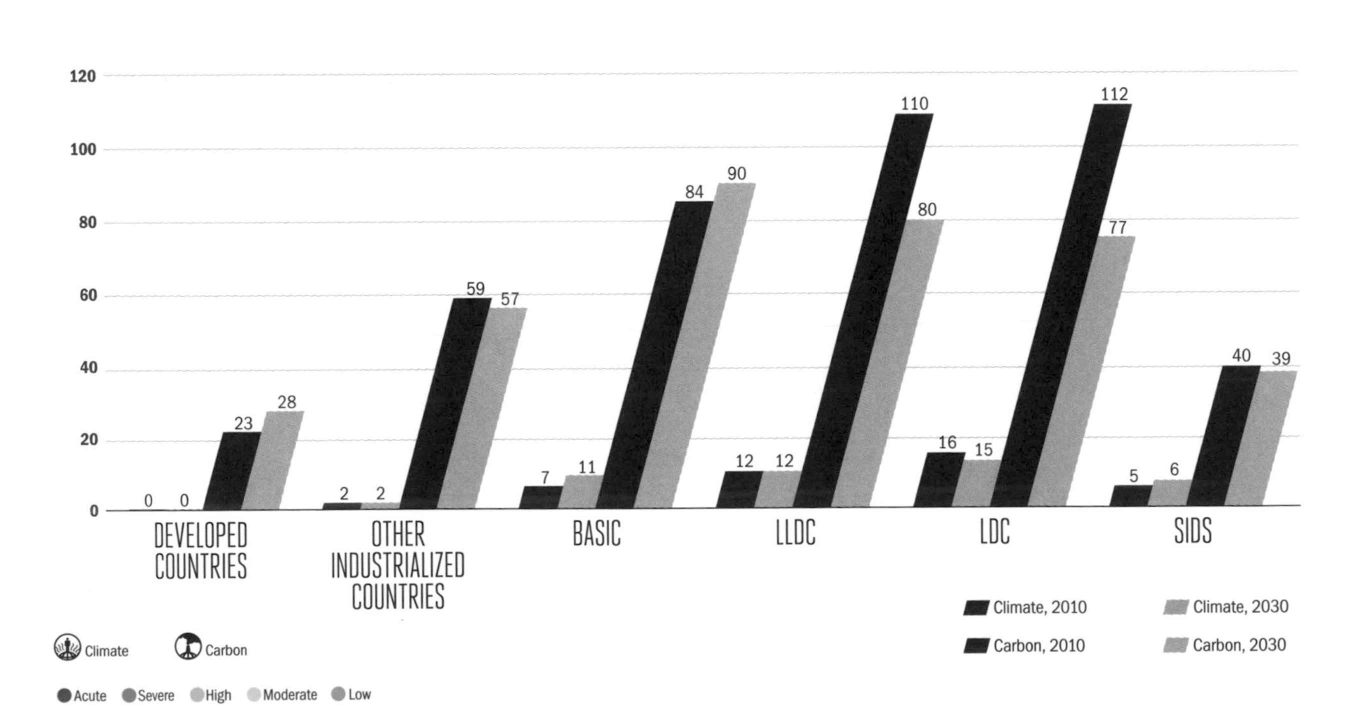

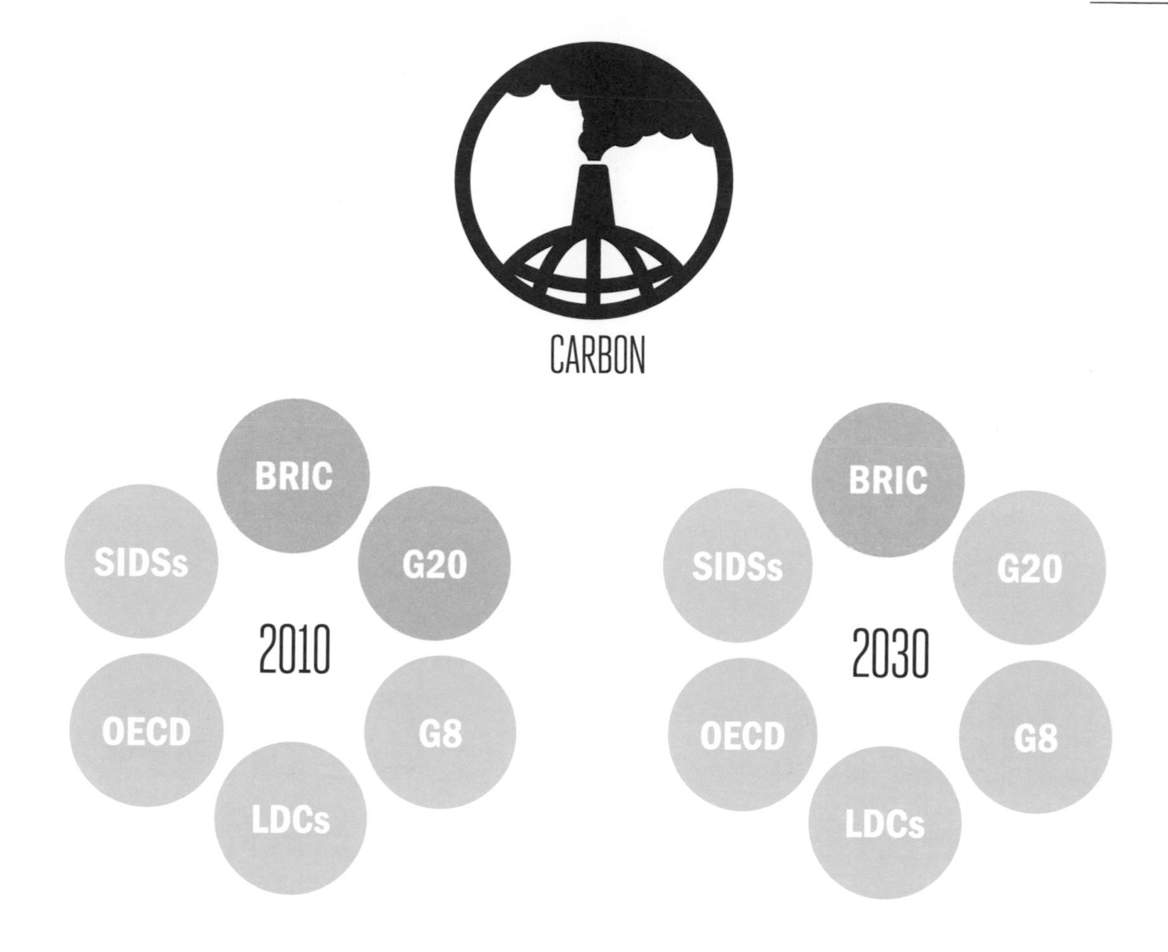

COSTS DUE TO CLIMATE AND CARBON, % OF GDP

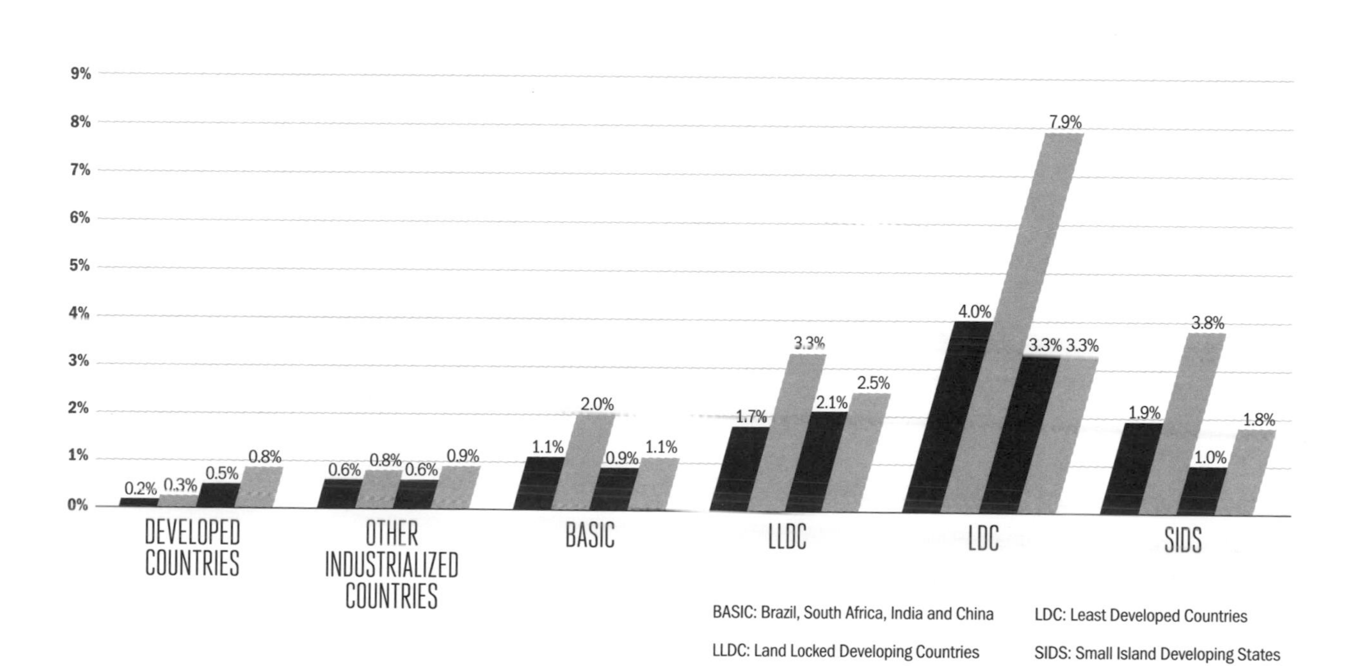

BASIC: Brazil, South Africa, India and China

LLDC: Land Locked Developing Countries

LDC: Least Developed Countries

SIDS: Small Island Developing States

HOTSPOTS

CLIMATE

2010		2030
182,000	INDIA	333,000
17,000	PAKISTAN	37,000
26,000	NIGERIA	31,000
17,000	DR CONGO	25,000
15,000	BANGLADESH	21,000
10,000	ETHIOPIA	16,000
9,000	INDONESIA	13,000
8,000	AFGHANISTAN	13,000
7,000	MYANMAR	11,000
6,000	SUDAN/SOUTH SUDAN	8,000
6,000	TANZANIA	8,000
5,000	UGANDA	7,000
4,000	MOZAMBIQUE	6,000
4,000	ANGOLA	5,000
3,000	BRAZIL	5,000
3,000	COTE D'IVOIRE	5,000
3,000	NIGER	4,000
4,000	CAMERON	4,000
3,000	BURKINA FASO	4,000
3,000	CHAD	4,000

2010		2030
72	CHINA	727
89	INDIA	680
48	MEXICO	368
36	INDONESIA	282
21	THAILAND	166
14	VIETNAM	159
15	MALAYSIA	119
16	BRAZIL	118
45	UNITED STATES	116
13	PHILIPPINES	102
15	NIGERIA	94
11	COLOMBIA	87
11	VENEZUELA	84
11	PAKISTAN	81
7	BANGLADESH	69
17	RUSSIA	61
7	IRAN	50
5	MYANMAR	39
7	ARGENTINA	38
5	SOUTH AFRICA	32

Climate   Carbon   Economic Cost (billion PPP USD)

CARBON

2010		2030
1,379,000	CHINA	1,643,000
923,000	INDIA	1,059,000
148,000	PAKISTAN	234,000
123,000	INDONESIA	184,000
177,000	NIGERIA	168,000
99,000	BANGLADESH	118,000
84,000	AFGHANISTAN	114,000
81,000	UNITED STATES	112,000
107,000	ETHIOPIA	94,000
84,000	DR CONGO	91,000
98,000	RUSSIA	77,000
55,000	VIETNAM	65,000
50,000	BRAZIL	64,000
34,000	TURKEY	49,000
25,000	IRAN	48,000
32,000	PHILIPPINES	46,000
40,000	MYANMAR	45,000
34,000	JAPAN	41,000
39,000	ANGOLA	40,000
42,000	UKRAINE	39,000

2010		2030
71	CHINA	451
114	UNITED STATES	305
42	BRAZIL	298
39	INDIA	129
19	INDONESIA	121
22	RUSSIA	119
11	MEXICO	73
10	ARGENTINA	71
9	MALAYSIA	67
8	PERU	58
19	CANADA	53
6	COLOMBIA	46
10	ANGOLA	40
5	GABON	33
4	VENEZUELA	33
4	BOLIVIA	31
10	AUSTRALIA	26
4	THAILAND	19
9	JAPAN	18
5	PAKISTAN	18

MILLENNIUM DEVELOPMENT GOALS

END EXTREME POVERTY & HUNGER

UNIVERSAL EDUCATION

GENDER EQUALITY

CHILD MORTALITY

Floods & landslides · Storms · Diarrheal infections · Heat & cold illnesses · Hunger · Malaria & vector-borne · Meningitis · Drought · Biodiversity

Desertification · Heating and Cooling · Labour productivity · Sea-level rise · Agriculture · Fisheries · Tourism · Water · Forestry · Hydro Energy

Biodiversity · Fisheries · Oil sands · Air pollution · Indoor smoke · Oil Spills · Water

MATERNAL HEALTH

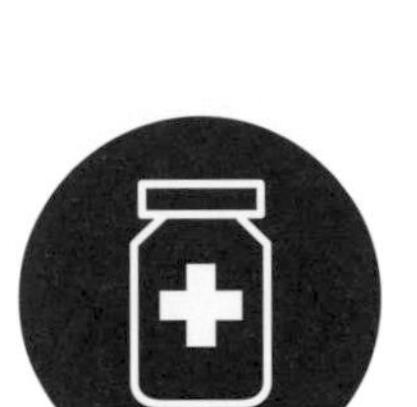

COMBAT HIV/AIDS & INFECTIOUS DISEASES

INJUSTICE

    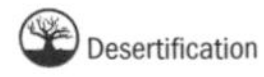   

Floods & landslides · Storms · Diarrheal infections · Heat & cold illnesses · Hunger · Malaria & vector-borne · Meningitis · Wildfires
Permafrost · Forestry · Tourism · Desertification · Fisheries · Sea-level rise · Hydro Energy · Transport · Biodiversity
Heating & Cooling · Drought · Labour Productivity · Water · Agriculture

2010 2030 2010 2030

EUROPE

EASTERN EUROPE

NORTHERN EUROPE

WESTERN EUROPE

SOUTHERN EUROPE

AMERICAS

CARIBBEAN

CENTRAL AMERICA

NORTH AMERICA

SOUTH AMERICA

ASIA-PACIFIC

AUSTRALASIA

CENTRAL ASIA

EAST ASIA

MIDDLE EAST

PACIFIC

RUSSIA/NORTH ASIA

SOUTH ASIA

SOUTHEAST ASIA

AFRICA

CENTRAL AFRICA

EAST AFRICA

NORTH AFRICA

SOUTHERN AFRICA

WEST AFRICA

CLIMATE FINANCE

PRIORITY

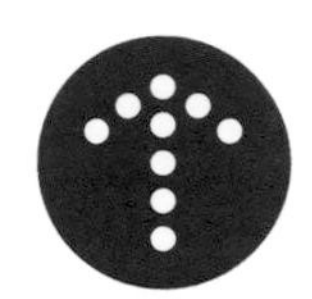

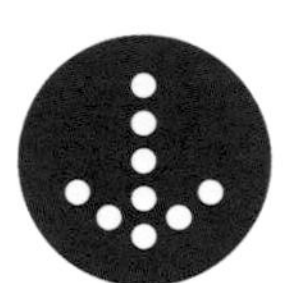
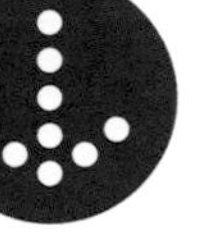

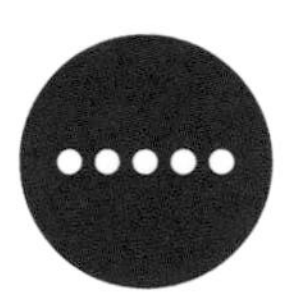

Climate

 Floods & landslides  Storms  Diarrheal infections 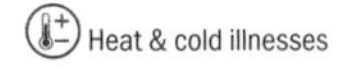 Heat & cold illnesses  Hunger  Malaria & vector-borne  Meningitis  Wildfires

 Permafrost  Forestry Tourism Desertification Fisheries Sea-Level Rise Hydro Energy  Transport  Biodiversity

Heating & Cooling Drought  Labour Productivity  Water  Agriculture

In 2010, developed countries provided 14 billion dollars of their Official Development Assistance (ODA) as climate finance, a significant increase from around 7 billion in 2009. However, the degree to which these resources are "new and additional" as agreed at the international climate change talks at Copenhagen and Cancún is seriously in question. The Fast Start Finance target of 30 billion dollars over the three years from 2010 to 2012 would imply approximately 10 billion dollars' worth of new climate finance per year. While collectively climate finance for 2010 was a respectable 7 billion dollars higher than in 2009, only 5 billion is derived from increases in donors' ODA volumes - i.e. approximately 2 billion dollars of those resources have been either diverted or reclassified from existing ODA flows.

If, however, other commitments related to ODA are taken into account, the level of "additionality" and new finance diminishes considerably. In the 1970s, a collective commitment to provide 0.7% of the Gross National Income (GNI) of developed countries as ODA to developing countries was agreed to in the UN General Assembly. That commitment has been consistently met by a handful of developed country donors since the mid-1970s and has been reconfirmed in numerous official international contexts. The 2005 G8 summit at Gleneagles and the UN 2005 World Summit, which launched the Millennium Development Goals for 2015, saw a spate of new ODA commitments - including countries far behind the 0.7% target - all attempts to reach 0.7% by 2015, with interim ODA volume goals for 2010.

Only 2 billion dollars of new climate finance for 2010 is actually additional to these targets for progressing towards 0.7% of GNI or flows above that - commitments that had already been made by the same group of countries in order to support the achievement of the Millennium Development Goals, among other sustainable development priorities, such as Agenda 21. Given that today still only a fraction of countries have actually provided in excess of 0.7% GNI as ODA, just 1 billion dollars of new climate finance alone can be considered additional to this particular commitment.

To the degree, therefore, that commitments on climate finance are delivering, they are also unquestionably at the expense of previous commitments to related sustainable development priorities. Neither is the picture for 2011 likely to be substantively different, since under preliminary reporting, overall ODA has increased by just 3.9%, broadly enough to keep up with one year of global inflation over this period as reported by the International Monetary Fund. Furthermore, almost 90% of this finance was targeted towards mitigation activities, with 14% committed to adaptation - a clear discrimination versus the agreements made at Copenhagen and Cancún, whereby it was firmly agreed that there would be a balance of resources for the two purposes.

Financial flows in the form of aid or climate finance have been central to policy debate and intergovernmental negotiations for responses to sustainable development challenges and climate change. But ODA-related flows are only a fraction of the picture. Investment linked to projects of the UNFCCC's Clean Development Mechanism, for instance, are now several times the level of climate finance through ODA. More than half of ODA is, in any case, concessional debt - and a possible liability. More than half of all CDM projects, on the other hand, are estimated to result in a technology transfer of one form or another - a further bonus. Despite this, the CDM arguably absorbs much less of the attention of policy makers than finance. This is partly ascribed to the faltering political support currently enjoyed by the Kyoto Protocol mechanism. But the fact that China to-date accounts for almost 80% of all CDM investments by volume, and India for another 15%, does mean all other developing countries capture just over 5% of any investment flows. Many countries have no CDM projects at all and no national capacity to register CDM projects.

In an ongoing financial and economic crisis that runs parallel to time-restricted policy windows for addressing core global concerns such as climate change, a heavy reliance on further delivery through ODA finance is clearly a restrictive avenue of action. The example of the CDM also demonstrates the large-scale impact possible through policy frameworks with a bearing in the private sector, as opposed to ODA finance efforts, even when these are only moderately effective (given CDM coverage limitations alone). Effective policies for technology development and transfer, capacity building and regulatory mechanisms have the potential to yield significant impact in terms of implementation of sustainable development visions, including in the climate agenda, the Rio agenda an otherwise.

Climate change finance from developed countries to developing countries is reported by all donors as a part of their Official Development Assistance (ODA). This analysis was based on the Organization of Economic Co-operation and Development's (OECD) CRS database - the only truly comprehensive and comparable source of financial tracking available, although it is exclusively a donor reporting mechanism. Research focused on the latest data accessible, which is for the year 2010. 2010 is also the first year of so-called Fast Start Finance - additional commitments to climate change finance agreed at the UN Climate Summit at Copenhagen (COP15) and further confirmed at the next Summit in Cancún (COP16). The analysis has benefitted from the Rio markers for climate change used by donor governments and the OECD. Only finance to projects reported to have climate change as a principal objective were included in the analysis so as to retain comparability with sector-based development finance analysis, where partially related funding is ignored. That focus also partly addresses further concerns over the misrepresentation and double-counting of a share of climate finance as reported by other recent independent research into the topic. The approach used here represents just one perspective on monitoring international climate finance flows; other methodologies could have been chosen and would have likely yielded different results and conclusions.

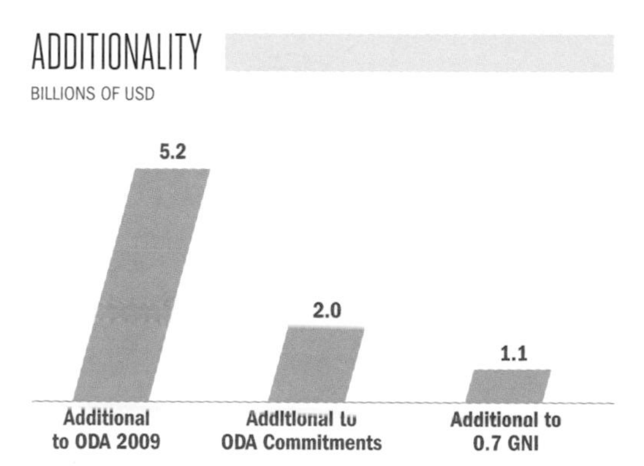

INDICATOR OVERVIEW

Impact Areas	Indicators	Confidence	Severity	Surge	Injustice	Priority	Gender Bias	Affected Country Group: A	Affected Country Group: R
CLIMATE									
	DROUGHT	✓	⚠⚠	▶					
	FLOODS & LANDSLIDES	✓	⚠⚠	▶▶			♀		
	STORMS	✓	⚠⚠⚠	▶▶					
	WILDFIRES	✓	⚠	II					
	BIODIVERSITY	✓	⚠⚠⚠⚠	▶▶▶					
	DESERTIFICATION	✓	⚠⚠	▶					
	HEATING & COOLING	✓	⚠	▶▶					
	LABOUR PRODUCTIVITY	✓	⚠⚠⚠⚠	▶▶▶			♀♂		
	PERMAFROST	✓	⚠⚠⚠	▶▶					
	SEA-LEVEL RISE	✓	⚠⚠⚠⚠	▶▶▶					
	WATER	✓	⚠⚠⚠	◀◀					
	DIARRHEAL INFECTIONS	✓	⚠⚠⚠	▶					
	HEAT & COOL ILLNESSES	✓	⚠⚠	◀					
	HUNGER	✓	⚠⚠⚠⚠	▶					
	MALARIA & VECTOR BORNE	✓	⚠⚠	II					
	MENINGITIS	✓	⚠⚠	▶					
	AGRICULTURE	✓	⚠⚠⚠⚠	▶▶▶					
	FISHERIES	✓	⚠⚠⚠	▶▶▶					
	FORESTRY	✓	⚠⚠	▶▶					
	HYDRO ENERGY	✓	⚠	◀◀					
	TOURISM	✓	⚠⚠	II					
	TRANSPORT	✓	⚠⚠	▶					
WORLD									
CARBON									
	OIL SANDS	✓	⚠⚠	▶▶					
	OIL SPILLS	✓	⚠⚠⚠	◀					
	BIODIVERSITY	✓	⚠⚠⚠⚠	▶▶▶					
	CORROSION	✓	⚠⚠	▶					
	WATER	✓	⚠⚠	◀					
	AIR POLLUTION	✓	⚠⚠⚠⚠	▶▶▶					
	INDOOR SMOKE	✓	⚠⚠⚠⚠	◀◀			♀		
	OCCUPATIONAL HAZARDS	✓	⚠⚠⚠	▶			♂		
	SKIN CANCER	✓	⚠⚠	▶					
	AGRICULTURE	✓	⚠⚠	◀◀◀					
	FISHERIES	✓	⚠⚠	▶▶▶					
	FORESTRY	✓	⚠⚠⚠	▶▶					
WORLD									

A Absolute (largest overall share of total negative impact) R Relative (highest share of total losses vs. GDP/per capita) Mo Model ES Emission scenario Additional mortality – yearly average

Info		Change		Impact				
Mo	ES	Mortality	$	#	2010 Mortality	2030 Mortality	2010 $	2030 $
Corti et al., 2009; Hoekstra et al., 2010; Rubel and Kottek, 2010; Sheffield and Wood, 2007	SRES A1B (IPCC, 2007)		71%	10			5,000	20,000
Kharin et al., 2007	SRES A1B (IPCC, 2007)	4%	231%	8	2,750	3,500	10,000	95,000
Donat et al, 2011; Mendelsohn et al., 2011	IPCC SRES A1B (IPCC, 2000)	24%	129%	7	2,500	3,500	15,000	100,000
Krawchuk et al., 2009	IPCC SRES A2 (IPCC, 2000)		106%	14			-15	-90
Baumgartner et al., 2012; Thomas et al., 2004	IPCC SRES A1B (IPCC, 2000)		74%	3			80,000	400,000
Hansen et al., 2007	IPCC SRES A1B (IPCC, 2000)		56%	11			5,000	20,000
Isaac et al., 2008	TIMER/IMAGE reference scenario for the ADAM project (Isaac et al. 2008)		19%	22			-35,000	-75,000
Euskirchen, 2006; Kjellstrom et al., 2009	SRES A2 (IPCC, 2000)		174%	1			300,000	2,500,000
Hoekstra et al., 2010; Nelson et al., 2001	UKTR GCM-based scenario (Nelson et al., 2001)		71%	5			30,000	150,000
DIVA, 2003	A1F1 (IPCC, 2000)		115%	2			85,000	550,000
Hoekstra et al., 2010; McKinsey and Company, 2009; Nohara, 2006; Portmann et al., 2010; Rosengrant et al., 2002	IPCC SRES A1B (IPCC, 2000)		68%	12			15,000	15,000
McMichael et al., 2004	S750 (IPCC, 2007)	56%		15	85,000	150,000		
Curriero et al., 2002; Knutti et al., 2008; Toulemon and Barbieri, 2006; Van Noort et al., 2012	IPCC SRES A1B (IPCC, 2000)	20%		16	35,000	35,000		
McMichael et al., 2004	S750 (IPCC, 2007)	42%		17	225,000	380,000		
McMichael et al., 2004	S750 (IPCC, 2007)	15%		18	20,000	20,000		
Adamo et al., 2011; Sheffield and Wood, 2008	SRES A1B (IPCC, 2000)	25%		19	30,000	40,000		
Cline, 2007	Cline, 2007		157%	4			50,000	350,000
Cheung et al., 2010; O´Reilly et al., 2003	SRES A1B (IPCC, 2000)		355%	6			15,000	150,000
US Forest Service (2010)	SRES A1B (IPCC, 2000)		182%	9			5,000	45,000
Lehner, 2003; Nohara, 2006	SRES A1B (IPCC, 2000)		134%	21			-5,000	-25,000
ECLAC, 2011; Steiger, 2011	SRES A1B (IPCC, 2000)			20				
Jonkeren et al, 2011; Nohara et al, 2006	SRES A1B (IPCC, 2000)		96%	13			1,000	5,000
					400,250	632,000	575,985	4,299,910

Info		Change		Impact				
Mo	ES	Mortality	$	#	2010 Mortality	2030 Mortality	2010 $	2030 $
CAPP, 2011; CERES, 2010			12%	5			5,000	25,000
Muehlenbachs et al., 2011; Schmidt, 2004; Westwood, 2010			5%	3			10,000	40,000
Costanza, 2006; Hooper, 2012; Reilly, 2008			109%	1			300,000	1,750,000
OECD, 2012			24%	7			1,000	5,000
OECD, 2012			18%	6			5,000	10,000
Bell et al., 2007; OECD, 2012; Sheffield et al., 2011		32%		8	1,400,000	2,100,000		
OECD, 2012		17%		9	3,100,000	3,100,000		
BP, 2012; Mathers and Loncar, 2006		26%		10	55,000	80,000		
Martens, 1998; WHO IARC, 2005		87%		11	20,000	45,000		
Avnery, 2011; Hansen et al., 2007; Ramanathan et al., 2008; World Bank, 2005			494%	12			15,000	-150,000
IGBP-DIS SoilData(V.0), 2008; OECD,2012			203%	2			10,000	75,000
Costanza et al., 1997; OECD, 2012; Reilly, 2008; Wentzel, 1982			5%	4			30,000	85,000
					4,575,000	5,325,000	376,000	1,840,000

$ Additional economic costs in 2010 USD (negative numbers show gains) (thousands) – yearly average

\# Order no. of impact by overall economic scale versus the climate section (or carbon section for carbon indicators)

A VERY SHORT **HISTORY** OF CLIMATE SCIENCE

CLIMATE CHANGE HAS BEEN SUBJECT TO SCIENTIFIC AND POPULAR DEBATE FOR WELL OVER A CENTURY. The greenhouse effect was first proven by Irish physicist John Tyndall in 1859. The possibility of human-engineered global warming was raised by the Nobel Laureate Swedish chemist Svante Arrhenius in 1896 (Tyndall, 1869; Arrhenius, 1896). Arrhenius initially concluded that a doubling of atmospheric carbon dioxide (to over 550ppm) might result in 5-6 degrees Celsius (9-11° Fahrenheit) of warming. This estimation is closely aligned with current science: the prediction falls just outside the confidence intervals of the latest reference scenarios of the Intergovernmental Panel on Climate Change (IPCC) (Arrhenius, 1896; IPCC, 2000). At the then current rates of emissions Arrhenius thought the process might take millennia. However, a decade later, after observing the intervening rise in industrial CO_2 emissions, Arrhenius revised the warming timeframe to just a few centuries (Arrhenius, 1908).

In the 1930s, English engineer Guy Stewart Callendar was the first to report an actual warming trend and to ascribe it to human activities. The "Callender effect", estimated then as an annual temperature increase of 0.005°C, was still not on timescales relevant to people but might usefully impede the onset of a new ice age (Callendar, 1938; Weart, 2011). Subsequent technological progress improved monitoring of CO_2 and temperature, boosting evidence for human-induced climate change. This led the American physicist Gilbert Plass to assert in 1956 that a doubling or halving of atmospheric CO_2 would lead to an increase or decrease in temperature of around 3.5°C or 6.3°F (Kaplan, 1952; Plass, 1956). It was thought warming would be evident by the end of the century. By the mid-1980s, records of atmospheric CO_2 and temperature frozen in time kilometres deep in Antarctic ice cores confirmed the relationship between GHG emissions and climate change on the basis of 150,000 years of meteorological history (Lorius et al., 1986; Mayewski and White, 2002). By the end of the century, the record had been extended to over 400,000 years, strengthening the conclusions, and confirming the unprecedented nature of contemporary levels of CO_2 in the Earth's atmosphere (Petit et al., 1999).

By 1990, and publication of the first assessment report by the IPCC, the scientific community had reached a firm understanding and generalized level of agreement over the basic characteristics of climate change, the central role of human activities in shaping it and the potential danger for people alive today (IPCC, 1990). It constituted a wake-up call to policy-makers to address climate change. In 1992, the UN Framework Convention on Climate Change marked the international community's first step towards a serious response (UNFCCC, 1992). At the turn of the century, warming of the planet and the increase of GHG emissions in faithful synchrony was observationally manifest (IPCC, 2001). By 2007, it had become scientifically indisputable (IPCC, 2007).

THE
LONDON, EDINBURGH, AND DUBLIN
PHILOSOPHICAL MAGAZINE
AND
JOURNAL OF SCIENCE.

[FIFTH SERIES.]

APRIL 1896.

XXXI. *On the Influence of Carbonic Acid in the Air upon the Temperature of the Ground.* By Prof. SVANTE ARRHENIUS *.

I. *Introduction : Observations of* Langley *on Atmospherical Absorption.*

A GREAT deal has been written on the influence of the absorption of the atmosphere upon the climate. Tyndall † in particular has pointed out the enormous importance of this question. To him it was chiefly the diurnal and annual variations of the temperature that were lessened by this circumstance. Another side of the question, that has long attracted the attention of physicists, is this : Is the mean temperature of the ground in any way influenced by the presence of heat-absorbing gases in the atmosphere? Fourier ‡ maintained that the atmosphere acts like the glass of a hot-house, because it lets through the light rays of the sun but retains the dark rays from the ground. This idea was elaborated by Pouillet § ; and Langley was by some of his researches led to the view, that "the temperature of the earth under direct sunshine, even though our atmosphere were present as now, would probably fall to −200° C., if that atmosphere did not possess the quality of selective

* Extract from a paper presented to the Royal Swedish Academy of Sciences, 11th December, 1895. Communicated by the Author.
† 'Heat a Mode of Motion,' 2nd ed. p. 405 (Lond., 1865).
‡ *Mém. de l'Ac. R. d. Sci. de l'Inst. de France*, t. vii. 1827.
§ *Comptes rendus*, t. vii. p. 41 (1838).

Phil. Mag. S. 5. Vol. 41. No. 251. *April* 1896. S

266 Prof. S. Arrhenius *on the Influence of Carbonic Acid*

TABLE VII.—*Variation of Temperature caused by a given Variation of Carbonic Acid.*

Latitude.	Carbonic Acid=0·67.					Carbonic Acid=1·5.					Carbonic Acid=2·0.					Carbonic Acid=2·5.					Carbonic Acid=3·0.				
	Dec.–Feb.	March–May.	June–Aug.	Sept.–Nov.	Mean of the year.	Dec.–Feb.	March–May.	June–Aug.	Sept.–Nov.	Mean of the year.	Dec.–Feb.	March–May.	June–Aug.	Sept.–Nov.	Mean of the year.	Dec.–Feb.	March–May.	June–Aug.	Sept.–Nov.	Mean of the year.	Dec.–Feb.	March–May.	June–Aug.	Sept.–Nov.	Mean of the year.
70–60	−2·9	−3·0	−3·4	−3·1	−3·1	3·3	3·4	3·8	3·6	3·52	6·0	6·1	6·0	6·1	6·05	7·9	8·0	7·9	8·0	7·95	9·1	9·3	9·4	9·4	9·3
60–50	−3·0	−3·2	−3·4	−3·3	−3·22	3·4	3·7	3·6	3·8	3·62	6·1	6·1	5·8	6·1	6·02	8·0	8·0	7·6	7·9	7·91	9·8	9·5	9·0	9·5	9·3
50–40	−3·2	−3·3	−3·3	−3·4	−3·3	3·7	3·8	3·4	3·7	3·65	6·1	6·1	5·5	6·0	5·92	8·0	7·9	7·0	7·9	7·7	9·5	9·4	8·6	9·2	9·17
40–30	−3·4	−3·4	−3·2	−3·3	−3·32	3·7	3·6	3·3	3·5	3·52	6·0	5·8	5·4	5·6	5·7	7·9	7·6	6·9	7·3	7·42	9·3	9·0	8·2	8·8	8·82
30–20	−3·3	−3·2	−3·1	−3·1	−3·17	3·5	3·3	3·2	3·5	3·47	5·6	5·4	5·0	5·2	5·3	7·2	7·0	6·6	6·7	6·87	8·7	8·3	7·5	7·9	8·1
20–10	−3·1	−3·1	−3·0	−3·1	−3·07	3·5	3·2	3·1	3·2	3·25	5·2	5·0	4·9	5·0	5·02	6·7	6·6	6·3	6·6	6·52	7·9	7·5	7·2	7·5	7·52
10–0	−3·1	−3·0	−3·0	−3·0	−3·02	3·2	3·2	3·1	3·1	3·15	5·0	5·0	4·9	4·9	4·95	6·6	6·4	6·3	6·4	6·42	7·4	7·3	7·2	7·3	7·3
0–(−10)	−3·0	−3·0	−3·1	−3·0	−3·02	3·1	3·1	3·2	3·2	3·15	4·9	4·9	5·0	5·0	4·95	6·4	6·4	6·6	6·6	6·5	7·3	7·3	7·4	7·4	7·35
−10–(−20)	−3·1	−3·1	−3·2	−3·1	−3·12	3·2	3·2	3·2	3·2	3·2	5·0	5·0	5·2	5·1	5·07	6·6	6·6	6·7	6·7	6·65	7·4	7·5	8·0	7·6	7·62
−20–(−30)	−3·1	−3·2	−3·3	−3·2	−3·2	3·2	3·2	3·4	3·3	3·27	5·2	5·3	5·5	5·4	5·35	6·7	6·8	7·0	7·0	6·87	7·9	8·1	8·6	8·3	8·22
−30–(−40)	−3·3	−3·3	−3·4	−3·4	−3·35	3·4	3·5	3·7	3·5	3·52	5·5	5·6	5·8	5·6	5·62	7·0	7·2	7·7	7·4	7·32	8·6	8·7	9·1	8·8	8·8
−40–(−50)	−3·4	−3·4	−3·3	−3·4	−3·37	3·6	3·7	3·8	3·7	3·7	5·8	6·0	6·0	6·0	5·95	7·7	7·9	7·9	7·9	7·85	9·1	9·2	9·4	9·3	9·25
−50–(−60)	−3·2	−3·3	—	—	—	3·8	3·7	—	—	—	6·0	6·1	—	—	—	7·9	8·0	—	—	—	9·4	9·5	—	—	—

THE MONITOR

THE MONITOR EXPLAINED

THE CLIMATE VULNERABILITY MONITOR

In mid 2010, the first Climate Vulnerability Monitor (or, "the Monitor") was commissioned on the initiative of the founding chair of the Climate Vulnerable Forum, the Maldives, as an independent global study of the gathering climate change crisis. The Monitor provides a framework for understanding global vulnerability to climate-related concerns. It enables a weighing of the possible costs, benefits and needs associated with different ways to address this crisis. The framework is grounded in third-party research by dozens of other research groups and scientists assimilated in the Monitor.

Subtitled "The State of the Climate Crisis", the first Monitor was issued in December 2010 in conjunction with the UN climate change talks in Cancún. DARA developed the report, and two external advisory bodies were formed to solicit wide-ranging third-party input. A second edition of the Monitor was subsequently commissioned in November 2011 at the Ministerial Meeting of the Climate Vulnerable Forum held in Dhaka, Bangladesh. DARA was mandated to develop the second edition of the Monitor, overseen by a joint Steering Group comprising Climate Vulnerable Forum and DARA officials and with continued input from external advisory bodies.

ITS PURPOSE

The Monitor was first assembled to contribute to a fuller understanding of the global climate crisis and to support communities facing serious challenges as a result of this emerging concern. It aims to inform the public and policymakers and help shape more effective climate change policies. The Monitor's second edition essentially measures the global impact of climate change and the carbon economy in socio-economic terms, both for today and for the near future. In doing so, it reveals information that enables a comparison of the vulnerability of different countries around the world to climate-related effects. It highlights the key issues at hand, assesses the scale of the problem overall and in its different aspects and anticipates the rates of change and the distribution of effects across various countries. The report is not an attempt to "predict" the future but to explore what implications current patterns of core economic and social activities hold for the near future. Its estimations of socio-economic impact should be considered broad indications as opposed to precision appraisals.

The Monitor is a country-level tool that also provides for sub-regional, regional, geopolitical and global analysis. The development of the Monitor's second edition further benefitted from in-country research conducted in Ghana and Vietnam; key insights from these exercises are detailed in the relevant sections of this report and have also been used to support analysis elsewhere. The country studies provide an idea of how the Monitor's information can be employed in national contexts. However, the Monitor is *not* a replacement for regional, national and sub-national analysis in any respect. Any global study involves use of highest-common-denominator information across countries for the sake of comparability. The Monitor is therefore most accurate at the international level and least accurate at sub-national levels. At all levels, however, it is designed to serve as complementary input and as a reference point.

The body of data amassed here could also help establish possible relationships, causal and otherwise, between climate-related phenomena and social and political vulnerabilities, such as propensity to armed violence, instability and migration. This report, for instance, particularly focuses on the relationships between climate-related impacts and transnational flows of climate change finance and of progress towards the Millennium Development Goals for 2015, the international community's leading objectives for poverty reduction.

Finally, as the first edition of the Monitor made clear, this report can be improved upon in the future. In spite of its 19th century roots, the science and analysis of climate change is still a relatively new field of study as conventionally defined, and it is evolving rapidly. Several of the indicators in this report rely on information that was not available when the first Monitor was being developed only two years ago. Only a few of the indicators in the report rely on studies published prior to the last major IPCC report in 2007. Its practical shelf-life depends on how quickly this highly active and interdisciplinary field continues to advance.

ITS USERS

The Monitor is specifically prepared to serve as a resource to Climate Vulnerable Forum officials tasked with negotiations and policy development related to climate change. The Monitor has also been used by analysts, policy makers, senior representatives and topic specialists from the following groups:

- Civil society organizations
- Development Aid agencies and intergovernmental and international non-governmental humanitarian and development organizations
- Financial institutions, such as investment banks
- Government climate change, environment, foreign affairs and resources or planning departments
- Heads of state and government
- Journalists, commentators, bloggers and the wider media
- Lead climate change negotiators active in the UN talks
- Members or representatives of parliaments in developed and developing countries
- NATO member military intelligence institutions and strategic studies groups
- Research institutions and think tanks with a development, humanitarian or environment focus

APPLICATIONS

The data and perspectives the Monitor provides have been used for a number of applications, including policy development guidance, resource allocation, financial analysis and communication on climate-change issues.

Policy Development

With respect to policy development, the Monitor serves as an additional reference for helping national policy makers and international organizations design and calibrate programmes to respond to climate change. This is particularly valuable in lower-income developing countries, where local decision makers might otherwise not be able to afford a third-party reference to compare with the analysis of other foreign consultants and external experts (Ayers, 2010).

A brief review of National Adaptation Programmes for Action lodged with the UN Framework Convention on Climate Change (UNFCCC) highlights the differences and gaps between countries' existing policies and the assessment here. Labour Productivity, the most serious climate effect in the Monitor, is barely considered. Cooling of indoor space is also a non-issue in most cases. Perhaps more alarming is recent World Health Organization research highlighting that just 3% of resources for priority projects in Least Developed Countries and small island states target health (WHO, 2010). If these policies had been developed while consulting reference publications like the Monitor, oversights and missed priorities would likely have been more readily avoided. And the impact of national policies addressing climate

change might have been enhanced. Another example is the international humanitarian system. The Climate section on Environmental Disasters estimates that in less than 20 years, climate change could cause thousands of deaths and hundreds of billions of dollars in damage due to a further aggravation of weather (this is after accounting for any anticipated reductions in risk as wealth increases). Is the humanitarian system prepared for such rapid increases in the scale of emergencies? Are more capacities, resources and institutional coordination needed to ensure the international community is prepared?
Climate change means the world now operates in a highly variable and dynamically evolving natural environment where the future will constantly be different from the past. International policies of all kinds will have to account for such evolutions in medium- to long-term planning in order to remain effective. Climate change should be taken into account when setting agendas and making policies at the village, regional and global level. And decision makers will need to draw on as many different forward-looking studies, such as the Monitor, as possible.

Climate Finance

Because it compares current and future levels of vulnerability to climate change, the Monitor can help decision makers prioritize where to spend their resources. This not only relates to legal obligations under the UNFCCC that developed countries have assumed to help developing countries. It also relates to countries being able to see the benefits and pitfalls of how they allocate resources across various sectors or strategies. There is however no internationally accepted definition of "vulnerable" countries among intergovernmental agencies such as the UNFCCC. Nor is the Monitor an attempt to establish a fixed definition. The Monitor does, however, provide arguments for why a wide range of countries - particularly developing and least developed, land-locked, or small island developing states - may have very serious climate-related vulnerabilities. 15 billion dollars of climate finance currently flows each year from taxpayers in developed countries to developing countries, including just over 2 billion dollars for support to adapt to climate change impacts. Are those resources being allocated according to who is most vulnerable? Are those resources being prioritized according to the co-benefits they would deliver to the environment or human health?
There are almost no comprehensive, up-to-date tools for assessing the near-term effects of climate change and the carbon economy and how they differ from country to country. And yet international actors have to make choices about where to focus energies and resources today - and have been doing so for over a decade now. Despite the imperfections of such tools, including this one, policy makers without this kind of reference are passing equally imperfect or worse judgements on these issues or are allowing political, cultural, strategic or military factors to play a determining role in climate change investment decisions. Some combination of all approaches is most likely. However, adding reference points from independent assessments can enrich the decision-making landscape and support more effective and cost-efficient policy.

Business and Investment

This report estimates the extent to which climate change has already affected the global economy, determining the wealth and growth prospects of different countries. As climate change accelerates and triggers new effects, it could have an even larger impact on a country's economic state. The Monitor provides a range of insights into the risks different countries will face on this front in the near term. Those insights are of interest both for the purpose of analysing a country's overall risk and for developing investment strategies.

Communication

The Monitor is useful to the lay person as a broad introductory work as well as to politicians and advocates across a variety of organizations that can use the data and analysis to question new or prevailing policies, be they government, corporate or otherwise.

FOCUS AND STRUCTURE

Years
2010 and 2030

Countries
184

Assessments
A global examination of wide-ranging negative and positive effects across two separate climate-related themes.
Climate: The impact of climate change on society.
Carbon: The independent impact of the carbon economy on society (separate from climate change).

Climate Vulnerability Levels
An indicator of the level of vulnerability of a country, region or group to a particular climate or carbon stress in relation to levels experienced by other countries.

Acute Severe High Moderate Low
Most vulnerable *Least vulnerable*

Impact Areas

- **Environmental Disasters:** Economic and health effects of environmental disasters generated or worsened by human activity.
- **Habitat Change:** Economic effects of shifts and changes to the environment.
- **Health Impact:** Health and economic effects for different diseases grouped by illness or cause.
- **Industry Stress:** Economic effects experienced by specific sectors of the economy.

CLIMATE INDICATORS

ENVIRONMENTAL DISASTERS
- Drought
- Floods and Landslides
- Storms
- Wildfires

HABITAT CHANGE
- Biodiversity
- Desertification
- Heating and Cooling
- Labour Productivity
- Permafrost
- Sea-Level Rise
- Water

HEALTH IMPACT
- Diarrheal Infections
- Heat & Cold Illnesses
- Hunger
- Malaria & Vector-Borne
- Meningitis

INDUSTRY STRESS
- Agriculture
- Fisheries
- Forestry
- Hydro Energy
- Tourism
- Transport

CARBON INDICATORS

ENVIRONMENTAL DISASTERS
- Oil Sands
- Oil Spills

HABITAT CHANGE
- Biodiversity
- Desertification
- Corrosion
- Water

HEALTH IMPACT
- Air Pollution
- Indoor Smoke
- Occupational Hazards
- Skin Cancer

INDUSTRY STRESS
- Agriculture
- Fisheries
- Forestry

KEY CONCEPTS AND DEFINITIONS

CLIMATE

Climate is taken to mean the average weather. The classical time period used by the World Meteorological Organization to determine the climate is 30 years. So the climate is the average weather over a given period of 30 years. Parameters such as temperature, rainfall and wind can be examined to determine key characteristics of the state of the climate at different periods in time, and to identify variation across time periods. The section of the Monitor labelled "Climate" is concerned with the socio-economic effects of a changing climate.

CLIMATE CHANGE

Climate change is a change in average weather. For the purpose of this study, it is assumed that human activities are the principal and overwhelming - if not exclusive - cause of the contemporary warming of the climate, in accordance with the broad consensus and more recent evidence on this subject (IPCC, 2007; Rohde et al., 2012; Muller, 2012).

According to the United Nations Framework Convention on Climate Change (UNFCCC), climate change occurs "in addition to natural climate variability observed over comparable time periods" (UNFCCC, 1992). The Monitor controls for natural variability in a number of ways, including by judging all impacts against a 1975 baseline period (i.e. the change in temperature and other variables versus the 1975 climate), even though considerable warming of the climate system had occurred well prior to 1975. Therefore the Monitor's assessment of climate change should be understood to align with that of the UNFCCC.

Climate change is caused by alterations to the composition of the Earth's atmosphere, in particular, through emissions of GHGs such as CO_2, and through changes to the land, such as through deforestation and land conversions. The process is additionally tempered by a range of positive or negative environmental feedbacks, for instance the extent of heat-reflective sea ice in the Arctic. Climate change has as its consequences a wide variety of environmental, social and economic effects, many of which are the subject of this report. These consequences are the exclusive focus of the first part of the Monitor's assessment, labelled "Climate".

CLIMATE VULNERABILITY

Climate vulnerability, or vulnerability to climate change, is taken to mean the degree to which a community experiences harm as a result of a change in climate. These communities may be regional, sub-regional, national, sub-national, or other. Vulnerability encapsulates socio-economic concerns, such as income levels, access to information, education, social safety nets and other meaningful determinants of the resilience of a given community. It also encapsulates environmental or so-called "bio-physical" factors, such as geographic location, topography, natural resource supplies, vegetation and otherwise. A community's vulnerability in all these respects may be determined intrinsically, for example, through a local government's aversion to corruption, or exogenous factors, such as globalized markets.

The definition of "vulnerability" used here aligns closely with the IPCC definition, termed "outcome vulnerability" - higher levels of harm are the outcome in large part of higher levels of vulnerability, and vice versa, impacts are lower where vulnerability is lower (IPCC, 2007; Füssel, 2009). The Monitor's concept of vulnerability, therefore, is a composite of exposure and vulnerability and may also be referred to as "risk" (Peduzzi et al., 2012a).

CARBON

Carbon dioxide (CO_2) is a principal greenhouse gas along with numerous other "heat-trapping" pollutants, such as methane, black carbon or nitrous oxide. Like these other pollutants, CO_2 is typically generated as a by-product of combustion when carbon-based fuels - e.g. coal, oil, charcoal/wood, natural gas - are burned. So the terms "carbon" and "carbon economy" have come to embody the problem at the root of the climate challenge and are used here as a blanket name for all greenhouse pollutants that are related to human activity and can cause climate change, or detract from resolving it. Not covered under the rubric of "Carbon" is the full breadth of socio-economic impacts related to the industrial economy. Toxic factory refuse, industrial solvent disposal and waste, or agricultural pesticides and other such issues are deliberately not considered here.

The Monitor also assumes that any societal or environmental costs of a low-carbon economy, i.e. externalities of renewable or low-emissions energy solutions, are negligible with respect to this framework of analysis, since carbon intensive energy modes generate 10 to 100+ times greater negative externalities for the environment and society than low-carbon alternatives (IPCC, 2012b).

ADAPTATION

Adaptation is understood as actions that help communities or their ecosystems cope with a changing climate, in particular, steps that reduce any losses or harm inflicted. The IPCC defines adaptation as an adjustment in natural or human systems to reduce the harm or exploit the benefits of actual or expected climatic stimuli or their effects.

MITIGATION

Mitigation is broadly understood as action that stems global warming, i.e. that mitigates the warming effect. The IPCC defines mitigation as human intervention to reduce the sources or enhance the sinks of greenhouse gases. Mitigation policies could be programmed to minimize the negative (and positive) impacts measured in the Carbon part of the Monitor.

In the scenarios and indicators of the Climate and Causes section, the Monitor has factored in carbon use or emissions according to reference scenarios - the IPCC's mid to high A1B scenario is the most common assumption used (IPCC SRES, 2000). Although there is variation from indicator to indicator, the Monitor does assume communities have a baseline capacity to adapt and that a degree of forced adaptation is already occurring. This is seen in various socio-economic datasets that underlie certain indicators. So, for instance, the level of mortality risk for Bangladesh estimated by the UN reflects the current sum of exposure and vulnerability there, including any efforts that have been made to adapt to a changing climate. The Climate Water indicator is another example, where the line between impact and adaptation blurs since the assumption is that the next cheapest option will be chosen to replace lost water resources at cost and according to demand, so the value of water lost or gained is its market value. In addition, the Monitor has made various dynamic adjustments, such as adjusting a community's vulnerability measure due to its economic growth prospects. For Climate and Carbon health indicators, for instance, there is strong evidence that many diseases decline as countries gain in wealth, so that is accounted for in the Monitor (Mathers and Loncar, 2005).

USING THE MONITOR

The Monitor is divided into three main parts: first, a region-by-region, then country-by-country overview of the assessment for all 184 countries included in the analysis; then the two key sections, Climate and Carbon. These detailed sections provide data and an explanation for each indicator and detail the principal causes and effects for each instance.
The Monitor's second edition is not directly comparable with the 2010 Monitor because updates to the methodology, including a significant expansion in the breadth of analysis, make the new edition substantially more comprehensive than the original.
The country studies follow the Climate section, as their focus relates primarily to the Monitor's Climate assessment. And the report provides an analysis of the interrelationships between Climate and Carbon as a bridge between the two sections.
The reader will find country-level information for each of the report's 34 indicators. The data tables and the upper map of each indicator groups countries by their level of vulnerability. The level given, which is for 2030, assumes that no deliberately scaled-up attempts will be made to reduce risks. The climate change impact in 2030 is understood to be largely committed because the oceans have absorbed a certain amount of heat that they will release back into the atmosphere, ensuring continued warming for decades to come (Hansen et al., 2005). Figures in absolute terms are given either in mortality or US dollars (2010 PPP) or both. Other metrics are provided for some of the indicators where appropriate and feasible.
The values given represent this research project's best estimates of possible country-level outcomes. Larger countries invariably have larger impacts when measured in absolute terms, but the level of vulnerability registered identifies the intensity of the effects relative to size. The figures are basically averages and, despite the impression of precision they convey, it's important to note that it is nearly impossible to achieve any real precision. All figures should be considered plausible but simply a broad indication of the level of impact that could be expected.

CONFIDENCE

It is also important to note, when reviewing information at the indicator level, that each indicator has been assigned a level of "Confidence" and, in the case of the Climate section, "Regional Climate Uncertainty". Confidence is noted as "Robust" (highest confidence), "Indicative", or "Speculative" (least confidence). That evaluation is based on judgements that are explained in this book's Navigator and in more detail in the Monitor's methodological annex at: <www.daraint.org/cvm2/method>.
Localized Uncertainties
Climate outcomes are deemed more certain for some regions than for others. Therefore, the Climate section includes maps of regional climate uncertainty (lower map). These indicate the level of disagreement among leading climate models by region on whether there will be increases or decreases in the main driving climate variables, such as rainfall or temperature. When uncertainty is "Limited", it denotes for instance that less than 10% of models disagree for that region on an increase or decrease. When it is "Considerable", more than one third of models disagree. This information is particularly relevant for indicators based on highly uncertain climate parameters, such as rainfall. A lot more rain or a lot less would make a significant difference for any response to climate change, and different models sometimes show little agreement on such key points (Tebaldi et al., 2011).
Uncertainty related to the degree of change is not represented in these maps but is one of the factors accounted for in the Confidence evaluation. The Monitor's assessment is based on the average point of models whenever a group of these was available. An exception is the model drawn on for the Storms indicator, specifically for tropical cyclones. The models available gave such completely opposing outputs that a mean was uninformative. The model most aligned with observational evidence was chosen instead (Mendelsohn et al., 2012; IPCC, 2007). This disagreement is captured in regional uncertainty maps, where most key areas of the globe affected by tropical cyclones (although not North America) carry "Considerable" uncertainty. The Storms indicator is labelled "Speculative" in part due to discord on the scale of changes predicted by different models.

COUNTRY-LEVEL INTERPRETATION

When consulting the Monitor at the country level, readers are encouraged to take advantage of these multi-point considerations. If an indicator is "Speculative" and the country of interest is within a region with "Considerable" uncertainty on the direction of change, the assessment provided in the Monitor should be treated with much more caution than if the inverse confidence and uncertainty values had been given. However, just because models disagree does not mean that the values provided could not be potential future outcomes. Responses to the impacts of climate change should ideally be robust to a range of different outcomes (Dessai et al., 2009). Therefore, planning should be capable of coping with at least the level of impact suggested here. Countries with negative or very low impacts projected for low confidence, high uncertainty indicators like Storms should also respond with caution. The model chosen for Storms predicts a decrease of cyclone activity in the Pacific basin, the likelihood of which has been confirmed by other studies, although there is no consensus on any clear trend (Mendelsohn et al., 2012; Callaghan and Power, 2010; IPCC, 2012a). Given the levels of uncertainty and lack of agreement among experts, it is likely wiser to take more precautions than the Monitor indicates as necessary.

KEY TO THE MONITOR

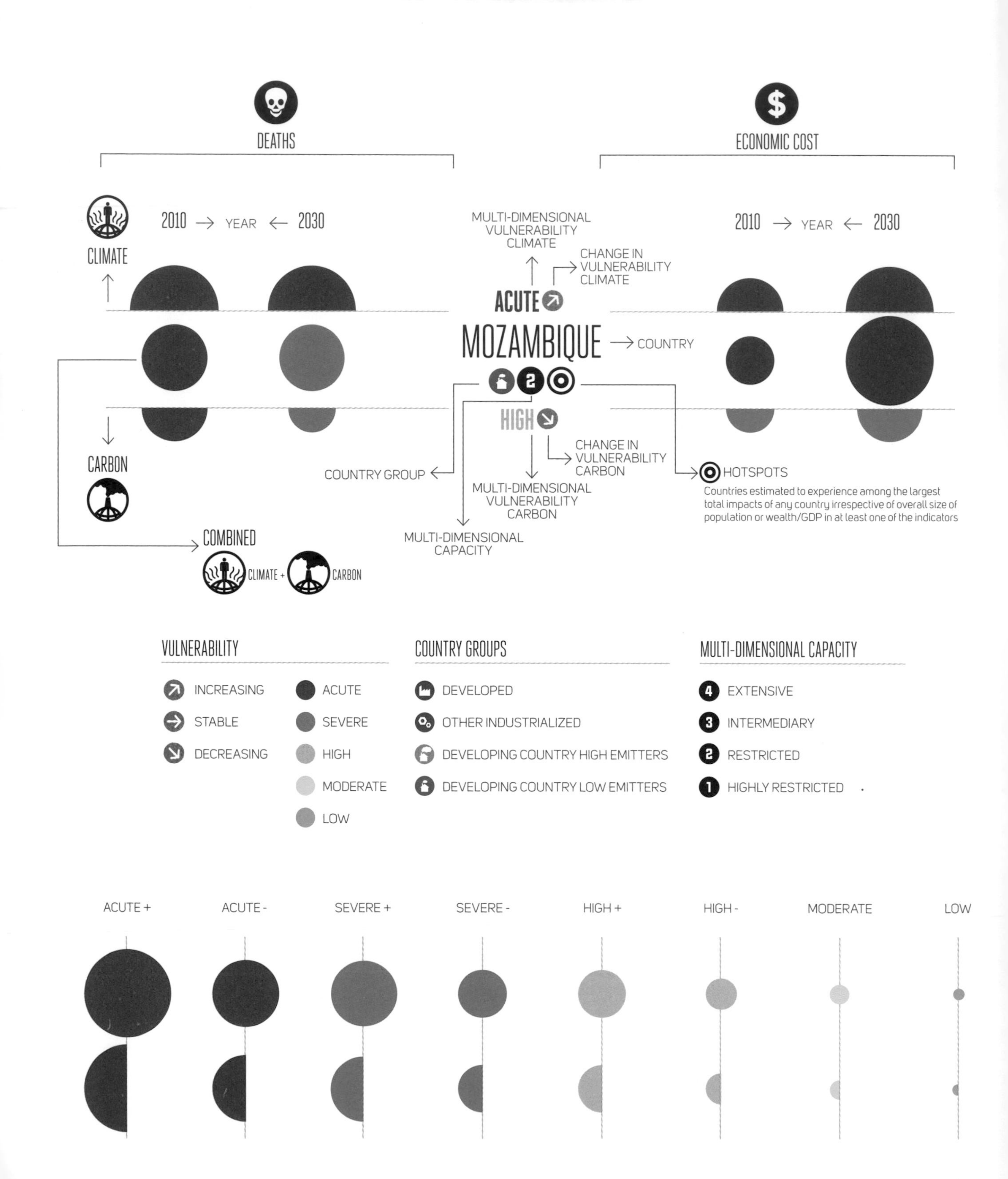
DEATHS
ECONOMIC COST
2010 → YEAR ← 2030
2010 → YEAR ← 2030
CLIMATE
CARBON
COMBINED
CLIMATE +
CARBON
MULTI-DIMENSIONAL VULNERABILITY CLIMATE
CHANGE IN VULNERABILITY CLIMATE
ACUTE
MOZAMBIQUE
COUNTRY
HIGH
CHANGE IN VULNERABILITY CARBON
MULTI-DIMENSIONAL VULNERABILITY CARBON
COUNTRY GROUP
MULTI-DIMENSIONAL CAPACITY
HOTSPOTS
Countries estimated to experience among the largest total impacts of any country irrespective of overall size of population or wealth/GDP in at least one of the indicators
VULNERABILITY
INCREASING
STABLE
DECREASING
ACUTE
SEVERE
HIGH
MODERATE
LOW
COUNTRY GROUPS
DEVELOPED
OTHER INDUSTRIALIZED
DEVELOPING COUNTRY HIGH EMITTERS
DEVELOPING COUNTRY LOW EMITTERS
MULTI-DIMENSIONAL CAPACITY
EXTENSIVE
INTERMEDIARY
RESTRICTED
HIGHLY RESTRICTED
ACUTE +
ACUTE -
SEVERE +
SEVERE -
HIGH +
HIGH -
MODERATE
LOW

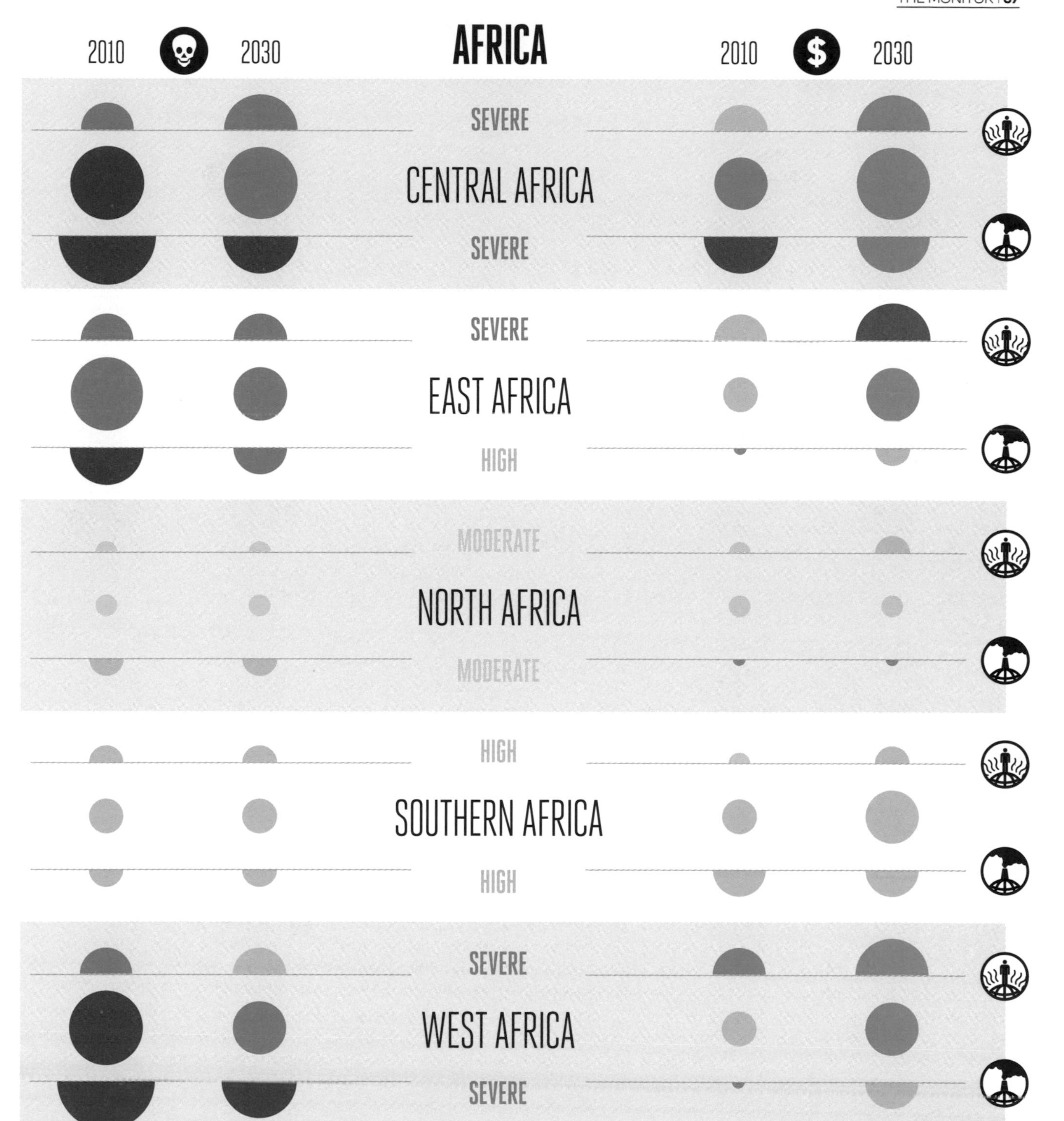
2010
2030
AFRICA
2010
2030
SEVERE
CENTRAL AFRICA
SEVERE
SEVERE
EAST AFRICA
HIGH
MODERATE
NORTH AFRICA
MODERATE
HIGH
SOUTHERN AFRICA
HIGH
SEVERE
WEST AFRICA
SEVERE

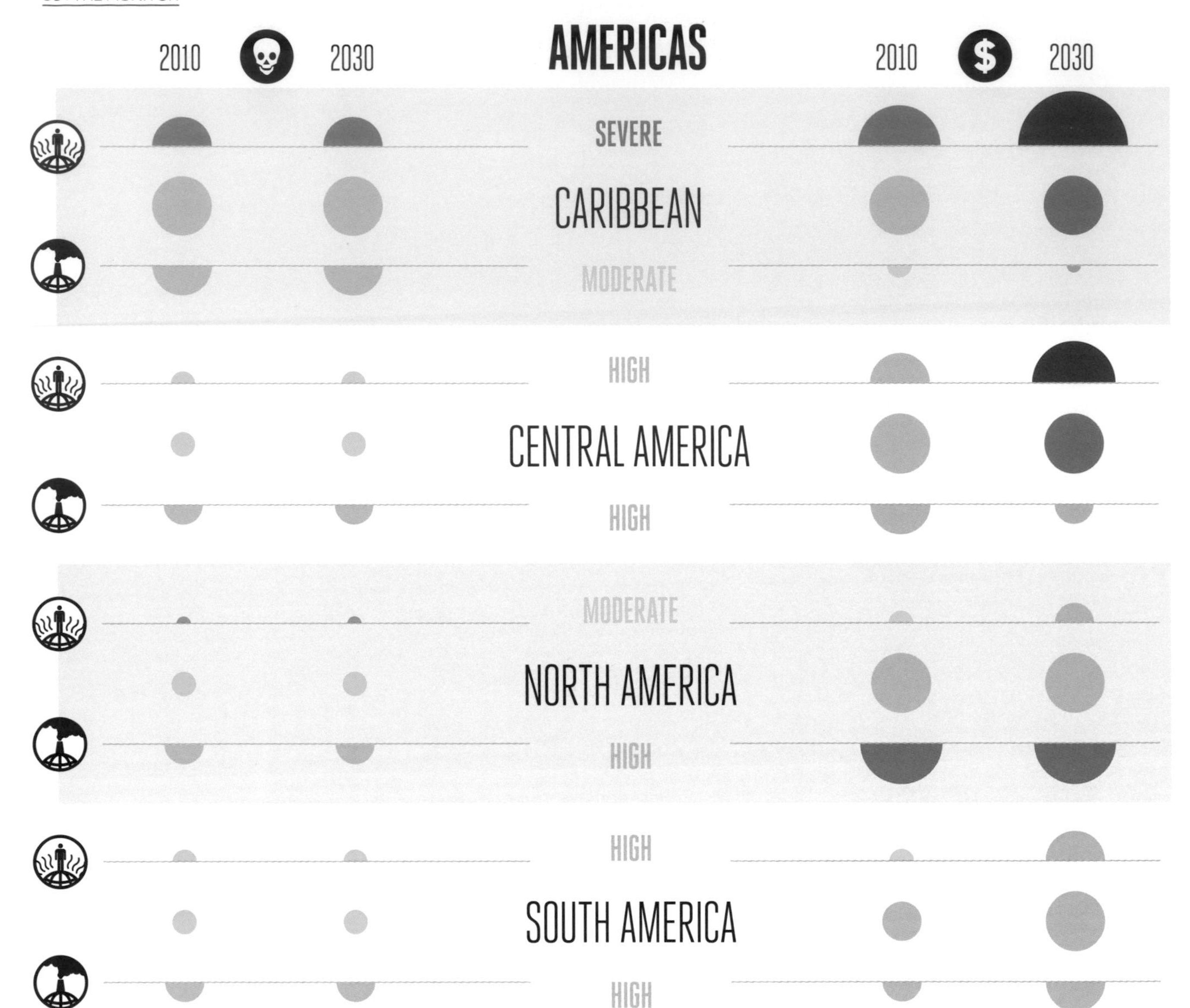
AMERICAS
2010
2030
2010
$
2030
SEVERE
CARIBBEAN
MODERATE
HIGH
CENTRAL AMERICA
HIGH
MODERATE
NORTH AMERICA
HIGH
HIGH
SOUTH AMERICA
HIGH

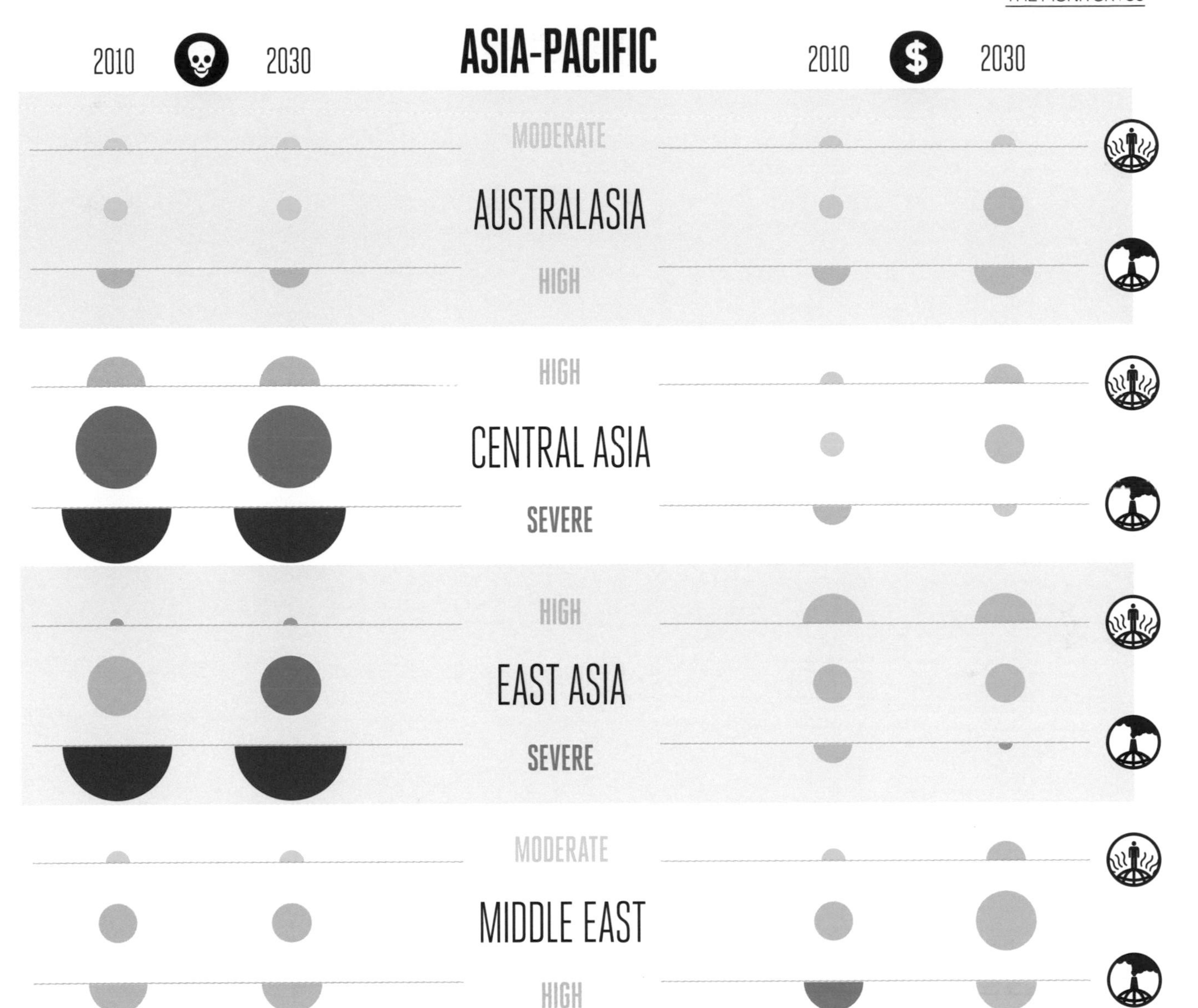
2010
2030
ASIA-PACIFIC
2010
2030
MODERATE
AUSTRALASIA
HIGH
HIGH
CENTRAL ASIA
SEVERE
HIGH
EAST ASIA
SEVERE
MODERATE
MIDDLE EAST
HIGH

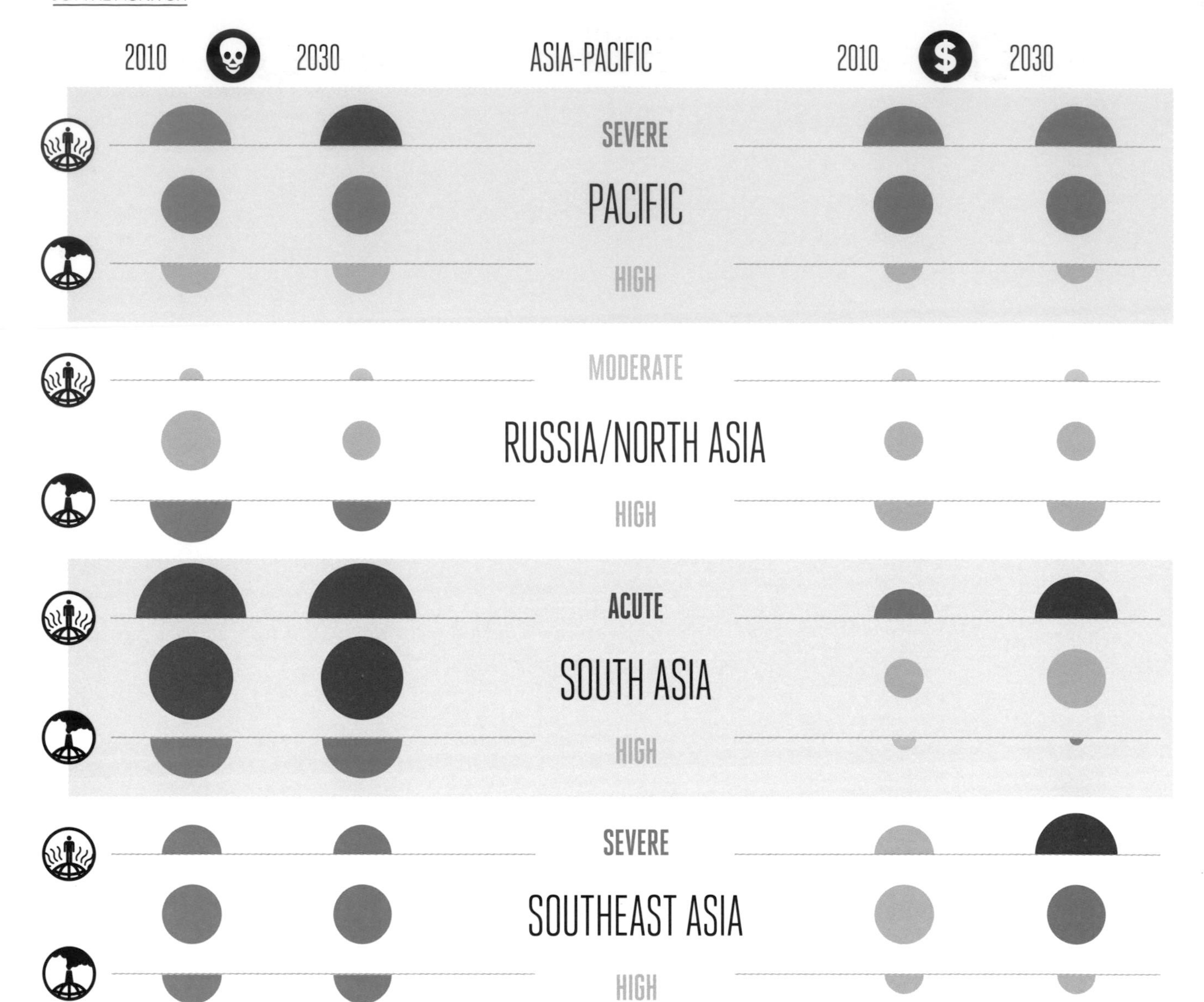
2010
2030
ASIA-PACIFIC
2010
$
2030
SEVERE
PACIFIC
HIGH
MODERATE
RUSSIA/NORTH ASIA
HIGH
ACUTE
SOUTH ASIA
HIGH
SEVERE
SOUTHEAST ASIA
HIGH

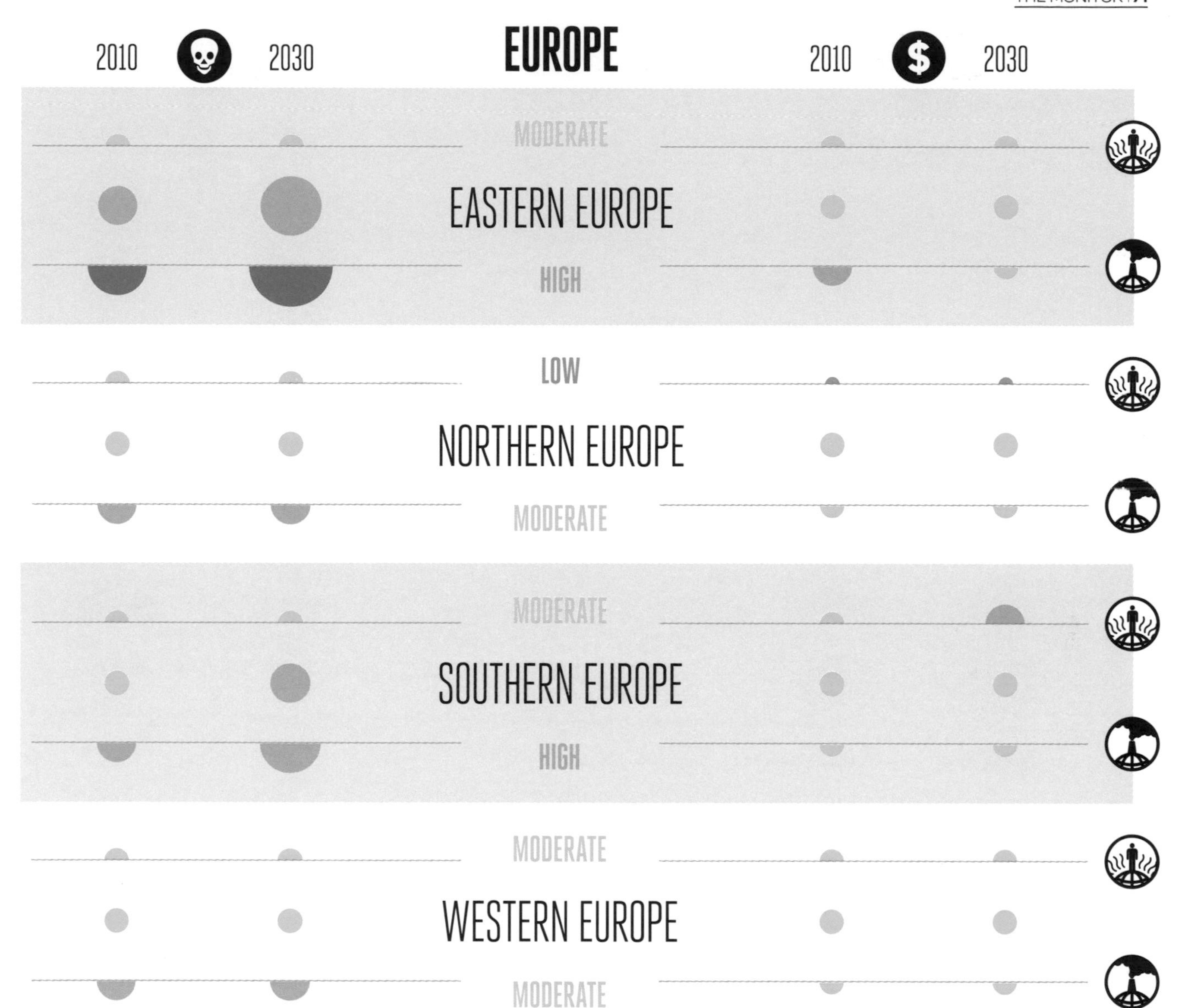
2010
2030
EUROPE
2010
2030
MODERATE
EASTERN EUROPE
HIGH
LOW
NORTHERN EUROPE
MODERATE
MODERATE
SOUTHERN EUROPE
HIGH
MODERATE
WESTERN EUROPE
MODERATE

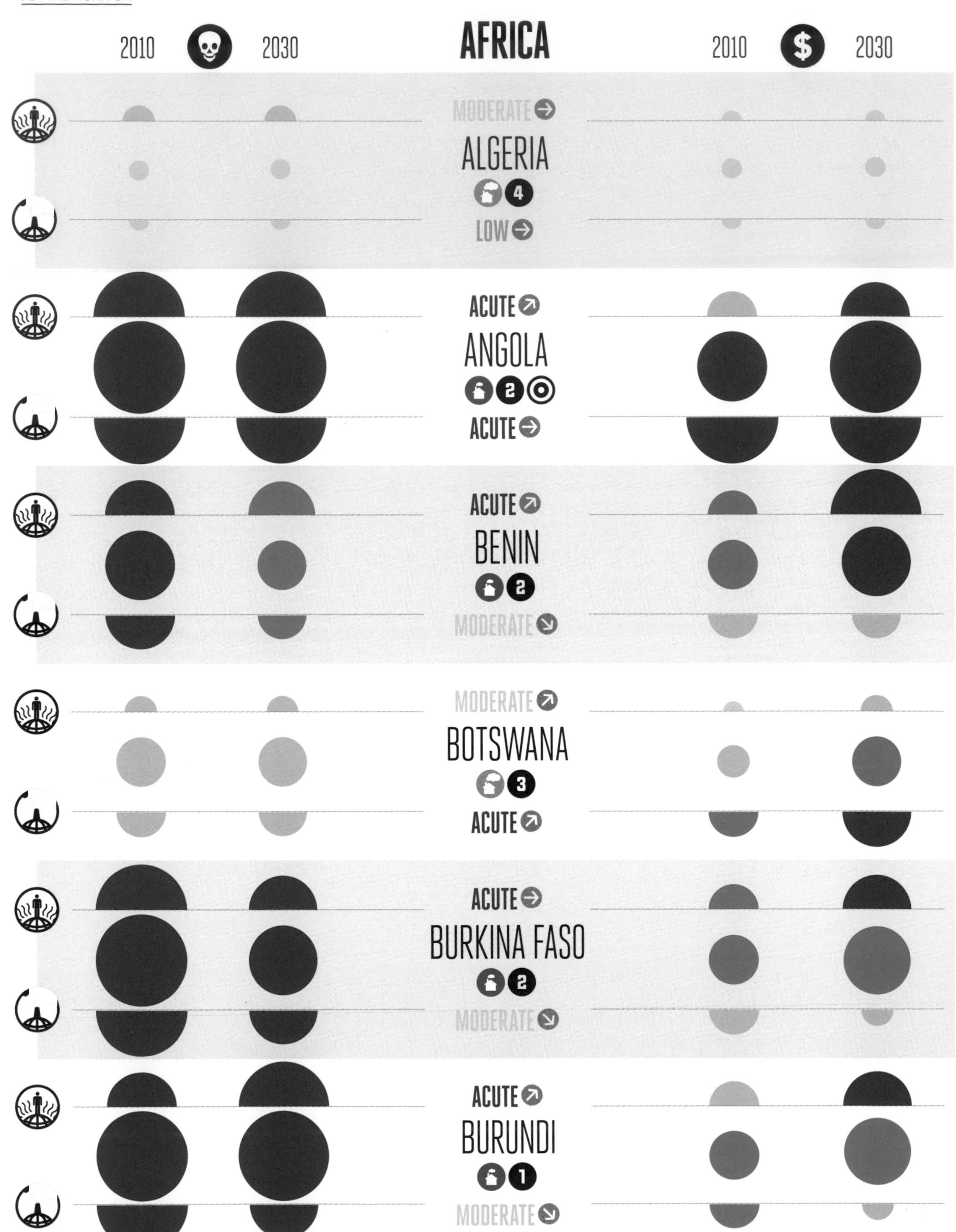
2010
2030
AFRICA
2010
$
2030
MODERATE
ALGERIA
4
LOW
ACUTE
ANGOLA
2
ACUTE
ACUTE
BENIN
2
MODERATE
MODERATE
BOTSWANA
3
ACUTE
ACUTE
BURKINA FASO
2
MODERATE
ACUTE
BURUNDI
1
MODERATE

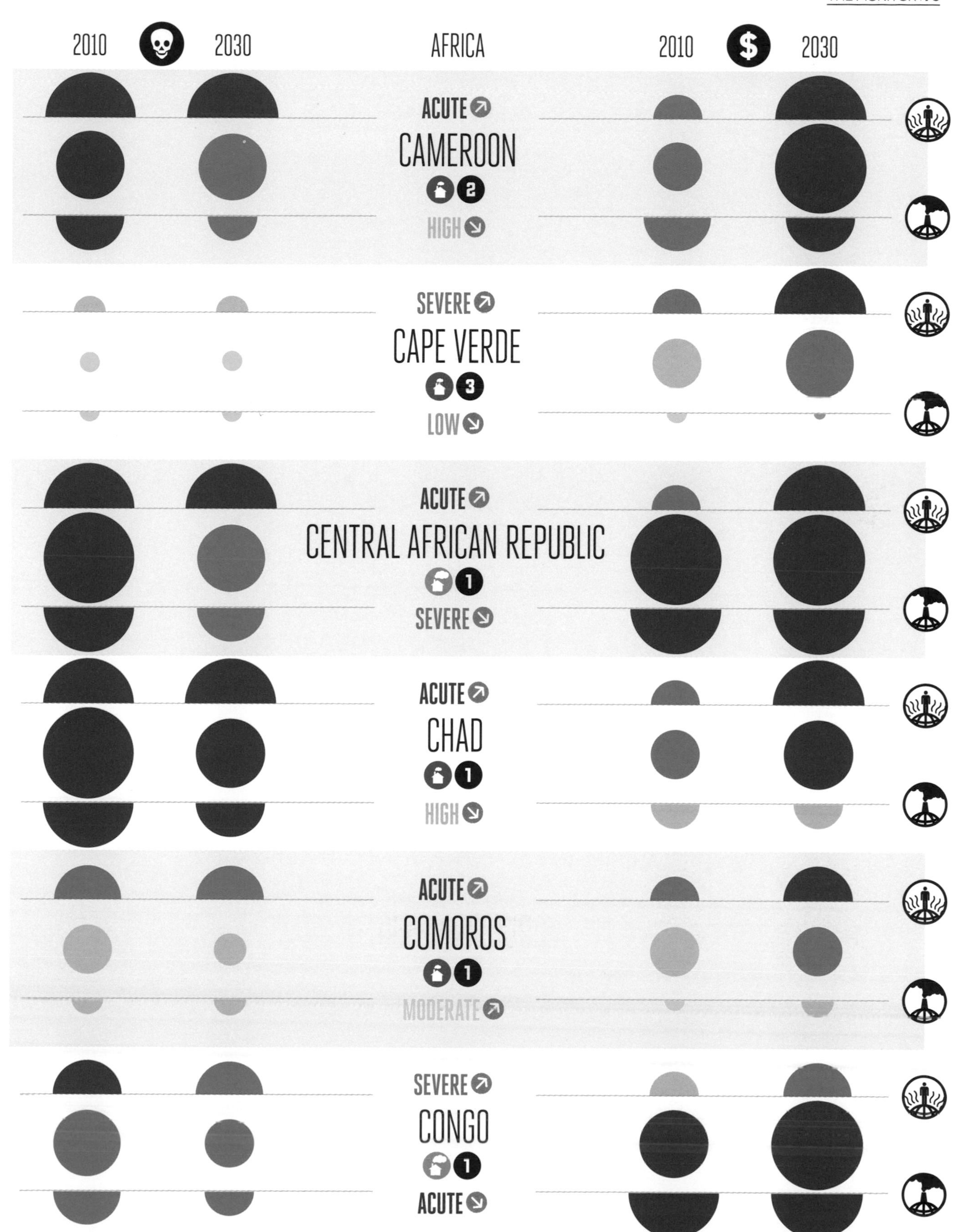
2010
2030
AFRICA
2010
2030
ACUTE
CAMEROON
2
HIGH
SEVERE
CAPE VERDE
3
LOW
ACUTE
CENTRAL AFRICAN REPUBLIC
1
SEVERE
ACUTE
CHAD
1
HIGH
ACUTE
COMOROS
1
MODERATE
SEVERE
CONGO
1
ACUTE

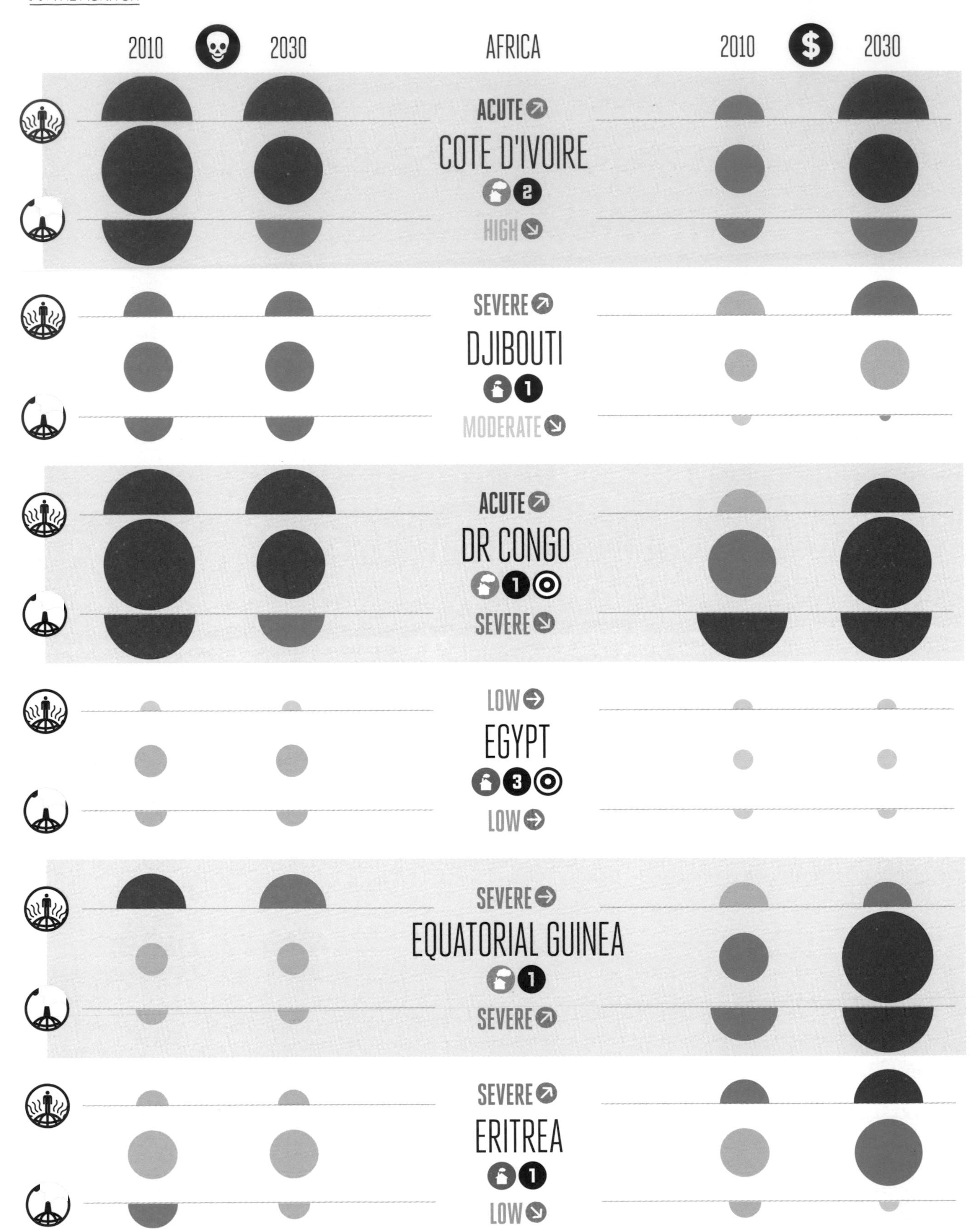
2010
2030
AFRICA
2010
$
2030
ACUTE
COTE D'IVOIRE
2
HIGH
SEVERE
DJIBOUTI
1
MODERATE
ACUTE
DR CONGO
1
SEVERE
LOW
EGYPT
3
LOW
SEVERE
EQUATORIAL GUINEA
1
SEVERE
SEVERE
ERITREA
1
LOW

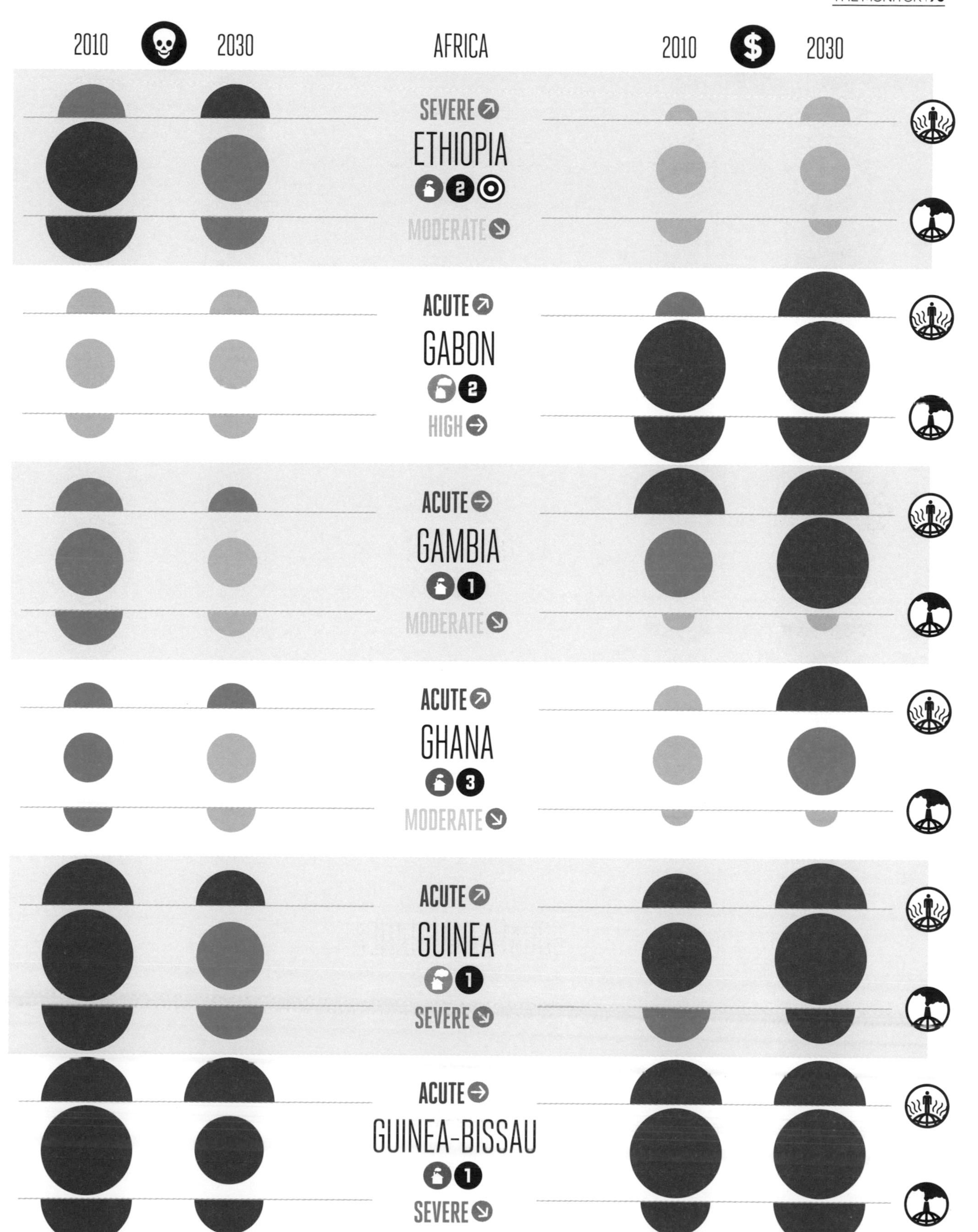
2010
2030
AFRICA
2010
$
2030
SEVERE
ETHIOPIA
2
MODERATE
ACUTE
GABON
2
HIGH
ACUTE
GAMBIA
1
MODERATE
ACUTE
GHANA
3
MODERATE
ACUTE
GUINEA
1
SEVERE
ACUTE
GUINEA-BISSAU
1
SEVERE

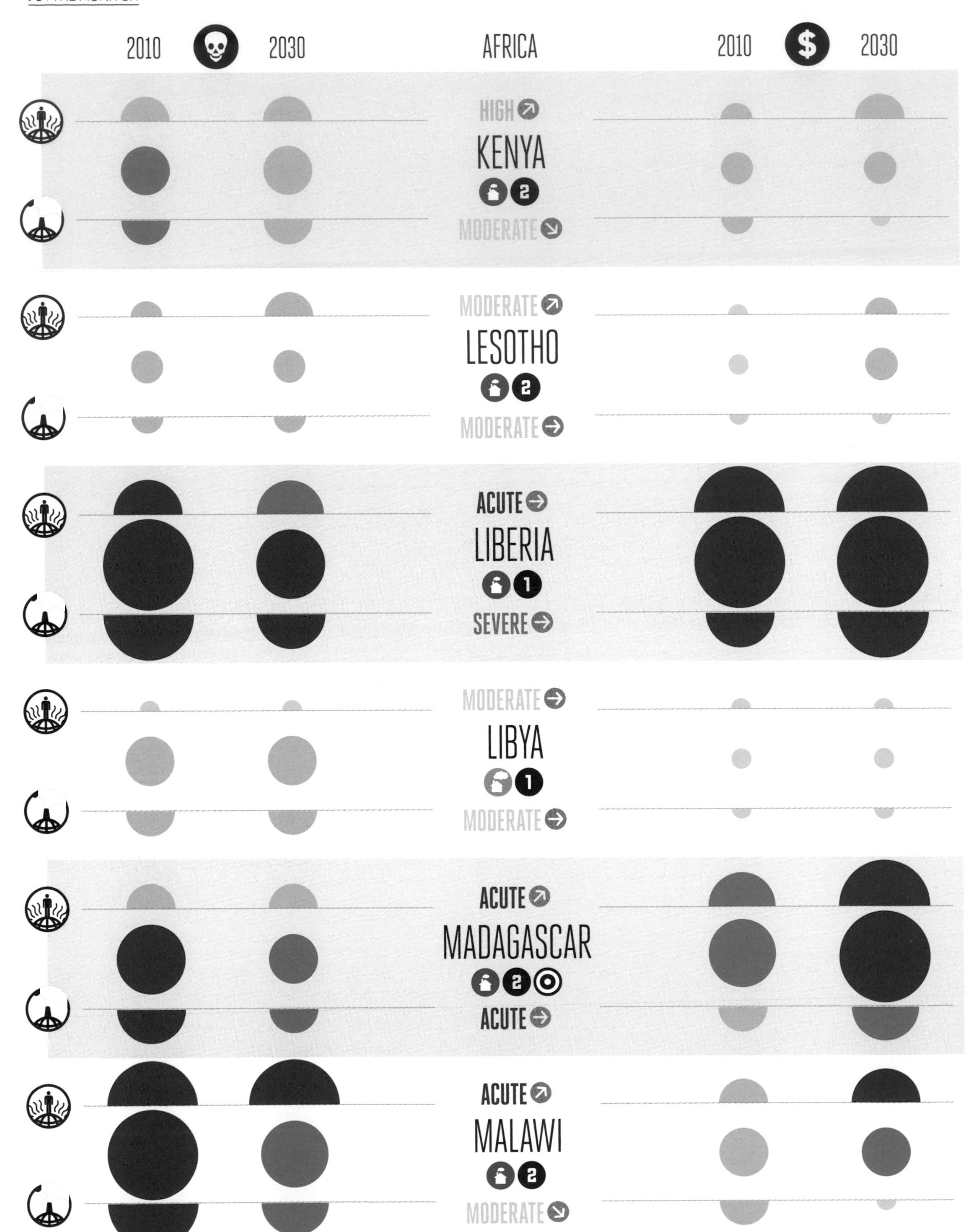
2010
2030
AFRICA
2010
$
2030
HIGH
KENYA
2
MODERATE
MODERATE
LESOTHO
2
MODERATE
ACUTE
LIBERIA
1
SEVERE
MODERATE
LIBYA
1
MODERATE
ACUTE
MADAGASCAR
2
ACUTE
ACUTE
MALAWI
2
MODERATE

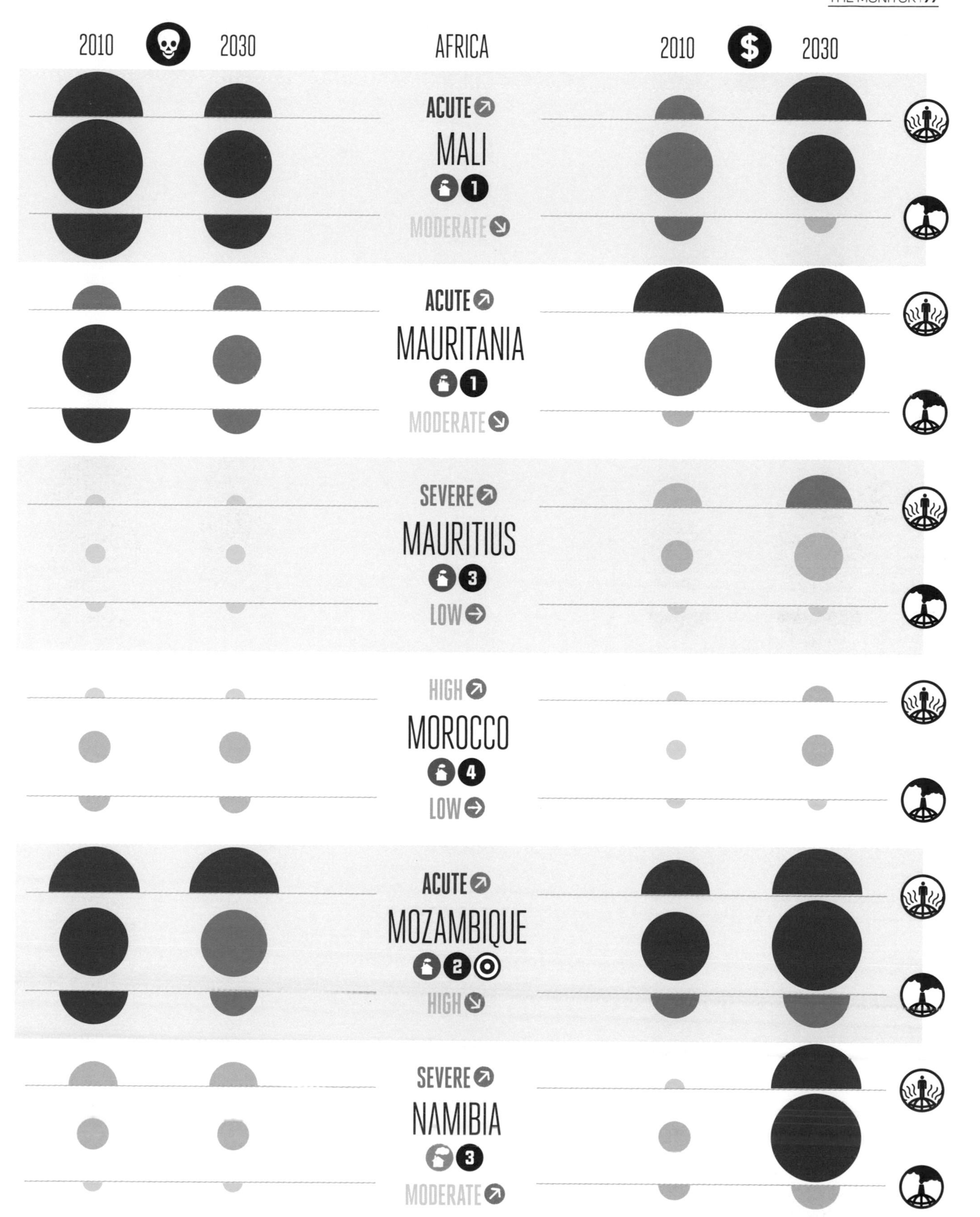
2010
2030
AFRICA
2010
2030
ACUTE
MALI
1
MODERATE
ACUTE
MAURITANIA
1
MODERATE
SEVERE
MAURITIUS
3
LOW
HIGH
MOROCCO
4
LOW
ACUTE
MOZAMBIQUE
2
HIGH
SEVERE
NAMIBIA
3
MODERATE

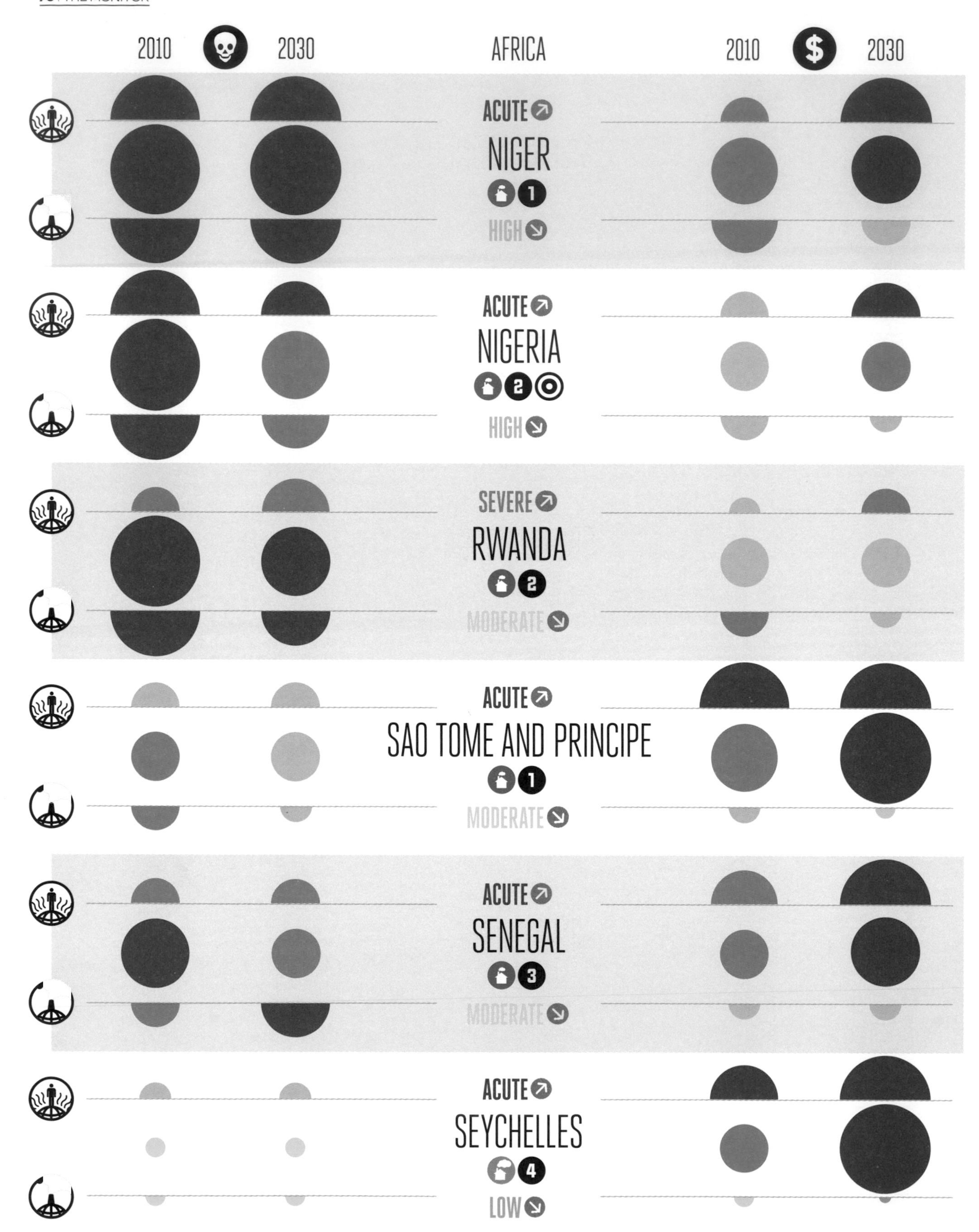
2010
2030
AFRICA
2010
$
2030
ACUTE
NIGER
1
HIGH
ACUTE
NIGERIA
2
HIGH
SEVERE
RWANDA
2
MODERATE
ACUTE
SAO TOME AND PRINCIPE
1
MODERATE
ACUTE
SENEGAL
3
MODERATE
ACUTE
SEYCHELLES
4
LOW

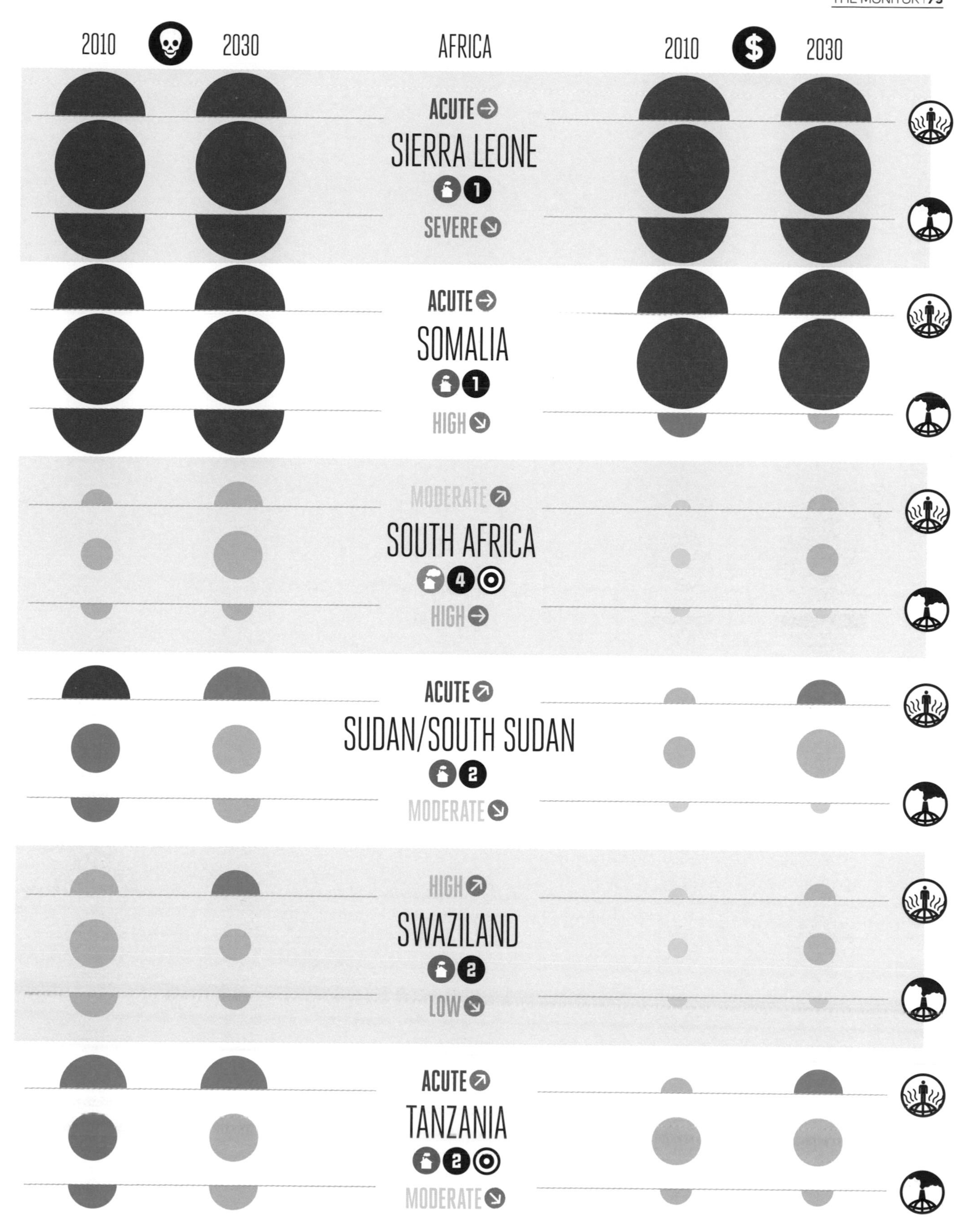
2010
2030
AFRICA
2010
2030
ACUTE
SIERRA LEONE
1
SEVERE
ACUTE
SOMALIA
1
HIGH
MODERATE
SOUTH AFRICA
4
HIGH
ACUTE
SUDAN/SOUTH SUDAN
2
MODERATE
HIGH
SWAZILAND
2
LOW
ACUTE
TANZANIA
2
MODERATE

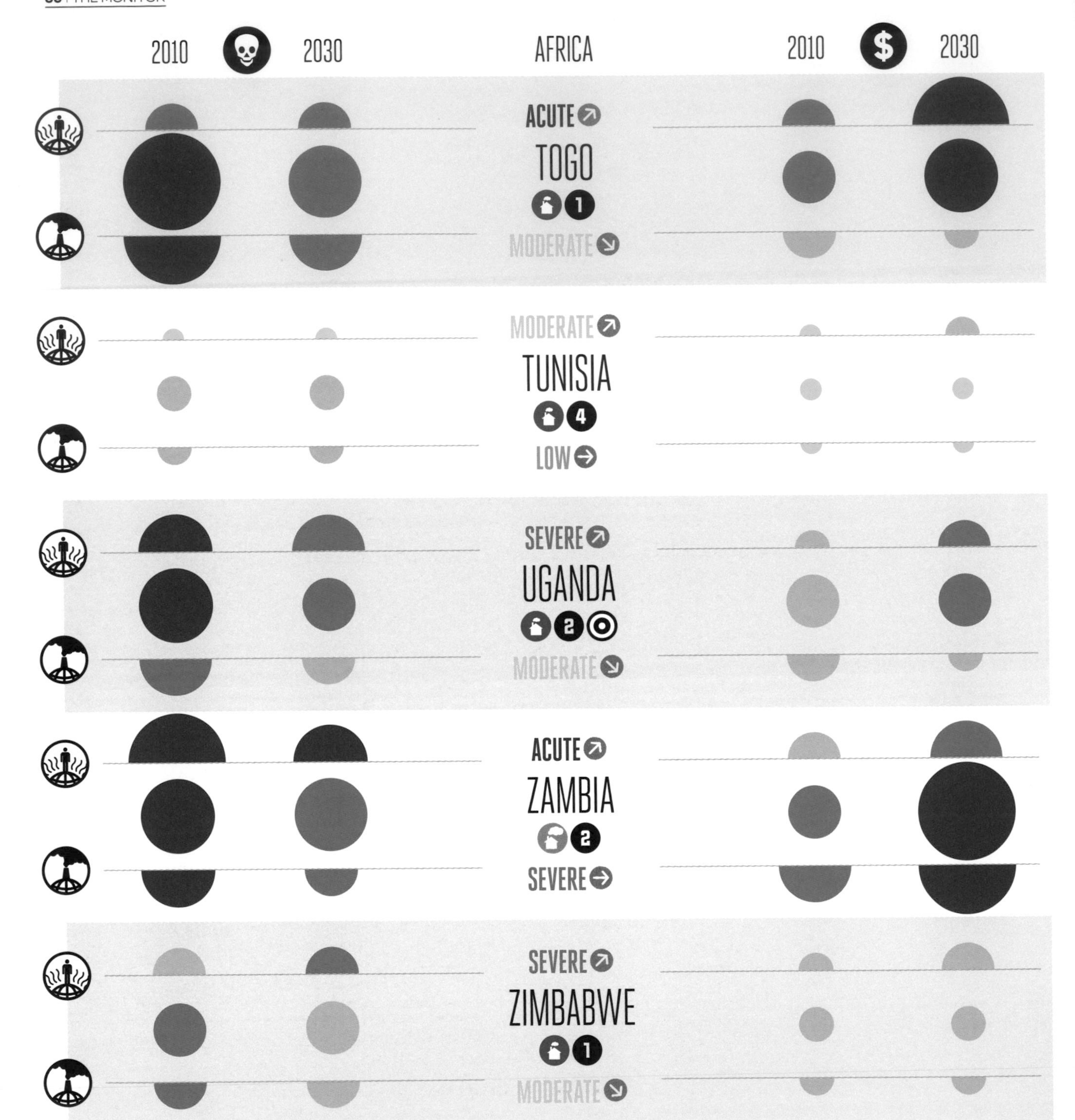
2010
2030
AFRICA
2010
2030
ACUTE
TOGO
1
MODERATE
MODERATE
TUNISIA
4
LOW
SEVERE
UGANDA
2
MODERATE
ACUTE
ZAMBIA
2
SEVERE
SEVERE
ZIMBABWE
1
MODERATE

AMERICAS

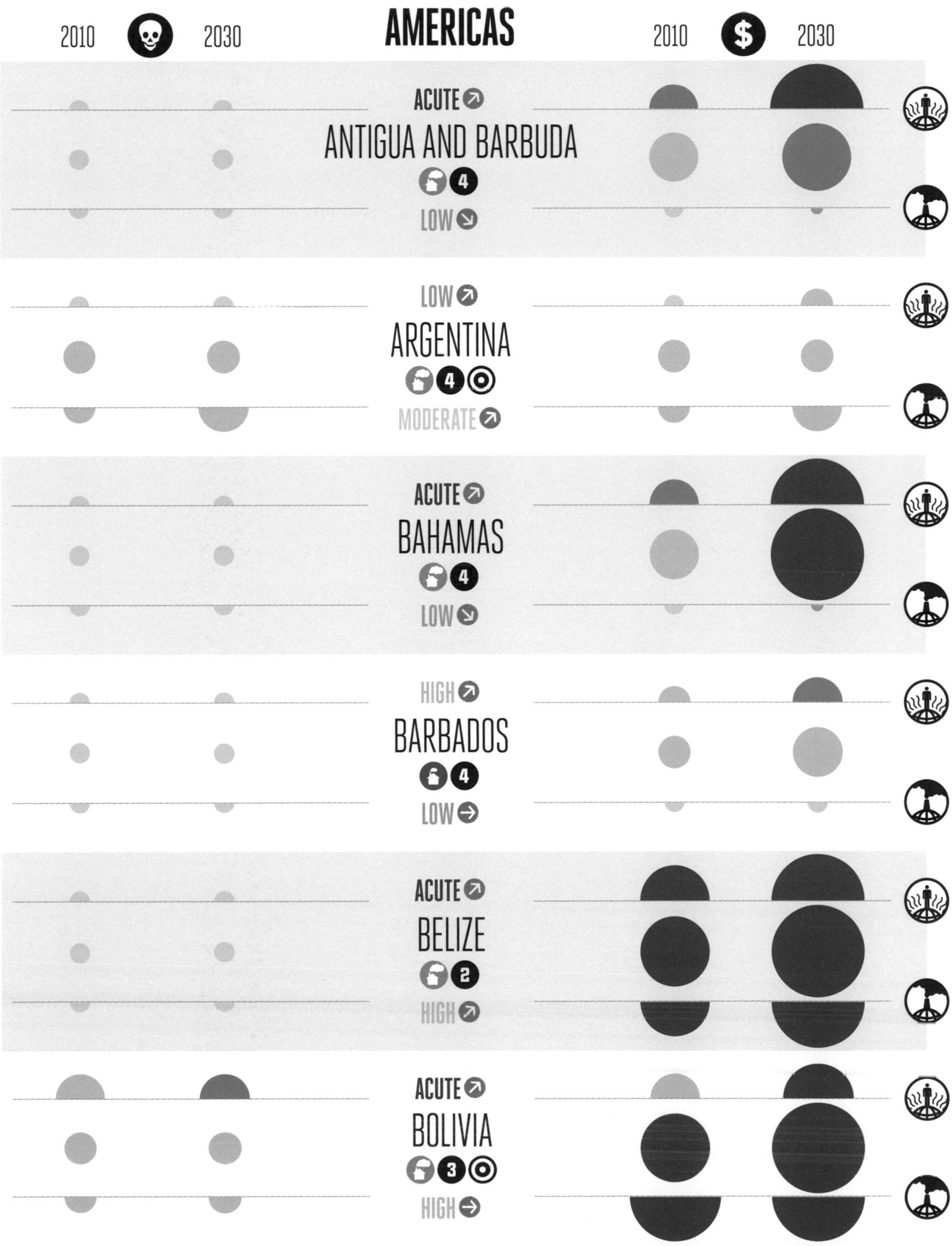

2010 2030 2010 $ 2030

ACUTE
ANTIGUA AND BARBUDA
4
LOW

LOW
ARGENTINA
4
MODERATE

ACUTE
BAHAMAS
4
LOW

HIGH
BARBADOS
4
LOW

ACUTE
BELIZE
2
HIGH

ACUTE
BOLIVIA
3
HIGH

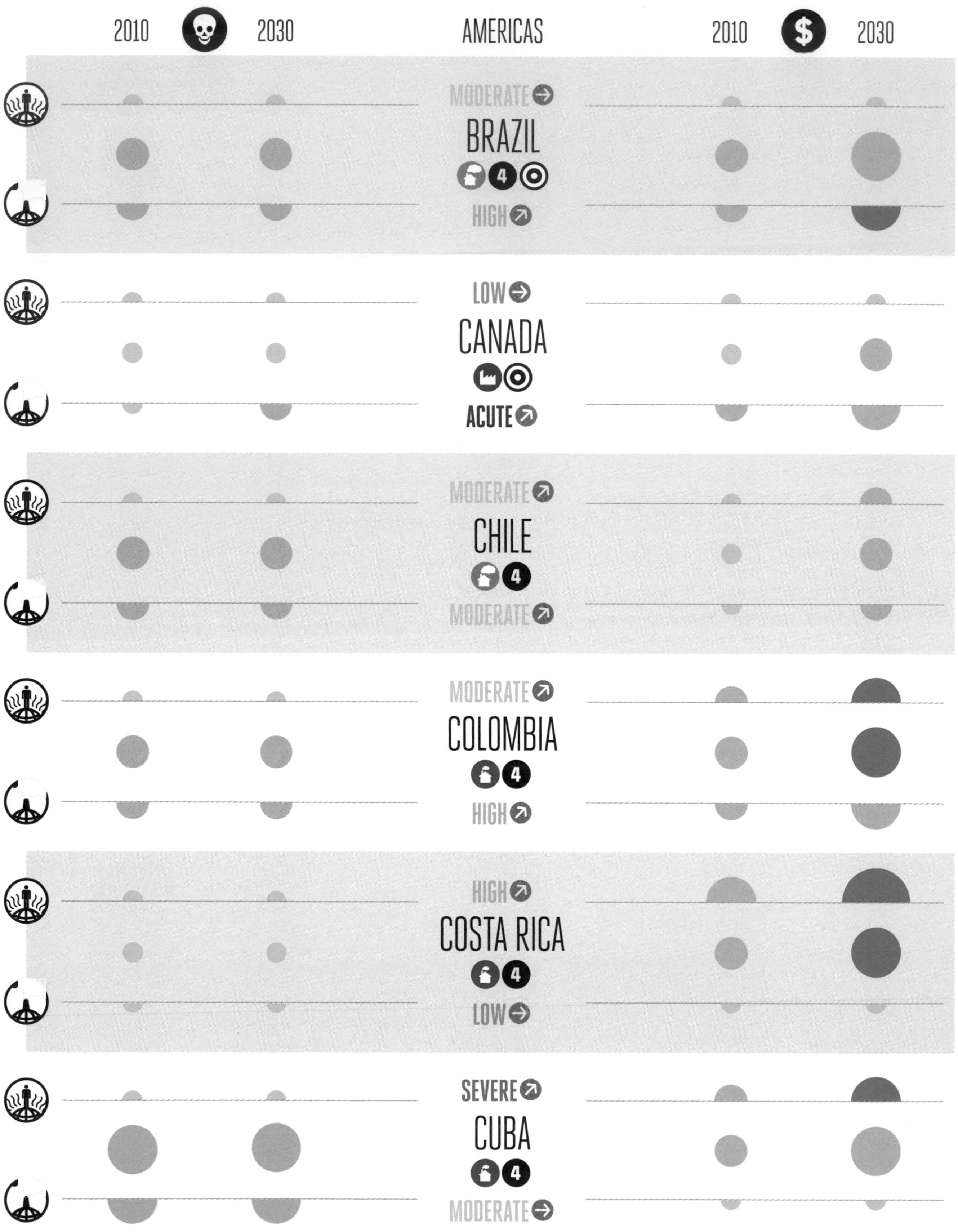

2010 2030 AMERICAS 2010 2030

MODERATE
BRAZIL
4
HIGH

LOW
CANADA
ACUTE

MODERATE
CHILE
4
MODERATE

MODERATE
COLOMBIA
4
HIGH

HIGH
COSTA RICA
4
LOW

SEVERE
CUBA
4
MODERATE

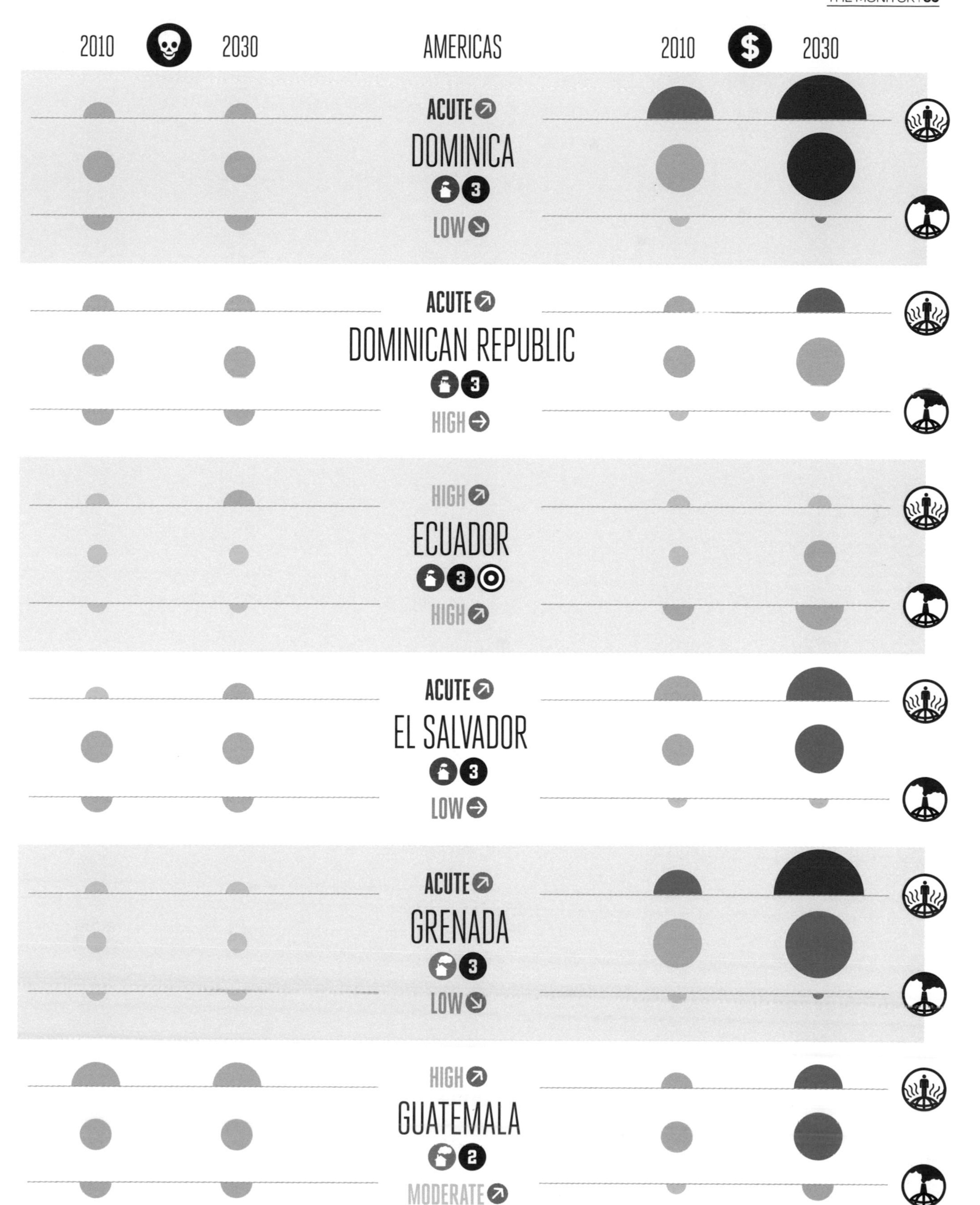
2010
2030
AMERICAS
2010
2030
ACUTE
DOMINICA
3
LOW
ACUTE
DOMINICAN REPUBLIC
3
HIGH
HIGH
ECUADOR
3
HIGH
ACUTE
EL SALVADOR
3
LOW
ACUTE
GRENADA
3
LOW
HIGH
GUATEMALA
2
MODERATE

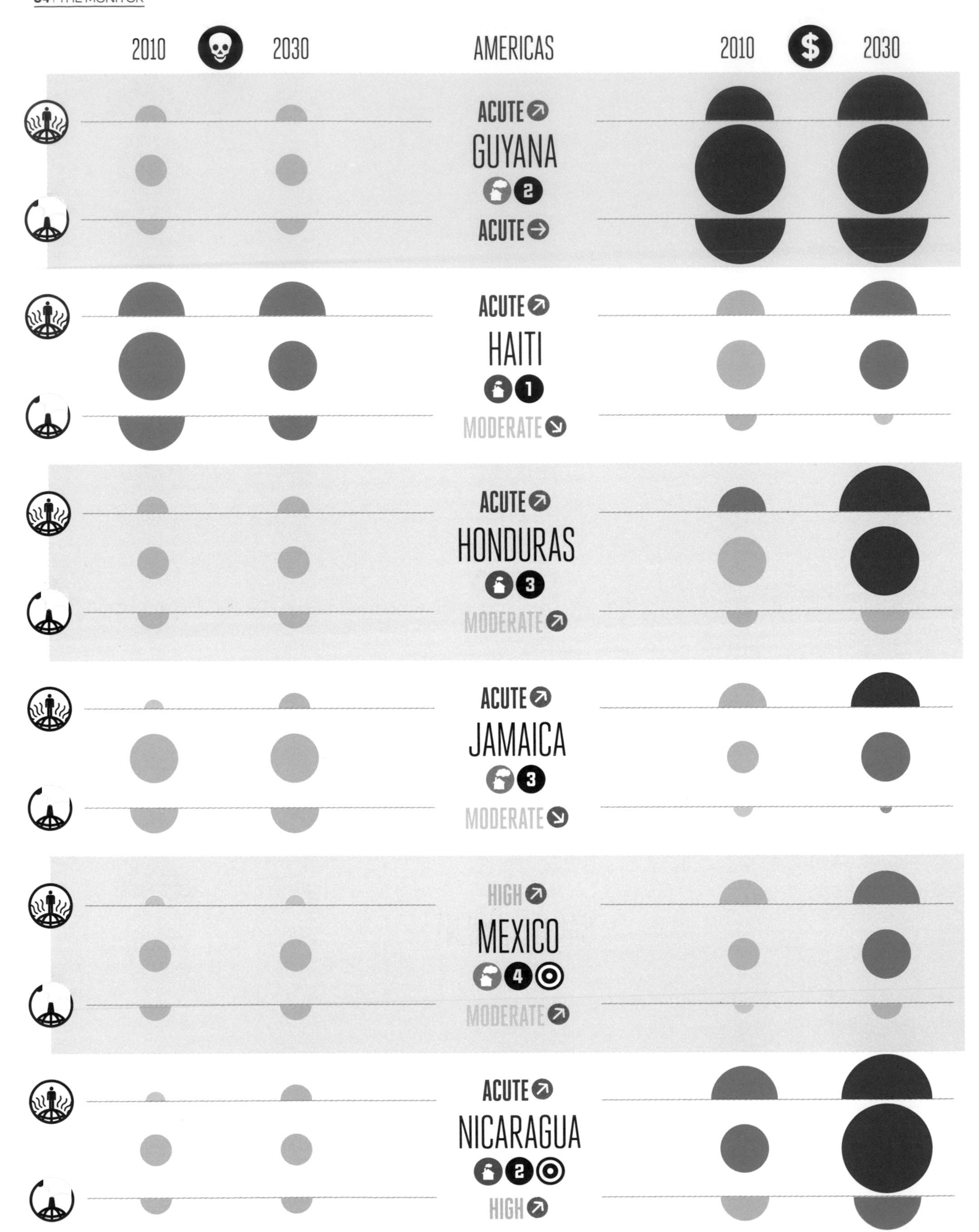
2010
2030
AMERICAS
2010
$
2030
ACUTE
GUYANA
2
ACUTE
ACUTE
HAITI
1
MODERATE
ACUTE
HONDURAS
3
MODERATE
ACUTE
JAMAICA
3
MODERATE
HIGH
MEXICO
4
MODERATE
ACUTE
NICARAGUA
2
HIGH

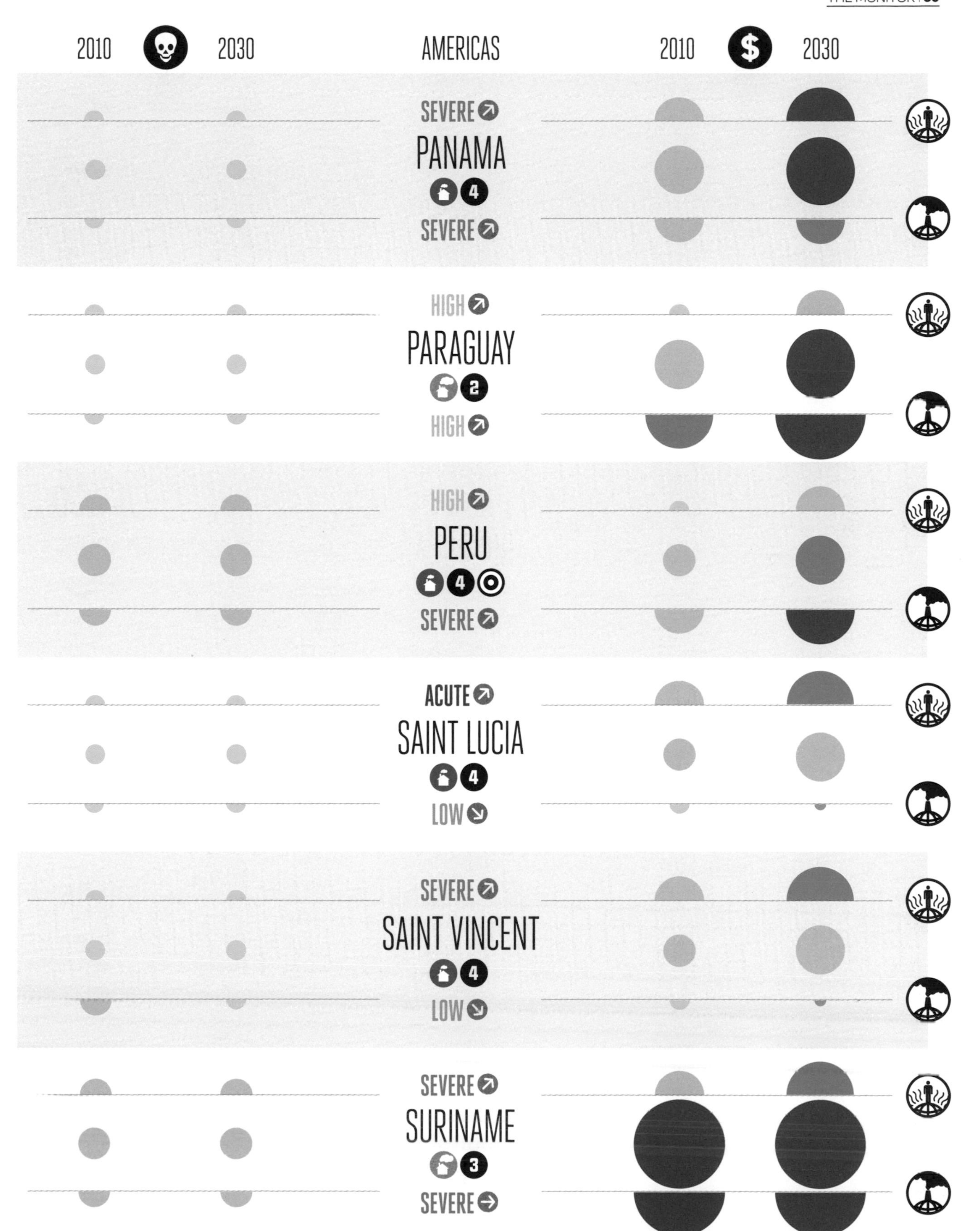
2010
2030
AMERICAS
2010
2030
SEVERE
PANAMA
4
SEVERE
HIGH
PARAGUAY
2
HIGH
HIGH
PERU
4
SEVERE
ACUTE
SAINT LUCIA
4
LOW
SEVERE
SAINT VINCENT
4
LOW
SEVERE
SURINAME
3
SEVERE

2010
2030
AMERICAS
2010
$
2030
MODERATE
TRINIDAD AND TOBAGO
3
LOW
LOW
UNITED STATES
HIGH
MODERATE
URUGUAY
4
MODERATE
HIGH
VENEZUELA
4
MODERATE

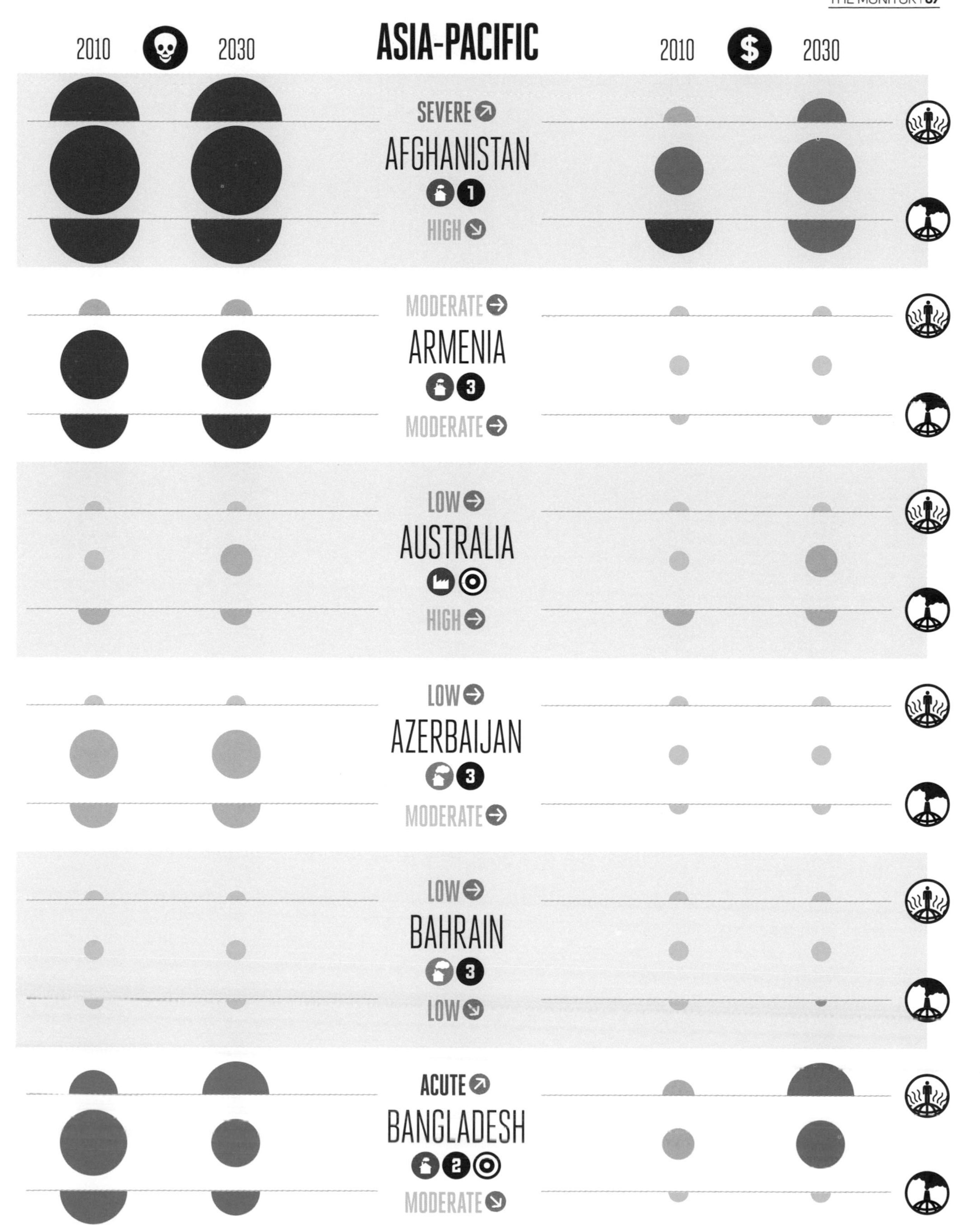
2010
2030
ASIA-PACIFIC
2010
$
2030
SEVERE
AFGHANISTAN
1
HIGH
MODERATE
ARMENIA
3
MODERATE
LOW
AUSTRALIA
HIGH
LOW
AZERBAIJAN
3
MODERATE
LOW
BAHRAIN
3
LOW
ACUTE
BANGLADESH
2
MODERATE

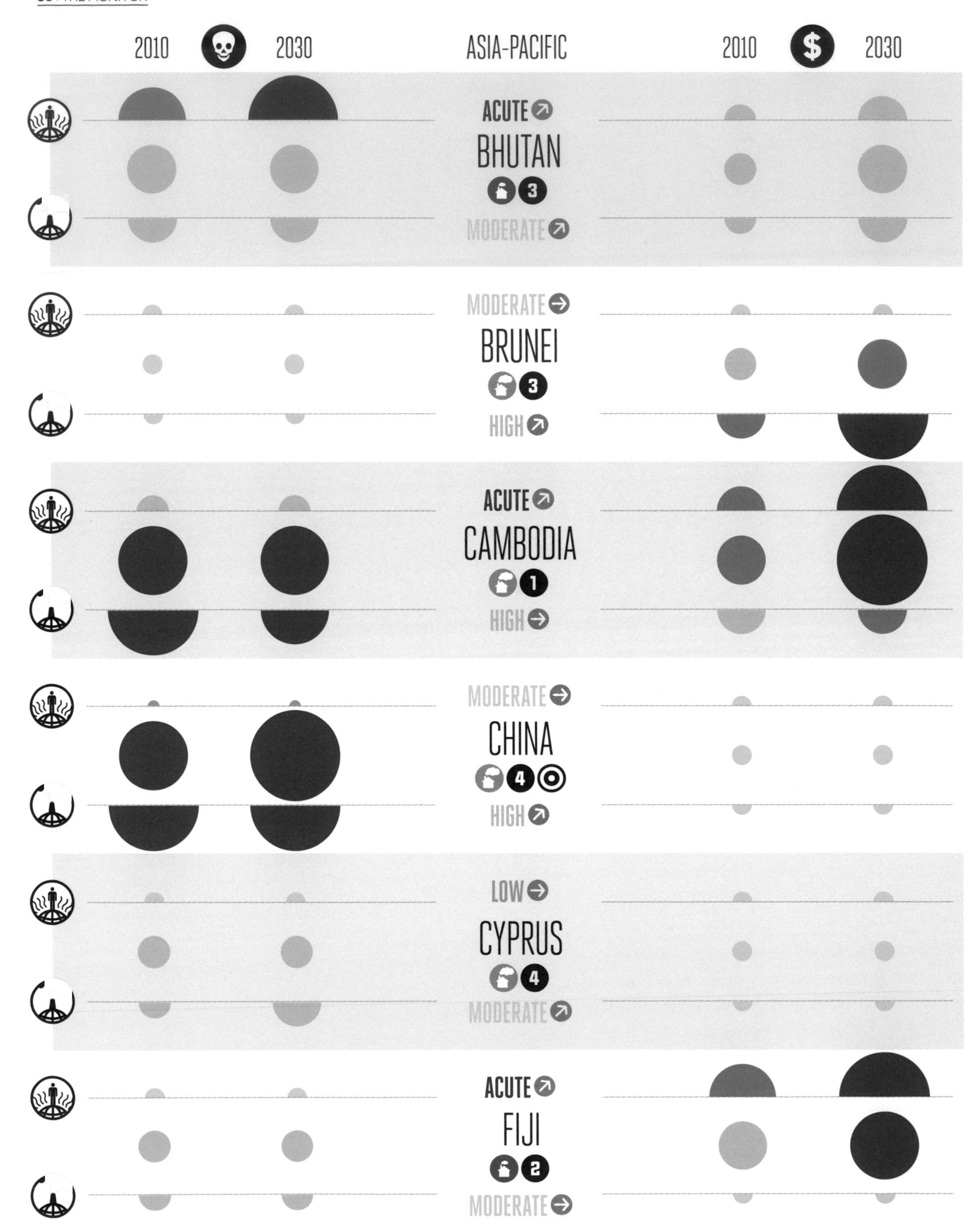
2010
2030
ASIA-PACIFIC
2010
$
2030
ACUTE
BHUTAN
3
MODERATE
MODERATE
BRUNEI
3
HIGH
ACUTE
CAMBODIA
1
HIGH
MODERATE
CHINA
4
HIGH
LOW
CYPRUS
4
MODERATE
ACUTE
FIJI
2
MODERATE

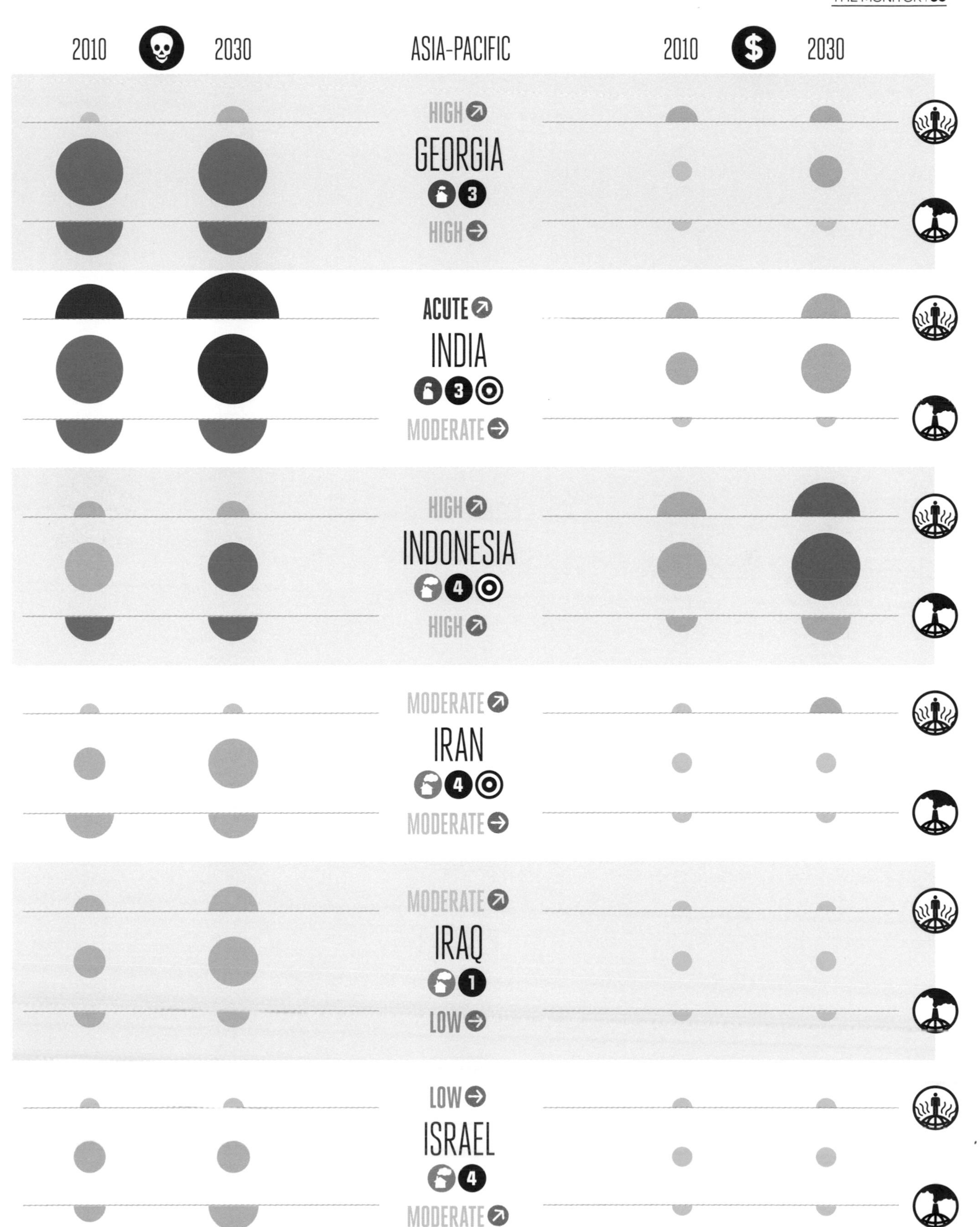
2010
2030
ASIA-PACIFIC
2010
$
2030
HIGH
GEORGIA
3
HIGH
ACUTE
INDIA
3
MODERATE
HIGH
INDONESIA
4
HIGH
MODERATE
IRAN
4
MODERATE
MODERATE
IRAQ
1
LOW
LOW
ISRAEL
4
MODERATE

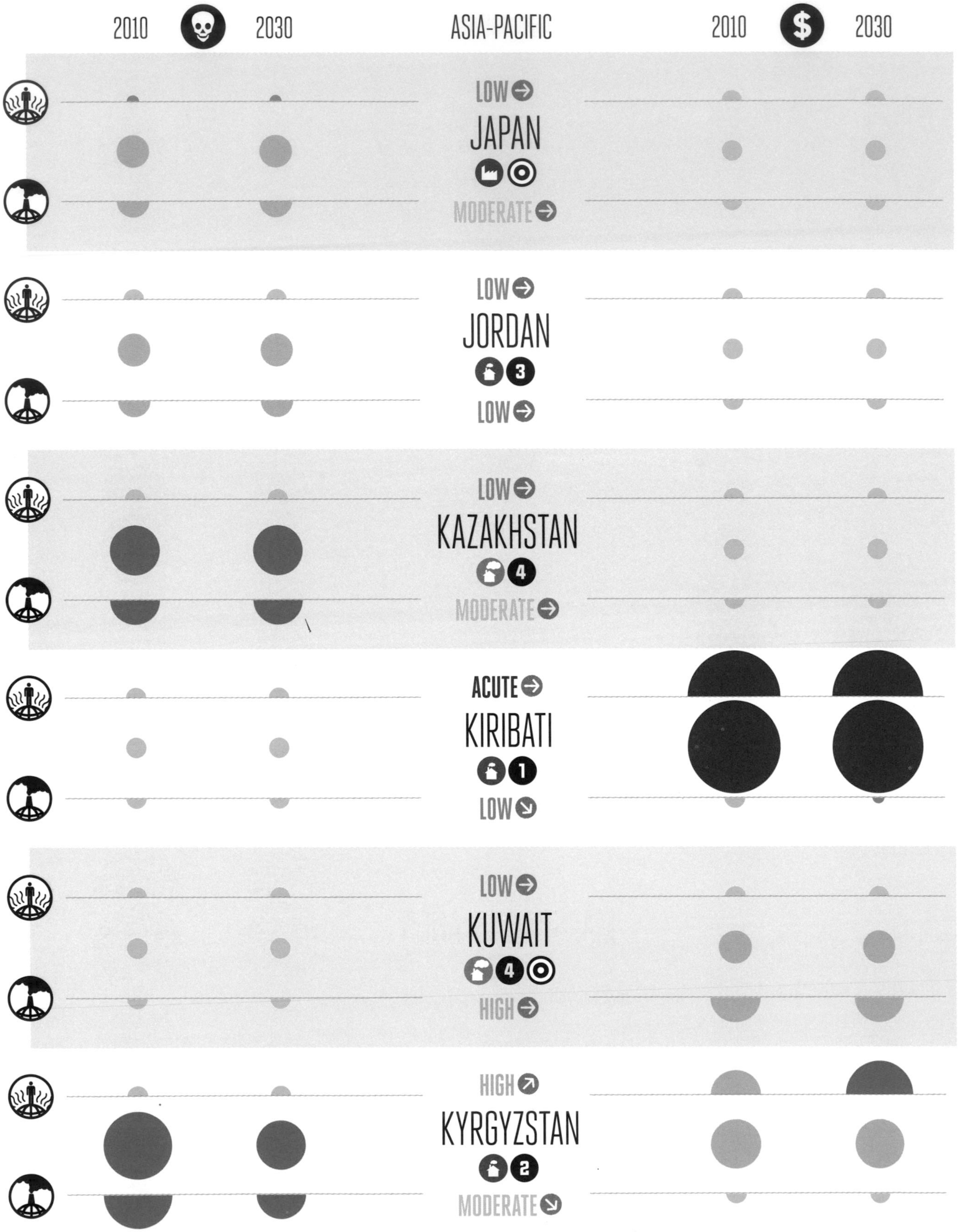

2010 2030 ASIA-PACIFIC 2010 2030

LOW
JAPAN
MODERATE

LOW
JORDAN
3
LOW

LOW
KAZAKHSTAN
4
MODERATE

ACUTE
KIRIBATI
1
LOW

LOW
KUWAIT
4
HIGH

HIGH
KYRGYZSTAN
2
MODERATE

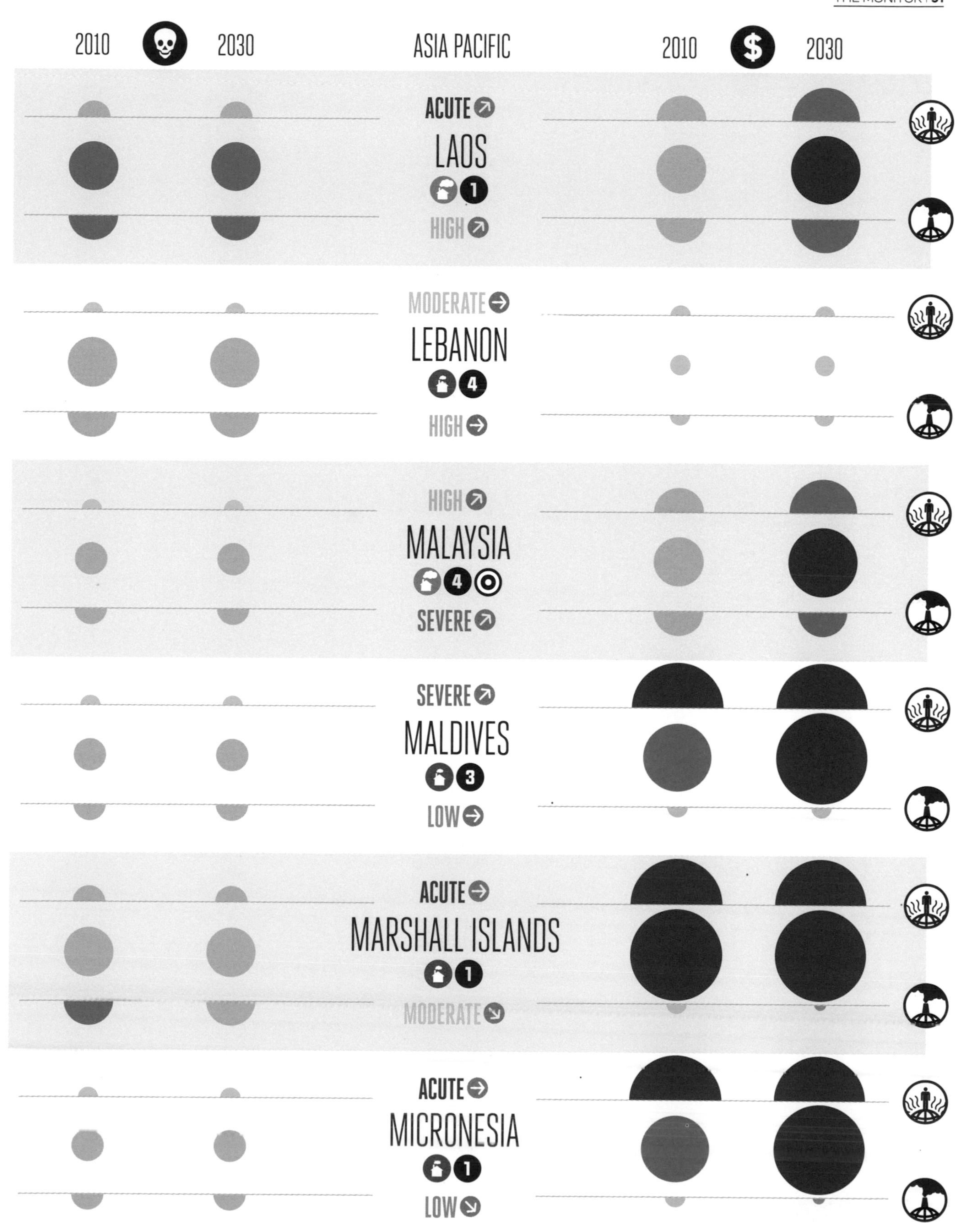
2010
2030
ASIA PACIFIC
2010
$
2030
ACUTE
LAOS
1
HIGH
MODERATE
LEBANON
4
HIGH
HIGH
MALAYSIA
4
SEVERE
SEVERE
MALDIVES
3
LOW
ACUTE
MARSHALL ISLANDS
1
MODERATE
ACUTE
MICRONESIA
1
LOW

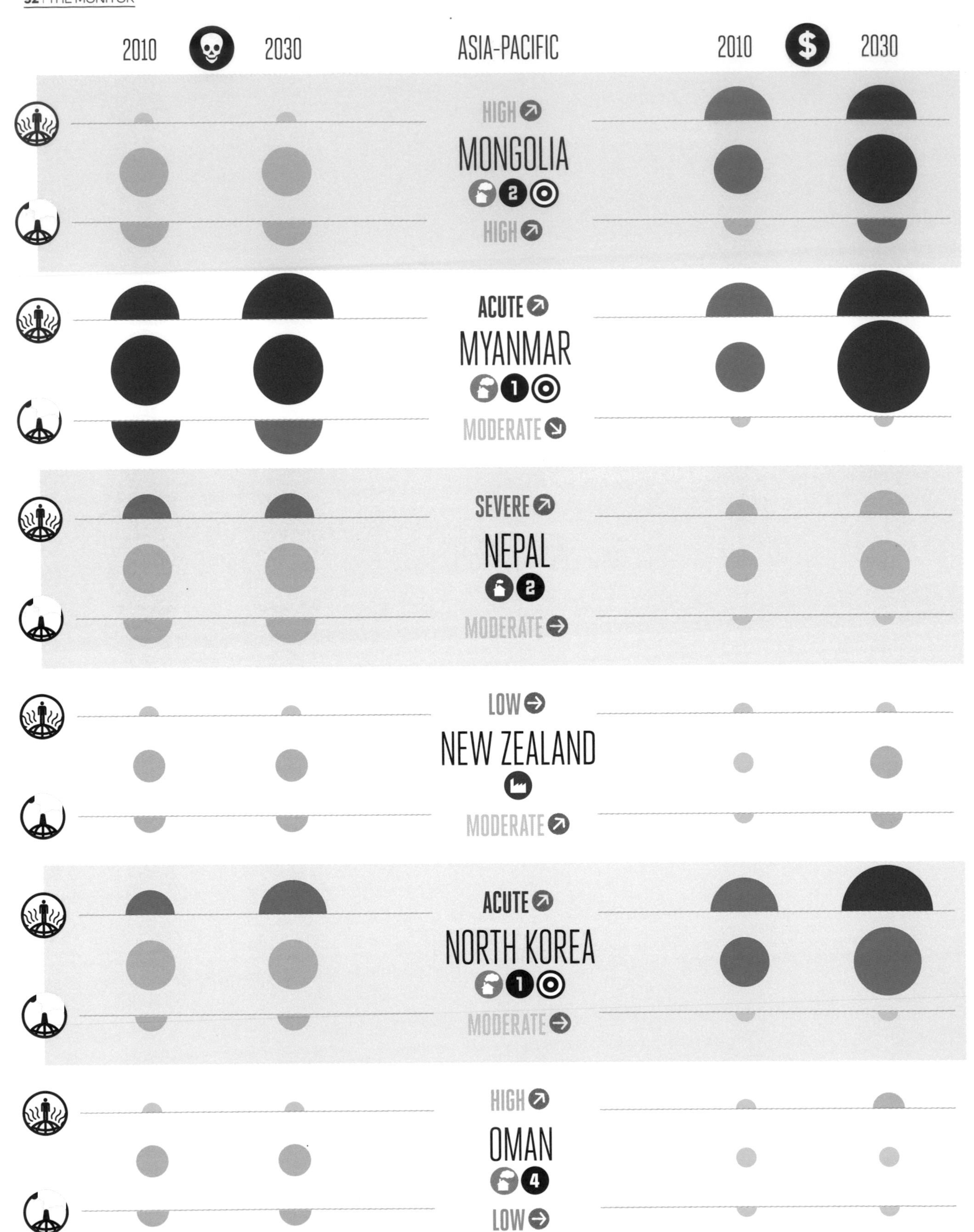
2010
2030
ASIA-PACIFIC
2010
$
2030
HIGH
MONGOLIA
2
HIGH
ACUTE
MYANMAR
1
MODERATE
SEVERE
NEPAL
2
MODERATE
LOW
NEW ZEALAND
MODERATE
ACUTE
NORTH KOREA
1
MODERATE
HIGH
OMAN
4
LOW

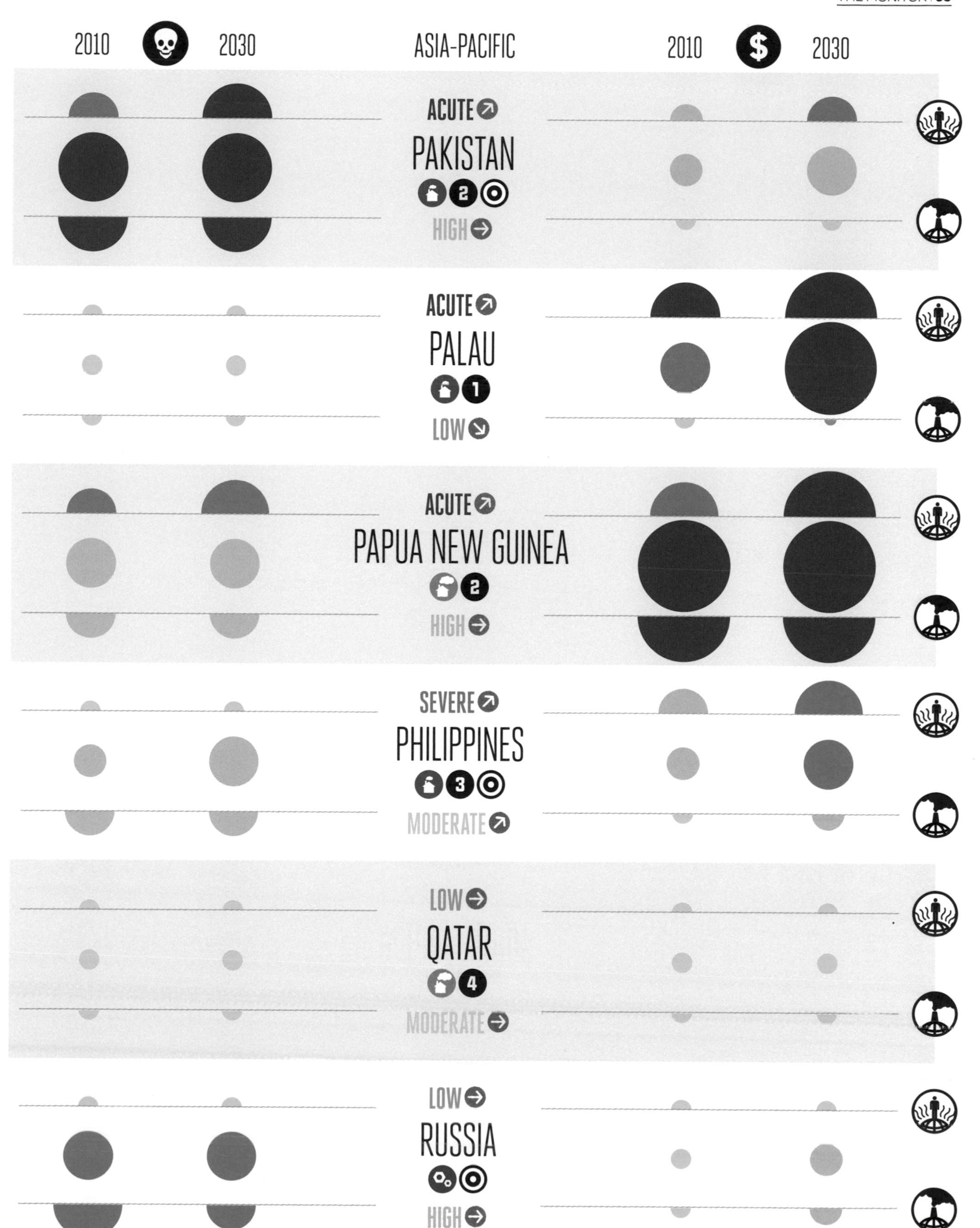
2010
2030
ASIA-PACIFIC
2010
$
2030
ACUTE
PAKISTAN
2
HIGH
ACUTE
PALAU
1
LOW
ACUTE
PAPUA NEW GUINEA
2
HIGH
SEVERE
PHILIPPINES
3
MODERATE
LOW
QATAR
4
MODERATE
LOW
RUSSIA
HIGH

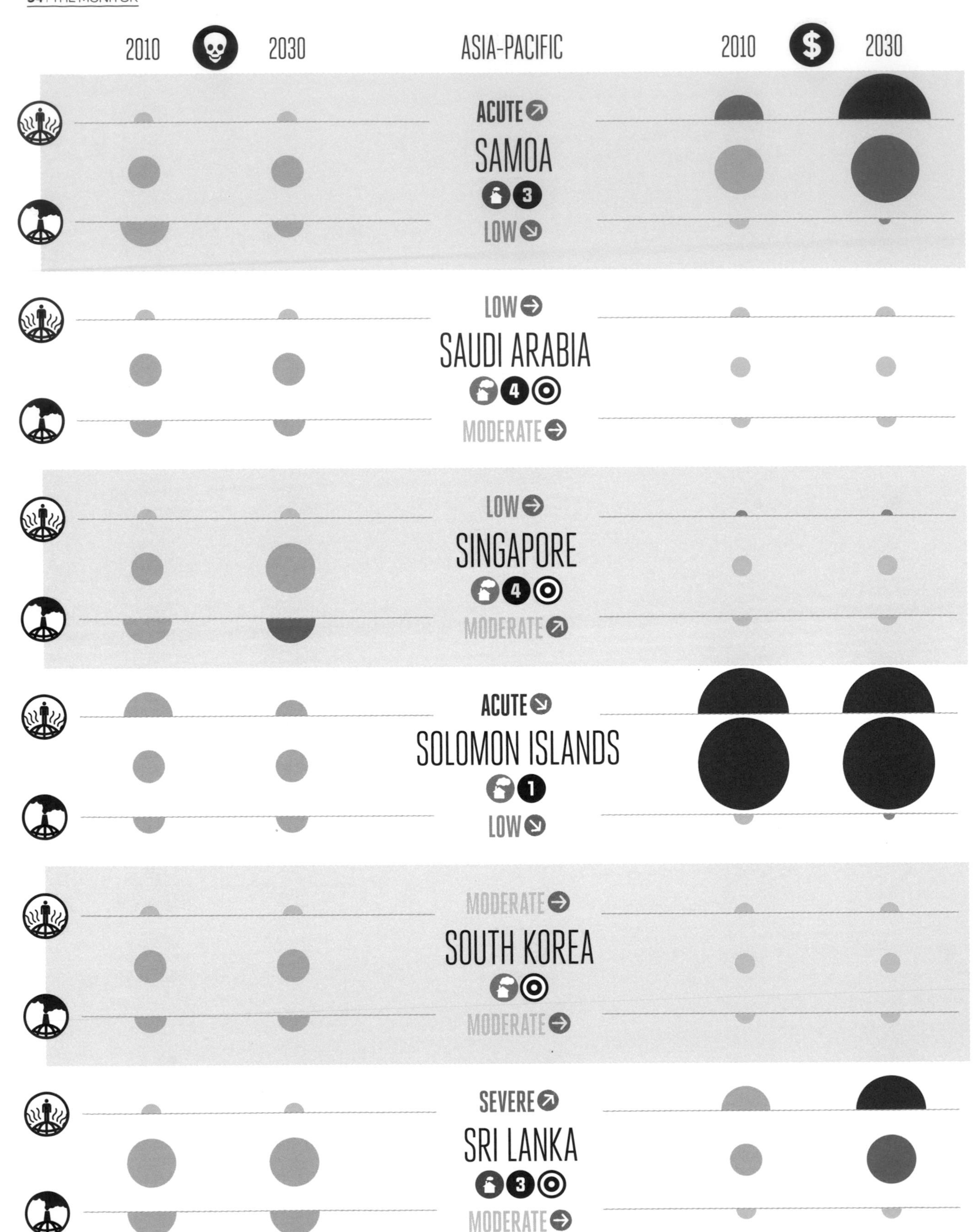
2010
2030
ASIA-PACIFIC
2010
$
2030
ACUTE
SAMOA
3
LOW
LOW
SAUDI ARABIA
4
MODERATE
LOW
SINGAPORE
4
MODERATE
ACUTE
SOLOMON ISLANDS
1
LOW
MODERATE
SOUTH KOREA
MODERATE
SEVERE
SRI LANKA
3
MODERATE

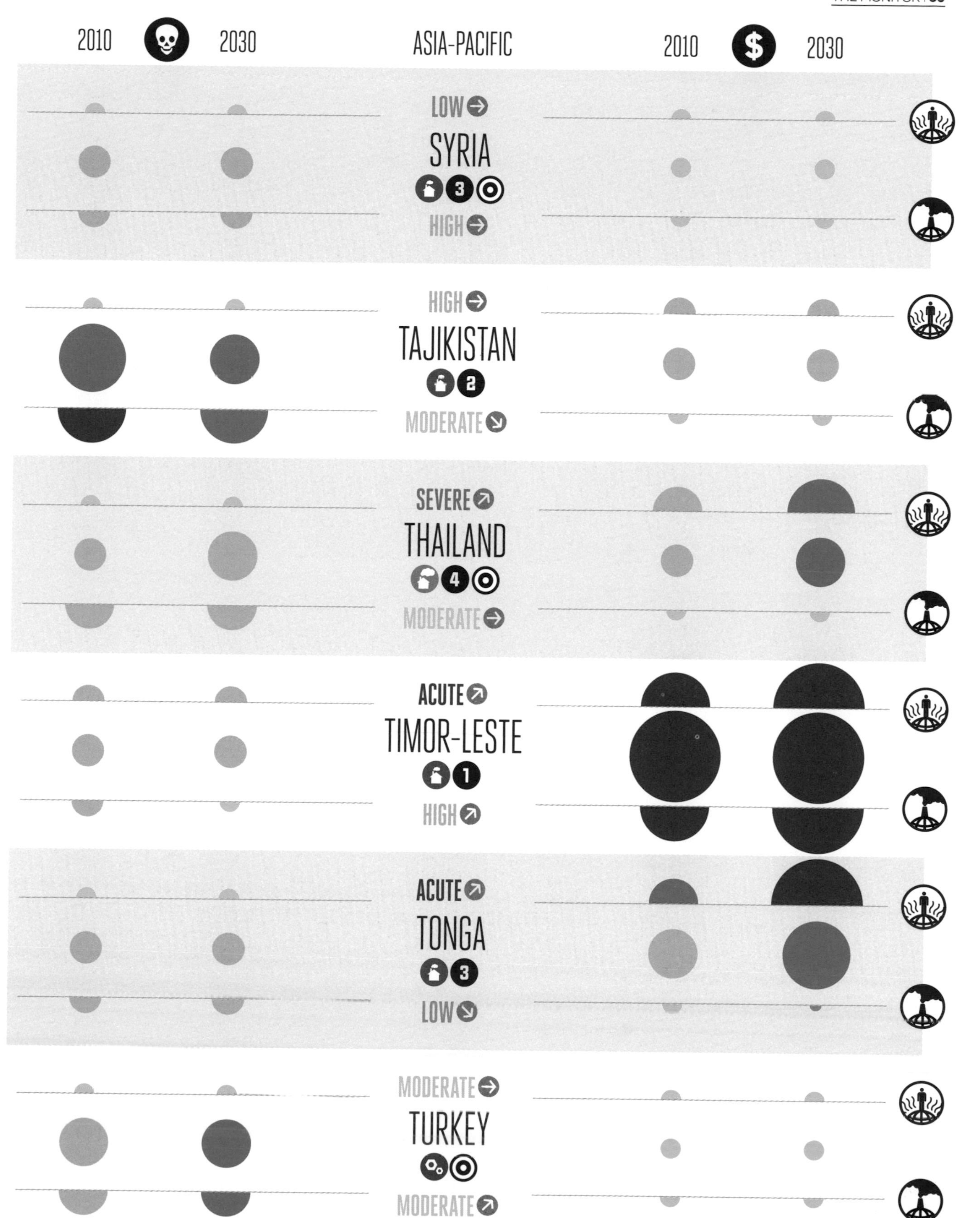
2010
2030
ASIA-PACIFIC
2010
2030
LOW
SYRIA
3
HIGH
HIGH
TAJIKISTAN
2
MODERATE
SEVERE
THAILAND
4
MODERATE
ACUTE
TIMOR-LESTE
1
HIGH
ACUTE
TONGA
3
LOW
MODERATE
TURKEY
MODERATE

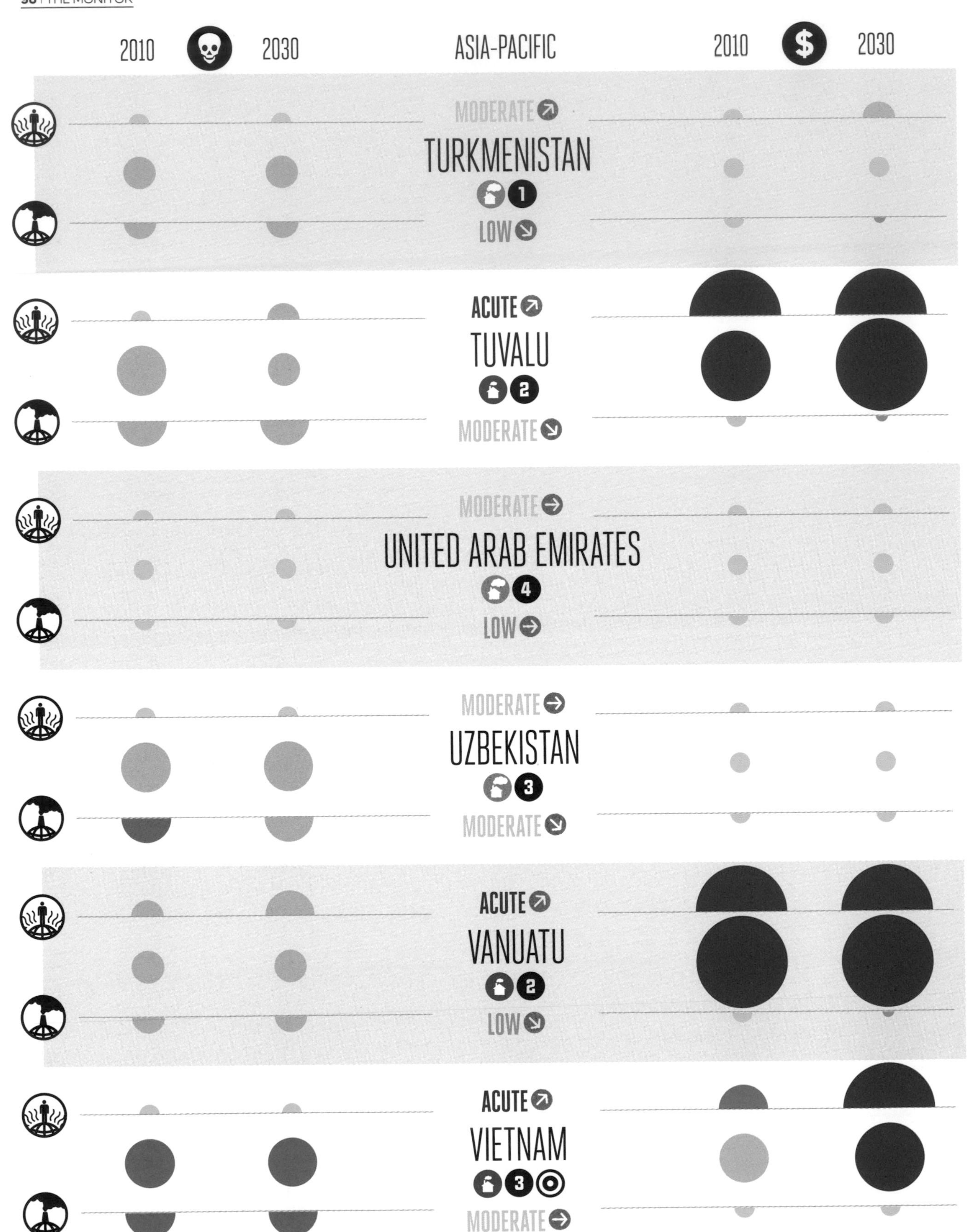
2010
2030
ASIA-PACIFIC
2010
$
2030
MODERATE
TURKMENISTAN
1
LOW
ACUTE
TUVALU
2
MODERATE
MODERATE
UNITED ARAB EMIRATES
4
LOW
MODERATE
UZBEKISTAN
3
MODERATE
ACUTE
VANUATU
2
LOW
ACUTE
VIETNAM
3
MODERATE

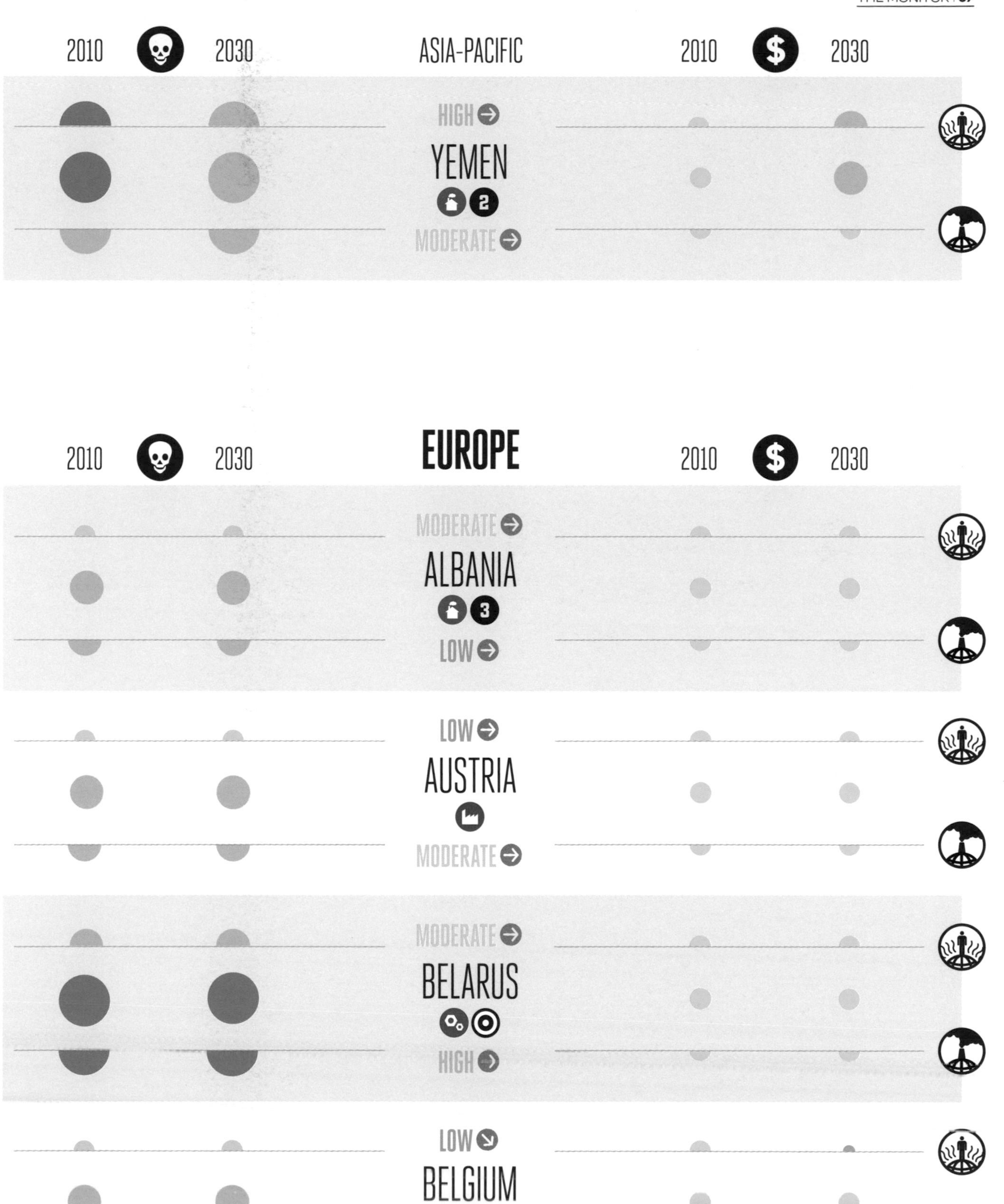
2010
2030
ASIA-PACIFIC
2010
2030
HIGH
YEMEN
2
MODERATE
2010
2030
EUROPE
2010
2030
MODERATE
ALBANIA
3
LOW
LOW
AUSTRIA
MODERATE
MODERATE
BELARUS
HIGH
LOW
BELGIUM
MODERATE

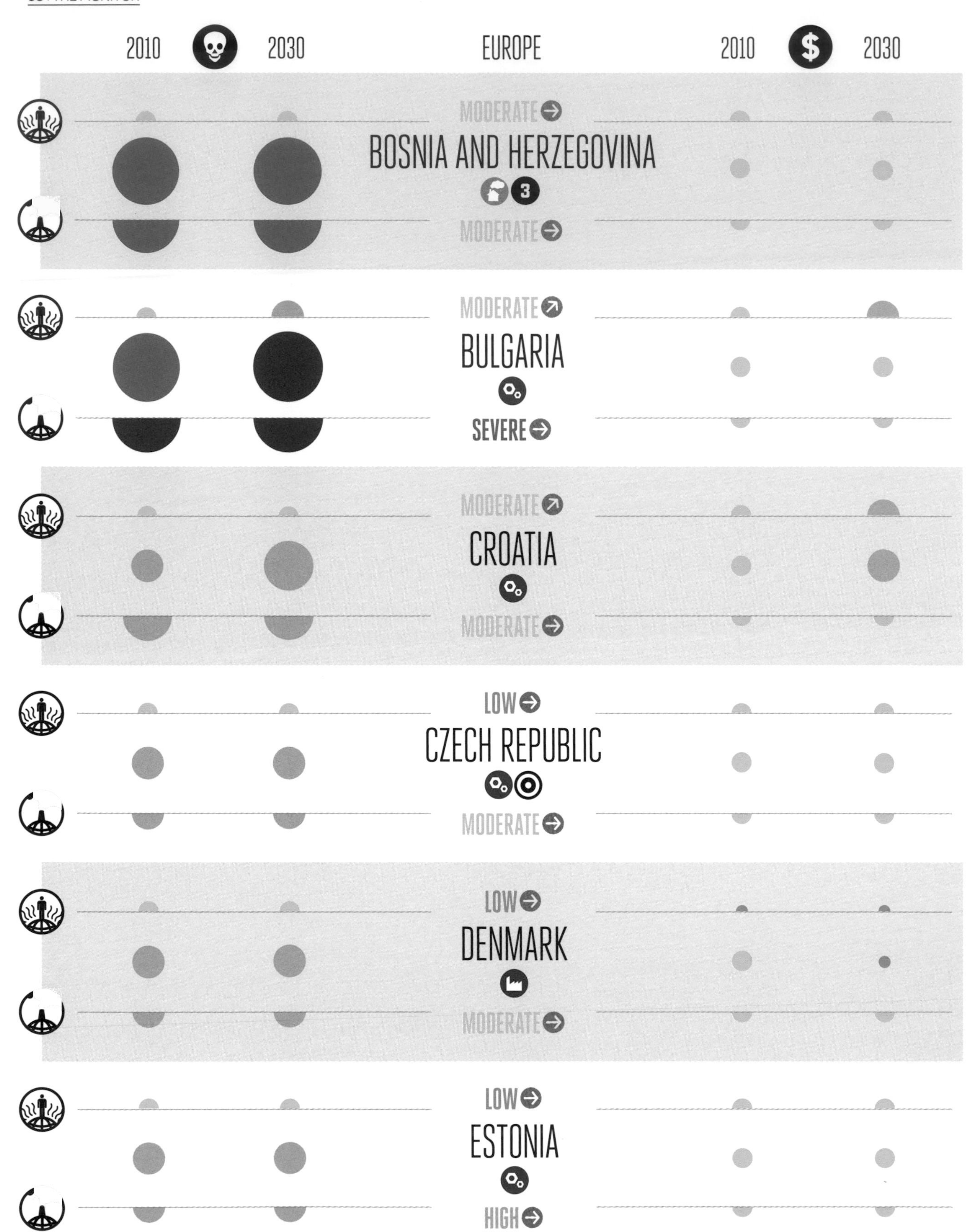
2010
2030
EUROPE
2010
2030
MODERATE
BOSNIA AND HERZEGOVINA
3
MODERATE
MODERATE
BULGARIA
SEVERE
MODERATE
CROATIA
MODERATE
LOW
CZECH REPUBLIC
MODERATE
LOW
DENMARK
MODERATE
LOW
ESTONIA
HIGH

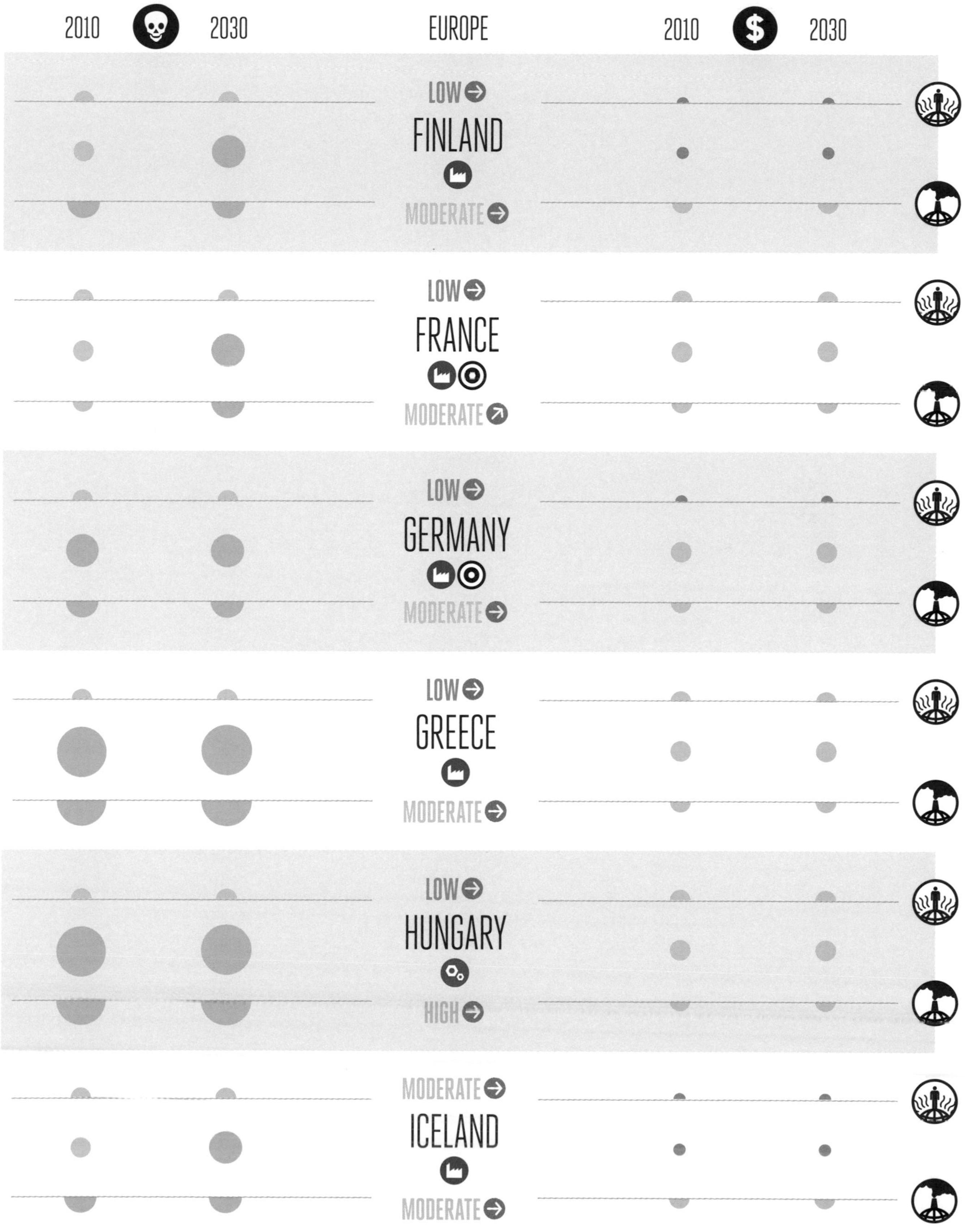

2010 2030 EUROPE 2010 2030

LOW
FINLAND
MODERATE

LOW
FRANCE
MODERATE

LOW
GERMANY
MODERATE

LOW
GREECE
MODERATE

LOW
HUNGARY
HIGH

MODERATE
ICELAND
MODERATE

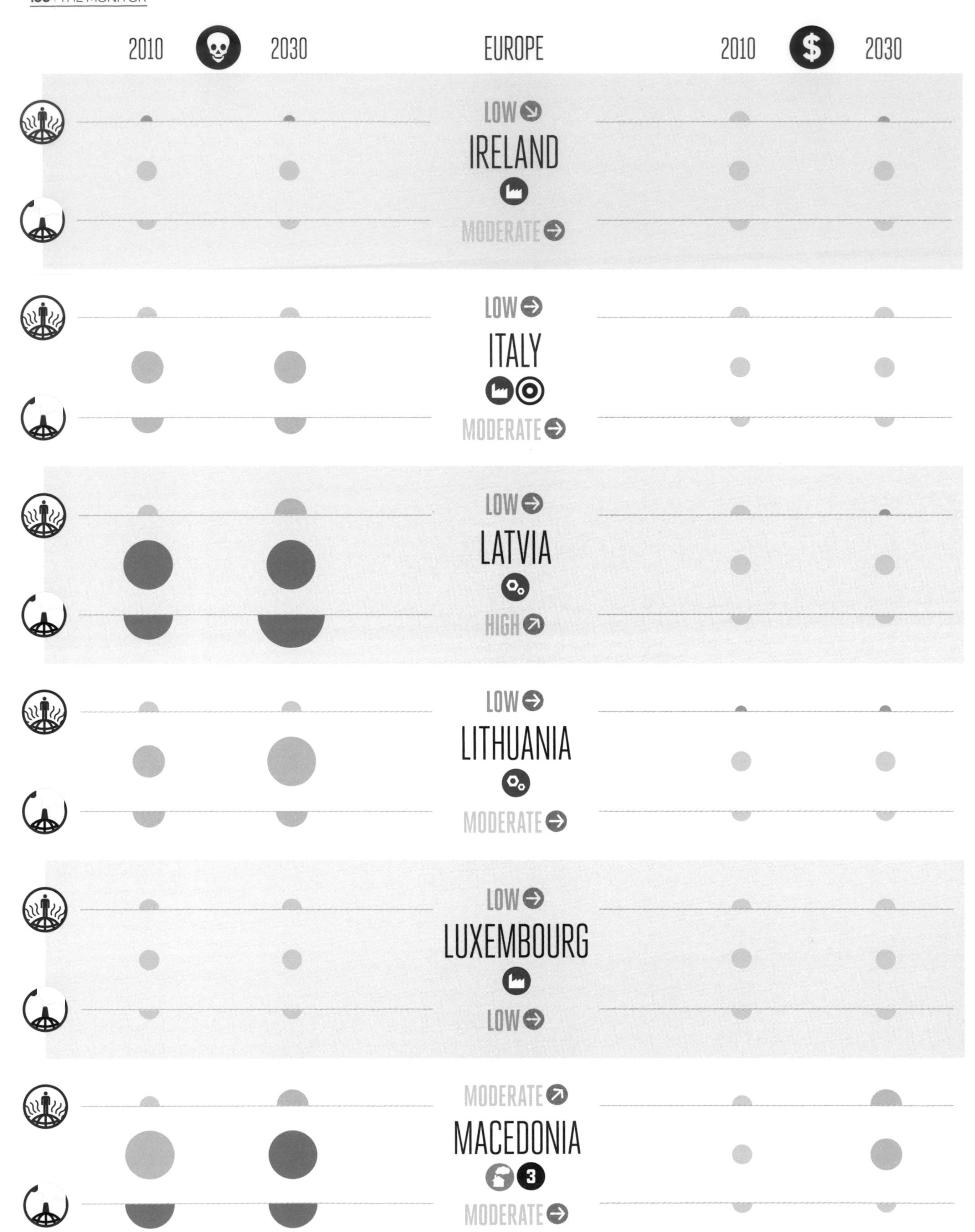
2010
2030
EUROPE
2010
2030
LOW
IRELAND
MODERATE
LOW
ITALY
MODERATE
LOW
LATVIA
HIGH
LOW
LITHUANIA
MODERATE
LOW
LUXEMBOURG
LOW
MODERATE
MACEDONIA
3
MODERATE

2010
2030
EUROPE
2010
$
2030
LOW
MALTA
LOW
HIGH
MOLDOVA
2
MODERATE
LOW
NETHERLANDS
MODERATE
LOW
NORWAY
MODERATE
LOW
POLAND
MODERATE
LOW
PORTUGAL
MODERATE

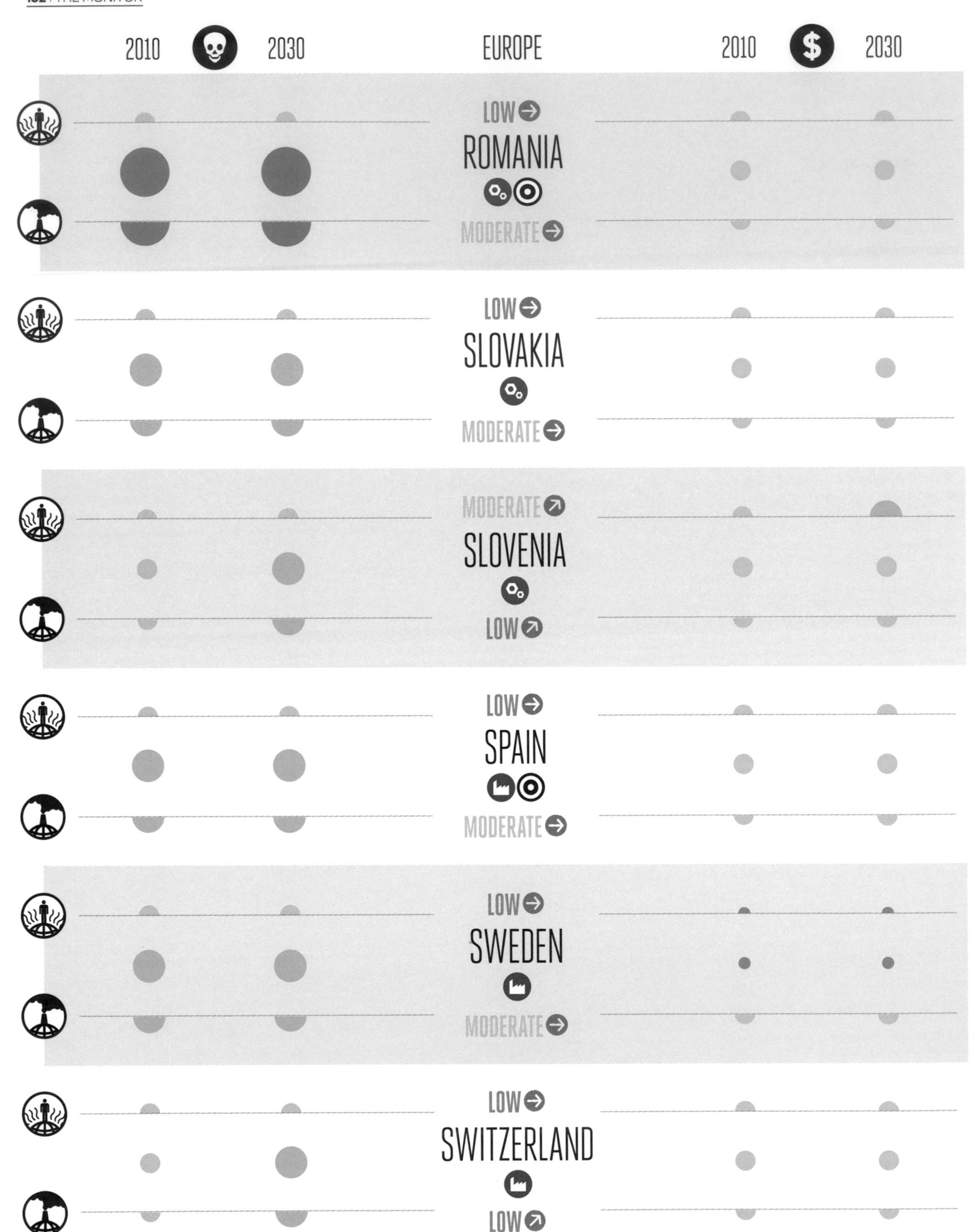
2010
2030
EUROPE
2010
2030
LOW
ROMANIA
MODERATE
LOW
SLOVAKIA
MODERATE
MODERATE
SLOVENIA
LOW
LOW
SPAIN
MODERATE
LOW
SWEDEN
MODERATE
LOW
SWITZERLAND
LOW

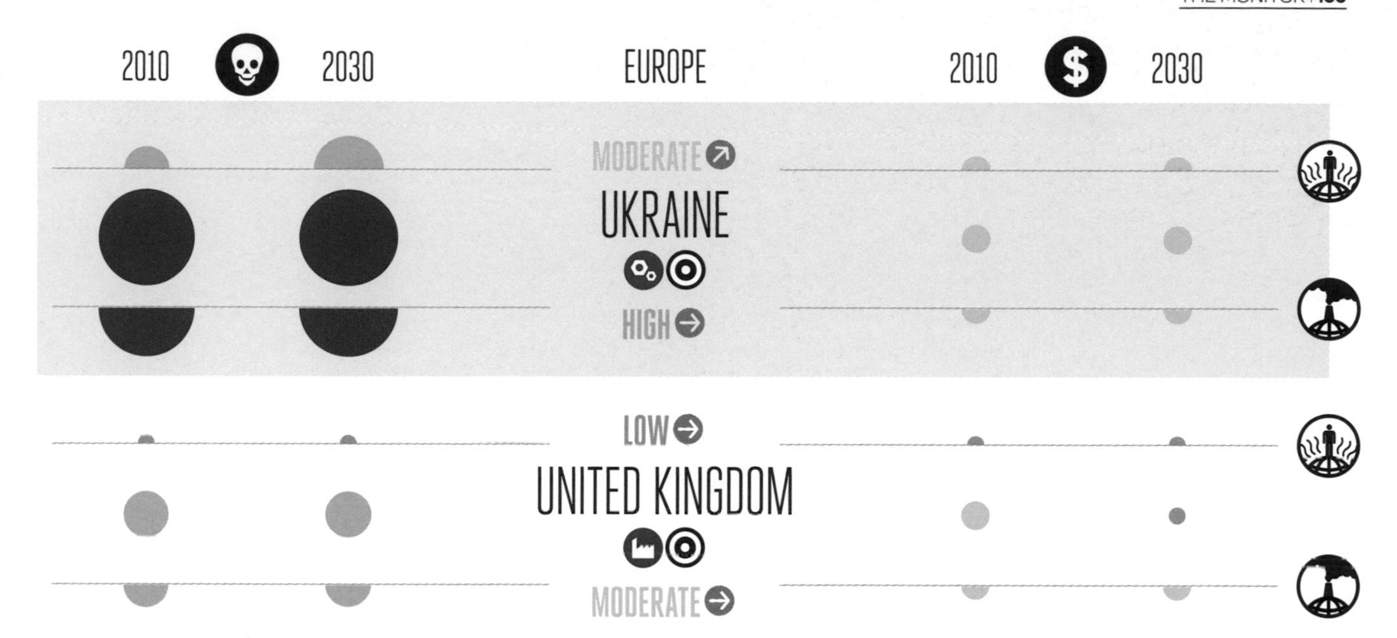
2010
2030
EUROPE
2010
2030
MODERATE
UKRAINE
HIGH
LOW
UNITED KINGDOM
MODERATE

CLIMATE

ENVIROMENTAL DISASTERS

DROUGHT

FLOODS & LANDSLIDES

STORMS

$	5 BILLION LOSS	2010
	20 BILLION LOSS	2030
☠	2,750	2010
	3,500	2030
$	10 BILLION LOSS	2010
	95 BILLION LOSS	2030
☠	2,500	2010
	3,500	2030
$	15 BILLION LOSS	2010
	100 BILLION LOSS	2030
$	15 BILLION GAIN	2010
	92 BILLION GAIN	2030

DROUGHT

ESTIMATES GLOBAL CLIMATE IMPACT

2010 EFFECT TODAY

USD **LOSS** PER YEAR **5 BILLION**

2030 EFFECT TOMORROW

USD **LOSS** PER YEAR **20 BILLION**

ECONOMIC IMPACT

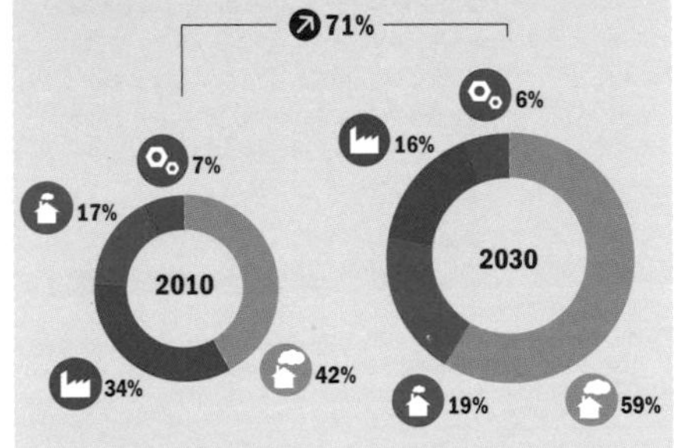

- As the planet's temperatures reach new highs drought will become more common and more severe
- Climate change also means more rain, but most of it is falling in the far north or far south where fewer people live, and much of this rain falls during the wet season while dry seasons tend to become drier
- When drought hits, agriculture comes under extreme pressure, crops may fail and livestock perish with important localized economic, health and social repercussions
- Catching and conserving water will be critical to ensure a resilient agricultural sector and food and water security during periods of extreme drought

RELATIVE IMPACT

2030
156
19

HOTSPOTS

2010		2030
800	CHINA	6,250
300	INDIA	1,500
200	IRAN	1,500
500	UNITED STATES	1,250
200	SPAIN	650

GEOPOLITICAL VULNERABILITY

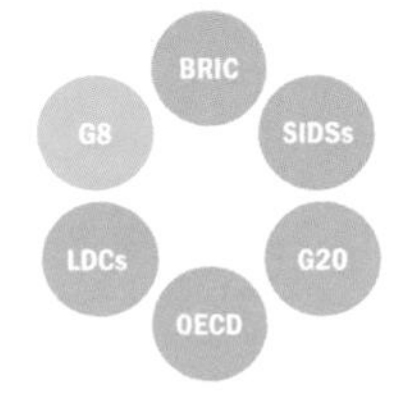

Economic Cost (2010 PPP non-discounted)
Developing Country Low Emitters
Developed
Developing Country High Emitters
Other Industrialized

$ = Losses per million USD of GDP

Change in relation to overall global population and/or GDP

Millions of USD (2010 PPP non-discounted)

F The increase in heat is already being experienced. It is virtually certain to increase in the coming years (IPCC, 2007). Parts of the world experiencing additional rainfall will also experience drought (Sheffield and Wood, 2008; Helm et al., 2010). Drought can diminish crop yields and kill livestock, generating serious economic losses for affected communities (Pandey et al. (eds.), 2007). Some of the world's major agriculturally productive regions, such as Brazil and Australia, are already affected (Saleska et al., 2011; LeBlanc et al., 2009). Deforestation and other forms of environmental degradation only worsen risk of drought (Turner et al., 2007). Reducing losses and safeguarding communities will require the tackling of these problems as well stimulating increased water availability through effective capture, storage and distribution measures and policies (McKinsey & Company, 2009). Displacing risks to the insurance industry would also alleviate the severity of losses to individuals and communities (Linnerooth-Bayer and Mechler, 2006).

CLIMATE MECHANISM

A hotter planet not unsurprisingly implies more drought (Sheffield and Wood, 2008). This is qualified by the fact that because of climate change there will also be more moisture and rain in the atmosphere (Allen and Ingram, 2002; Huntington, 2006; Kharin et al., 2007). Additional rain however tends to fall far north or south, where it is not lacking, and less rain tends to fall in the tropical areas of the planet which are already near thermal maximums and where a majority of the world's population live (Helm et al., 2010; Sherwood and Huber, 2010). In parts of the tropics, clouds are gaining in altitude and failing to deposit their moisture on mountain ranges (Malhi et al., 2008). As evidenced in cities, even if more rain falls, provided heat rises faster, any additional water would evaporate and not benefit the soil and its vegetation (Schmidt in Hao et al. (eds.), 2009). Hence, global aridity has increased and is expected to continue increasing, including in areas like the US, which have largely escaped the most severe forms of drought to date (Dai, 2011). Even where rainfall is declining, it is becoming more concentrated generating longer dry spells (Trenberth, 2011). Moreover, country level analysis in Vietnam for instance shows how in regions prone to extreme heat rain will likely decline in dry seasons and only increase in wet seasons when there will be an overabundance (Vietnam MONRE, 2010). Extreme forms of heat experienced today, such as the European heat wave of 2003, the Russian heat wave of 2010, or the extreme summer temperatures of 2011 in Texas would have been extremely unlikely to occur in the absence of climate change (Hansen et al., 2012).
When drought hits, plant productivity is directly affected and the mortality risk for livestock, such as cattle or birds, is greatly raised and indirectly can create vulnerabilities which invasive pests can exploit, further increasing damage (Chaves et al., 2009; Lesnoff et al., 2012; Wolf, 2009; Cherwin, 2009). Economic losses clearly result (Pandey et al. (eds.) 2007; Ding et al., 2011). Drought also damages buildings and infrastructure due to the shrinking and swelling of soil under extreme heat and aridity. This can lead to structural failure or accelerate asset depreciation (Corti et al., 2009).

IMPACTS

The global impact of climate change on drought is estimated to cause close to four billion dollars in damage a year in 2010, set to increase as a share of GDP to 2030 when average annual losses would reach close to 20 billion dollars a year. The impact is very widespread with some 160 countries experiencing high vulnerability to drought by 2030. There are many regions which are seriously affected, especially the wider Mediterranean basin and Black Sea, North Africa, the Middle East and southern and eastern Europe. In addition, parts of Central Asia and Southern Africa are also expected to experience severe effects. While mainly developing countries are affected, since developed nations in general are located geographically in the far north or south, a handful of major advanced economies are exposed to the most severe effects, in particular Spain, Portugal, Greece and Australia. Large numbers of least developed countries figure among those countries with Acute or Severe levels of vulnerability.
The largest total impact is felt in China whose estimated losses in 2010 of 800 million dollars would surpass six billion dollars a year in damage by 2030. Other countries with particularly large-scale impacts include India, Iran, the US, Spain, Mexico, Brazil and Russia – several are estimated to experience impacts in excess of 1 billion dollars in annual losses by 2030.

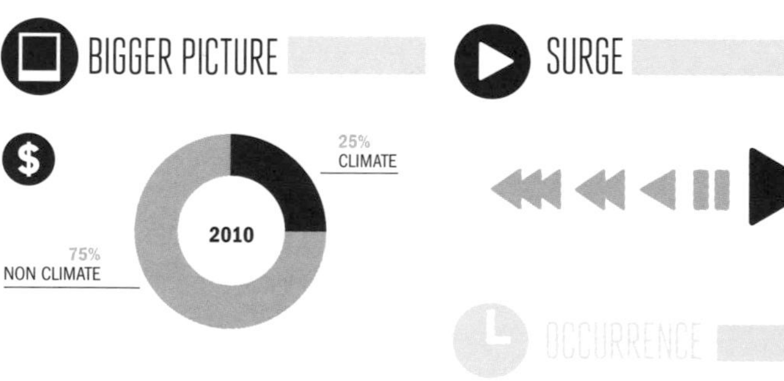

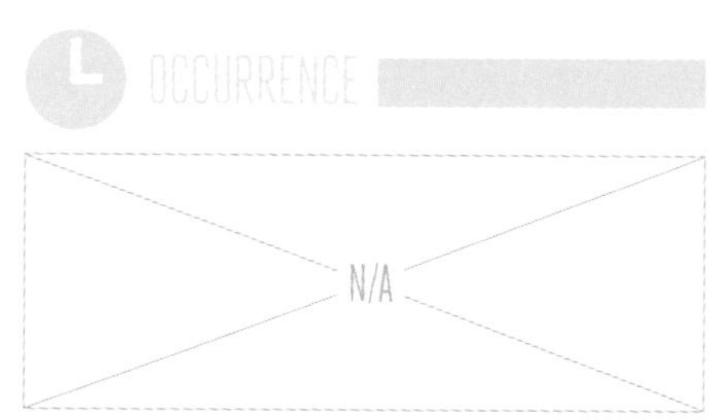

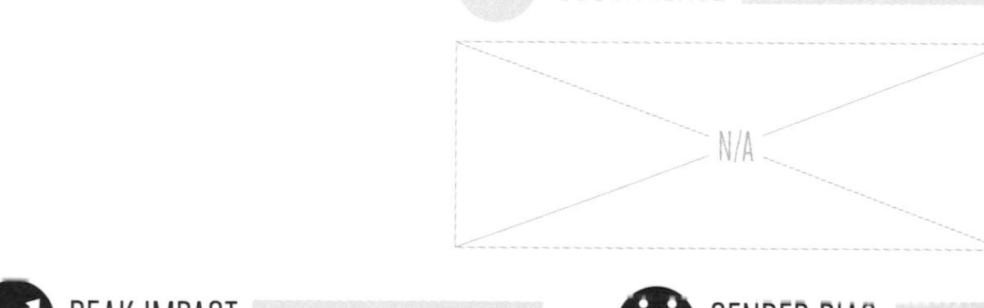

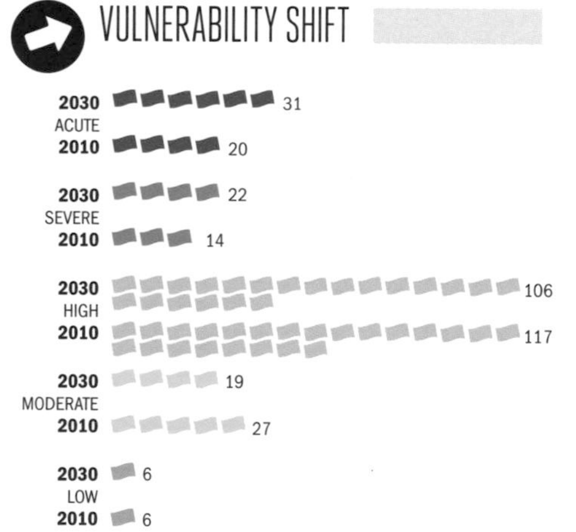

2002 MALAWI 500	2011 UNITED STATES 8,000
2006 CHINA 134	2009 CHINA 3,600
2005 BURUNDI 120	2002 AUSTRALIA 2,000
2004 KENYA 80	2004 BRAZIL 1,650
2002 UGANDA 79	2010 RUSSIA 1,400

INDICATOR INFORMATION

MODEL: Corti et al., 2009; Hoekstra et al., 2010; Rubel and Kottek, 2010; Sheffield and Wood, 2007

EMISSION SCENARIO: SRES A1B (IPCC, 2007)

BASE DATA: Corti et al., 2009; CRED EM-DAT, 2012

 = Millions of USD (historic)

 = 5 countries (rounded)

THE BROADER CONTEXT

Virtually all of the costliest drought years have occurred in the last two decades (CRED/EM-DAT, 2012). For statistical reasons it is still difficult to conclusively discern and pronounce on any global trends in drought losses; however the IPCC and insurance industry have reported increases in drought impact, and regional drought has become extreme in recent years (Quarantelli, 2001; IPCC, 2007; Bouwer, 2011). Major agricultural zones of Australia have experienced prolonged drought for a decade, not attenuated by a return to pre-drought levels of rainfall as the heat rises (LeBlanc et al., 2009). A 2010 drought in Brazil and across the Amazon regions was one of the worst ever (Saleska et al., 2011). The insurance industry is gauging growing losses as a result of drought-triggered soil subsidence and damage to buildings and infrastructure, estimated to cost €340 million per year in France alone (Swiss Re, 2010).

VULNERABILITIES AND WIDER OUTCOMES

Geography is a prime vulnerability, since countries in the far north receive considerably more rainfall (IPCC, 2007; Helm et al., 2010). Demand for water is another key determinant of vulnerability, since drought in the middle of the Sahara is of little consequence, while drought in the southern US, Europe or India is a major concern. Global water demand is expected to almost double by 2030, in particular due to increased water withdrawals in the agricultural sector – just as climate change will deprive many of the world's productive regions of water (McKinsey & Company, 2009; Sheffield and Wood, 2008). Land degradation from over-intensive agricultural exploitation or over-grazing and deforestation also greatly increase susceptibility to drought – another 30 % loss of forest in the Amazon could push the entire region into permanent aridity (Malhi et al., 2008). A lack of adequate irrigation and water infrastructure exacerbates drought since water captured in other periods of the year cannot be drawn upon during periods of prolonged aridity. In general, water-deprived economies have been understood to be less prosperous (Brown and Lall, 2006). The human health consequences of drought are principally accounted for under the Hunger indicator of the Monitor.

RESPONSES

Any response to drought must face up to two key concerns: 1) increasing water availability, and 2) dealing with building and infrastructure damage due to sinking or destabilized land. Increasing water availability will be met at the market cost of supplying water, which varies from region to region depending on the degree of water scarcity currently prevailing locally (McKinsey & Company, 2009). Effective governments would anticipate any shortfall and stimulate action to meet any expected water demand shortfall in order to avoid economic losses and loss of tax revenues. Addressing soil subsidence through design could involve the retrofitting of buildings to withstand soil movements linked to drought. Both drought and soil subsidence impacts can be dealt with by displacing risks to the insurance (and micro-insurance) industry through policies enabling businesses and home-owners to safeguard against potential damages (Swiss Re, 2011; Churchill and Matul, 2012).

THE INDICATOR

The indicator measures the impact of climate change on drought, defined as a consecutive sequence of months with "anomalously low soil moisture". It measures the change in both disaster damages and depreciation of property due to soil subsidence damages. The change in the number of droughts expected to occur is estimated using an ensemble of eight climate models (Sheffield and Wood, 2008). Baseline data for disaster damages is derived from the main international disaster database, but is known to be incomplete (CRED/EM-DAT, 2012). Accelerated depreciation of infrastructure due to soil subsidence uses a model based on France and extrapolated based on GDP per capita and population density, but excluding arid countries where the effect is considered less relevant (Corti et al., 2009; Hoekstra et al., 2010). Limitations and uncertainties relate to difficulties in estimating rainfall change for certain regions, the simplistic 1:1 damage assumption implied and to the extrapolation used for the soil subsidence indicator.

ESTIMATES COUNTRY-LEVEL IMPACT

COUNTRY	2010 ($)	2030 ($)
ACUTE		
Afghanistan	5	40
Armenia	5	25
Bolivia	5	45
Bosnia and Herzegovina	15	100
Cambodia	5	60
China	800	6,250
Croatia	15	85
Cuba	10	65
El Salvador	10	70
Gambia		1
Georgia	10	50
Greece	35	95
Guyana	1	15
Hungary	15	90
Iran	200	1,500
Lithuania	10	45
Mauritius	5	25
Moldova	10	65
Morocco	40	300
Mozambique	1	10
Namibia	1	10
Nicaragua	1	15
Peru	25	150
Portugal	45	150
Romania	20	100
South Africa	50	250
Spain	200	650
Tajikistan	5	20
Uruguay	5	40
Vietnam	40	350
Zimbabwe	1	10
SEVERE		
Australia	45	100
Azerbaijan	5	30
Bangladesh	15	75
Belarus	10	35
Benin	1	5
Costa Rica	1	15
Denmark	10	25
Ethiopia	5	20
Guatemala	5	20
Guinea	1	1
Guinea-Bissau		1
Honduras	1	10
India	300	1,500
Jamaica	1	5
Laos	1	5
Macedonia	1	5
Mexico	95	600
Pakistan	35	200
Sierra Leone		1
Swaziland		1
Thailand	40	200
Uzbekistan	5	30
HIGH		
Albania	1	5
Algeria	5	30
Angola	5	15
Antigua and Barbuda		
Argentina	25	150
Austria	10	10
Bahamas		1
Bahrain	1	5
Barbados		1
Belgium	10	15
Belize		1
Bhutan		1
Botswana	1	5
Brazil	95	550
Brunei	1	5
Bulgaria	5	20
Burkina Faso	1	1
Burundi		1
Cameroon	1	5
Cape Verde		
Central African Republic		1
Chile	15	70
Colombia	15	80
Comoros		
Congo	1	1
Cote d'Ivoire	1	5
Cyprus	1	1
Czech Republic	10	40
Dominica		
Dominican Republic	5	20
DR Congo	1	5
Ecuador	5	30
Egypt	10	50
Equatorial Guinea	1	5
Estonia	1	5
Fiji		1
Gabon	1	5
Germany	70	100
Ghana	5	15
Grenada		

($) Additional economic costs due to climate change (million USD PPP) - yearly average

CLIMATE VULNERABILITY

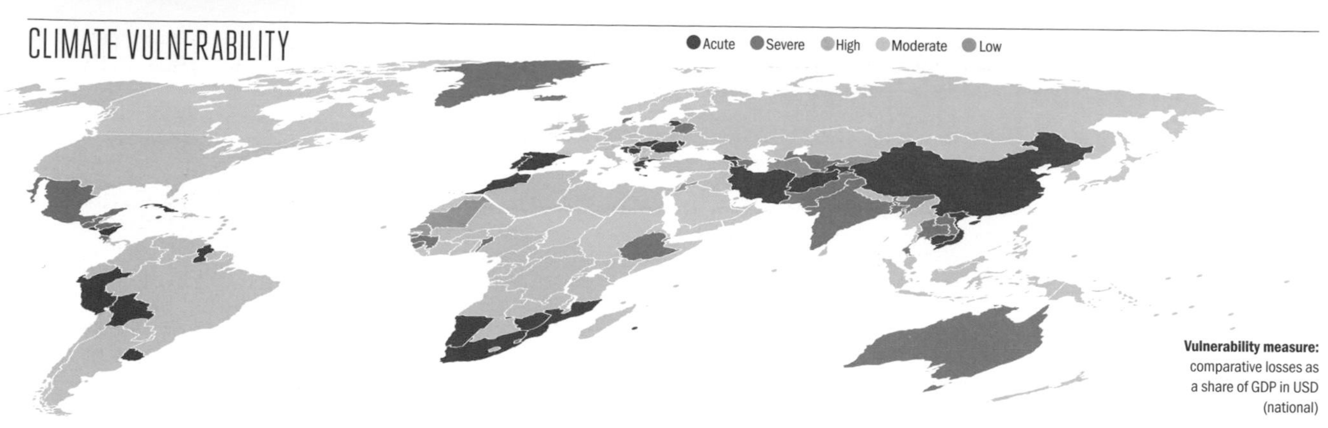

Vulnerability measure: comparative losses as a share of GDP in USD (national)

CLIMATE UNCERTAINTY

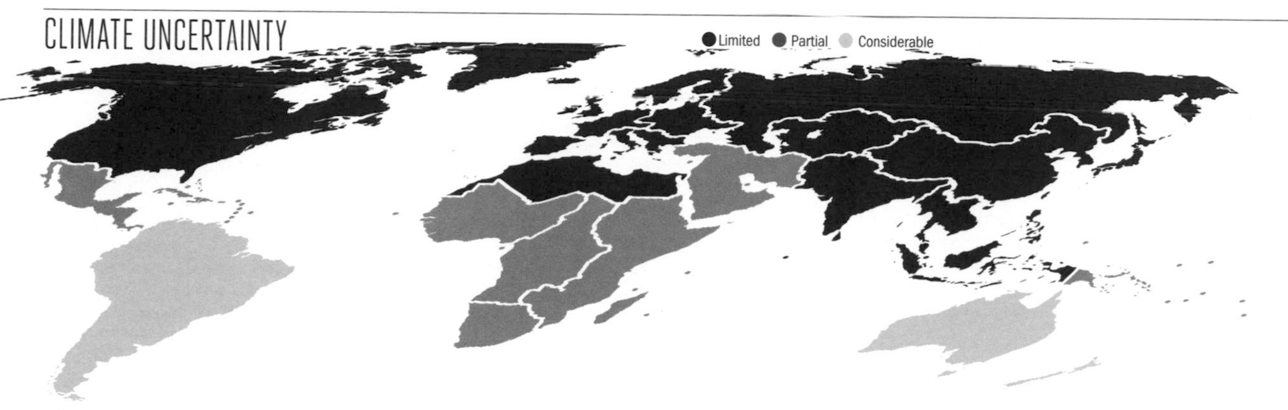

COUNTRY	$ 2010	$ 2030
Haiti	1	1
Iceland		1
Indonesia	40	200
Iraq	5	15
Ireland	5	5
Italy	55	150
Kazakhstan	5	20
Kenya	1	5
Kiribati		
Kuwait	5	20
Latvia	1	5
Lebanon	1	10
Lesotho		1
Liberia		
Libya	1	10
Madagascar	1	5
Malawi	1	1
Malaysia	20	80
Maldives		
Mali	1	1
Malta		1
Marshall Islands		
Micronesia		
Myanmar	1	10
Nepal	1	10
Netherlands	15	25
New Zealand	5	5
Nigeria	15	70
North Korea	1	10
Palau		
Panama	1	10
Papua New Guinea	1	1
Paraguay	1	5
Philippines	20	85
Poland	30	100
Qatar	5	20
Russia	90	400
Rwanda	1	1
Saint Lucia		1
Saint Vincent		
Samoa		
Sao Tome and Principe		
Seychelles		1
Singapore	10	40
Slovakia	5	15
Slovenia	1	10
Solomon Islands		
South Korea	55	250
Sri Lanka	5	25
Suriname		1
Tanzania	5	15
Timor-Leste		1
Togo		1
Tonga		
Trinidad and Tobago	1	5
Tunisia	5	15
Turkey	35	65
Tuvalu		
Ugondo	1	10
Ukraine	20	75
United Arab Emirates	5	25
United Kingdom	55	90
United States	500	1,250
Vanuatu		
Venezuela	10	45
Zambia	1	1
MODERATE		
Canada	25	45
Chad		
Eritrea		
Finland	1	1
France	45	75
Israel	1	15
Japan	90	150
Luxembourg	1	1
Mongolia		1
Niger		1
Norway	1	5
Oman	1	5
Saudi Arabia	1	10
Somalia		
Sudan/South Sudan	1	10
Sweden	5	10
Switzerland	5	10
Syria	1	5
Yemen	1	5
LOW		
Djibouti		
Jordan		
Kyrgyzstan		
Mauritania		
Senegal		
Turkmenistan		

FLOODS & LANDSLIDES

ESTIMATES GLOBAL CLIMATE IMPACT

2010 EFFECT TODAY

DEATHS PER YEAR **2,750**

USD LOSS PER YEAR **10 BILLION**

2030 EFFECT TOMORROW

DEATHS PER YEAR **3,500**

USD LOSS PER YEAR **95 BILLION**

CONFIDENCE
INDICATIVE

SEVERITY
AFFECTED
INJUSTICE
PRIORITY
MDG EFFECT

- Heavy rainfall, the main trigger of flooding and landslides, is on the rise
- Spring comes earlier and releases more water from mountains and glaciers which adds further to flood risks
- Future increases in these effects may coincide, generating more mega disasters of the scale of the 2010 Pakistan floods
- Comprehensive risk reduction efforts in implementation of the Hyogo Framework for Action are helping to reduce vulnerabilities, even as world population and exposed infrastructure expand
- Parallel efforts are not being made to deliberately adjust humanitarian relief systems to growing flood dange

MORTALITY IMPACT

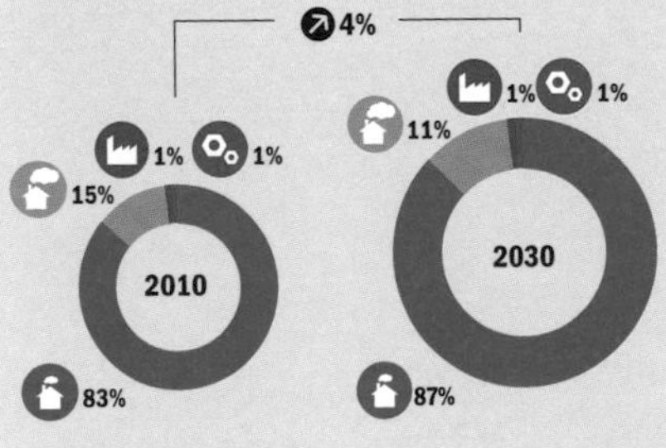

ECONOMIC IMPACT

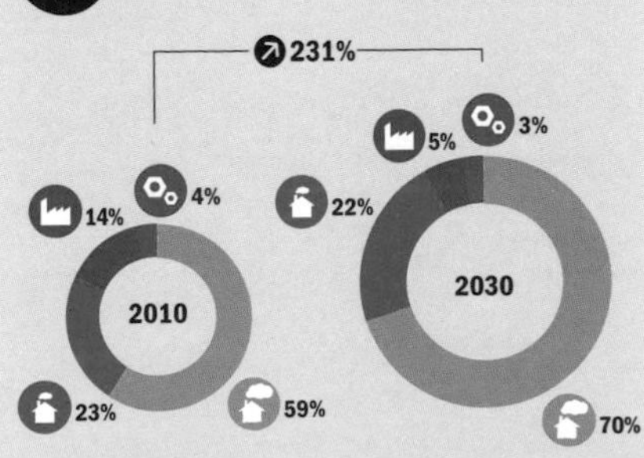

RELATIVE IMPACT

2010: 130 | 6

2030: 82 | 7

$ 2010: 52 | 4

$ 2030: 104 | 6

GEOPOLITICAL VULNERABILITY

LDCs
BRIC
G20
G8
OECD
SIDSs

HOTSPOTS

Deaths: 2010 | 2030

2010		2030
2,000	INDIA	2,500
200	CHINA	150
75	BANGLADESH	100
50	VIETNAM	55
30	PAKISTAN	45

$: 2010 | 2030

2010		2030
4,500	CHINA	50,000
1,250	INDIA	10,000
550	NORTH KOREA	6,750
350	PAKISTAN	3,250
300	BANGLADESH	2,750

Deaths | Economic Cost (2010 PPP non-discounted)
Developing Country Low Emitters | Developed
Developing Country High Emitters | Other Industrialized

= Deaths per 100 million
$ = Losses per 100,000 USD of GDP
Change in relation to overall global population and/or GDP

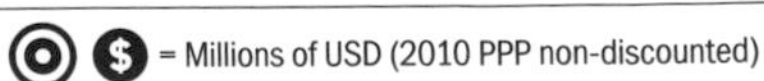
= Millions of USD (2010 PPP non-discounted)

Flooding is a common natural hazard from increases in rainfall due to climate change. Floods are expected to worsen practically everywhere, even in areas facing declining annual rainfall, as heavy downpours become more common (IPCC, 2007). More floods mean more deaths and injuries, more damaged property and infrastructure, and growing disruption of economic activities. Where large countries like China, Pakistan, or the US are affected, the lives of millions of people may be disrupted and billions of dollars of economic damage inflicted (CRED/EM-DAT, 2012). However, the risk of death due to flooding is heavily concentrated in low-income countries, which face significant risks of setbacks in development gains, with women particularly vulnerable (UNISDR, 2011; Nelleman et al., 2011). Highly cost-effective including "low-regrets" measures to limit damages and speed recovery are also inaccessible to many for lack of the capacity and up-front resources to implement them (IPCC, 2012a). Social and political factors, including illiteracy and the over-exploitation of resources often exacerbate these problems (UNISDR, 2009).

CLIMATE MECHANISM

A warmer planet means a more active hydrological system, as water is evaporated faster from oceans and land, generating cloud and rainfall (Dore, 2005; Kharin et al., 2007). That means more rain overall and more energy in general in the global climate system as it heats up, leading to heavier downpours of rain, more variable or erratic rainfall, and more frequent heavy precipitation. Coupled with an earlier spring that discharges more water as glaciers continue to decline, the implications are that risk of flooding and landslides caused by weather, and not earthquakes or otherwise, are on an increase (Hidalgo et al., 2009; Radi⊠ and Hock, 2011; IPCC, 2007; Mirza et al., 2003; Jonkman et al., 2008; Bouwer et al., 2010). The evidence base for the flood trend is low, in particular due to inadequate gauge station records and confounding information linked to land use and engineering (IPCC, 2012a). The increase in heavy rainfall during short periods of time is assured and is not only the main trigger of flooding, but the main input variable to early warning tools to predict flooding (Prudhomme et al., 2002; Harris et al., 2007).

IMPACTS

Globally, climate change is already estimated to be responsible for close to an average of 3,000 deaths per year and around 10 billion dollars in economic losses through flooding and landslides. For every death, there can be as many as 10,000 people in need of emergency assistance; each year, over 25 million more people are affected than in earlier periods when climate change was not so marked. Over the next 20 years, the climate-related flood death toll is expected to increase only modestly to 3,500 deaths per year with economic losses more than tripling as a share of global GDP, reaching 95 billion dollars per year by 2030.

Approximately two-thirds of these losses are incurred in China and India alone. Populous emerging economies in Asia, such as Bangladesh, Pakistan, and Vietnam are particularly vulnerable, as are mountainous developing countries, such as Bhutan and Nepal. Effects are widely distributed around the world, with the number of countries labeled "Acute" doubling by 2030. Low-lying small island states, such as the Maldives, are unaffected by non-coastal flooding and landslides, whereas mountainous small islands, such as Haiti or Fiji are at high risk.

THE BROADER CONTEXT

The significance of socio-economic determinants of risk mean climate change is only one factor in the scale of damage generated by so-called natural disasters. Mortality risk due to extreme weather is known to fall over time with rising incomes (Peduzzi et al., 2012). However, economic losses show increases in recent years (CRED/EM-DAT, 2012; Munich Re, 2012). These observations support the UN's analysis that as socio-economic development improves, fewer people are killed, but infrastructure is at greater risk (UNISDR, 2009 and 2011).

VULNERABILITIES AND WIDER OUTCOMES

Vulnerability levels are often dictated by socio-economic development standing and the associated effectiveness of governments in putting in place measures that can limit dangers for populations. Poorly located, unprotected flood plain settlements are also at high risk, but sound governance should prevent or rationalize this type of development. Environmental degradation and unwise patterns of land

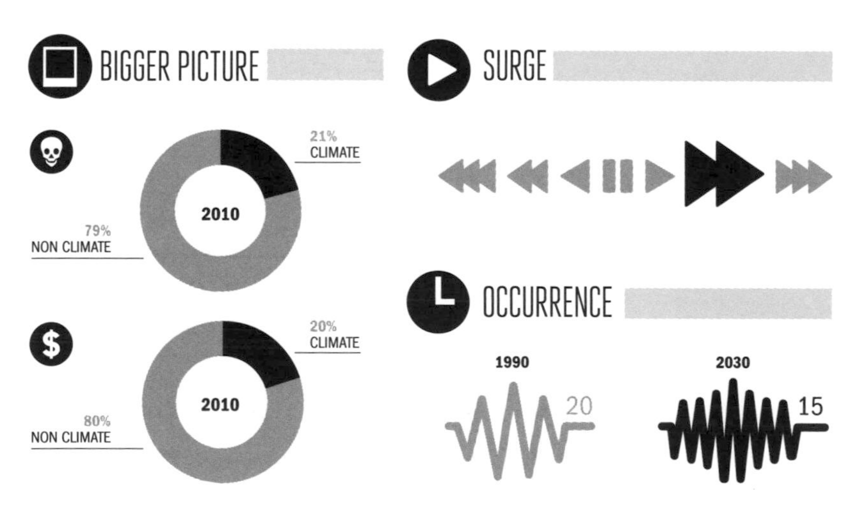

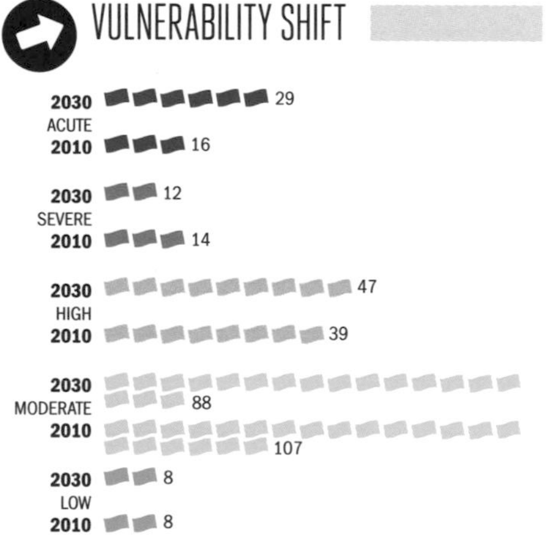

2010 CHINA 18,930
2002 GERMANY 11,600
2008 UNITED STATES 10,002
2010 PAKISTAN 9,500
2007 UNITED KINGDOM 8,448

INDICATOR INFORMATION

MODEL: Kharin et al., 2007

EMISSION SCENARIO: SRES A1B (IPCC, 2007)

BASE DATA: CRED EM-DAT, 2012; Munich Re NATCAT, 2010 (economic data); UNEP GRID, 2012 (mortality data)

 = Millions of USD (historic)

 Estimated time between major weather events (years)

 = 5 countries (rounded)

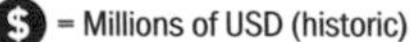

usage, particularly deforestation, further exacerbate localized vulnerabilities, for example, by destabilizing hillsides and by increasing the flow of rainwater over land—effects especially significant in developing countries (Brashshaw et al., 2007). High rates of urbanization, common in most developing countries around the world today, often lead rural-urban migrants to settle in flood plain shanty towns adjacent to major urban centres, adding to the level of risk (Quarantelli, 2003).

Flooding carries serious consequences for economic activity, especially for lower-income communities where insurance that otherwise speeds economic rebound is least prevalent (Dodman and Satterthwaite, 2008). Harm to poverty-reduction efforts has been shown to result more from widespread and regularly occurring small- to medium-scale disasters, since they repeatedly frustrate development progress, even though freak, high-profile, catastrophes typically receive more attention (Lavell, 2008). Flood damage—particularly ecological and social costs or diffuse disruptions to broad economic activities—is also difficult to fully quantify, and in extreme cases can persist for months (Messner and Meyer, 2005).

RESPONSES

Like other disasters, floods are considered to have three core components: hazard, exposure, and vulnerability. Hazard is a variable largely beyond immediate human control, so responses either aim to decrease vulnerability or exposure to hazard, or both. Measures such as rapid early warning systems, disaster education, building codes and their regulation, environmental protection against deforestation and land degradation, insurance for infrastructure or other economic assets, flood defences and storm drains, strengthening of local ecosystems, disaster volunteer programmes all reduce vulnerabilities, but may demand resources which many countries simply do not possess. Under pressure of economic and population growth, most increases in exposure are inevitable. But strategic municipal planning for infrastructure development can help minimize the extent of new exposure to risk. Urban centres with elevated population densities are also high-dividend opportunities for reducing possible disasters, provided urban authorities are willing and able to meet the needs of their residents in managing risks (Dodman and Satterthwaite, 2008).

The capacity of governments to develop and implement a range of risk-reduction measures is considered a fundamental determinant of the success of national disaster prevention and recovery strategies; this includes the ability to incorporate considerations of disaster risk into wide-ranging state agendas, from education to municipal planning and fiscal tools. Capacity to do so is also most deficient in highly vulnerable, low-income settings (Ahrens and Rudolph, 2006).

A number of low-income countries, such as Bangladesh have nevertheless managed to reduce levels of vulnerability through cost-effective community and volunteer-based efforts, as alternatives to more resource-intensive measures (Khan, 2007). On the other hand, recent floods along the Mississippi and Missouri rivers in the US have shown how even the highly developed countries can be overwhelmed by large-scale events (Olson and Morton, 2012). New extremes and delays in policy changes to increase resilience mean that the world's humanitarian system should prepare for serious increases in flood response in the years ahead.

THE INDICATOR

The indicator combines exposure to floods and landslides with modeled mortality risk for estimations of deaths with socio-economic adjustments. For economic losses, a combination of 20 years of disaster data from different sources is relied upon as a baseline. The indicator then estimates how the change in, or increases in the occurrence of, heavy precipitation events would alter the current picture of flood and landslide risk. Uncertainty regarding precipitation change in some areas is an impediment to reliable national-level estimates of these changes. Likewise, country-specific variation in the effects of increased heavy rainfall is not accounted for, except through the worsening of the pre-existing topography of risk, as reflected in historic and modeled disaster data. Although records of floods are unreliable, models of the effects of climate change on heavy precipitation and observed rainfall changes do reveal the increasing trend (IPCC, 2007, IPCC, 2012a; Kharin et al.).

ESTIMATES COUNTRY-LEVEL IMPACT

COUNTRY	2010	2030	2010	2030	2010	2030
ACUTE						
Bangladesh	75	100	300	3,000	600,000	900,000
Bhutan	1	1		1	15,000	25,000
Bolivia	1	1	30	300	10,000	15,000
Cambodia	10	10	20	200	65,000	65,000
China	200	150	4,500	50,000	2,000,000	1,500,000
Comoros	5	10			45,000	85,000
Dominica	1	1			2,500	3,000
Ecuador	1	5	30	300	25,000	30,000
Fiji	1	1	1	10	4,000	3,500
Guyana			10	100	2,000	1,500
Haiti	5	5	5	35	30,000	40,000
India	2,000	2,500	1,000	10,000	20,000,000	25,000,000
Kyrgyzstan	1	1	5	35	9,500	15,000
Laos	5	10	1	15	55,000	70,000
Macedonia			5	50	1,500	1,000
Moldova	1	1	15	100	5,500	5,000
Mozambique	1	5	10	85	20,000	30,000
Nepal	10	15	15	150	85,000	100,000
North Korea	10	10	550	6,500	100,000	85,000
Pakistan	30	45	350	3,000	300,000	450,000
Saint Lucia	1	1		1	6,000	6,000
Sao Tome and Principe	1	1			15,000	25,000
Solomon Islands	1	1			5,000	9,000
Tajikistan	5	5	40	300	30,000	45,000
Timor-Leste	1	1			25,000	25,000
Turkmenistan	5	10	5	25	55,000	80,000
Vanuatu		1		1	2,500	4,000
Vietnam	50	55	150	2,000	500,000	500,000
Yemen	1	1	35	250	7,500	25,000
SEVERE						
Afghanistan	5	10	5	35	55,000	90,000
Armenia	1	1		1	20,000	25,000
Belize				1	1,500	2,000
Costa Rica	1	1	5	55	6,500	10,000
Czech Republic			55	350	2,000	1,500
Guatemala	5	10	5	60	45,000	90,000
Honduras	1	1	5	70	15,000	20,000
Iran	10	10	200	1,500	40,000	50,000
Myanmar	35	45	5	40	250,000	350,000
Slovenia			15	95	2,000	1,500
Thailand	15	10	100	1,000	150,000	100,000
Zimbabwe	1	1	5	25	15,000	25,000
HIGH						
Albania	1	1	1	10	5,000	6,500
Argentina	5	5	70	700	15,000	20,000
Australia	1	1	65	200	2,500	5,500
Austria	1	1	30	90	5,000	6,500
Azerbaijan	1	1	5	30	10,000	10,000
Belarus	1	1	5	35	6,500	5,500
Benin	1	1	1	5	7,500	15,000
Brunei					1,500	1,500
Bulgaria	1	1	10	70	3,000	1,500
Burkina Faso	1	1	1	15	3,000	7,500
Burundi	1	1		1	10,000	20,000
Cape Verde					1,500	2,000
Colombia	10	10	50	450	35,000	45,000
Croatia	1	1	10	85	4,000	3,000
Dominican Republic	1	1	1	25	7,500	8,000
El Salvador	1	5		1	20,000	30,000
Equatorial Guinea		1			2,000	3,500
Gabon	1	1			1,500	3,000
Georgia	1	1	1	10	30,000	20,000
Indonesia	25	30	75	650	250,000	250,000
Italy	1	1	150	500	5,500	7,000
Jamaica	1	1	1	20	3,500	4,000
Liberia	1	1			5,500	15,000
Madagascar	5	5	1	15	30,000	55,000
Malawi	1	1	1	5	15,000	25,000
Malaysia	5	5	20	200	15,000	15,000
Malta			1	1	200	300
Mauritius		1			1,500	1,500
New Zealand	1	1	5	15	4,500	9,500
Nicaragua	1	5	1	5	20,000	40,000
Niger	1	5	1	10	10,000	25,000
Papua New Guinea	1	5	1	5	30,000	40,000
Peru	5	5	15	150	15,000	20,000
Philippines	25	25	30	300	200,000	250,000
Poland	1	1	85	600	5,500	4,000
Romania	1	1	40	300	8,500	6,000
Sierra Leone	1	5		1	15,000	30,000
Somalia	1	5	1	1	20,000	45,000
South Korea	5	5	95	800	25,000	20,000
Sri Lanka	5	5	15	150	45,000	40,000
Sudan/South Sudan	5	5	5	40	40,000	55,000
Suriname					550	650
Swaziland		1			3,000	4,000
Switzerland	1	1	25	75	2,000	3,000
Ukraine	1	1	40	300	25,000	15,000
Uzbekistan	10	15		1	95,000	150,000
Venezuela	5	5	30	300	15,000	15,000
MODERATE						
Algeria	5	5	5	60	15,000	20,000
Angola	1	5		1	20,000	45,000
Bahamas						
Bahrain				1	650	850

Additional mortality due to climate change - yearly average
Additional economic costs due to climate change (million USD PPP) - yearly average

CLIMATE VULNERABILITY

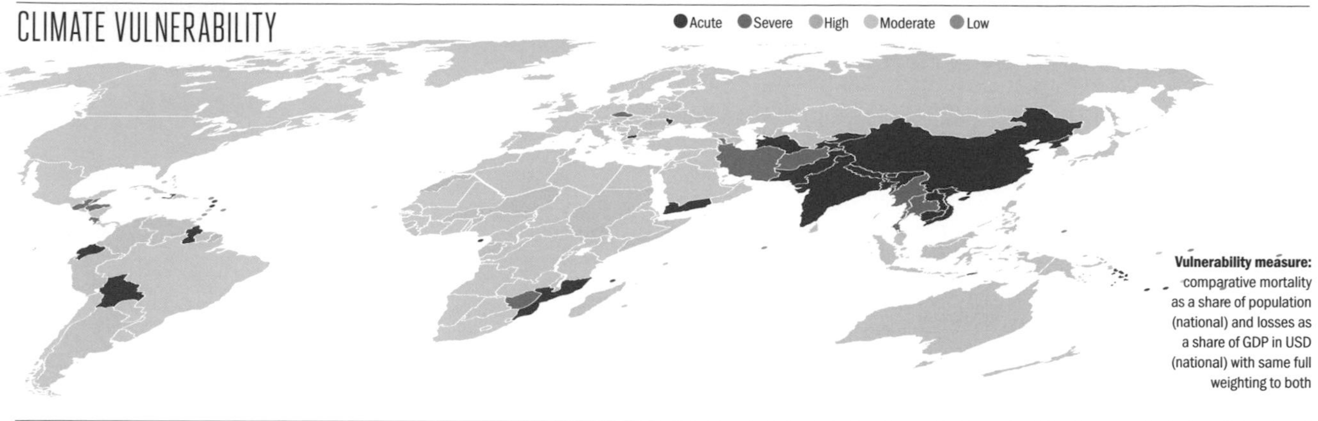

Vulnerability measure: comparative mortality as a share of population (national) and losses as a share of GDP in USD (national) with same full weighting to both

CLIMATE UNCERTAINTY

Limited · Partial · Considerable

COUNTRY	2010	2030	2010	2030	2010	2030
Belgium		1	1	5	1,500	2,000
Bosnia and Herzegovina	1	1	1	5	3,000	2,000
Botswana				1	650	700
Brazil	5	10	20	200	30,000	30,000
Cameroon	5	5		1	35,000	50,000
Canada	1	5	30	100	9,000	20,000
Central African Republic	1	1			6,000	9,500
Chad	1	1		1	9,500	20,000
Chile	1	1	5	50	4,000	4,500
Congo	1	1			7,000	15,000
Cote d'Ivoire	1	1			20,000	30,000
Cuba	1	1	1	20	2,500	2,500
Cyprus					750	1,500
Denmark				1	250	350
Djibouti					200	250
DR Congo	10	25		1	90,000	200,000
Egypt	5	10	5	30	65,000	80,000
Eritrea	1	1			4,500	7,500
Estonia					750	450
Ethiopia	10	15	1	5	75,000	160,000
Finland				1		
France	1	1	60	200	9,000	15,000
Gambia					1,000	1,500
Germany	1	1	100	350	4,500	6,500
Ghana	1	1	1	5	6,500	10,000
Greece	1	1	10	30	2,000	3,000
Guinea	1	5		1	15,000	25,000
Guinea-Bissau					950	1,500
Hungary			10	65	1,500	900
Iceland				1	150	250
Iraq	5	5			35,000	60,000
Ireland		1	5	15	1,000	2,500
Israel		1	1	5	1,500	2,000
Japan	5	5	150	400	20,000	35,000
Jordan				1	2,000	3,000
Kazakhstan	1	5	5	30	10,000	15,000
Kenya	5	5	1	10	40,000	50,000
Kuwait					150	200
Latvia					1,000	750
Lebanon	1	1			3,000	3,000
Lesotho					3,500	3,500
Libya			1	5	650	850
Lithuania					1,000	900
Luxembourg				1	200	500
Mali	1	1			10,000	20,000
Mauritania		1		1	2,000	4,500
Mexico	10	10	55	500	40,000	40,000
Micronesia						
Mongolia	1			1	4,500	3,500
Morocco	1	1	5	30	15,000	20,000
Namibia				1	1,000	1,500
Netherlands	1	1	15	40	2,000	3,500
Nigeria	10	15	1	20	85,000	150,000
Norway			1	5	700	1,000
Oman		1		1	1,500	3,000
Panama	1	1	1	5	2,000	2,000
Paraguay	1	1		1	10,000	20,000
Portugal	1	1	10	30	2,000	3,000
Qatar					300	350
Russia	10	5	75	550	35,000	25,000
Rwanda	1	1			15,000	25,000
Saint Vincent						
Samoa						
Saudi Arabia		1	10	90	1,500	3,000
Senegal	1	1	1	5	9,500	15,000
Seychelles						
Singapore			1	5		
Slovakia	1		5	30	2,500	2,000
South Africa	1	1	5	35	5,500	4,500
Spain	1	1	10	35	4,000	5,500
Sweden				1	400	600
Syria	1	5			30,000	45,000
Tanzania	1	5	1	10	20,000	30,000
Togo	1	1		1	5,000	9,000
Tonga						
Trinidad and Tobago				1	650	600
Tunisia		1	5	45	3,500	4,000
Turkey	5	10	30	100	15,000	35,000
Uganda	1	5		1	15,000	35,000
United Arab Emirates	1	1	1	20	2,500	3,000
United Kingdom	1	1	100	350	3,500	5,500
United States	5	5	600	2,000	15,000	35,000
Uruguay	1	1	1	5	1,500	1,600
Zambia	1	1		1	10,000	20,000
LOW						
Antigua and Barbuda						
Barbados						
Grenada						
Kiribati						
Maldives						
Marshall Islands						
Palau						
Tuvalu						

Additional persons affected/in need of emergency assistance due to climate change - yearly average

STORMS

ESTIMATES GLOBAL CLIMATE IMPACT

2010 EFFECT TODAY

DEATHS PER YEAR **2,500**

USD LOSS PER YEAR **15 BILLION**

2030 EFFECT TOMORROW

DEATHS PER YEAR **3,500**

USD LOSS PER YEAR **100 BILLION**

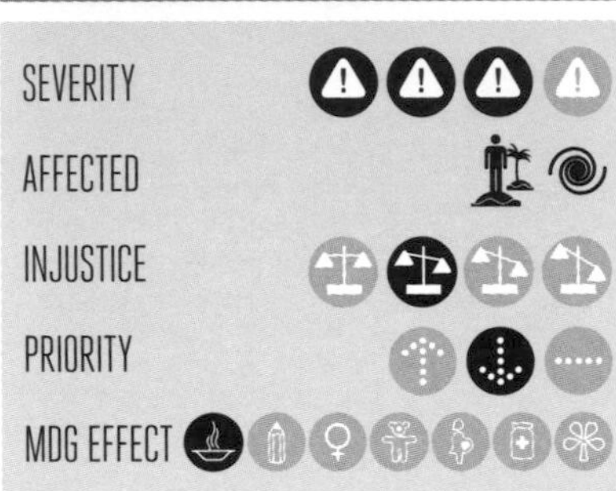

- All weather is affected by climate change because the Earth's atmosphere is warmer, moister, and more active today than in the recent past
- As a result, storms are becoming more extreme both in and outside of the tropics and will cause greater damage
- The location and extent of the additional damage is difficult to predict, as experts and their studies differ in their conclusions
- Countries already exposed to tropical cyclones or immediately adjacent to cyclone belts should prepare for growing risks and damages, especially in coastal areas

MORTALITY IMPACT

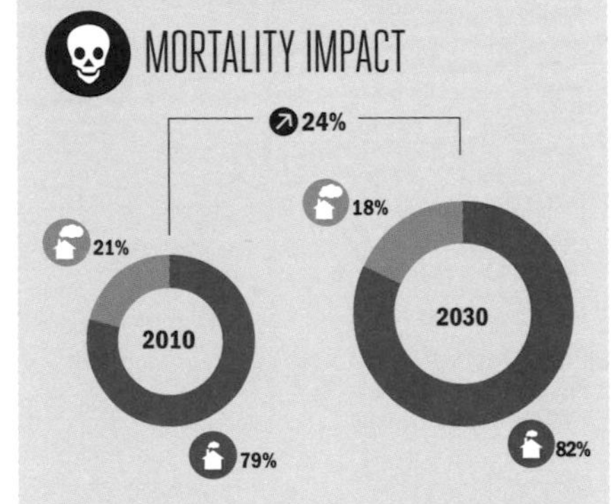

ECONOMIC IMPACT

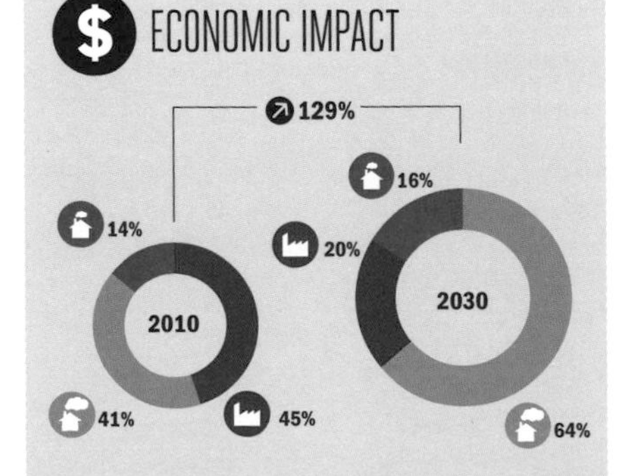

RELATIVE IMPACT

2010: 82
2030: 93 | 1
$ 2010: 27 | 2
$ 2030: 58 | 2

GEOPOLITICAL VULNERABILITY

SIDSs, G8, OECD, G20, BRIC, LDCs

HOTSPOTS

Deaths (2010 / 2030)

	2010	2030
BANGLADESH	1,750	2,500
MYANMAR	500	600
INDIA	150	150
MADAGASCAR	50	100
PHILIPPINES	45	60

Economic cost (2010 / 2030)

	2010	2030
CHINA	4,750	50,000
JAPAN	4,000	10,000
UNITED STATES	2,500	8,250
NORTH KOREA	550	5,750
SOUTH KOREA	600	4,750

Deaths | Economic Cost (2010 PPP non-discounted)
Developing Country Low Emitters | Developed
Developing Country High Emitters | Other Industrialized

= Deaths per 10 million
$ = Losses per 10,000 USD of GDP
Change in relation to overall global population and/or GDP

=Millions of USD (2010 PPP non-discounted)

Whether or not specific events can be identified as "caused" by climate change, all weather is now affected by a global climate system that is warmer, more active, and wetter (Trenberth, 2012). As a result, it is evident that storms are generally becoming more extreme, particularly in terms of wind speeds and quantity of rainfall. Moreover, there is a pole-ward shift to the north and south of cyclone storm tracks, as parts of the world adjacent to the tropics are experiencing more "tropical" weather. Where vulnerabilities to more severe storms are accentuated by environmental and income-related factors—such as for high-risk urban slums in low-lying coastal areas—the dangers of these changes are much higher (IPCC, 2012a). Corresponding measures will need to offset the additional risk by reducing community vulnerabilities and, where possible, limiting exposure, to storm hazards (UNISDR, 2009 and 2011). Increased emergency assistance should also be foreseen in the coming years and decades.

CLIMATE MECHANISM

Climate change increases air and sea temperatures, boosting the level of moisture in the atmosphere; this leads to acceleration of the planet's hydrological system, heavier precipitation, higher maximum winds and a general tendency to more extreme weather (IPCC, 2007). These hallmarks have been recognized in storms, including cyclones (IPCC, 2012a). Whether or not there has been a change in the frequency or overall number of cyclones in recent years can side-track the focus on other important factors, such as wind speed changes (Knutson et al. in Chan et al. (eds.), 2010). Simply counting the change in the number of cyclones often leads to the conclusion that there is less cyclone activity, since there is generally understood to be a slight increase in the most extreme cyclones, such as categories 3 to 5, but an overall decrease in the total number of cyclones since the reduction in less severe storms is expected to be greater (Knutson et al., 2010). It is not surprising that an increase in the most extreme cyclones, as measured on the well-known Saffir-Simpson scale results in fewer cyclones overall, since the scale itself is static, measures overall power, and is a rough proxy for the size of storms (Dolan and David, 1992; Irish et al., 2008). Larger more powerful storms absorb and dissipate considerably more energy than smaller ones, whose declining numbers have been attributed to an overall decline in cyclone frequency in recent times (IPCC, 2012a). Nor is the ultimate number of storms as important as the intensity or size of those storms: in the US, 85% of all cyclone damage is caused by the most extreme storms (Rudeva and Gulev, 2007; Pielke et al., 2008). A large share of the damage caused by cyclones is the result of storm surge, or inundations from rainfall, high winds, and freak waves caused by major storms, which have been worsened by heavier rainfall and sea-level rise, both of which are fuelled by climate change (Dasgupta et al., 2009).

IMPACTS

The impact of climate change on both tropical cyclones and major storms outside of the tropics (extra-tropical cyclones) is estimated to already cost 15 billion dollars and to be responsible for an average of almost 2,500 deaths each year, with around 1.5 million people affected and in need of emergency assistance.

In global terms, the number of countries experiencing extreme effects is limited, particularly since the great majority of losses relate to tropical cyclones, which are a serious concern for only 30 to 40 countries in the world's cyclone belts. A dozen countries in Asia, Africa, the Pacific, and the Caribbean are estimated to suffer Acute or Severe vulnerability to climate change-aggravated storm effects. The countries most vulnerable cut across the socio-economic spectrum from Japan to major emerging economies, such as China, least developed countries such as Madagascar, or small island developing states, such as Haiti.

Bangladesh is currently estimated to suffer the greatest human impact of these effects, with over 1,000 additional casualties due to climate change on an averaged yearly basis—major storms do not occur annually, but once in every 5 to 20 years. Myanmar and India are estimated to suffer the next greatest share of additional casualties. In overall economic terms, China, Japan, the US, North Korea, and South Korea experience the greatest estimated losses, incurring between 2 and 5 billion dollars a year in damages. A number of small island countries, such as Antigua and Barbuda, Dominica, Grenada, and Vanuatu are identified as experiencing the most severe economic and human loss

BIGGER PICTURE

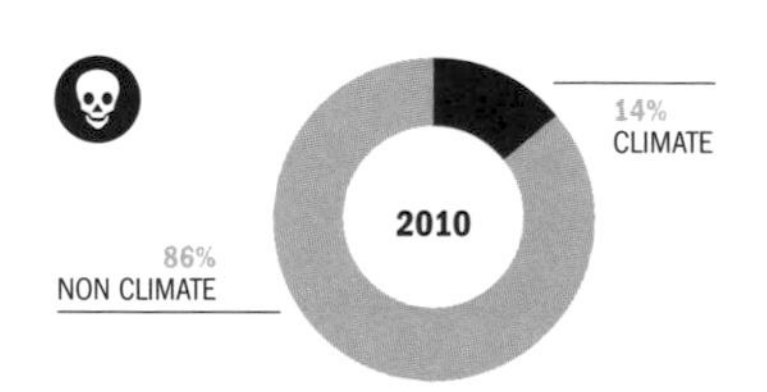

SURGE

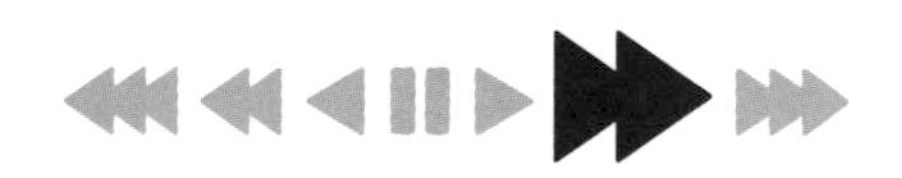

OCCURRENCE

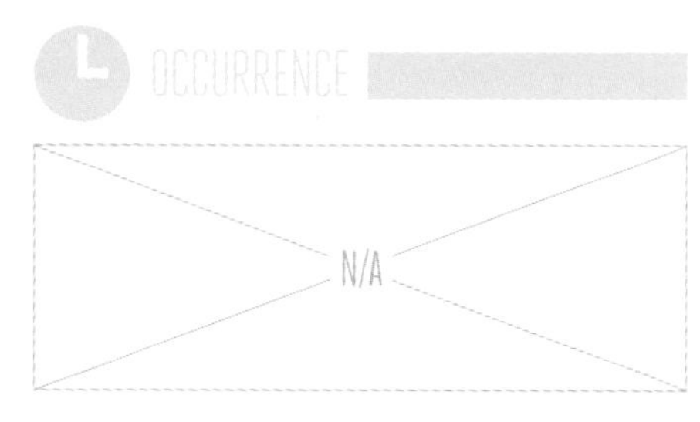

VULNERABILITY SHIFT

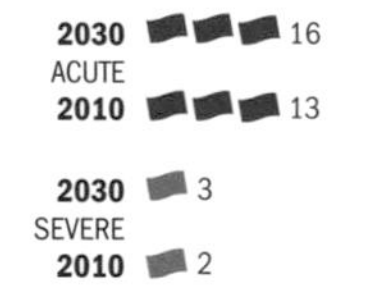

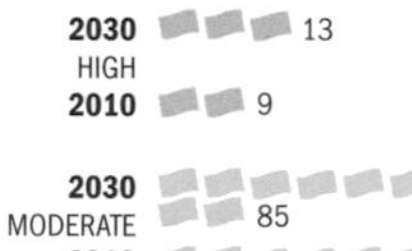

PEAK IMPACT

Year	Country	Deaths	Year	Country	Millions USD
2008	MYANMAR	138,366	2005	UNITED STATES	158,230
2007	BANGLADESH	4,275	2004	JAPAN	15,144
2004	HAITI	2,757	2005	MEXICO	7,910
2005	UNITED STATES	1,882	2006	CHINA	7,859
2004	PHILIPPINES	1,861	2000	NORTH KOREA	6,000

GENDER BIAS

INDICATOR INFORMATION

MODEL. Donat et al, 2011; Mendelsohn et al., 2011

EMISSION SCENARIO: SRES A1B (IPCC, 2000)

BASE DATA: Tropical storms: Mendelsohn et al., 2011 (economic); Peduzzi et al., 2012 (mortality). Extra-tropical storms: CRED EM-DAT, 2012; Munich Re NATCAT, 2010 (economic)

 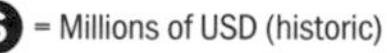
= Millions of USD (historic)

 = 5 countries (rounded)

Acute · Severe · High · Moderate · Low

relative to size. Several countries located on the Central American isthmus, such as Belize, El Salvador, and Honduras are exposed to tropical cyclones originating in both the Caribbean/Atlantic and Pacific Oceans, and are estimated to suffer extreme effects.

THE BROADER CONTEXT

As with other weather-related disasters, two key trends provide the context for the changes in extreme weather hazards which researchers increasingly attribute to climate change: 1) reductions in vulnerability due to continued economic growth especially in developing countries; and 2) an increase in the number of people and the amount of infrastructure exposed to extreme weather, due to the combined effects of population growth, urbanization, and economic development (UNISDR, 2011; Peduzzi et al., 2012). Correcting for these developments and other inconsistencies, evolution in reporting systems and biases in the statistical record have led to mixed interpretations of whether the scale of impacts due to climate change are increasing or decreasing (Mendelsohn et al., 2011; Pielke et al., 2008). The insurance industry has been registering greater and greater losses from weather-related catastrophes, including storms, over the past several years (Swiss Re, 2010, 2011, and 2012).

VULNERABILITIES AND WIDER OUTCOMES

Particularly noteworthy in terms of environmental vulnerabilities to storms are low-lying coastal communities which will bear the brunt of the increasing effects of climate change on heavy rainfall, wave height, and storm surge during cyclones (Füssel in Edenhofer et al. (eds.), 2012). Significantly altering the risk profile of countries are existing protection levels and capacities embodied in infrastructure, early warning systems, social and community response, support networks and levels of awareness about disasters. Likewise, government capacity to manage risks, as well as land use and environmental planning and protection can all affect the level of vulnerability, e.g., inappropriate urbanization or the clearing of coastal mangrove forests, which otherwise provide protection against winds and storm surges (UNISDR, 2009 and 2011; IPCC, 2012a). Migration patterns are fuelling rapid and inappropriate urbanization, leading to growing settlements in high-risk coastal flood zones, which themselves are seeing a depletion in natural protection, as from the destruction of mangrove forests (Donner and Rodriguez, 2008; Füssel in Edenhofer et al. (eds.), 2012). Where insurance coverage is low, the ability of affected communities to rebound from disasters is greatly inhibited (Dodman and Satterthwaite, 2008). This is especially a concern among developing and lower-income countries, such as small island developing states, where the scale of impact can also generate important setbacks for development (Pelling and Uitto, 2001).

RESPONSES

Numerous preventive measures can be taken to reduce key vulnerabilities and minimize naturally increasing exposures to disaster. Possible efforts include education and communication programmes, promotion of community volunteer emergency organizations, supporting governments to develop and implement action plans to manage risks through sensible municipal planning, constructing protective infrastructure, reinforcing environmental protection to limit risk-multiplication, and promoting access to insurance products. Better management of urbanization and urban-rural migration flows would also help lower risks for coastal mega-cities (de Sherbinin et al., 2007). Progress in human development and poverty reduction will inevitably enhance capacities to withstand serious storms and limit the damage to the highest risk groups, requiring integrated strategies regarding climate change, disaster risk, and development strategies (Schipper and Pelling, 2006).

THE INDICATOR

Although the increasing severity of weather including tropical and extra-tropical cyclones is well established, the indicator is considered speculative because there is considerable disagreement among the models predicting change in cyclone intensity for different regions of the world. With the exception of the North Atlantic, where evidence of an increase in extreme weather is strongest, predictions of changes in cyclone activity in the Indian and Pacific oceans differ widely (Mendelsohn et al., 2011; IPCC, 2012a).

ESTIMATES COUNTRY-LEVEL IMPACT

COUNTRY	Mortality 2010	Mortality 2030	Costs 2010	Costs 2030	Affected 2010	Affected 2030
ACUTE						
Antigua and Barbuda			30	250	700	650
Bangladesh	1,750	2,500	150	1,250	400,000	600,000
Belize			30	250	550	700
Dominica			15	150	-90	-100
Dominican Republic	10	10	200	1,750	20,000	20,000
El Salvador			250	1,750	5	15
Grenada			25	200	-35	-60
Haiti	15	20	25	200	5,750	8,500
Honduras	1	1	200	1,500	200	350
Jamaica		1	100	800	1,000	2,500
Madagascar	50	100	40	250	150,000	300,000
Myanmar	500	600	1	20	10,000	15,000
Nicaragua	1	1	50	350	250	550
North Korea			550	5,750	2,250	-950
Tonga		1			-3,750	20,000
Vanuatu	5	10		-1	7,250	15,000
SEVERE						
Mauritius	1	1	25	150	500	400
Saint Lucia			1	20	15	10
Samoa		1		-1	750	5,750
HIGH						
Bahamas		1			400	450
China	1	-5	4,750	50,000	100,000	-250,000
Cuba	-1	-1	100	850	-75,000	-200,000
Japan	-10	-20	4,000	10,000	-10,000	-30,000
Marshall Islands					55	650
Micronesia					1	25
Mozambique	15	25	1	15	150,000	200,000
Oman			75	550		
Pakistan	5	5	250	2,250	4,500	8,750
Palau					200	450

COUNTRY	Mortality 2010	Mortality 2030	Costs 2010	Costs 2030	Affected 2010	Affected 2030
Solomon Islands	1	1			8,500	20,000
South Korea		-1	600	4,750	-25	-200
Yemen			25	200		
MODERATE						
Albania						
Algeria				1		
Argentina			1	10		
Armenia						
Australia	1	1	-1	-1	100,000	150,000
Austria			5	10		1
Azerbaijan						
Belarus						
Belgium			1	10	1	1
Bolivia						
Bosnia and Herzegovina						
Botswana						
Bulgaria						
Canada			1	5		
Chile			1	10		
Costa Rica			1	10	950	1,250
Croatia						
Cyprus						
Czech Republic			1	5	550	1,000
Denmark			5	15	10	20
Djibouti						
Ecuador						
Egypt						
Estonia			1	1		
Finland				1		
France		1	40	95	3,250	6,000
Georgia				1		
Germany			100	350	25	50

COUNTRY	Mortality 2010	Mortality 2030	Costs 2010	Costs 2030	Affected 2010	Affected 2030
Greece			1	5		
Guyana				1		
Hungary				1		
Iceland						
India	150	150	550	4,250	300,000	350,000
Iran			250	1,750		
Ireland			1	1		
Israel			1	10		
Italy			1	5		
Jordan				1		
Kazakhstan						
Kuwait			1	15		
Kyrgyzstan						
Latvia			1	10	400	750
Lebanon			1	5		
Lithuania				1	250	500
Luxembourg			1	1		
Macedonia						
Malawi				1		
Malta						
Mexico	10	15	150	1,250	70,000	85,000
Moldova			1	5		
Mongolia						
Namibia						
Netherlands			1	5	90	200
Norway			1	5		
Panama					25	30
Paraguay						
Peru			1	10		
Philippines	45	60	15	100	200,000	250,000
Poland			1	10	1	1
Qatar			1	10		

Additional mortality due to climate change - yearly average; Additional economic costs due to climate change (million USD PPP) - yearly average

STORMS

CLIMATE VULNERABILITY

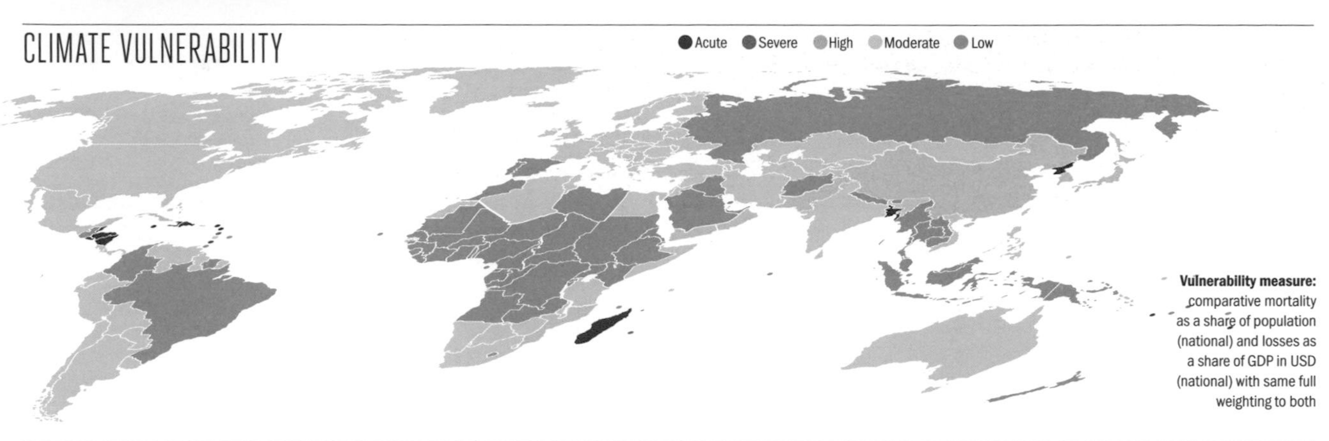

Vulnerability measure: comparative mortality as a share of population (national) and losses as a share of GDP in USD (national) with same full weighting to both

CLIMATE UNCERTAINTY

Limited Partial Considerable

COUNTRY	2010	2030	2010	2030	2010	2030
Romania			1	1		
Saint Vincent			1	5	-150	-150
Seychelles				1		
Slovakia			1	5		
Slovenia			1	5		
Somalia				1		
South Africa			5	20		
Sri Lanka			5	35	2,500	60
Swaziland						
Sweden			5	10	10	15
Switzerland			5	15	65	100
Syria						
Tajikistan			1	15		
Tanzania			15	90		
Tunisia						
Turkey						
Turkmenistan						
Ukraine			1	5		
United Kingdom			20	60	55	150
United States	1	1	2,500	8,250	4,750	6,500
Uruguay				1		
Uzbekistan						
Venezuela				1		
Vietnam	10	10	-5	-75	15,000	15,000
Zimbabwe	1	5			6,500	15,000
LOW						
Afghanistan						
Angola						
Bahrain			-5	-35		
Barbados				1	-90	-250
Benin						
Bhutan						

COUNTRY	2010	2030	2010	2030	2010	2030
Brazil						
Brunei						
Burkina Faso						
Burundi						
Cambodia						
Cameroon						
Cape Verde						
Central African Republic						
Chad						
Colombia						
Comoros						
Congo						
Cote d'Ivoire						
DR Congo						
Equatorial Guinea						
Eritrea						
Ethiopia						
Fiji	1	-1	-10	-75	5,250	-2,000
Gabon						
Gambia						
Ghana						
Guatemala		1	-1	-10	150	250
Guinea						
Guinea-Bissau						
Indonesia			-50	-400		
Iraq						
Kenya				-1		
Kiribati						
Laos	1	1	-5	-35	5,750	8,750
Lesotho						
Liberia						
Libya						

COUNTRY	2010	2030	2010	2030	2010	2030
Malaysia			-1	-10		
Maldives				-1	5	15
Mali						
Mauritania						
Morocco						
Nepal						
New Zealand			-5	-15	150	150
Niger						
Nigeria						
Papua New Guinea						
Portugal						
Russia	-1	-5	1	10	-150	-300
Rwanda						
Sao Tome and Principe						
Saudi Arabia			-30	-250		
Senegal						
Sierra Leone						
Singapore						
Spain			-1	-10		
Sudan/South Sudan						
Suriname						
Thailand			-5	-35	750	850
Timor-Leste						
Togo			-1	-10		
Trinidad and Tobago		-1			-250	-1,250
Tuvalu						
Uganda						
United Arab Emirates			-10	-85		
Zambia						

Additional persons affected/in need of emergency assistance due to climate change - yearly average

WILDFIRES

ESTIMATES GLOBAL CLIMATE IMPACT

2010 EFFECT TODAY

USD GAIN PER YEAR **15 MILLION**

2030 EFFECT TOMORROW

USD GAIN PER YEAR **90 MILLION**

ECONOMIC IMPACT

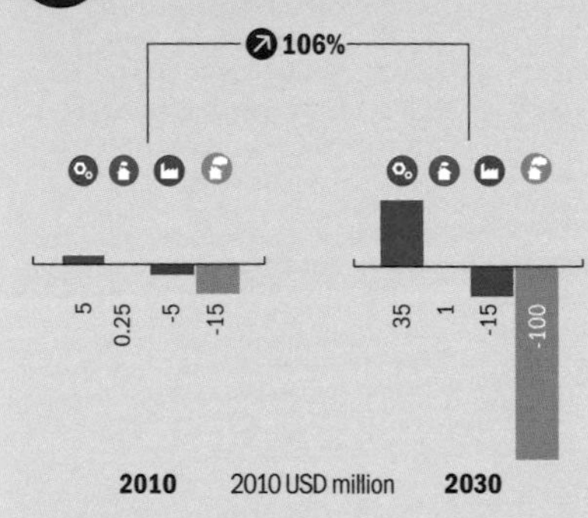

- Global impact of climate change on wildfires may have a neutral effect as a warmer planet brings more rain, dampening fires
- Shifts in wildfire may occur where forested areas become drier and hotter, severely affecting populated parts of Russia, Mongolia, or Australia
- The marginal effect of climate change is difficult to predict because of wind and rain uncertainties and because good international data monitoring fire damages is lacking
- Wildfire occurrence has links to now more prevalent heat extremes and drought which increase the probability of fires

RELATIVE IMPACT

2 2010

2 2030

$$$$ 25 | 1 2010

$$$$$$ 49 | 1 2030

HOTSPOTS

2010		2030
5	RUSSIA	40
1	MONGOLIA	15
0	NICARAGUA	1
0	SOUTH AFRICA	1
1	CANADA	1

GEOPOLITICAL VULNERABILITY

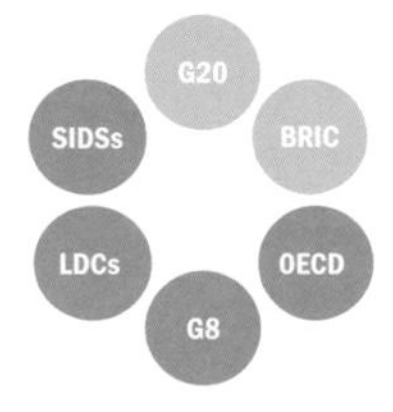

Economic Cost (2010 PPP non-discounted)
Developing Country Low Emitters
Developed
Developing Country High Emitters
Other Industrialized

= Deaths per 100 million
$ = Losses per 10 million USD of GDP
Change in relation to overall global population and/or GDP

Wildfires—the uncontrolled burning of forests, grasslands or brush—will generally become more frequent and damaging for drought-prone parts of the world. But it is certain that climate change will reduce disturbances from wildfires in some areas where rainfall is significantly increasing. The 2010 wildfires in Russia, as well as the recent fires in Australia, Greece, and the US, are clearly linked to warm, dry temperatures, if not drought (UNISDR, 2011). However, the additional losses incurred by those worst affected are likely to be offset on a global scale by a reduction in wildfire activity in other parts of the world. It is expected that Vietnam may see increased rainfall in some seasons, but declining rain and rising heat during the dry periods would favour wildfire onset, even if more rain overall falls in a given year (Vietnam MONRE, 2010). Tackling an additional burden of wildfire in affected areas will be great, since suppressing fires is costly: the US Forest Service spent 1 billion dollars on fire suppression in the year 2000 alone, with costs growing significantly over time—2.5 million dollars in losses were reported for that year. But expenditures were undoubtedly warranted in most cases, since wildfires can be extremely deadly: in February 2009, one series of fires alone in Australia killed 180 people (WFLC, 2004; CRED/EM-DAT, 2012).

CLIMATE MECHANISM

Wildfires are affected by three key factors: 1) availability of vegetation to burn; 2) environmental conditions, such as temperature, wind, and humidity or rainfall but also topography and ecosystem type—tropical forests for example are more humid and burn less than temperate forests; and 3) varying ignition sources of fires (Krawchuk et al., 2009). Climate change affects all of these elements: it influences vegetation growth and health along with the expanse of different ecosystem areas (Gonzalez et al., 2010). In regions with less rain and more heat, the declining vegetation will offer less available material for burning and will ultimately reduce disturbances from wildfires. Heat is increasing relatively uniformly around the world due to climate change. Less predictable rainfall and vegetation changes add considerable uncertainty to whether or not fires ultimately retreat or advance with global warming. Climate change has also been shown to potentially alter electrical activity in the atmosphere, giving rise to lightning, the principal initial trigger of wildfires (Reeve and Toumi, 1999).

IMPACTS

Drawing on recent research, the Monitor estimates the global impact of climate change on wildfire to be close to zero in 2010 and in 2030 (Krawchuk et al., 2009). Estimates of impact include around 3 million dollars of additional losses a year in 2010, and some 15 million dollars of additional losses in 2030. "Gains" of 25 and 150 million dollars a year in 2010 and 2030, respectively, outweigh considerably any losses incurred elsewhere in the world, but overall totals are small. "Gains" represent avoided wildfires that would have taken place without climate change. The largest negative effects in absolute terms are estimated to occur in Russia, Mongolia, Canada, Australia, and South Africa, while the US and Indonesia are expected to reap the most benefits overall. Within large countries like the US, it is possible that increased fire activity may well be experienced in certain areas but will be counterbalanced with decreased activity in other parts of the country. In general, wildfires mainly concern industrialized or developed countries.

THE BROADER CONTEXT

There has been a considerable increase in wildfire damage recorded in recent years (CRED/EM-DAT, 2012). However, improvements in the actual reporting systems themselves—advances in technology and information sharing—have allowed the reporting of increasing numbers of phenomena (UNISDR, 2009). However, satellite analysis has shown that the annual burned area has grown since the 1970s (UNEP, 2002). Several other factors, such as land usage change, could be contributing to increasing fire damage. As with other weather-related disasters, growing exposure to wildfires through economic development, population growth, and an expansion in infrastructure at risk should also increase damages.

VULNERABILITIES AND WIDER OUTCOMES

Countries with large areas of non-tropical vegetation and a propensity to drought are particularly vulnerable to the effects of climate change

BIGGER PICTURE

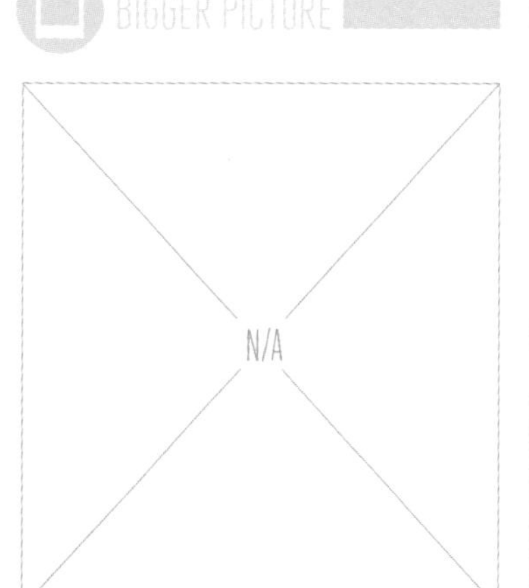

SURGE

OCCURRENCE

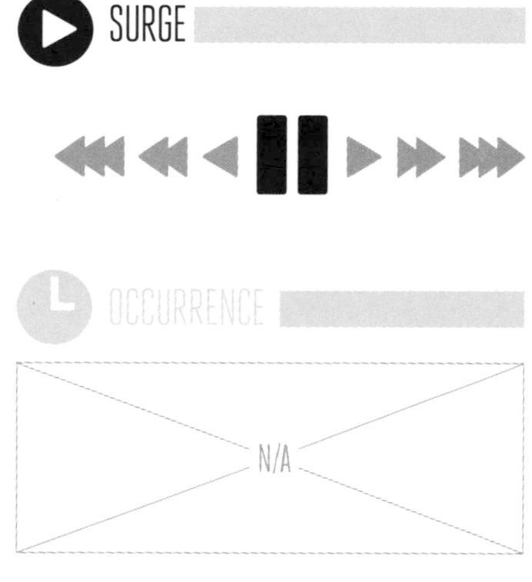

VULNERABILITY SHIFT

	Year	Countries
ACUTE	2030	7
	2010	2
SEVERE	2030	5
	2010	5
HIGH	2030	4
	2010	8
MODERATE	2030	11
	2010	12
LOW	2030	157
	2010	157

PEAK IMPACT

Year	Country	Deaths
2009	AUSTRALIA	180
2007	GREECE	70
2010	RUSSIA	61
2008	MOZAMBIQUE	49
2010	ISRAEL	44

Year	Country	Millions of USD
2003	UNITED STATES	3,500
2005	SPAIN	2,050
2010	RUSSIA	1,800
2007	GREECE	1,750
2003	PORTUGAL	1,730

GENDER BIAS

INDICATOR INFORMATION

MODEL: Krawchuk et al., 2009

EMISSION SCENARIO: SRES A2 (IPCC, 2000)

BASE DATA: CRED EM-DAT, 2012

= Millions of USD (historic)

Acute Severe High Moderate Low

= 5 countries (rounded)

on wildfires. Coniferous forests are especially risky areas for fire outbreak during extended warm, dry periods (Cruz and Alexander, 2010).
The full extent of increased wildfires is difficult to estimate, but given the incredible potential for the rapid and uncontrolled spread of fires, growing fire dangers in some parts of the world could carry serious risks for public safety. The 2010 Russian wildfires, for example, burned some 4,000 hectares of land– contaminated, moreover, by radioactive material from the Chernobyl disaster–the full consequences of which are not yet known; the fires also threatened functioning nuclear power plants and research facilities (Munich Re, 2010).

RESPONSES

Responding to wildfires is extremely costly requires highly sophisticated technology. Some early detection and warning systems are capable of identifying a fire within 5 minutes of its ignition (Bridge, 2010). Thus, such systems represent an investment that could significantly reduce overall expenditures on suppressing fires that would otherwise end up destroying thousands or millions of hectares. Fire safety and education programmes may reduce the potential for fires set by human hands by up to 80% (UNEP, 2002).
Of course, as is well known, not all wildfires are bad. Natural habitats have evolved to cope with wildfires over time and to support biodiversity and processes of regeneration (Parker et al., 2006). Therefore, many countries also practice what is called "prescribed burning," effectively a "let-burn" policy, in which human settlements are not endangered. But while such practices may lower fire prevention costs and help support ecosystems, if fires subsequently reach a large-scale and deviate to threaten settlements, the costs of fire suppression can rapidly and counter-productively escalate (UNEP, 2002).

THE INDICATOR

The indicator relies on a high-resolution global pyrogeography model for the effect of climate change on fire disturbances, used to estimate impact for populated areas (Krawchuk et al., 2009). Limitations relate to uncertain future rainfall and the restricted socio-economic base data set, which may underestimate costs (CRED/EM-DAT, 2012). Regarding base data, the major wildfires that affected Russia in 2010 are recorded in the reference database at 1.8 billion dollars in losses and 61 deaths. The major reinsurer, Munich Re, on the other hand estimates the total cost of the fires at 3.3 billion dollars and over 50,000 indirect deaths from both extreme heat and the significantly higher than normal air particle loads and their effect on chronic respiratory and cardiovascular disease sufferers (Munich Re, 2010). Historical base data would also give a misleading trend if fires spread to areas where damage in the past was unusual, underestimating future losses.

ESTIMATES COUNTRY-LEVEL IMPACT

COUNTRY	2010 $	2030 $
ACUTE		
Australia	0.25	0.50
Guinea-Bissau		
Israel		
Mongolia	1	15
Mozambique		
Nepal		
South Africa	0.25	1
SEVERE		
Nicaragua	0.25	1
Paraguay		
Poland		
Russia	5	40
Slovakia		
HIGH		
Argentina		
Greece		
Mexico		
Swaziland		
MODERATE		
Bhutan		
Brazil		
Canada	0.50	1
Central African Republic		
Chile		
DR Congo		
Lebanon		
Philippines		
South Korea		
Sudan/South Sudan		
Turkey		
LOW		
Afghanistan		
Albania		
Algeria		
Angola		
Antigua and Barbuda		
Armenia		
Austria		
Azerbaijan		
Bahamas		
Bahrain		
Bangladesh		
Barbados		
Belarus		
Belgium		
Belize		
Benin		
Bolivia		
Bosnia and Herzegovina		
Botswana		
Brunei		
Bulgaria	-0.25	-1
Burkina Faso		
Burundi		
Cambodia		
Cameroon		
Cape Verde		
Chad		
China		
Colombia		
Comoros		
Congo		
Costa Rica		
Cote d'Ivoire		
Croatia		
Cuba		
Cyprus		
Czech Republic		
Denmark		
Djibouti		
Dominica		
Dominican Republic		
Ecuador		
Egypt		
El Salvador		
Equatorial Guinea		
Eritrea		
Estonia		
Ethiopia		
Fiji		
Finland		
France		
Gabon		
Gambia		
Georgia		
Germany		
Ghana		
Grenada		
Guatemala		
Guinea		
Guyana		
Haiti		
Honduras		
Hungary		

$ Additional economic costs due to climate change (million USD PPP) - yearly average

CLIMATE VULNERABILITY

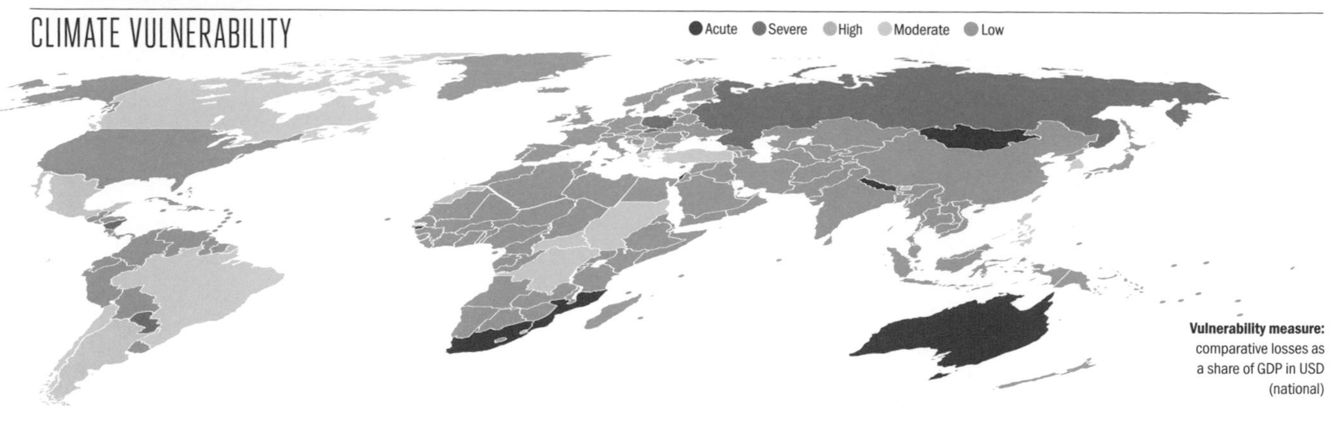

CLIMATE UNCERTAINTY

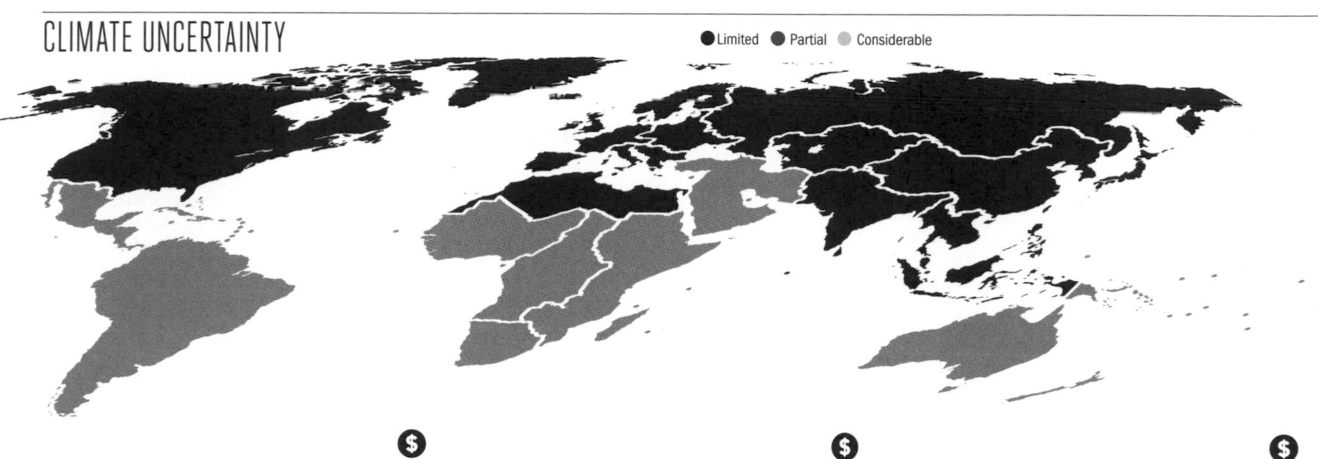

COUNTRY	2010	2030
Iceland		
India		
Indonesia	-20	-150
Iran		
Iraq		
Ireland		
Italy	-1	-1
Jamaica		
Japan		
Jordan		
Kazakhstan		
Kenya		
Kiribati		
Kuwait		
Kyrgyzstan		
Laos		
Latvia		
Lesotho		
Liberia		
Libya		
Lithuania		
Luxembourg		
Macedonia		
Madagascar		
Malawi		
Malaysia	-0.25	-1
Maldives		
Mali		
Malta		
Marshall Islands		
Mauritania		
Mauritius		
Micronesia		
Moldova		
Morocco		
Myanmar		
Namibia		
Netherlands		
New Zealand		
Niger		
Nigeria		
North Korea		
Norway		
Oman		
Pakistan		
Palau		
Panama		
Papua New Guinea		
Peru		
Portugal	-0.25	-1
Qatar		
Romania		
Rwanda		
Saint Lucia		
Saint Vincent		
Samoa		
Sao Tome and Principe		
Saudi Arabia		
Senegal		
Seychelles		
Sierra Leone		
Singapore		
Slovenia		
Solomon Islands		
Somalia		
Spain	-0.25	-1
Sri Lanka		
Suriname		
Sweden		
Switzerland		
Syria		
Tajikistan		
Tanzania		
Thailand		
Timor-Leste		
Togo		
Tonga		
Trinidad and Tobago		
Tunisia		
Turkmenistan		
Tuvalu		
Uganda		
Ukraine		
United Arab Emirates		
United Kingdom		
United States	-5	-15
Uruguay		
Uzbekistan		
Vanuatu		
Venezuela		
Vietnam		
Yemen		
Zambia		
Zimbabwe		

HABITAT CHANGE

BIODIVERSITY

DESERTIFICATION

HEATING & COOLING

LABOUR PRODUCTIVITY

PERMAFROST

SEA-LEVEL RISE

WATER

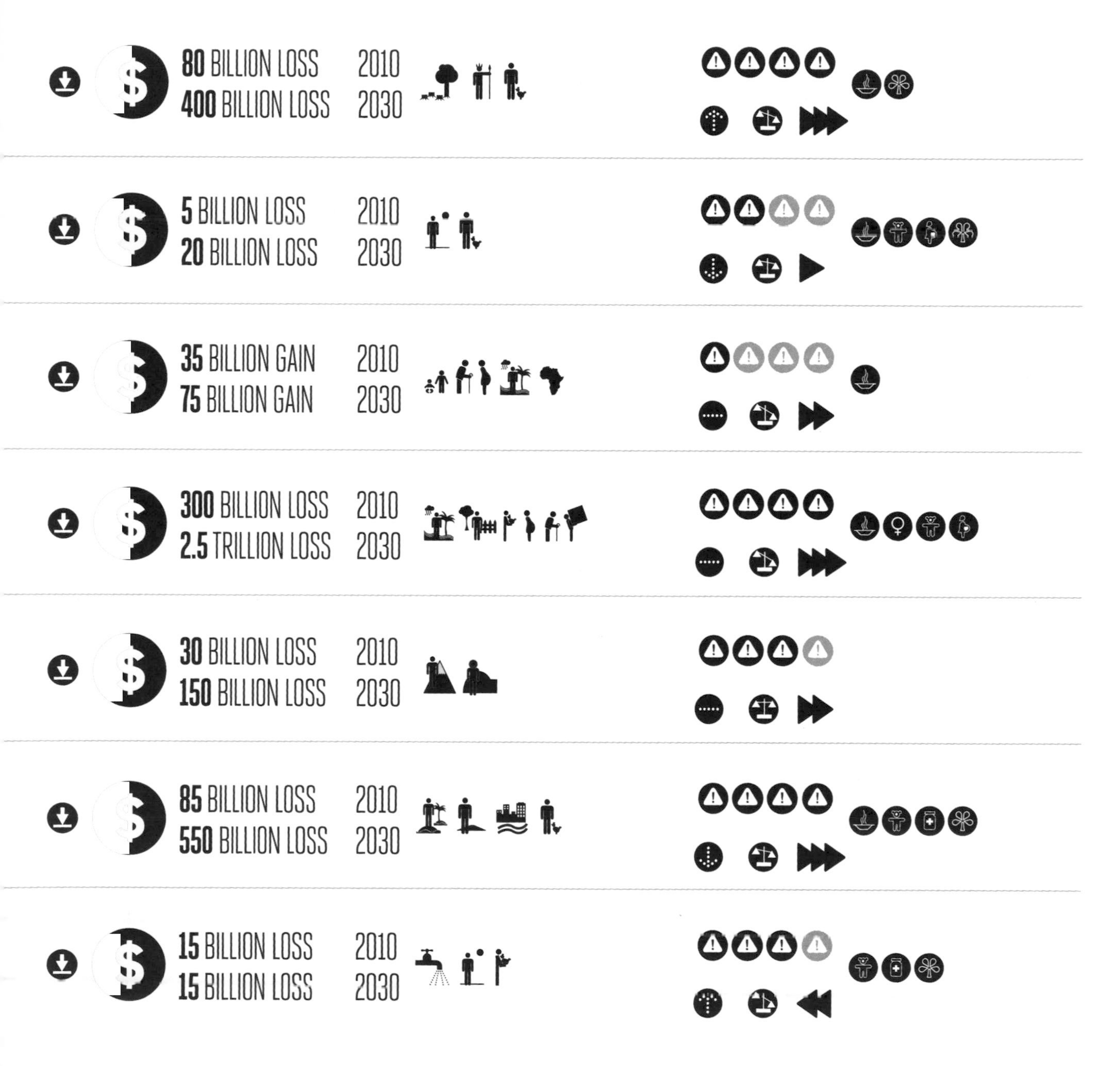
80 BILLION LOSS 2010
400 BILLION LOSS 2030
5 BILLION LOSS 2010
20 BILLION LOSS 2030
35 BILLION GAIN 2010
75 BILLION GAIN 2030
300 BILLION LOSS 2010
2.5 TRILLION LOSS 2030
30 BILLION LOSS 2010
150 BILLION LOSS 2030
85 BILLION LOSS 2010
550 BILLION LOSS 2030
15 BILLION LOSS 2010
15 BILLION LOSS 2030

BIODIVERSITY

ESTIMATES GLOBAL CLIMATE IMPACT

2010 EFFECT TODAY

USD **LOSS** PER YEAR **80 BILLION**

2030 EFFECT TOMORROW

USD **LOSS** PER YEAR **400 BILLION**

ECONOMIC IMPACT

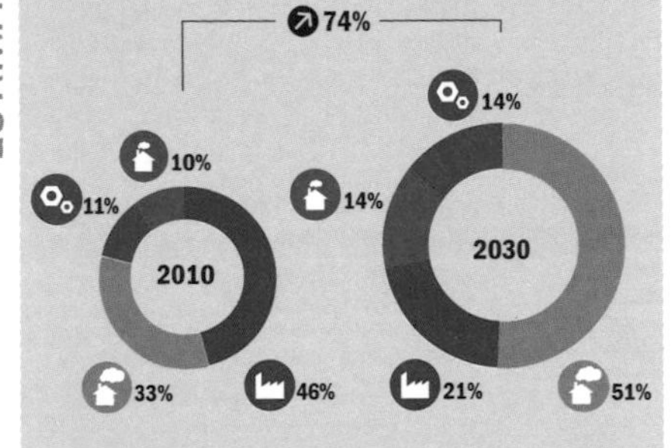

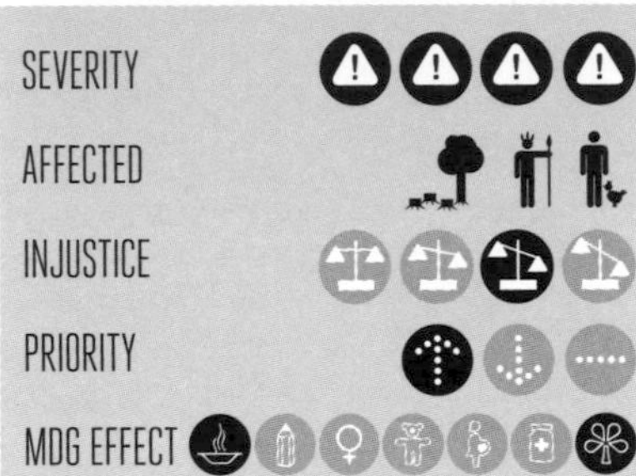

- Richness of life in the world's ecosystems is currently in full decline as human activities from toxic pollution to deforestation and destruction of natural habitats for agricultural land persist
- Climate change forces biological zones to face weather conditions that are unsuitable for their plant, animal, insect, and other species, hastening decline and extinction
- Biodiversity loss has significant market value and on a large scale will slow the world's economic growth
- Limiting non-climate dangers to biodiversity, such as deforestation, will be the basis of an effective response to the impact of climate change

RELATIVE IMPACT

HOTSPOTS

2010	Country	2030
25,000	USA	45,000
4,250	CHINA	45,000
3,500	BRAZIL	30,000
3,250	IRAN	25,000
3,250	RUSSIA	25,000

GEOPOLITICAL VULNERABILITY

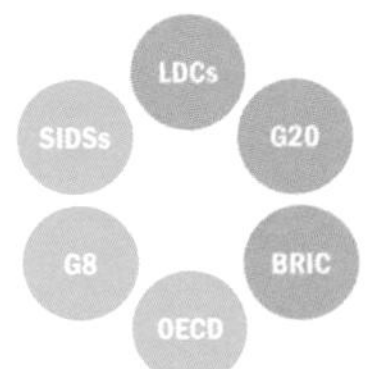

Developing Country Low Emitters | Developed

Developing Country High Emitters | Other Industrialized

 = Losses per 10,000 USD of GDP

Change in relation to overall global population and/or GDP

The international definition of biodiversity is "variability among living organisms" (CBD, 1992). Biodiversity has both market and non-market value—such as aesthetic and other non-traded values—principally through the integral role of biodiversity in sustaining ecosystems (Boyd and Banzhaf, 2007). The agricultural sector is particularly dependent on ecosystem services, such as water, pollination, and pest control. If removed, they will incur predictable market-based costs, since compensating measures must be taken at market cost. Experts have estimated that a 30% species loss can generate some 10% of lost plant production affecting agricultural outputs (Hooper et al., 2012). Global biodiversity loss has become not only a conservation issue, but a large-scale and serious macroeconomic problem. UNEP estimates current global environmental damages at over 6 trillion dollars (Garfunkel ed., 2010). As one of the costliest impacts of climate change assessed here, losses can only worsen unless comprehensive solutions are found (IPCC, 2007; Bellard et al., 2012).

CLIMATE MECHANISM

The world's main biological zones, or biomes, from tropical woodlands, to grass steppes, and temperate deciduous forests, have taken thousands of years to establish rich habitats for an unimaginable variety of natural species. These zones are distinguished one from another by precise climate and geographical characteristics (Sala et al., 2000). The planet is warming at rates faster than in much of the Earth's recent past and the growing human presence in the environment limits the scope for biomes and their inhabitants to shift to new areas or adapt to changing climates (IPCC, 2007; Pereira et al., 2010). Some species will become invasive, establishing themselves in new areas where others are in decline (Vilà et al. in Canadell et al. (eds.), 2007; Hellmann et al., 2008). As climates become unsuitable, endemic species of all kinds which have evolved to thrive in a specific habitat will be locked into declining biological zones with reduced geographic range. As that area shrinks, species decline at a predictable rate, reducing biodiversity (Thomas et al., 2004). Climate change could conceivably also bring some biodiversity benefits in isolated cases, but on a global scale the impacts are clearly understood by experts to be negative (Bellard et al., 2012). Valuing the market worth of ecosystems and their so-called "services" is difficult, not least since it involves putting a price tag on ecological life (Farber et al., 2002). But in a surrogate market—in which consumers would be charged for the benefits many now enjoy without cost—around half of the losses estimated here might be considered to have value (Sutton and Constanza, 2002; Curtis, 2004).

IMPACTS

The scale of the estimated impact on biodiversity from climate change are substantial: around 80 billion dollars a year at present. By 2030, that estimate will nearly double as a share of global GDP, approaching 400 billion dollars a year in losses.

Although the impact is estimated to affect developing countries more severely, biodiversity loss will occur in virtually every region, since the world's entire climate is in rapid shift. However, lower-income countries are more dependent on ecosystem services, increasing the damage potential for populations lower on the socio-economic scale. Large countries incur the most damages, especially the US, China, Brazil, Iran, and Russia. The US is estimated to incur one quarter of all losses today, at over 20 billion US dollars a year. Impacts are most severe as a share of GDP for countries in Africa and Central Asia, many of which could experience losses equivalent to more than 1% of GDP by 2030.

THE BROADER CONTEXT

The long-term decline of biodiversity is well established and continues as a clear trend. For example, since the 1970s, the fall in the abundance of vertebrate species has been almost one third. The World Conservation Union's (IUCN) "Red List" of endangered species reveals some 20,000 species of animals and plants at high risk for extinction. Decline of natural habitats due to human activities is also a continuing trend around the world, although destruction of tropical forests and mangroves has shown signs of slowing in some areas (SCBD, 2010). Deforestation is still a major global concern and threatens biodiversity (Busch et al., 2011). High demand for food and biofuels, driven by population and economic growth is an important driver of land change and degradation

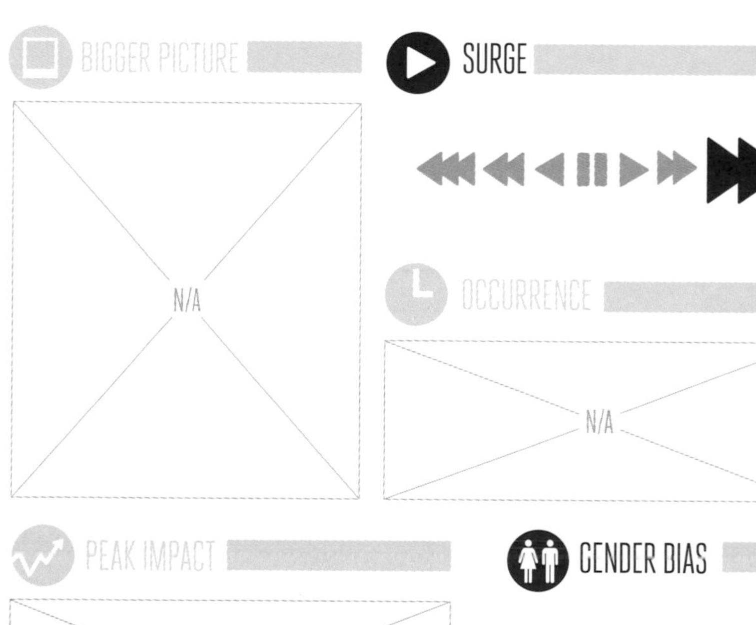

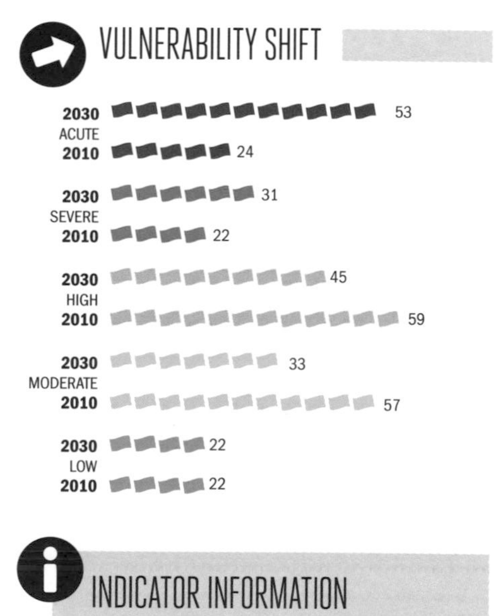

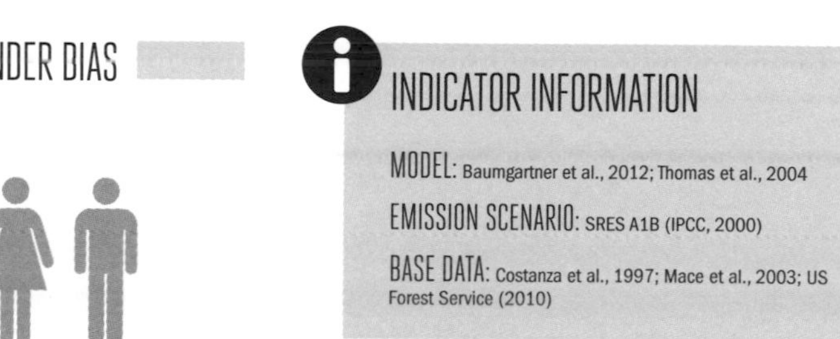

INDICATOR INFORMATION
MODEL: Baumgartner et al., 2012; Thomas et al., 2004
EMISSION SCENARIO: SRES A1B (IPCC, 2000)
BASE DATA: Costanza et al., 1997; Mace et al., 2003; US Forest Service (2010)

= 5 countries (rounded)

Acute Severe High Moderate Low

and deforestation (Gisladottir and Stocking, 2005).

VULNERABILITIES AND WIDER OUTCOMES

Assessments of the IUCN Red List show that the destruction of habitat by converting wild areas and forests into agricultural land are among the most significant contributors to biodiversity loss (Stuart et al., 2004; Brook et al., 2008). Unsustainable extraction of water resources further affects inland water-based ecosystems, especially those designed to meet the growing demand for water in the agricultural sector (Brinson and Malvarez, 2002). Agricultural and industrial pollutants are a further important source of stress (SCBD, 2010). The biomes most at risk due to climate change include scrubland, temperate deciduous forest, warm mixed forest, temperate mixed forest, and savannah (Thomas et al., 2004). Countries with high concentrations of these biomes have high vulnerability to biodiversity loss from climate change, even if current environmental conservation is sound. Lower-income countries, and those whose indigenous populations depend more heavily on ecosystems and wild areas, such as native forest, for their livelihood, are also highly vulnerable (Munasinghe, 1993; Salick and Byg, 2007).

Countries like Brazil that are already suffering large-scale biodiversity losses from forest destruction will increasingly experience double pressures from climate change (Miles et al., 2004). Biodiversity loss from climate change will slow the progress of human development in the worst-affected developing countries and will cause tangible economic losses worldwide by reducing ecosystem services (Roe and Elliot, 2004).

RESPONSES

Biodiversity loss due to climate change can be offset through measures that reduce other major biodiversity threats. Where those threats are already minimized, boosting conservation efforts, creating nature preserves, and reversing the fragmentation of habitats through the establishment of biodiversity corridors may help stem losses (Tabarelli et al., 2010). The principal response areas include promoting protection and sustainable management of forests, rationalizing and enhancing efficiencies in water usage, and managing toxic pollutants from industrial waste, agricultural fertilizers, and pesticides (Tilman et al., 2002). Interventions aimed at controlling invasive species, which can accelerate local biodiversity losses among endemic species, have shown to be effective and can complement other efforts (Veitch and Clout (eds.), 2004).

For many of the worst-affected communities in lower-income countries, capacity to implement such measures will be a major hurdle and international support will be vital. As with other systemic challenges, mainstreaming biodiversity considerations into decision making at different levels will be crucial to more effective solutions (Cowling et al., 2008). Social support should also be foreseen for indigenous groups and other communities which are heavily reliant on the fastest declining ecosystems (Salick and Byg, 2007).

Promising trends are visible in the global fight against biodiversity loss: protected and sustainable forest areas continue to grow incrementally and biodiversity aid has increased significantly in the past five years (SCBD, 2010). But the need is far greater than the response to date and most forms of biodiversity loss are irreversible (IPCC, 2002; Thomas et al., 2004). As climate change accelerates the decline, the urgency to respond effectively has never been greater.

THE INDICATOR

The indicator measures the proportion of species doomed to future extinction in different biomes around the world on account of the contraction of geographical climate-determined range size and future biome distribution due to climate change (Thomas et al., 2004). The exact time lag between threatened extinctions and their full realization varies and is not fully understood, although estimates exist (Brooks et al., 1999). Since the process of biodiversity loss due to climate change is continuous, in reality only a proportion of the estimated losses would be incurred at a date later than indicated. The indicator pairs biodiversity loss information and vegetation change with estimations of the lost economic value to determine a scale of economic losses in affected economies and the world (Mace et al. in Hassan et al. (eds.), 2005; US Forest Service, 2010; Costanza et al., 1997).

ESTIMATES COUNTRY-LEVEL IMPACT

COUNTRY	$ 2010	$ 2030	Contraction 2010	Contraction 2030
ACUTE				
Afghanistan	80	650	-10,000	-20,000
Angola	400	2,500	-60,000	-100,000
Argentina	3,000	20,000	-35,000	-70,000
Belarus	700	4,250	-550	-1,250
Belize	15	100	-450	-850
Bhutan	45	350	-250	-450
Bolivia	500	4,000	-35,000	-65,000
Botswana	150	750	-1,500	-3,000
Burkina Faso	60	400	-4,500	-9,250
Central African Republic	35	200	-5,500	-10,000
Chad	200	1,250	-20,000	-40,000
Chile	800	6,250	-15,000	-30,000
Congo	80	500	-400	-750
Djibouti	10	75	-550	-1,250
DR Congo	55	350	-20,000	-45,000
Equatorial Guinea	60	400	-400	-850
Eritrea	20	100	-2,750	-5,750
Estonia	85	400	-150	-300
Gabon	100	650	-4,000	-8,000
Georgia	55	350	-2,750	-5,500
Guinea	30	200	-4,250	-8,500
Guinea-Bissau	5	40	-600	-1,250
Guyana	65	300	-3,500	-7,250
Iran	3,250	25,000	-10,000	-20,000
Kazakhstan	950	5,000	-5,750	-10,000
Kyrgyzstan	90	600	-1,250	-2,500
Latvia	150	700	-600	-1,250
Lithuania	200	1,250	-200	-400
Macedonia	65	450	-2,000	-4,000
Mali	100	750	-20,000	-40,000
Mauritania	70	450	-15,000	-35,000
Mongolia	150	1,500	-3,000	-6,250
Mozambique	80	550	-35,000	-70,000
Namibia	100	600	-2,250	-4,250
Nicaragua	40	300	-1,500	-2,750
Niger	55	350	-20,000	-40,000
Oman	200	1,750	-2,000	-3,750
Papua New Guinea	65	500	-1,250	-2,500
Paraguay	100	900	-10,000	-25,000
Peru	800	6,250	-4,000	-8,250
Senegal	75	500	-3,250	-6,500
Solomon Islands	10	80	-75	-150
Somalia	85	550	-15,000	-30,000
South Africa	1,750	10,000	-5,250	-10,000
Sudan/South Sudan	300	2,000	-45,000	-90,000
Suriname	30	150	-2,750	-5,500
Tajikistan	45	300	-450	-850
Timor-Leste	10	85	-1,500	-3,250
Turkmenistan	350	2,000	-8,000	-15,000
Uruguay	200	1,250	-400	-800
Yemen	150	1,250	-3,250	-6,500
Zambia	65	400	-85,000	-150,000
Zimbabwe	75	500	-9,500	-20,000
SEVERE				
Albania	40	250	-50	-100
Armenia	35	250	-700	-1,500
Azerbaijan	200	1,250	-2,000	-4,000
Bosnia and Herzegovina	70	500	-1,500	-3,000
Brazil	3,500	30,000	-200,000	-450,000
Bulgaria	250	1,500	-5,250	-10,000
Cameroon	85	550	-2,250	-4,250
Colombia	650	4,750	-5,500	-10,000
Croatia	150	1,250	-1	-5
Cyprus	35	100	-55	-100
Ecuador	150	1,250	-2,750	-5,250
Ethiopia	150	1,000	-25,000	-55,000
Kenya	100	700	-950	-2,000
Laos	30	300	-1,250	-2,500
Lesotho	5	40	-25	-50
Liberia	1	20	-1,750	-3,750
Madagascar	40	250	-1,000	-2,250
Mexico	2,500	20,000	-50,000	-100,000
Morocco	300	2,000	-10,000	-20,000
Panama	75	550	-1,750	-3,500
Romania	350	2,500	-200	-350
Russia	3,250	25,000	-70,000	-150,000
Slovakia	200	1,250	-450	-900
Swaziland	10	55	-45	-90
Syria	200	1,500	-1,250	-2,250
Tanzania	150	850	-10,000	-20,000
Tunisia	150	1,250	-4,000	-7,750
Turkey	1,500	4,750	-4,750	-9,750
Ukraine	700	4,750	-800	-1,500
Uzbekistan	100	850	-7,250	-15,000
Venezuela	550	4,000	-25,000	-55,000
HIGH				
Algeria	150	1,000	-55,000	-100,000
Australia	1,250	2,250	-50,000	-100,000
Austria	300	800	-1,000	-2,000
Benin	20	100	-6,000	-10,000
Brunei	20	150	-100	-250
Cambodia	40	450	-1,500	-3,000
Canada	2,250	4,000	-60,000	-100,000
Costa Rica	35	300	-700	-1,500
Cote d ,Ivoire	40	250	-3,500	-6,750

$ Additional economic costs due to climate change (million USD PPP) - yearly average

Contraction of biological zones due to climate change (km^2) - yearly average

CLIMATE VULNERABILITY

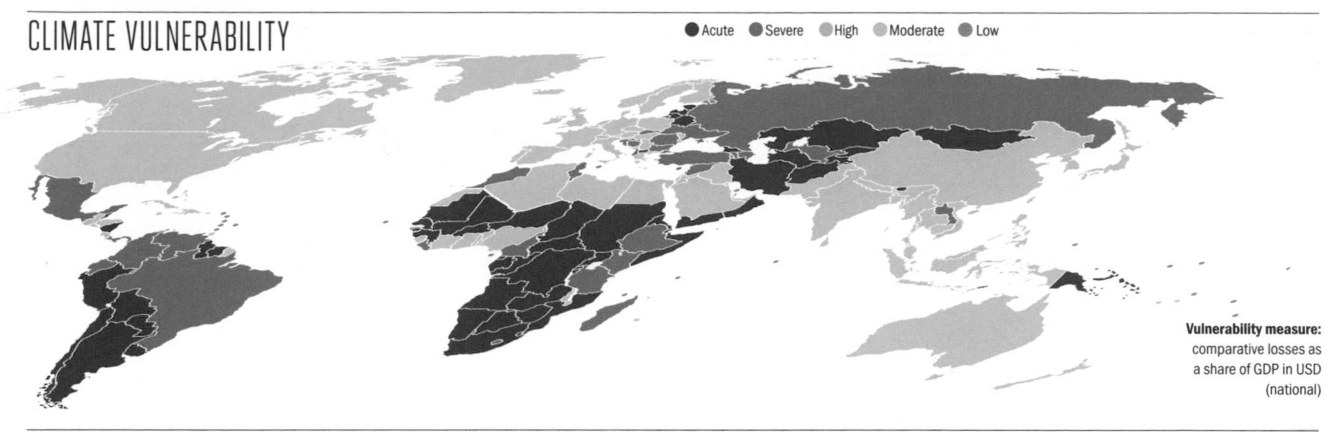

Vulnerability measure: comparative losses as a share of GDP in USD (national)

CLIMATE UNCERTAINTY

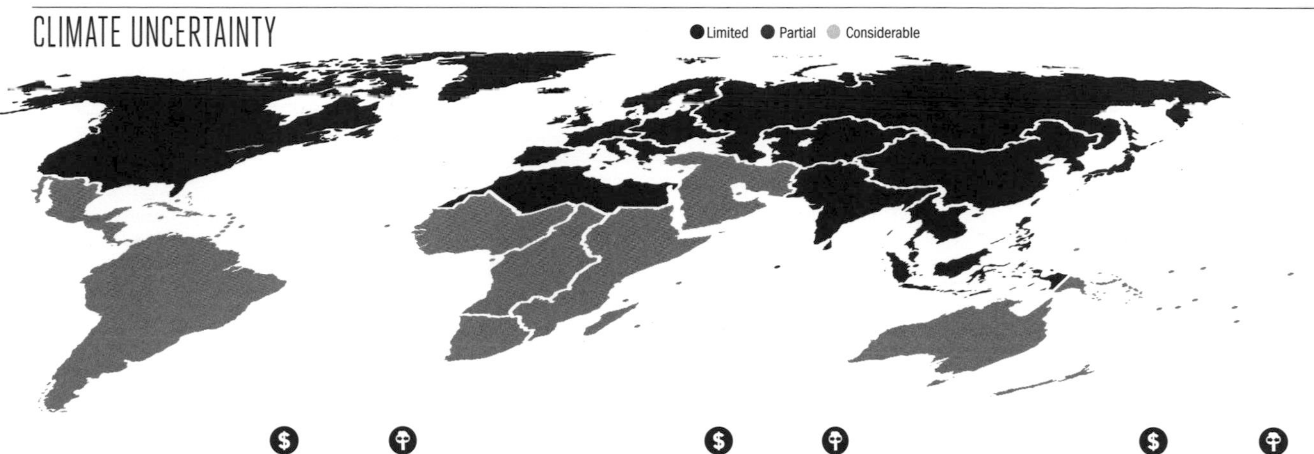

	$			
COUNTRY	2010	2030	2010	2030
Cuba	85	650	-2,250	-4,250
Czech Republic	250	1,750	-750	-1,500
Denmark	150	400	-30	-60
Fiji	5	35	-50	-95
Finland	150	400	-2,750	-5,250
France	1,750	5,000	-15,000	-25,000
Gambia	5	20	-200	-400
Ghana	55	350	-3,000	-6,000
Greece	400	1,250	-3,750	-7,250
Honduras	45	350	-2,500	-5,250
Hungary	150	950	-750	-1,500
Iceland	20	40	-5	-10
Indonesia	500	3,750	-5,000	-10,000
Iraq	85	650	-2,750	-5,500
Ireland	300	550	-350	-650
Libya	100	750	-40,000	-85,000
Malawi	10	60	-600	-1,250
Malaysia	350	2,750	-7,000	-15,000
Moldova	15	85	-300	-650
Myanmar	45	350	-20,000	-35,000
Nepal	25	200	-200	-400
New Zealand	250	400	-50	-100
Nigeria	200	1,250	-5,250	-10,000
Norway	250	500	-500	-950
Pakistan	300	2,250	-2,000	-4,000
Poland	700	4,750	-2,500	-5,000
Portugal	200	650	-3,750	-7,250
Sierra Leone	5	40	-600	-1,250
Slovenia	75	500	-600	-1,250
Spain	1,500	4,250	-15,000	-30,000
Sweden	400	950	-3,250	-6,500
Thailand	350	2,500	-7,750	-15,000

	$			
COUNTRY	2010	2030	2010	2030
Togo	5	30	-450	-950
Uganda	25	200	-250	-500
United States	25,000	45,000	-25,000	-50,000
Vanuatu	1	5	-30	-65
MODERATE				
Bahamas	5	35	-500	-950
Bangladesh	20	150	-100	-250
Belgium	100	350	-350	-750
Burundi	1	5	-650	-1,250
China	4,250	45,000	-60,000	-100,000
Dominican Republic	30	250	-3,750	-7,250
Egypt	10	60	-25,000	-50,000
El Salvador	15	100	-450	-950
Germany	1,000	3,000	-1,250	-2,500
Guatemala	30	250	-1,250	-2,750
Haiti	1	20	-200	-400
India	1,500	10,000	-15,000	-30,000
Israel	30	200	-150	-250
Italy	700	2,000	8,500	-15,000
Jamaica	5	40	-400	-750
Japan	900	2,500	-4,500	-9,250
Jordan	5	35	-550	-1,000
Lebanon	15	100	-65	-150
Luxembourg	15	40	-30	-80
Mauritius	5	20	-50	-100
Netherlands	150	400	-500	-1,000
North Korea	15	150	-1,750	-3,500
Philippines	95	750	-350	-650
Rwanda	1	10	-650	-1,250
Saudi Arabia	150	1,250	-15,000	-25,000
Singapore	10	70	-15	-30
South Korea	500	4,000	-550	-1,000

	$			
COUNTRY	2010	2030	2010	2030
Sri Lanka	30	250	-1,250	-2,750
Switzerland	70	200	-300	-600
Trinidad and Tobago	5	45	-200	-350
United Arab Emirates	20	150	-500	-1,000
United Kingdom	1,000	3,000	-1,500	-3,000
Vietnam	70	750	-150	-300
LOW				
Antigua and Barbuda				
Bahrain				
Barbados				
Cape Verde				
Comoros				
Dominica				
Grenada				
Kiribati				
Kuwait				
Maldives				
Malta				
Marshall Islands				
Micronesia				
Palau				
Qatar				
Saint Lucia				
Saint Vincent				
Samoa				
Sao Tome and Principe				
Seychelles				
Tonga				
Tuvalu				

DESERTIFICATION

ESTIMATES GLOBAL CLIMATE IMPACT

2010 EFFECT TODAY

USD LOSS PER YEAR **5 BILLION**

2030 EFFECT TOMORROW

USD LOSS PER YEAR **20 BILLION**

ECONOMIC IMPACT

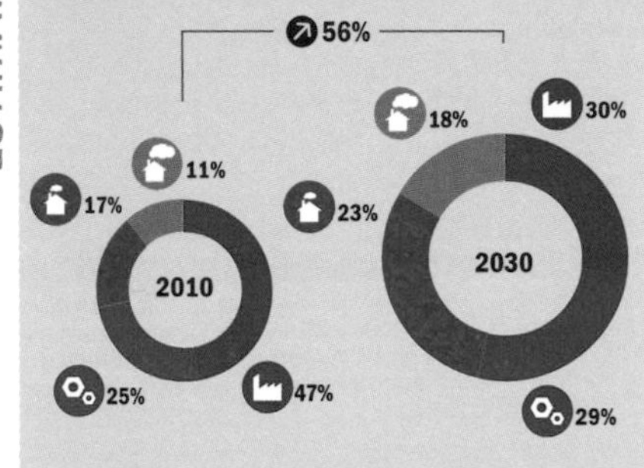

- Desertification will worsen already dry areas as heat rises and rainfall declines
- Although global climate change brings more rain, most of it will fall in the far north and south, while rainfall in the tropical zones, home to much of the world's drylands, is likely to decline as heat rises
- Millions of hectares of agricultural land in these areas are experiencing an increase in aridity, compounding other degradation taking place
- Climate change in the world's drylands will further impede human development progress for some of the world's poorest groups
- Sustainable land management strategies can help prevent desertification, but restoration of already degraded lands is difficult and costly

RELATIVE IMPACT

$$$$$ $$$$$$$$$$ 2010
150 / 2

$$$ $$$$$$$$$$ 2030
123 / 2

HOTSPOTS

2010 $ 2030

2010	Country	2030
600	MEXICO	4,500
450	UKRAINE	2,750
500	AUSTRALIA	1,500
200	RUSSIA	1,250
450	ITALY	1,250

GEOPOLITICAL VULNERABILITY

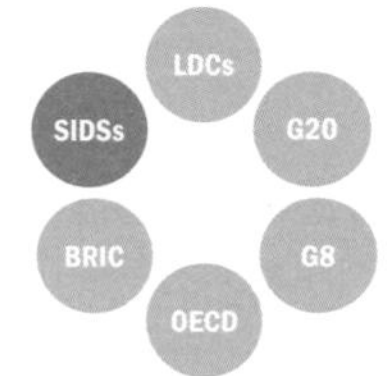

Economic Cost (2010 PPP non-discounted)
Developing Country Low Emitters
Developed
Developing Country High Emitters
Other Industrialized

$ = Losses per 100,000 USD of GDP

Change in relation to overall global population and/or GDP

$ = Millions of USD (2010 PPP non-discounted)

Desertification is degradation of drylands. The UN has defined "drylands" broadly as areas of land with an aridity index—a measure of rainfall versus evaporation—below a certain low-end threshold (UN, 2011). More than half the planet's productive land is considered drylands. Covering around 40% of the earth's land surface, drylands are home to some 2 billion people, nearly all in developing countries, and are responsible for more than 40% of global food production (UNCCD, 2011). As climate change intensifies heat and limits rainfall in drylands, already rampant land degradation in these areas will worsen (Evans and Geerken, 2004; Adeel et al., 2005; Zika and Erb, 2009). The UN and Christian Aid have estimated that anywhere between 25 and 700 million people could be displaced due to expected water stress and environmental degradation, including 50 million people affected by desertification over the next decade (Christian Aid, 2007; WWAP, 2009; UNCCD, 2010). Such groups have been campaigning for greater application of sustainable land and water resource management in order to combat this alarming development.

CLIMATE MECHANISM

A range of socio-economic and environmental processes are involved in land degradation in dry areas, including declining water availability, soil erosion and nutrient depletion, among others (Geist and Lambin, 2004). Climate observations and models indicate that many of the world's dry regions are becoming hotter and drier as global warming intensifies (Hansen et al, 2007; McCluney et al., 2011). A loss in net moisture or rainfall is a key factor in the degradation of dry land (Evans and Geerken, 2004). As a result, many non-arid lands will become arid, while affected arid lands will become even drier. On the other hand, where there are substantial increases in rainfall on existing drylands, such zones will improve and become more humid. Overall, the changes will be negative, since rainfall change is more likely to degrade the world's existing dryland, especially in Africa (IPCC, 2007 and 2007b; Helm et al., 2010). Where lands degrade, agricultural productivity and livelihoods will be severely affected (Fraser et al., 2011).

IMPACTS

The impact of climate change on desertification is expected to be widespread, affecting around 40 countries by 2030. The economic impact of land degradation is estimated at 5 billion dollars a year today, increasing to some 20 billion dollars annually and a larger share of global GDP by 2030.

Climate change-driven desertification is already estimated to affect some 5 million people worldwide, doubling to 10 million by 2030.

The range of worst affected countries is varied, with West Africa particularly hard hit. Countries such as Benin, Burkina Faso, Gambia, Guinea-Bissau, Mali, Niger, and Senegal top the list of those suffering the most extreme effects. A number of developed and industrialized countries are also affected from Australia to the Mediterranean, and Black Sea countries such as Bosnia and Herzegovina, Croatia, Russia and the Ukraine.

The bulk of global costs will occur in Organization for Economic Co-operation and Development (OECD) countries, including Italy, Spain and Turkey. However, Mexico is the country with the greatest total losses, reaching an estimated 5 billion dollars a year by 2030.

Countries acutely vulnerable to climate change include a large number of least developed and landlocked developing countries (LDCs and LLDCs), a particular cause for concern from a poverty/development perspective.

THE BROADER CONTEXT

Desertification itself is a serious global concern. The Secretariat of the UN Convention to Combat Desertification has been sounding the alarm on highly damaging changes underway in many of the world's drylands. They call attention, for instance, to 12 million hectares, including 75 billion tons of fertile soil, a principal global resource, lost each year as a result of desertification and drought (UNCCD, 2010). The extent to which climate change is rendering these regions hotter and drier (or wetter) will be its main, primarily negative, contribution to an already large-scale and multifaceted concern. Aside from climate change, the most widely cited causes of desertification include land-use issues such as deforestation, overcultivation, overgrazing, and unsustainable irrigation practices (Adeel et al, 2005). Natural variability in weather regimes can also result in

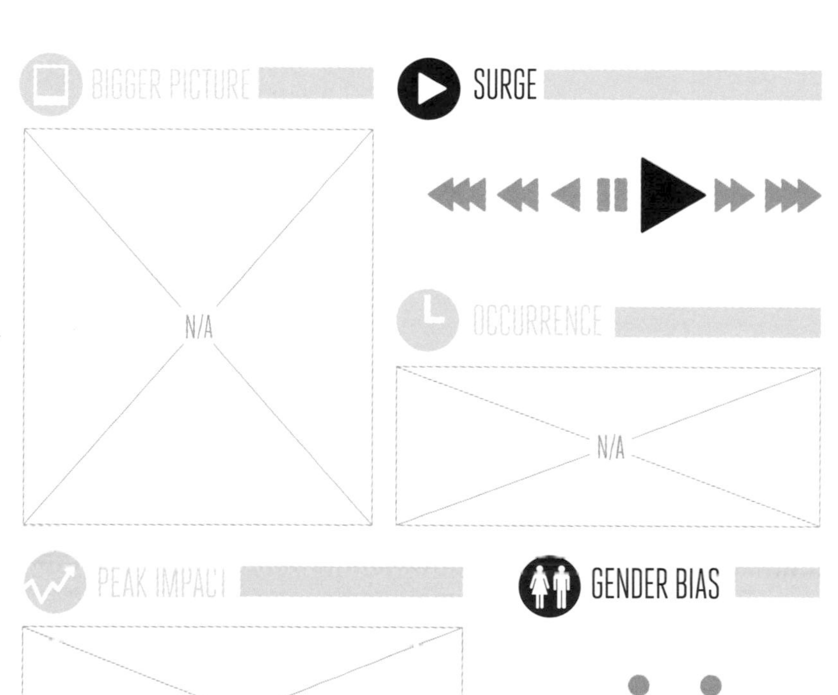

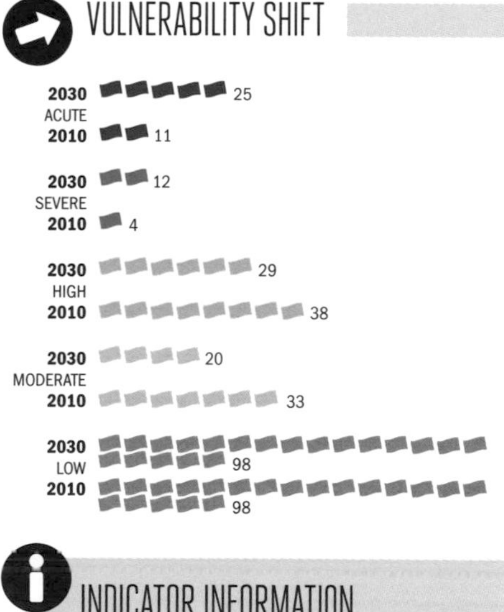

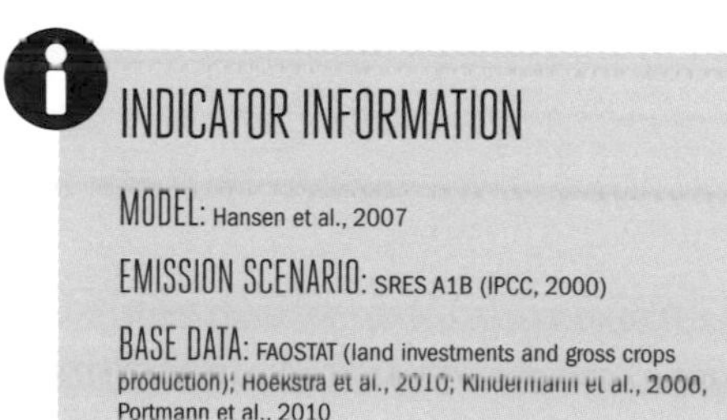

INDICATOR INFORMATION
MODEL: Hansen et al., 2007
EMISSION SCENARIO: SRES A1B (IPCC, 2000)
BASE DATA: FAOSTAT (land investments and gross crops production); Hoekstra et al., 2010; Kindermann et al., 2000, Portmann et al., 2010

= 5 countries (rounded)

Acute Severe High Moderate Low

large-scale short-term fluctuations in the primary productivity of drylands, both positive and negative (Hughes and Diaz, 2008).

Vulnerabilities and Wider Outcomes

Drylands exist around the world. Where they have been well managed, as in parts of southern Europe, they are fertile and productive. Where drylands are poorly managed, the opposite situation can develop as their susceptibility to degradation increases (Oygard et al., 1999). Given the overwhelming share of populated dryland areas within developing countries and LDCs or LLDCs, the capacity to promote and regulate sound policies can be an important factor in successful management (Esikuri ed., 1999).

Poverty can be viewed as a driver of desertification, when communities become locked in a vicious cycle that exacerbates deforestation for lack of alternative livelihoods. It can also be viewed as an outcome of desertification when, for example, households suffer losses of land, soil, or crop productivity due to desertification. As productive possibilities decline and populations in dryland areas continue to grow, these regions will likely expand as suppliers of seasonal and/or permanent migration (Johnson et al. (eds.), 2006). Poverty and health indicators for populations living in dryland areas are low, compared to other climatic zones (Adeel et al., 2005; Verstraete et al., 2009).

RESPONSES

Supporting dryland communities to adapt will require offsetting the additional heat and/or loss of rainfall brought about by climate change. Degradation prevention is preferable to costly restoration projects that seek to return vegetation and environmental integrity to degraded lands, often with limited results (Puigdefaabregas, 1998). Desertification control measures have had little success and have led experts to propose developmental approaches that foster technology uptake, investment, best practice land management replication, and boosting and diversifying incomes of dryland populations to better cope with change (Mortimore, 2003). Water capture, conservation and storage, increasing vegetation through reforestation, and the control of deforestation, and prevention of overgrazing and other soil-damaging processes can all contribute to enhanced resilience of drylands and their communities (Adeel et al., 2005). Improved monitoring of drylands would also facilitate better macro policy analysis and development (Reynolds et al., 2011).

THE INDICATOR

The indicator measures the value loss (or gain) in rapidly degraded (or improving) dryland agricultural zones resulting from an increase (or decrease) in aridity, due to temperature and rainfall changes brought about through global warming (Hansen et al., 2007). It is broadly indicative of how desertification is likely to unfold as a result of climate change. The amount of new agricultural lands accruing from deforestation is also accounted for. While projections of the key variable of rainfall are uncertain, there scientists are virtually unanimous about the direction of change (wet or dry) for a number of the world's key dryland regions, such as the Mediterranean basin.

ESTIMATES COUNTRY-LEVEL IMPACT

COUNTRY	2010	2030	2010	2030	2010	2030
ACUTE						
Albania20	100	300	600	35,000	80,000	
Australia	500	1,500	7,000	15,000	20,000	45,000
Benin	15	100	1,500	3,000	100,000	350,000
Bosnia and Herzegovina	65	450	1,750	3,250	100,000	250,000
Burkina Faso	10	50				
Costa Rica	25	200	550	1,250	50,000	150,000
Cote d'Ivoire	15	95				
Croatia	100	800	2,000	3,750	150,000	300,000
Cuba	65	450	1,250	2,500	150,000	250,000
Dominica	1	10	20	35	1,750	3,750
Gambia	1	10				
Guinea	5	30				
Guinea-Bissau	1	5				
Liberia	1	5				
Mali	5	45				
Mexico	600	4,500	10,000	20,000	600,000	1,500,000
New Zealand	150	500	2,750	5,750	45,000	100,000
Nicaragua	15	100	550	1,000	25,000	65,000
Niger	5	30				
Panama	90	700	1,500	3,250	75,000	200,000
Sierra Leone	1	10				
Timor-Leste	25	200	650	1,250	50,000	100,000
Togo	10	45	1,250	2,500	150,000	400,000
Ukraine	450	2,750	9,000	20,000	700,000	1,000,000
Uruguay	20	150	400	800	7,750	15,000
SEVERE						
Angola	25	150	1,250	2,500	20,000	65,000
Belize	1	5	20	40	250	650
Cape Verde	1	5	50	100	6,000	15,000
Dominican Republic	30	200	650	1,250	150,000	300,000
Egypt	250	1,250	2,000	4,000	150,000	400,000
Greece	100	350	1,500	2,750	100,000	250,000
Honduras	10	75	350	750	25,000	65,000
Italy	450	1,250	6,250	10,000	1,000,000	2,500,000
Madagascar	10	45	1,000	2,000	35,000	100,000
Senegal	10	50	750	1,500	50,000	150,000
Tunisia	30	200	450	950	30,000	75,000
Turkey	350	950	6,250	15,000	600,000	1,500,000
HIGH						
Afghanistan	5	30	500	1,000	25,000	80,000
Algeria	45	350				
Antigua and Barbuda		1	5	5	750	1,750
Bahrain	5	25				
Bulgaria	10	80	150	350	10,000	20,000
Chile	40	300	700	1,500	15,000	40,000
Cyprus	5	10	40	85	5,000	10,000
Ecuador	20	150	400	850	25,000	60,000
France	400	1,250	5,250	10,000	600,000	1,500,000
Ghana	10	65	750	1,500	75,000	200,000
Iraq	15	100				
Israel	25	200				
Jamaica	1	20	65	150	15,000	40,000
Jordan	5	30				
Lebanon	5	50				
Libya	15	100				
Malta	1	5	15	30	20,000	45,000
Morocco	30	200	1,250	2,500	85,000	200,000
Nigeria	60	350	4,250	8,500	750,000	2,000,000
Pakistan	70	400	1,500	3,250	350,000	1,000,000
Peru	55	400	1,250	2,250	25,000	65,000
Portugal	30	90	450	900	55,000	100,000
Russia	200	1,250	3,250	6,250	25,000	50,000
Saudi Arabia	75	550				
Slovenia	10	75	100	250	10,000	25,000
Spain	200	600	2,750	5,500	250,000	450,000
Sudan/South Sudan	20	150				
Syria	15	95				
United Arab Emirates	30	200				
MODERATE						
Bahamas		1	1	5	70	150
Bangladesh	5	20	150	300	150,000	400,000
Brazil	70	550	2,250	4,500	50,000	100,000
Cameroon	1	10				
Central African Republic		1				
Chad	1	5				
China	75	750	2,000	4,000	300,000	600,000
Colombia	1	10	35	75	1,500	3,750
Congo	1	5				
DR Congo	1	5				
Equatorial Guinea	1	5				
Gabon	1	5				
Iran	1	20	35	70	1,500	4,000
Japan	40	100	500	950	150,000	300,000
Mauritania		1	25	50	85	250
Namibia		1	15	25	35	95
Norway	1	1	10	20	150	350
Oman						1
Sao Tome and Principe						
United States	200	700	1,750	3,500	55,000	150,000
LOW						
Argentina	-250	-2,000	-3,750	-7,500	-55,000	-150,000
Armenia						
Austria						
Azerbaijan		-1	-5	-10	-600	-1,500
Barbados						

Additional economic costs due to climate change (million USD PPP) - yearly average

Additional land degraded due to climate change (km²) - yearly average

CLIMATE VULNERABILITY

Acute · Severe · High · Moderate · Low

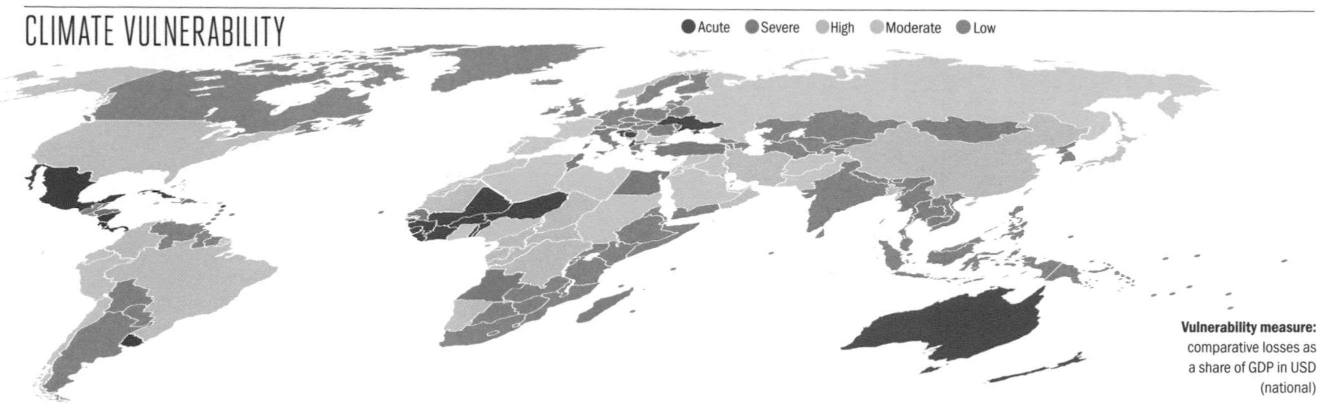

Vulnerability measure: comparative losses as a share of GDP in USD (national)

CLIMATE UNCERTAINTY

Limited · Partial · Considerable

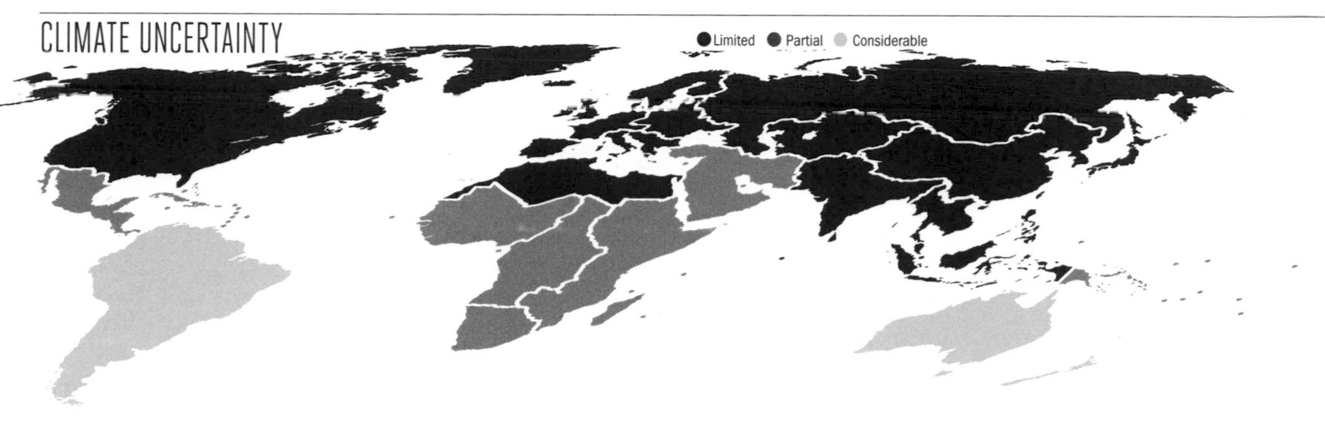

COUNTRY	2010	2030	2010	2030	2010	2030
Belarus						
Belgium						
Bhutan						
Bolivia						
Botswana	-5	-25				
Brunei						
Burundi	-1	-1				
Cambodia						
Canada	-5	-10	-35	-70	-100	-250
Comoros		-1	-75	-150	-30,000	-90,000
Czech Republic						
Denmark						
Djibouti		-1				
El Salvador						
Eritrea	-1	-1				
Estonia						
Ethiopia	-10	-65				
Fiji						
Finland						
Georgia						
Germany						
Grenada						
Guatemala						
Guyana						
Haiti						
Hungary						
Iceland						
India	-40	-300	-1,750	-3,500	-650,000	-1,500,000
Indonesia	-5	-50	-400	-750	-50,000	-100,000
Ireland						
Kazakhstan	-5	-45	-150	-300	-950	-2,000
Kenya	-10	-50				
Kiribati						
Kuwait						
Kyrgyzstan						
Laos		-1	-15	-30	-400	-1,000
Latvia						
Lesotho		-1	-15	-30	-1,000	-2,000
Lithuania						
Luxembourg						
Macedonia						
Malawi	-1	-10				
Malaysia						
Maldives						
Marshall Islands						
Mauritius	-5	-40	-90	-200	-55,000	-150,000
Micronesia						
Moldova						
Mongolia						
Mozambique			-5	-10	-150	-350
Myanmar	-5	-35	-650	1,250	50,000	-100,000
Nepal						
Netherlands						
North Korea	-1	-10	-100	-200	-20,000	-45,000
Palau						
Papua New Guinea						
Paraguay						
Philippines						
Poland						
Qatar						
Romania						
Rwanda	-1	-10				
Saint Lucia						
Saint Vincent						
Samoa						
Seychelles		-1				
Singapore						
Slovakia						
Solomon Islands						
Somalia			-1	-5	-20	-75
South Africa	-5	-25	-90	-200	-3,750	-7,000
South Korea	-250	-1,750	-2,000	-4,000	-1,000,000	-2,000,000
Sri Lanka						
Suriname						
Swaziland	-5	-20	-150	-300	-10,000	-25,000
Sweden						
Switzerland						
Tajikistan						
Tanzania			-1	-5	-150	-400
Thailand	-80	-650	-2,000	-4,000	-250,000	-600,000
Tonga						
Trinidad and Tobago						
Turkmenistan				-1	-1	-10
Tuvalu						
Uganda	-5	-30				
United Kingdom						
Uzbekistan						
Vanuatu						
Venezuela						
Vietnam	-80	-850	-3,500	-7,250	-950,000	-2,000,000
Yemen	-1	-1	-30	-55	-1,250	-5,250
Zambia	-1	-15				
Zimbabwe	-1	-10				

Additional persons affected due to climate change - yearly average

HEATING & COOLING

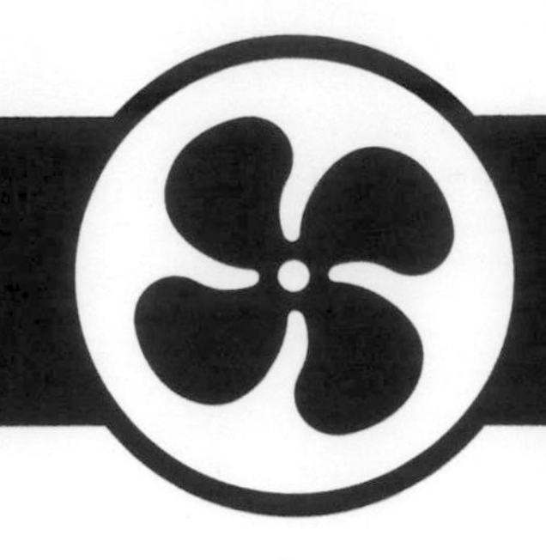

ESTIMATES GLOBAL CLIMATE IMPACT

2010 EFFECT TODAY

USD **GAIN** PER YEAR **35 BILLION**

2030 EFFECT TOMORROW

USD **GAIN** PER YEAR **75 BILLION**

ECONOMIC IMPACT

↘19%

	Developing Country Low Emitters	Developing Country High Emitters	Other Industrialized	Developed
2010	1.2	-2.2	-8	-25
2030	30	7.2	-50	-65

2010 USD billion

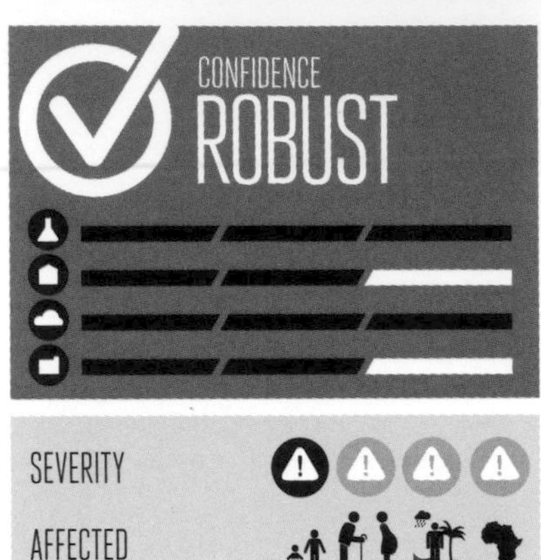

- The most certain outcome of global warming is rising heat
- As heat goes up, heating costs decrease and air conditioning costs rise
- In the cooler north, heating especially is mandatory and widespread, but in tropical zones, artificial cooling is not always a necessity
- Currently, the impact of rising heat on indoor space conditioning is a positive effect of climate change globally, as cost reductions in cooler countries outweigh cost increases in hotter countries
- Tropical countries still incur serious losses, and in the longer term, if climate change is not controlled, high cooling costs will overtake reductions in heating costs

RELATIVE IMPACT

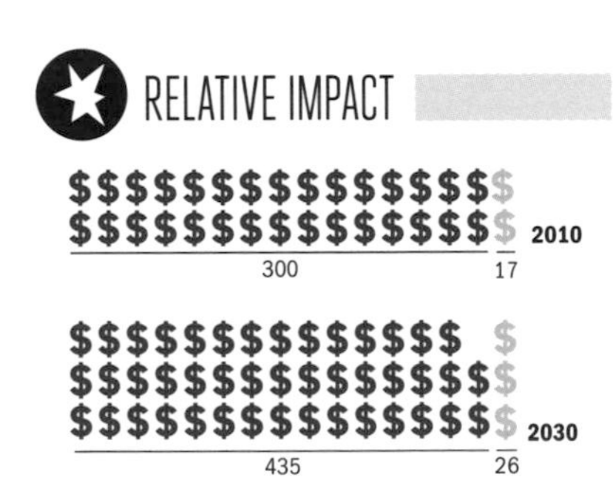

HOTSPOTS

2010		2030
800	INDIA	10,000
600	MEXICO	10,000
250	BRAZIL	5,000
350	SAUDI ARABIA	4,250
150	VIETNAM	3,750

GEOPOLITICAL VULNERABILITY

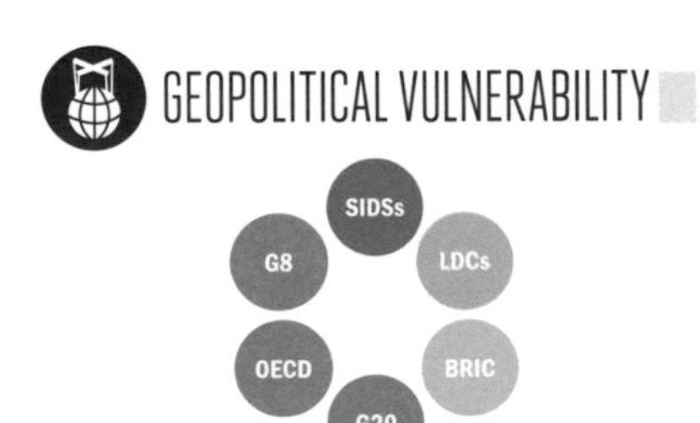

Economic Cost (2010 PPP non-discounted)

Developing Country Low Emitters

Developing Country High Emitters

Developed

Other Industrialized

$ = Losses per 100,000 USD of GDP

Change in relation to overall global population and/or GDP

= Millions of USD (2010 PPP non-discounted)

The heating and cooling of residential and non-residential indoor spaces are among the largest energy consumers globally (WRI, 2009). Energy demand for heating is currently ten times higher than for cooling (Isaac and van Vuuren, 2008). As a result, temperature rise is presently generating a net economic benefit for the world economy, since the lowering of heating costs due to milder winters or fewer cold days is more significant than any increase in air conditioning costs (Hansen et al., 2012). However, if climate change continues to the end of the century, rising heat and increased air conditioning demand in developing countries would generate net losses for the world (Isaac and van Vuuren, 2008). Today, the increasing costs faced by middle and lower income countries in tropical regions can represent a significant negative economic impact at a national level. As a result, cooler countries are seeing declining emissions or less growth in emissions at national levels, enabling them to better meet GHG reduction targets. In hotter countries, however, GHG emissions will be artificially inflated, making it more difficult to reduce them. In fact, meeting the rapidly growing demand for air-conditioning as incomes expand in developing countries is a significant challenge without climate change. Not meeting the challenge, including with climate change, will curtail the economic development and welfare of many lower and middle-income countries, for example through reduced productivity and greater exposure to heat related health risks (Kjellstrom et al., 2009; Akpinar-Ferrand and Singh, 2010).

CLIMATE MECHANISM

The planet's warming is virtually certain, resulting in more hot and fewer cold days and nights (IPCC, 2007). On average, winters are becoming shorter and milder, summers longer and hotter. Areas that rely on heating indoor space to maintain comfortable temperature levels will increasingly need less energy in a year as the cold wanes. On the other hand, areas that can benefit from year-round or seasonal air-conditioning to bring down indoor temperatures to comfortable levels will increasingly need more energy to maintain these levels as temperatures climb. Many industrialized countries will see benefits from reduced winter heating needs, however many of those same countries will also experience increased cooling needs (Miller et al., 2008). In the sub-tropics and tropics where most of the world's population resides, greater cooling costs far outweigh any heating fluctuations (Isaac and van Vuuren, 2008).

IMPACTS

The global impact of climate change on heating and cooling is currently estimated to benefit the global economy by more than 30 billion dollars each year. By 2030, the costs of heating and cooling are estimated to decline slightly as a share of global GDP, but reach over 70 billion dollars. This is a signal of what lies ahead, as increased demand for cooling will gradually overtake any benefits from lower heating costs.
In 2010, national losses amounted to some 5 billion dollars a year in additional costs, whereas gains in countries benefitting from lower heating costs amounted to 40 billion dollars a year. By 2030, annual losses are estimated to be over 70 billion dollars and gains at 150 billion dollars. Countries with the largest losses in 2030 are India and Mexico, each with over 10 billion in annual costs. The largest gains are in the United Kingdom, Russia, China, and Germany, with benefits ranging from 10 to 20 billion dollars or more each year.
Least developed and lower-income countries in Africa, Central America, the Caribbean, and the Pacific are particularly negatively impacted, with losses reaching from 0.5-1% of GDP by 2030.

THE BROADER CONTEXT

Energy demand for both heating and cooling is growing almost everywhere. Global demand for heating is expected to peak around 2030, while demand for cooling will continue to expand throughout the 21st century as incomes grow in tropical and sub-tropical developing countries (Isaac and van Vuuren, 2008). These increases and decreases would occur without climate change, since energy efficiencies are being realized in cooler countries where markets for heating and cooling equipment are saturated and population growth is slow or declining (UNECE, 2012). In developing countries air conditioning demand is far from saturated and is expected to increase rapidly as incomes rise and

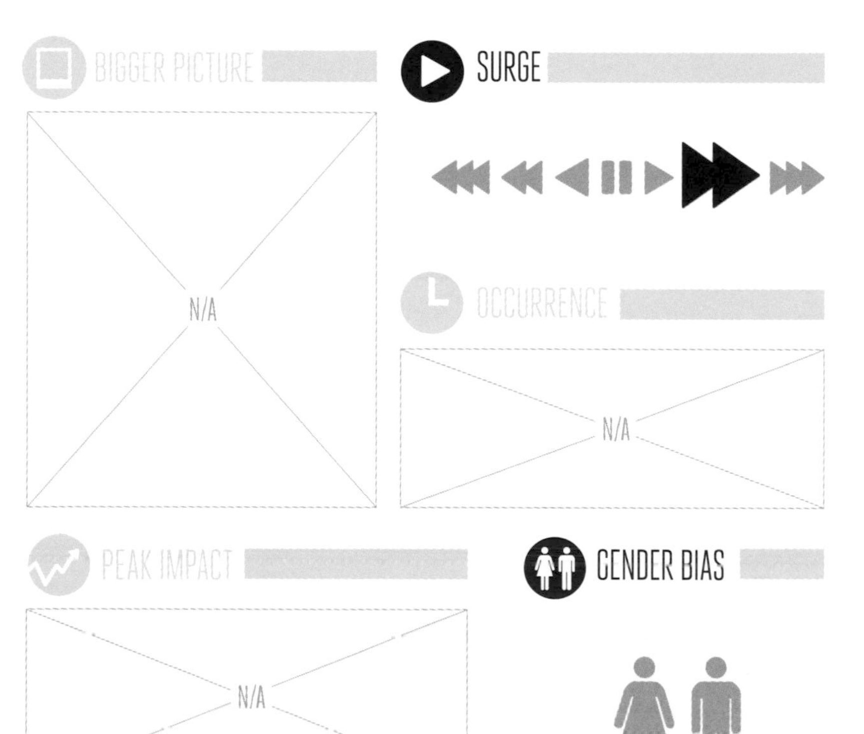

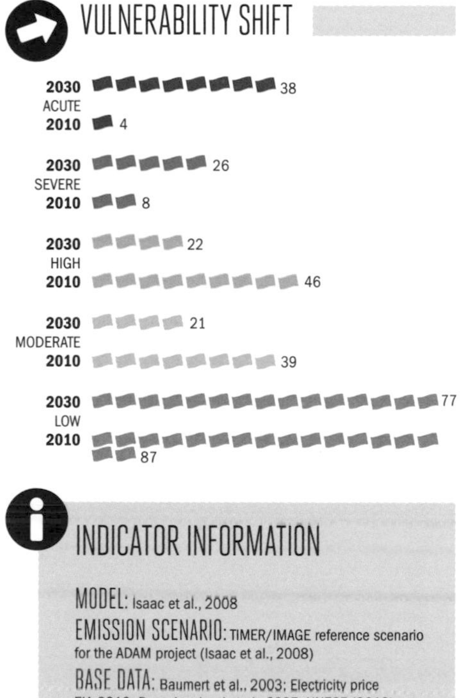

INDICATOR INFORMATION

MODEL: Isaac et al., 2008

EMISSION SCENARIO: TIMER/IMAGE reference scenario for the ADAM project (Isaac et al., 2008)

BASE DATA: Baumert et al., 2003; Electricity price EIA 2010; Perez-Lombard et al., 2007; UNECE (2012); Zmeureanu and Renaud, 2009

= 5 countries (rounded)

Acute Severe High Moderate Low

populations grow. Urban heat islands, growing in many places as a concern parallel to these other factors, are also exacerbating energy requirements (Kolokotroni et al., 2010; Memon et al., 2011).

VULNERABILITIES AND WIDER OUTCOMES

The world's hottest countries are most vulnerable to the impacts of climate change, since they already rely heavily on air-conditioning. Africa, Asia and the equatorial zones are particularly exposed since large populations and significant amounts of economic activity are located in warm zones.

If rising heat is not compensated by additional cooling that maintains at least the same level and progress in indoor climate control, economic productivity will fall more or less predictably (Kjellstrom et al., 2009a). Human welfare will be significantly affected through additional, serious impacts to human health from cardiovascular and chronic respiratory illnesses over and above what is already noted in the Health Impact section of this report (McMichael et al., 2006).

As is highlighted in this report's Ghana country study, people in the lowest-income communities are more likely to sleep outdoors on the hottest nights, increasing exposure to mosquito bites during peak vector activity periods (dusk and dawn) and promoting higher transmission rates of malaria. Heat stress also affects cognitive performance, mental stress, and depression among other psychological effects (Hancock et al., 2003; Hansen et al., 2008).

RESPONSES

Increases in heat are often offset by increased energy consumption on the part of those who can afford it, but at an additional energy cost. For those who cannot, social and economic welfare will be compromised by productivity and health effects, although it is unclear how the economic costs of lost productivity might compare with extra cooling costs (Yardley et al., 2011; Kjellstrom et al., 2009b). Since solutions for indoor space cooling are technically possible in many cases, international responses could focus on ensuring adequate indoor cooling for lower-income communities unable to do so at will, particularly in areas with high risk for malaria and vector-borne disease. Improving building insulation and energy efficiency in the tropics (not only in cold countries) to protect against heat (not only cold) would be an important, lower-emission option for adapting to the growing heat (Akpinar-Ferrand and Singh, 2010).

Heating and cooling is a clear example of a dual-focus adaptation-mitigation response area. Any mitigation project that ensures provision of cooling-related technologies to affected communities would also constitute an adaptation action. In terms of practical steps, increasing local shade-tree cover can have a positive effect on cooling buildings (Donovan and Butry, 2009). Cities could take greater advantage of the geothermal energy created as a result of the heat island effect to supply energy for cooling, since cities also heat the ground below, not only the air above. The potential energy supply has been estimated to exceed cooling demand requirements in several major cities (Zhu et al., 2010).

THE INDICATOR

The indicator maps residential/ non-residential heating demand changes. It is considered robust, given the certainty of the climate science community and model convergence on the main parameter of increasing heat, although humidity levels are also important (Wang et al., 2010). High quality energy consumption data gives a reasonable indication of the phenomenon's scale, but relies on the concept of heating and cooling degree-days, which are not fully accurate in terms of all demands, since wind, cloud cover, and humidity strongly influence heating and cooling behaviour (Baumert and Selman, 2003). While the same optimal temperature is assumed for different countries, it is argued that the optimal temperature varies by region, climate, and other conditions (Dear and Brager, 1998). Though the Indicator considers several dynamic variables, floor space size changes over time are not, though are understood to have a significant impact on future energy requirement estimates (Isaac et al., 2008; Clune et al., 2012).

ESTIMATE COUNTRY-LEVEL IMPACT

COUNTRY	$ 2010	$ 2030	⚡ 2010	⚡ 2030	2010	2030
ACUTE						
Antigua and Barbuda	1	25	15	65	15	55
Belize	1	30	15	55	1	10
Benin	15	150	100	300	85	200
Burkina Faso	45	400	250	600	150	350
Burundi	5	55	60	150	1	1
Cambodia	25	500	200	850	200	850
Central African Republic	5	55	40	100	5	15
Chad	45	350	150	350	150	350
Dominican Republic	65	950	450	1,750	350	1,250
Equatorial Guinea	25	200	150	400	95	250
Grenada	1	15	10	40	10	30
Guinea	15	100	95	250	25	60
Guinea-Bissau	1	20	15	45	15	35
Haiti	35	500	250	950	150	550
Honduras	25	400	200	750	65	250
Iraq	100	1,500	750	3,000	550	2,250
Jamaica	20	300	200	750	100	450
Laos	10	250	100	400	1	1
Liberia	5	50	40	100	25	65
Mali	30	250	200	550	65	150
Marshall Islands		5	1	10		
Mauritania	10	70	60	150	40	100
Micronesia	1	5	5	15		
Myanmar	75	1,250	650	2,750	100	450
Nicaragua	30	500	200	750	100	400
Niger	30	250	200	550	200	550
Panama	30	500	200	750	60	250
Papua New Guinea	20	350	200	900	85	350
Saint Lucia	1	25	15	65	15	50
Saint Vincent	1	15	10	35	5	20
Sao Tome and Principe		1	1	5	1	1
Senegal	30	250	200	550	150	400
Sierra Leone	10	75	65	150	30	80
Solomon Islands	1	25	15	65	15	55
Suriname	5	50	25	100	10	35
Togo	10	85	70	200	10	30
Tuvalu		1	1	1		
Yemen	200	2,250	1,500	4,750	1,000	3,250
SEVERE						
Bahrain	15	200	100	400	60	250
Cameroon	35	300	250	650	45	100
Cape Verde	1	10	5	15	5	10
Comoros	1	5	5	20	5	15
Cote d'Ivoire	35	300	300	750	150	350
Cuba	55	850	550	2,250	450	1,750
Dominica	1	10	5	25	5	15
DR Congo	15	150	400	1,000	1	5
El Salvador	20	300	150	600	50	200
Fiji	1	35	20	90	5	20
Gambia	5	25	20	60	15	40
Guyana	5	50	25	100	20	85
Kiribati		5	5	15	5	10
Mexico	600	10,000	6,250	30,000	3,000	15,000
Oman	45	550	350	1,250	250	800
Palau		1	1	5		
Philippines	200	3,000	1,500	6,500	800	3,250
Samoa	1	10	5	25	1	10
Saudi Arabia	350	4,250	2,500	9,000	2,000	7,250
Sudan/South Sudan	80	750	750	2,000	250	700
Tanzania	40	350	450	1,250	100	300
Uganda	40	300	150	450	25	70
United Arab Emirates	150	2,000	1,250	4,250	800	2,750
Vanuatu	1	10	5	25	5	20
Venezuela	200	3,000	1,500	6,250	400	1,500
Vietnam	150	3,750	1,500	6,000	550	2,500
HIGH						
Bahamas	1	30	20	80	15	60
Bangladesh	45	650	950	3,500	550	2,000
Barbados	1	30	20	80	20	70
Brazil	250	5,000	1,500	7,500	70	400
Brunei	5	50	25	100	20	85
Colombia	-40	1,250	-300	2,500	-55	450
Congo	5	60	50	100	10	25
Costa Rica	10	150	100	400	5	15
Ghana	30	250	350	900	60	150
Guatemala	5	150	30	300	10	100
India	800	10,000	15,000	65,000	15,000	55,000
Kuwait	55	650	400	1,500	450	1,500
Malaysia	65	1,000	550	2,250	350	1,500
Malta	1	10	15	30	10	25
Mozambique	10	90	150	400		
Nigeria	85	700	2,500	6,250	1,000	2,750
Paraguay	5	150	90	500		
Qatar	40	500	300	1,000	150	550
Singapore	60	1,000	300	1,250	200	900
Thailand	200	3,000	2,000	8,500	1,250	4,750
Timor-Leste	1	10	5	20		
Tonga		5	1	10	1	5
MODERATE						
Angola	15	150	95	350	20	75
Australia	150	550	1,750	4,000	1,500	3,750
Bhutan		1	-1	15		
Cyprus	1	15	5	65	5	50
Djibouti	-1	1	-5	1	-5	1
Egypt	-150	200	-1,250	550	-700	300

$ Additional economic costs due to climate change (million USD PPP) - yearly average

⚡ Additional/reduced energy load due to climate change (GWh) - yearly average

CLIMATE VULNERABILITY

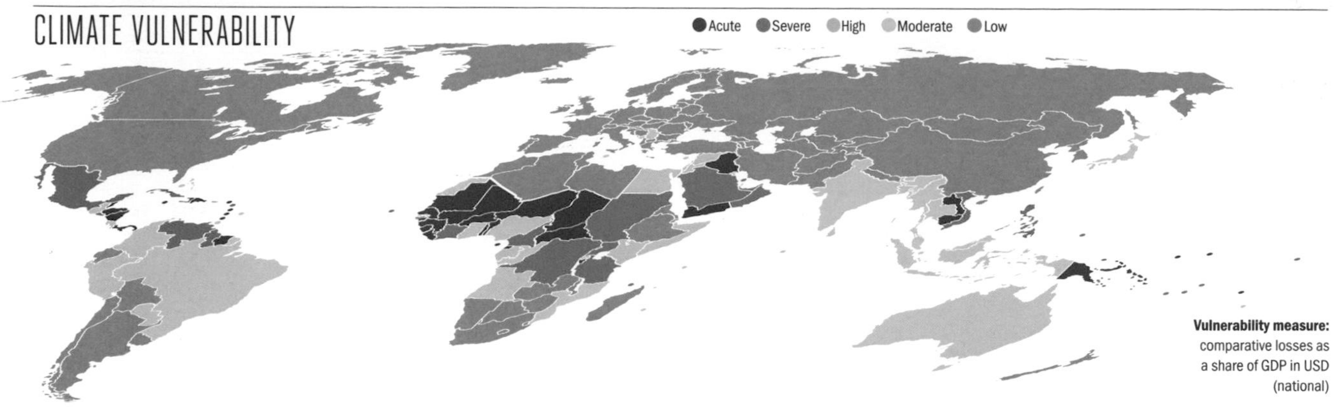

Vulnerability measure: comparative losses as a share of GDP in USD (national)

CLIMATE UNCERTAINTY

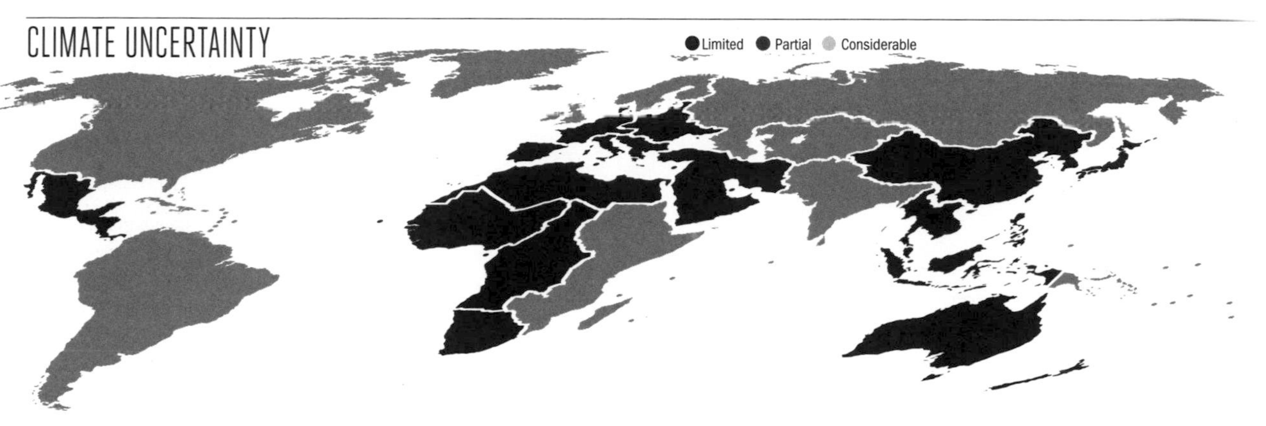

	$					
COUNTRY	2010	2030	2010	2030	2010	2030
Gabon	5	35	30	70	5	15
Indonesia	150	1,750	2,250	7,000	1,750	5,750
Israel	5	150	55	400	45	300
Japan	250	750	1,250	2,500	550	1,000
Jordan	-5	45	-50	95	-30	55
Kenya	-10	15	-60	35	-25	15
Maldives		5	-1	25	-1	20
Mauritius	1	20	20	45	10	30
Peru	5	450	35	900	10	200
Rwanda	-1	5	-15	10	-5	1
Seychelles		1	5	10	1	5
Somalia	-1	1	-10	5	-5	1
Sri Lanka	5	100	150	600	70	300
Syria	-25	55	-200	100	-100	70
Trinidad and Tobago	1	40	100	400	75	300
LOW						
Afghanistan	-30	-150	-650	-800	-150	-200
Albania	-20	-100	-95	-150	-1	-1
Algeria	-300	-1,750	-3,000	-4,500	-1,750	-2,750
Argentina	-65	-350	-3,000	-3,750	-1,000	-1,500
Armenia	-25	-150	-200	-300	-20	-40
Austria	-500	-1,500	-2,500	-4,750	-450	-850
Azerbaijan	-35	-200	-250	-400	-150	-250
Belarus	-350	-2,250	-1,750	-3,500	-1,500	-2,750
Belgium	-600	-1,750	-3,000	-5,250	-700	-1,250
Bolivia	-100	-800	-900	-1,750	-350	-650
Bosnia and Herzegovina	-85	-500	-450	-800	-350	-600
Botswana	-5	-30	-70	-100	-90	-150
Bulgaria	-250	-1,500	-1,250	-2,250	-800	-1,500
Canada	-550	-1,500	-6,750	-15,000	-1,250	-2,250
Chile	-400	-2,750	-2,000	-3,750	-850	-1,500
China	-2,750	-20,000	-60,000	-80,000	-50,000	-65,000
Croatia	-75	-450	-700	-1,250	-250	-400
Czech Republic	-700	-4,250	-3,500	-6,500	-2,500	-4,750
Denmark	-900	-2,500	-2,250	-4,000	-1,250	-2,500
Ecuador	-30	-10	-350	-20	-95	-5
Eritrea	-20	-100	-150	-300	-100	-200
Estonia	-40	-250	-150	-300	-150	-300
Ethiopia	-35	-200	-900	-1,500	-100	-150
Finland	-550	-1,500	-3,000	-5,500	-1,000	-1,750
France	-2,250	-6,250	-15,000	-25,000	-1,250	-2,000
Georgia	-1	-5	-5	-10	-1	-1
Germany	-8,000	-20,000	-30,000	-55,000	-15,000	-30,000
Greece	-25	-45	-250	-250	-200	-200
Hungary	-350	-2,250	-1,500	-2,750	-750	-1,250
Iceland	-40	-100	-150	-300		
Iran	-100	-350	-2,000	-2,000	-1,250	-1,250
Ireland	-300	-850	-1,250	-2,000	-500	-900
Italy	-2,000	-5,250	-6,500	-10,000	-3,250	-5,750
Kazakhstan	-150	-850	-2,500	-4,750	-2,500	-5,000
Kyrgyzstan	-10	-75	-250	-400	-20	-40
Latvia	-150	-950	-600	-1,000	-100	-200
Lebanon	-10	-15	-85	-30	-85	-20
Lesotho	-1	-10	-20	-35		
Libya	-55	-200	-500	-450	-500	-450
Lithuania	-300	-1,750	-1,250	-2,000	950	1,760
Luxembourg	-35	-100	-150	-300	-70	-150
Macedonia	-40	-250	-200	-350	-200	-300
Madagascar	-40	-150	-150	-200	-50	-60
Malawi	-1	-10	-80	-100	-10	10
Moldova	-65	-450	-350	-650	-250	-500
Mongolia	-40	-450	-350	-750	-500	-1,000
Morocco	-200	-1,000	-1,750	-2,500	-1,250	-1,750
Namibia	-15	-70	-100	-200	-25	-40
Nepal	-15	-80	-250	-450	-1	-1
Netherlands	-1,250	-3,500	-5,250	-9,500	-2,500	-4,500
New Zealand	-65	-200	-400	-750	-65	-150
North Korea	-150	-1,250	-1,250	-2,250	-650	-1,250
Norway	-350	-1,000	-2,250	-4,250	-35	-65
Pakistan	-65	-75	-1,500	-400	-700	-200
Poland	-1,250	-8,250	-6,750	-10,000	-7,000	-15,000
Portugal	-150	-400	-700	-1,250	-300	-550
Romania	-200	-1,250	-1,750	-3,250	-1,000	-2,000
Russia	-2,250	-15,000	-20,000	-45,000	-15,000	-25,000
Slovakia	-300	-1,750	-1,250	-2,500	-400	-750
Slovenia	-100	-650	-550	-1,000	-200	-400
South Africa	-200	-1,000	-3,250	-5,500	-3,000	-5,250
South Korea	-150	-1,250	-1,750	-3,500	-950	-2,000
Spain	-500	-1,250	-2,500	-4,000	-800	-1,250
Swaziland	-1	-15	-30	-50	-1	-1
Sweden	-1,250	-3,250	-5,000	-9,000	-150	-300
Switzerland	-400	-1,250	-2,750	-5,000	-20	-30
Tajikistan	-5	-15	-95	-90	-1	-1
Tunisia	-100	-550	-1,000	-1,500	-600	-850
Turkey	-550	-1,250	-3,250	-5,250	-1,750	-2,750
Turkmenistan	-5	-25	-100	150	100	-100
Ukraine	-1,250	-8,000	-6,250	-15,000	-3,000	-5,750
United Kingdom	-4,250	-10,000	-20,000	-35,000	-9,000	-15,000
United States	-650	-1,000	-5,750	-5,750	-3,500	-3,500
Uruguay	-40	-200	-250	-300	-60	-85
Uzbekistan	-40	-150	-750	-850	-500	-550
Zambia	-1	-5	-55	-45		
Zimbabwe	-30	-150	-250	-400	-150	-250

Additional CO_2 generated/reduced for heating and cooling due to climate change (Kt CO_2) - yearly average

LABOUR PRODUCTIVITY

ESTIMATES GLOBAL CLIMATE IMPACT

2010 EFFECT TODAY

USD **LOSS** PER YEAR **300** BILLION

2030 EFFECT TOMORROW

USD **LOSS** PER YEAR **2.5** TRILLION

ECONOMIC IMPACT

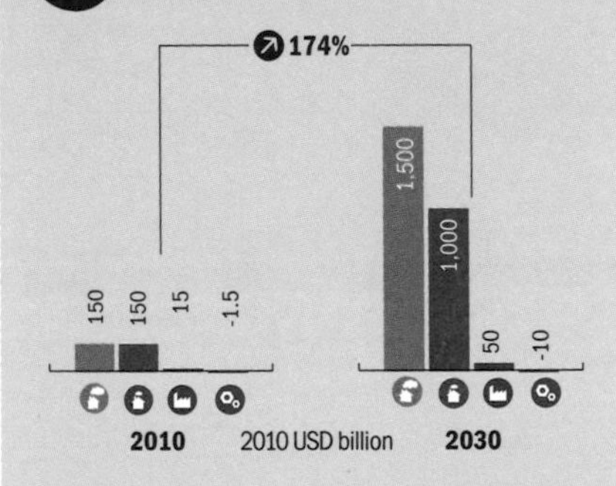

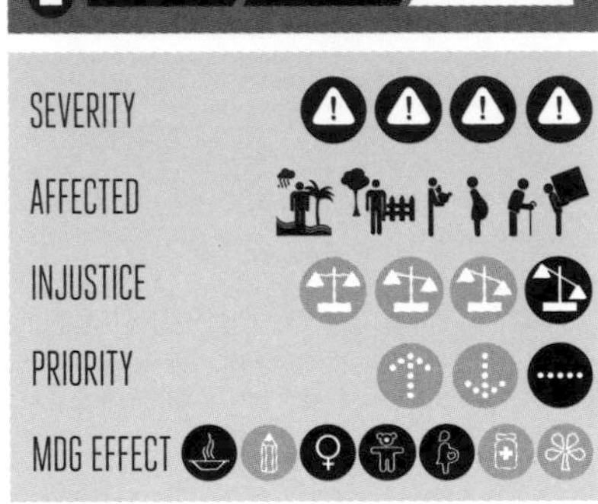

- People work less productively in hot conditions
- As the workplace warms, occupational heat exposure standards defined by the International Organization for Standardization (ISO) and other bodies are being breached
- Heat stress affects employees working outdoors or in non-cooled environments, except for the coldest and highest-altitude areas
- Effects are most serious for subsistence farmers in developing countries who cannot avoid daytime outdoor work
- Adapting to these changes can be cost-effective, such as through sun protection measures, but the full extent of adaptation is not well studied and could be extremely limited, especially for outdoor workers
- For indoor situations, air conditioning or insulation would need to be increased, but equally incur a cost

RELATIVE IMPACT

HOTSPOTS

2010		2030
55	INDIA	450
40	CHINA	450
35	MEXICO	250
30	INDONESIA	250
15	THAILAND	150

GEOPOLITICAL VULNERABILITY

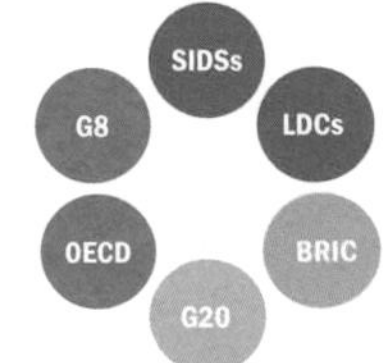

Economic Cost (2010 PPP non-discounted)
Developing Country Low Emitters
Developed
Developing Country High Emitters
Other Industrialized

$ = Losses per 10,000 USD of GDP

Change in relation to overall global population and/or GDP

$ = Billions of USD (2010 PPP non-discounted)

Labour productivity is one of the principal factors in contemporary economics, and a generalized loss of productivity results in economic loss (Samuelson and Nordhaus, 1948; Solow, 1956). Workers are less efficient and less productive when subjected to excess heat both outdoors and in inadequately climate-controlled working conditions (Ramsey, 1995; Pilcher et al., 2002; Niemelä et al., 2002; Hancock et al., 2007; Su et al., 2009). International ergonomic standards define highly specific thermal conditions for differing degrees of occupational exertion and stipulate clear threshold limits (ISO, 1989). Similar national standards are effective since the mid-1980s (NIOSH, 1986). Precise directives for personnel heat stress management are also imbedded in military operational guidelines, since it may affect combat outcomes (USDAAF, 2003). Science is more certain about the warming of the planet than any other aspect of climate change (IPCC, 2007). As the increase in hot days and hot nights continues, worker heat stress has the potential to become a significant drain on the world economy (Hansen et al., 2012; Kjellstrom et al., 2009a). Adapting to labour productivity impacts is costly, but not doing so will result in further costs through deteriorating health, cooling costs, or slower gains in competitiveness (Hanna et al., 2011a; CDC, 2008; Kjellstrom ed., 2009). Thus, incentives to adapt are high, but may be out of reach for three-quarters of the world's developing poor, who live in rural areas with few options (Kjellstrom et al., 2009b; Ravallion et al., 2007).

CLIMATE MECHANISM

As the planet warms, thresholds regulated in international and national occupational standards are increasing. Unless measures are taken, more hours of work will be needed to accomplish the same tasks, or more workers to achieve the same output (Kjellstrom et al., 2009a-b). Thermally optimal working conditions increase productivity (Fisk, 2000). Incremental increases in temperature are well understood, with business-as-usual economic development set to raise the average temperature by 3°C (5°F) above today's levels in 50-60 years (Betts et al., 2009). An additional 4°C (7°F) above that level—not ruled out for this century—would make outdoor activities of any kind impossible in large tropical areas of human habitation (Sokolov et al., 2009; Sherwood and Huber, 2010).

IMPACTS

The global impact of climate change on labour productivity is already estimated to cost the world economy 300 billion dollars a year—around 0.5% of global GDP. It is overwhelmingly the single most significant negative impact included in this assessment.

Hot and humid tropical and sub-tropical countries of Africa, Asia, Latin America, and the Pacific are already severely affected. The greatest total losses affect the world's major emerging economies: China, India, Indonesia, and Mexico, whose development due to labour productivity set-backs alone could be impeded by more than 200 billion dollars a year by 2030, when China and India's annual losses could approach half a trillion dollars each.

Approximately 0.6°C (1°F) of heat absorbed by the world's oceans will be released back into the atmosphere in the coming decades, effectively committing the world to a labour productivity loss estimated to reach 2.5 trillion dollars a year by 2030, stunting global GDP by over 1% (Hansen et al., 2005). Parts of West and Central Africa may even have 6% lower levels of GDP by 2030. Comparatively few people in colder zones of the planet, such as Australia and the United States, are expected to reap a modest gain in productivity: 3 billion dollars in 2010 and 18 billion dollars in 2030. The skewed workforce structure of developed economies, heavily reliant on low-exertion indoor work reduces vulnerability. However, numerous studies also indicate concern for exposed workers in developed countries (Graff Zivan and Neidell, 2011; Hanna et al., 2011a; Hübler et al., 2007).

THE BROADER CONTEXT

Labour productivity drives profitability and higher living standards (Ingene et al., 2010). Labour productivity is surging almost everywhere, even in the world's wealthiest and slowest growing economies (Jorgenson and Vu, 2011; OECD, 2012). Comparisons of labour productivity growth between the US (faster) and Europe (slower) have shown the importance of information technology (IT) as a positive driver (Ark

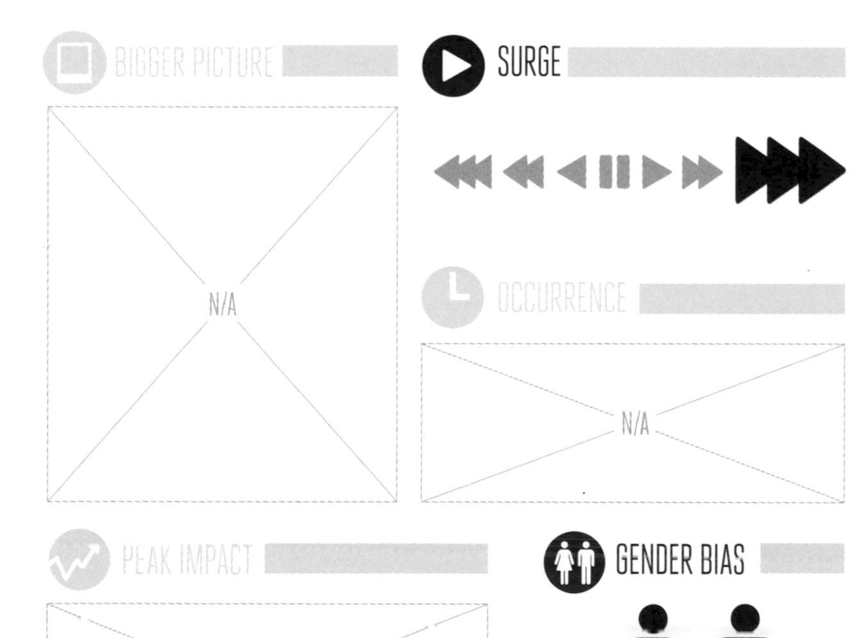

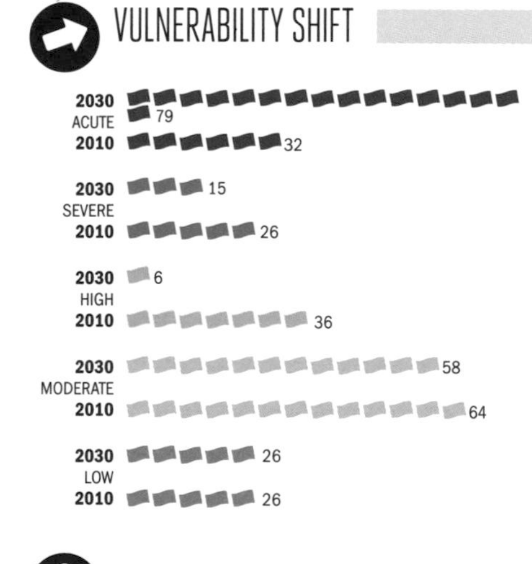

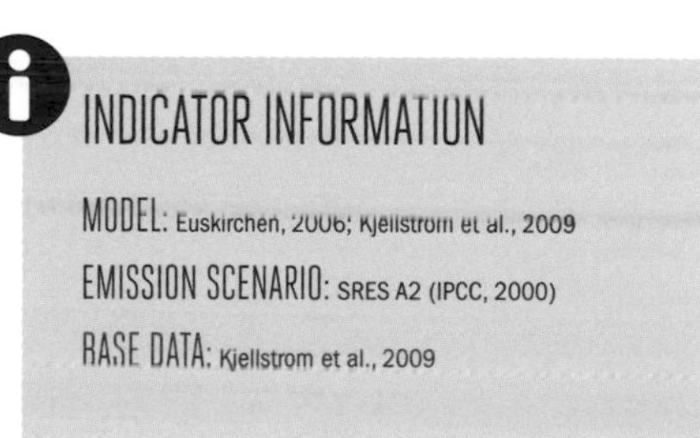

= 5 countries (rounded)

Acute Severe High Moderate Low

et al., 2008; Holman et al., 2008). Above all, climate change is limiting the productivity potential otherwise achievable by developing countries, as they make structural shifts in workforce employment towards higher productivity economic sectors (Kjellstrom et al., 2009a; McMillan and Rodrik, 2012).

VULNERABILITIES AND WIDER OUTCOMES

Geographical and structural vulnerabilities are determined by levels of income or human development. Geography is important since only the coldest zones experience gains, while the hottest ones approach the limits of physiological habitability (Sherwood and Huber, 2010). Structurally, economies with mostly outdoor workers are particularly vulnerable, as are economies with slower industrialization rates and few climate controlled workspaces—middle and low-income countries (Kjellstrom et al., 2009d). Some evidence indicates that women are less resistant to heat stress, while men are more exposed, due to the proportion of men in heavy, outdoor work (Luecke, 2006; ILO, 2011). Subsistence farmers typically inhabit geographically vulnerable regions and would need to commit to higher levels of activity in order to deliver equal output; however, since they need to see the land, displacing their working shifts into the cooler night hours is impossible (Kjellstrom ed., 2009). This raises food security concerns. Nutrition can compound matters by contributing to, or detracting from, labour productivity (Maturu, 1979).

RESPONSES

Six key strategy and measurement areas for adapting to growing thermal stress on the workforce follow:

1. Education and awareness campaigns directed at behavioural change of employees and workers to drink water (hydrate) and minimize sun exposure; e.g., municipal initiatives to increase tree cover and shade, or movable screens (McKinnon and Utley, 2005);
2. Strengthened labour institutions, guidelines, protection, regulations, and labour market policies for workers (Crowe et al. 2010; ILO, 2011);
3. Climate control to increase use of air conditioning or building insulation systems, assisting some indoor workers; not all indoor workplaces can be adequately cooled;
4. Gaining productivity by expanding use of IT, improving capital equipment, or modernizing agricultural technology (Storm and Naastepad, 2009; Wacker et al., 2006; Restuccia et al., 2004);
5. Fiscal and regulatory intervention to stimulate a faster structural transition of the economy away from outdoor labour; e.g., coordinating industrial systems or transitioning from natural resource-intensive growth plans that detract from macroeconomic productivity gains (Storm and Naastepad, 2009; McMillan and Rodrik, 2012);
6. Promotion of individual health to improve body thermal responses (Chan et al., 2012).

THE INDICATOR

Certainty about increasing temperature, the main climate variable at play, contributes to the robustness of the indicator, although humidity levels are another important determiner of thermal stress and are less certain (Wang et al., 2010). The indicator relies on a global/sub-regional scale model for estimating the loss of labour productivity, based on international labour standards and estimates of wet bulb globe temperature (WBGT) change for populations assumed to be acclimatized (Kjellstrom et al., 2009a). It takes into account both the productivity of outdoor and indoor workers, although the heaviest forms of labour are not considered. The changing structure of the workforce over time, in particular, the industrial shift of developing countries away from outdoor agriculture is also factored in. Productivity gains to countries in high latitudes that will experience a reduction in extreme cold were also accounted for, over and above the base model (Euskirchen et al., 2006).

ESTIMATES COUNTRY-LEVEL IMPACT

COUNTRY	$ 2010	$ 2030	2010	2030
ACUTE				
Afghanistan	350	3,000	29%	23%
Angola	2,500	15,000	52%	43%
Antigua and Barbuda	25	200	49%	38%
Bahamas	150	1,250	44%	35%
Bangladesh	3,500	30,000	44%	34%
Barbados	90	700	45%	35%
Belize	40	300	41%	32%
Benin	400	2,750	59%	48%
Bhutan	55	400	44%	34%
Burkina Faso	600	4,000	67%	54%
Cambodia	900	9,250	52%	40%
Cameroon	1,250	8,750	55%	45%
Cape Verde	60	400	50%	41%
Central African Republic	75	500	59%	48%
Chad	550	3,750	55%	45%
Colombia	9,750	75,000	40%	31%
Congo	350	2,500	53%	43%
Costa Rica	1,250	9,000	40%	31%
Cote d,Ivoire	1,000	7,250	53%	43%
Cuba	1,750	15,000	38%	30%
Dominica	15	100	49%	38%
Dominican Republic	1,250	9,500	38%	30%
DR Congo	500	3,250	54%	44%
El Salvador	950	7,500	38%	30%
Equatorial Guinea	500	3,250	65%	53%
Fiji	75	600	27%	18%
Gabon	500	3,250	41%	33%
Gambia	100	700	59%	48%
Ghana	2,000	15,000	55%	45%
Grenada	20	150	49%	38%
Guatemala	1,500	10,000	44%	34%
Guinea	350	2,000	57%	47%
Guinea-Bissau	55	350	55%	45%
Guyana	80	600	37%	29%
Haiti	150	1,250	41%	32%
Honduras	750	5,750	40%	31%
India	55,000	450,000	35%	27%
Indonesia	30,000	250,000	40%	31%
Jamaica	350	2,500	39%	30%
Kiribati	10	90	33%	23%
Laos	450	4,750	49%	38%
Liberia	50	350	48%	39%
Malaysia	10,000	95,000	37%	29%
Maldives	75	550	37%	28%
Mali	500	3,250	40%	32%
Marshall Islands	5	45	33%	23%
Mauritania	200	1,250	30%	24%
Mauritius	550	3,500	35%	27%
Mexico	35,000	250,000	39%	30%
Micronesia	10	90	33%	23%
Myanmar	2,250	15,000	48%	37%
Nepal	500	3,750	53%	41%
Nicaragua	400	3,000	40%	31%
Niger	350	2,250	50%	41%
Nigeria	10,000	75,000	42%	34%
Pakistan	6,500	50,000	33%	25%
Palau	5	25	33%	23%
Panama	1,000	7,750	41%	32%
Papua New Guinea	300	2,250	33%	23%
Philippines	10,000	85,000	38%	29%
Saint Lucia	30	250	49%	38%
Saint Vincent	20	150	49%	38%
Samoa	20	150	33%	23%
Sao Tome and Principe	10	60	58%	47%
Senegal	700	4,750	57%	46%
Seychelles	60	400	45%	35%
Sierra Leone	150	900	54%	44%
Solomon Islands	30	250	30%	21%
Sri Lanka	3,000	25,000	33%	26%
Suriname	70	500	33%	25%
Thailand	15,000	150,000	45%	35%
Timor-Leste	90	750	35%	27%
Togo	200	1,250	61%	50%
Tonga	15	100	33%	23%
Trinidad and Tobago	400	3,000	43%	34%
Tuvalu	1	5	33%	23%
Vanuatu	20	150	33%	23%
Venezuela	8,000	60,000	41%	32%
Vietnam	8,000	85,000	48%	37%
SEVERE				
Burundi	35	250	61%	50%
Comoros	10	55	43%	35%
Djibouti	20	150	56%	46%
Eritrea	40	250	62%	51%
Ethiopia	950	6,000	64%	52%
Kenya	700	4,750	48%	39%
Madagascar	200	1,250	67%	55%
Malawi	150	900	61%	50%
Mozambique	250	1,500	63%	51%
Rwanda	150	850	68%	55%
Somalia	65	400	42%	34%
Sudan/South Sudan	1,000	7,500	39%	32%
Tanzania	650	4,000	63%	51%
Uganda	450	3,000	60%	48%
Zambia	200	1,500	54%	43%

$ Additional economic costs due to climate change (million USD PPP) - yearly average

CLIMATE VULNERABILITY

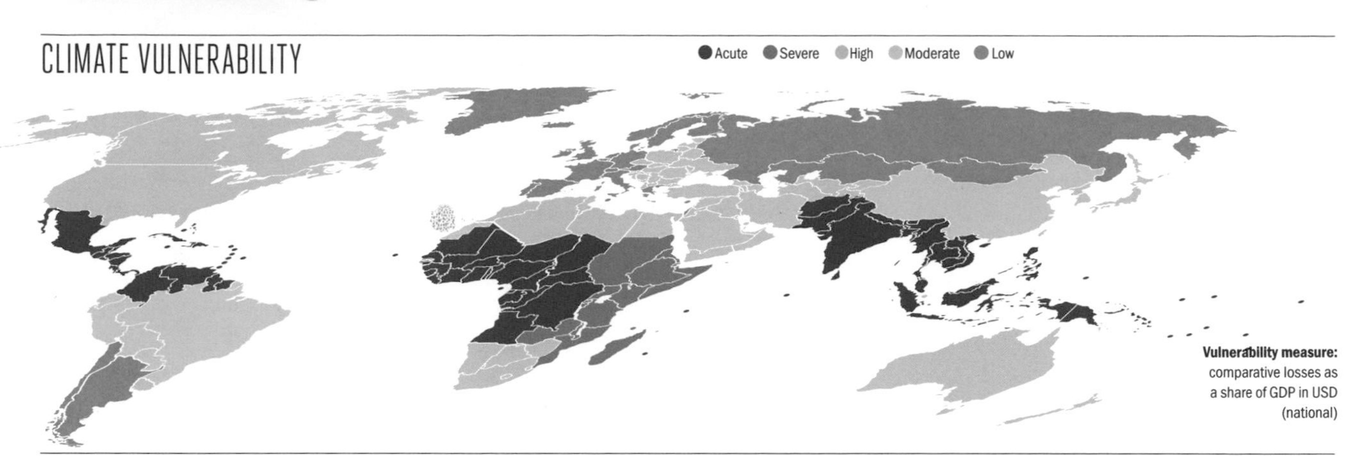

CLIMATE UNCERTAINTY

COUNTRY	$ 2010	$ 2030	🛈 2010	🛈 2030
HIGH				
Bolivia	200	1,750	46%	36%
Brazil	6,000	45,000	43%	34%
China	40,000	450,000	36%	25%
Ecuador	500	4,000	43%	33%
Paraguay	90	700	46%	36%
Peru	1,250	9,500	48%	37%
MODERATE				
Albania	1	5	5%	5%
Algeria	100	750	18%	12%
Armenia	5	40	25%	19%
Australia	45	100	6%	6%
Azerbaijan	35	200	36%	27%
Bahrain	10	60	31%	21%
Belarus	15	95	5%	5%
Bosnia and Herzegovina	1	5	4%	4%
Botswana	60	400	53%	43%
Brunei	1	15	6%	6%
Bulgaria	1	15	5%	5%
Canada	300	850	7%	7%
Croatia	1	15	5%	5%
Czech Republic	5	40	5%	5%
Egypt	200	1,000	21%	14%
Estonia	5	20	5%	5%
Georgia	10	60	32%	24%
Hungary	5	30	5%	5%
Iran	400	2,750	19%	13%
Iraq	30	250	16%	11%
Japan	400	1,000	6%	6%
Jordan	10	70	17%	12%
Kuwait	55	350	31%	21%
Kyrgyzstan	5	25	36%	27%
Latvia	5	25	5%	5%
Lebanon	25	150	20%	13%
Lesotho	5	50	39%	32%
Libya	40	250	23%	16%
Lithuania	5	45	5%	5%
Macedonia	1	5	4%	4%
Moldova	1	10	4%	4%
Morocco	65	450	21%	14%
Namibia	30	200	33%	27%
New Zealand	5	15	6%	6%
North Korea	90	900	37%	26%
Oman	25	150	26%	18%
Poland	15	100	5%	5%
Qatar	65	450	40%	27%
Romania	5	40	5%	5%
Saudi Arabia	200	1,250	22%	15%
Singapore	25	200	6%	6%
Slovakia	1	20	5%	5%
Slovenia	1	10	5%	5%
South Africa	1,250	7,250	32%	27%
South Korea	150	1,000	6%	6%
Swaziland	15	85	36%	30%
Syria	35	200	18%	12%
Tajikistan	5	25	35%	26%
Tunisia	40	250	19%	13%
Turkey	400	1,250	20%	14%
Turkmenistan	15	90	32%	24%
Ukraine	30	200	5%	5%
United Arab Emirates	95	600	36%	24%
United States	15,000	50,000	6%	6%
Uruguay	10	75	41%	32%
Uzbekistan	25	150	32%	24%
Yemen	20	150	20%	13%
Zimbabwe	25	150	69%	56%
LOW				
Argentina	-150	-1,000	38%	29%
Austria			6%	6%
Belgium			5%	5%
Chile	-50	-400	37%	29%
Cyprus			6%	6%
Denmark			6%	6%
Finland	-150	-500	6%	6%
France			5%	5%
Germany			6%	6%
Greece			5%	5%
Iceland	-10	-25	7%	7%
Ireland			5%	5%
Israel			5%	5%
Italy			4%	4%
Kazakhstan	-250	-1,750	40%	30%
Luxembourg			5%	5%
Malta			5%	5%
Mongolia	-15	-150	34%	26%
Netherlands			6%	6%
Norway	-200	-650	6%	6%
Portugal			6%	6%
Russia	-2,000	-15,000	6%	6%
Spain			5%	5%
Sweden	-300	-950	6%	6%
Switzerland			6%	6%
United Kingdom			6%	6%

🛈 Share of workforce particularly affected by climate change (%) - yearly average

PERMAFROST

ESTIMATES GLOBAL CLIMATE IMPACT

2010 EFFECT TODAY

USD LOSS PER YEAR **30** BILLION

2030 EFFECT TOMORROW

USD LOSS PER YEAR **150** BILLION

ECONOMIC IMPACT

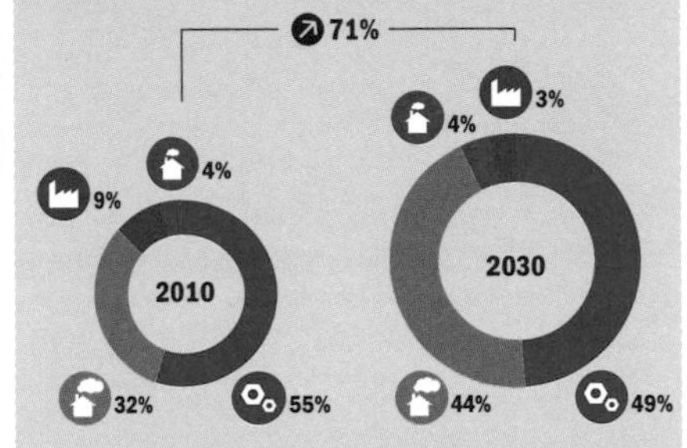

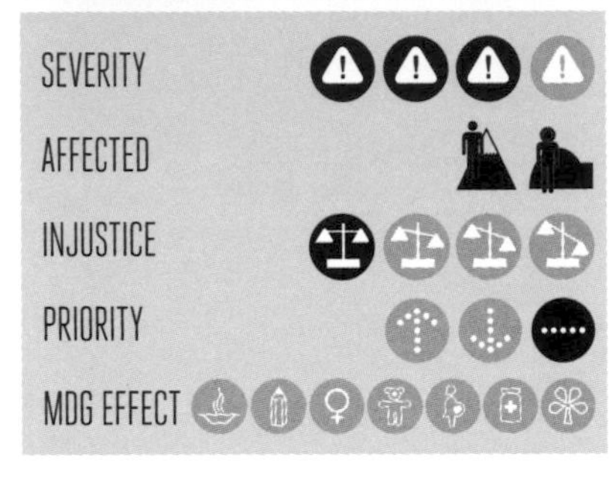

SEVERITY

AFFECTED

INJUSTICE

PRIORITY

MDG EFFECT

- One-quarter of the northern hemisphere's land is permanently frozen or frozen for extended periods
- The planet's warming has been most rapid in the far north, where rising heat simply melts permanently frozen land
- Infrastructure of every kind, from buildings, roads, and railways, to pipelines, airports, and power lines come under stress or are damaged when the rate of melting is accelerated
- The entire infrastructure of the far north and the world's coldest zones is affected
- Overall, the effect is estimated to accelerate by around 10–20% the rate of wear and tear on all exposed infrastructure in the near term

RELATIVE IMPACT

2010	437	4
2030	581	7

HOTSPOTS

2010	$	2030
15,000	RUSSIA	75,000
9,250	CHINA	65,000
600	MONGOLIA	4,000
1,750	CANADA	3,500
400	PAKISTAN	2,000

GEOPOLITICAL VULNERABILITY

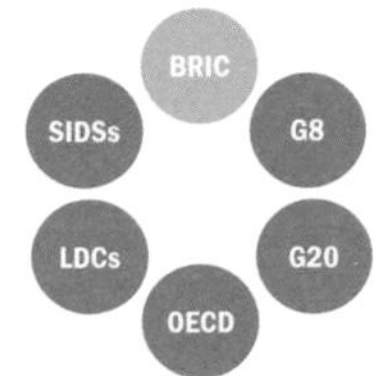

Economic Cost (2010 PPP non-discounted)
Developing Country Low Emitters
Developed
Developing Country High Emitters
Other Industrialized

$ = Losses per 10,000 USD of GDP

Change in relation to overall global population and/or GDP

$ = Millions of USD (2010 PPP non-discounted)

Permafrost thawing is one impact of climate change that does not spare some of the world's most advanced and industrialized countries. In some places rising heat is causing dry lands to degrade into desert. In the coldest parts of the world, the heat is instead causing land to melt and sink, damaging infrastructure as it subsides (Larsen and Goldsmith, 2007). Every conceivable type of infrastructure is at risk as permafrost melts, including buildings, roads, railways, and oil pipelines (Xu et al., 2010; Lin, 2011M; Feng and Liu, 2012). Preserving this infrastructure as growing heat adds to the stress is a major challenge for engineers and a serious cost for local communities (McGuire, 2009). In Alaska, for instance, two-thirds of the state roads budget is spent on permafrost repair alone (Stidger, 2001). In worst case scenarios, it is estimated that extreme permafrost thaw could force the relocation of entire communities (Romanovsky et al., 2010). Permafrost thawing through accelerated infrastructure replacement and repair will impose significant cost burdens on the world's coldest communities.

CLIMATE MECHANISM

As temperatures rise, regions nearer the poles are heating up the fastest (IPCC, 2007). Much of the land within the Arctic Circle is frozen on a permanent basis, or for more than 1–2 years. The permafrost region currently covers about one-quarter of earth's land area (Nelson et al., 2002); however, it is home to only a fraction of the world's population (Hoekstra et al., 2010). One-quarter of the land area of the northern hemisphere has a subterranean layer of ice built up under the soil which can melt when temperatures rise (Anisimov, 2009). The warming planet thaws otherwise permanently frozen land, destabilizes it, alters its ecosystem, and compromises the structural integrity of any buildings or infrastructure that have been constructed in these zones (Romanovsky et al., 2010). In this way, climate change is already accelerating the process by which key infrastructure in these areas requires repair or replacement (Larsen and Goldsmith, 2007).

IMPACTS

The impact of climate change on infrastructure in affected permafrost zones is estimated globally at 30 billion dollars a year in 2010. With the expected increase in temperatures through to 2030, losses associated with permafrost thawing are estimated to grow as a share of global GDP, amounting to approximately 150 billion dollars a year.

Countries worst affected include the US (because of Alaska), Canada, China (because of Tibet), Mongolia, Russia, and a number of Central Asian states (because of the Himalayas). As climate change intensifies, the same group of countries continues to be affected.

The largest total losses are incurred in Russia, China, Mongolia, and Canada. Losses for Russia and China are currently estimated at around 20 and 10 billion dollars respectively, and should grow to over 60 billion dollars each year by 2030.

Mongolia, Kyrgyzstan, and Bhutan are estimated to suffer the most severe effects as a share of GDP, with Mongolia and Kyrgystan's losses at over 4% of GDP by 2030, and Bhutan's in excess of 1% of GDP.

Some 10 million people are estimated to be affected by the impact of climate change on permafrost globally, a number that will more than double to nearly 25 million by 2030.

THE BROADER CONTEXT

Dealing with some degree of oscillation in permanently frozen land in the coldest zones of the planet is normal (Wei et al., 2009). It is the acceleration in these processes that incurs additional costs as temperatures rise. While the northernmost or coldest regions of the planet are sparsely inhabited, oil and gas exploitation has grown in permafrost regions in and around the Arctic Circle. Planned or constructed high value infrastructure in these regions will face growing risks (Pavlenko and Glukhareva, 2010). The same is true for the multi-billion dollar China–Tibet railway, built over partially unstable land across the Tibetan ranges and plateaux (Yang and Zhu, 2011).

VULNERABILITIES AND WIDER OUTCOMES

Communities and governments maintaining expensive public infrastructure in lower-middle income countries, such as Kyrgyzstan in Central Asia, will face a major development challenge in tackling accelerated infrastructure erosion. There is a lack of clarity on the extent to which insurance

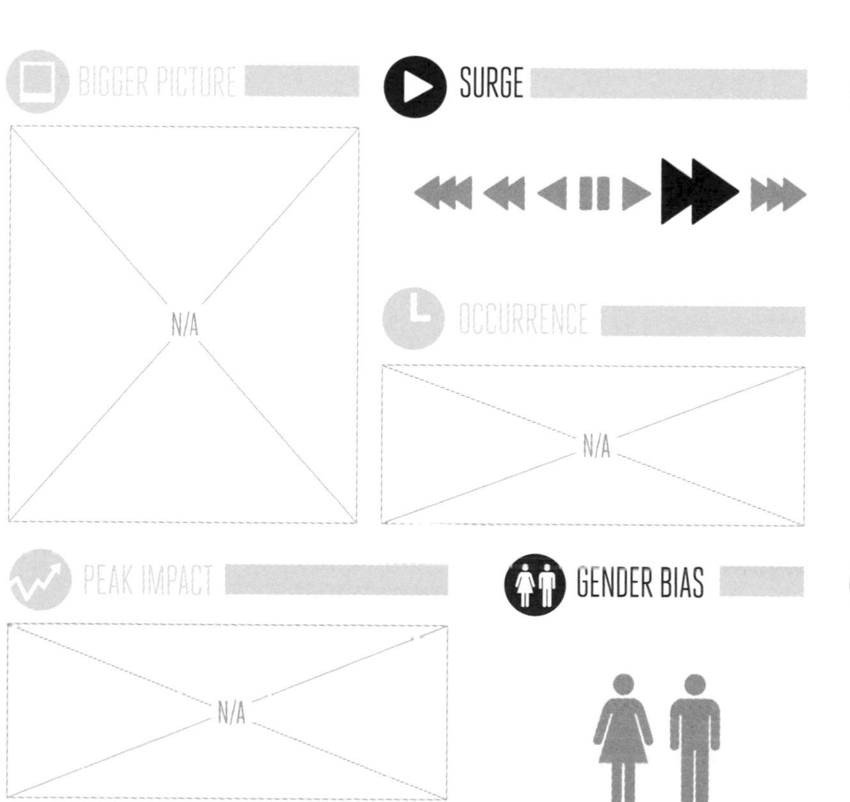

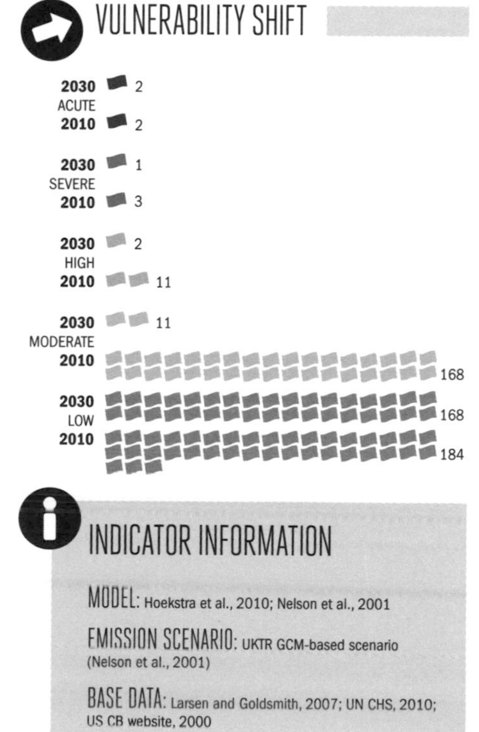

INDICATOR INFORMATION

MODEL: Hoekstra et al., 2010; Nelson et al., 2001

EMISSION SCENARIO: UKTR GCM-based scenario (Nelson et al., 2001)

BASE DATA: Larsen and Goldsmith, 2007; UN CHS, 2010; US CB website, 2000

= 5 countries (rounded)

Acute Severe High Moderate Low

policies are valid for permafrost erosion damage (Mills, 2005; Williams, 2011). Insurance coverage is growing, as incomes of developing countries expand, suggesting that for many of the worst affected areas, including Tibet, Mongolia, and Kyrgyzstan, a lack of insurance will heighten the impact of these changes (Kharas, 2010). Permanently frozen land also stores around half of the potential soil-derived emissions of greenhouse gases (GHGs), mostly in the form of methane, a highly potent GHG. As such, there is mounting concern that, as they thaw, the permafrost regions could become a major unmanageable driver of global climate change (Tarnocai et al., 2009).

RESPONSES

Adaptation to the thawing of permafrost is a challenge. Future planning might make non-essential infrastructure projects in transition zones less of a priority. For all existing infrastructure, there is a predictable accelerated depreciation and replacement cost that must be faced (Larsen and Goldsmith, 2007). Unlike sea-level rise, changes are likely to come faster, and no wall can prevent the retreat of frozen land which, as it thaws, will decimate any built infrastructure in affected areas. However, for certain types of infrastructure, such as pipelines or railways, measures can be taken to mitigate the extent of destabilising effects, especially when designing new infrastructure (Xu et al., 2010; Wei et al., 2009).

Public resources may be considered, for instance, to subsidise or back insurance schemes which allow risk to be managed in a more long-term framework, buffering communities from abrupt losses and enhancing the resilience of highly exposed groups (Verheyen, 2005). In worst cases, community relocation may be necessary (Romanovsky, 2010).

THE INDICATOR

The indicator is understood to be moderately robust. This is because clarity on the climate signal in one of the fastest warming regions of the world is pronounced, and the IPCC's stance on the possibility of extensive damage stemming from permafrost erosion is firm (IPCC, 2007). However, permafrost damage is for now a niche research area at best, and the indicator's robustness is compromised by being based on only one study and model from Alaska (Larsen and Goldsmith, 2007). Further uncertainties relate to the extrapolation of the damage estimations through income (GDP) metrics and population-weighted adjustments in order to simulate the damage effects in the other countries. Assumptions were also made by proxy for non-public infrastructure based on capital values of private infrastructure at risk, which could be an area for further improvement. Given the potential scale of the damage, the topic remains a clear research priority for additional enquiry in all respects.

ESTIMATES COUNTRY-LEVEL IMPACT

COUNTRY	$ 2010	$ 2030	Persons 2010	Persons 2030
ACUTE				
Kyrgyzstan	400	1,750	450,000	850,000
Mongolia	600	4,000	550,000	1,000,000
SEVERE				
Bhutan	45	250	20,000	40,000
HIGH				
Russia	15,000	75,000	4,500,000	9,500,000
Tajikistan	100	500	150,000	250,000
MODERATE				
Afghanistan	20	100	90,000	200,000
Canada	1,750	3,500	350,000	700,000
China	9,250	65,000	4,500,000	9,500,000
Finland	15	30	3,750	7,750
India	100	550	85,000	150,000
Kazakhstan	200	800	75,000	150,000
Nepal	65	300	150,000	300,000
Norway	100	200	20,000	40,000
Pakistan	400	2,000	350,000	750,000
Sweden	85	150	20,000	40,000
United States	650	1,250	90,000	200,000
LOW				
Albania				
Algeria				
Angola				
Antigua and Barbuda				
Argentina				
Armenia				
Australia				
Austria				
Azerbaijan				
Bahamas				
Bahrain				
Bangladesh				
Barbados				
Belarus				
Belgium				
Belize				
Benin				
Bolivia				
Bosnia and Herzegovina				
Botswana				
Brazil				
Brunei				
Bulgaria				
Burkina Faso				
Burundi				
Cambodia				
Cameroon				
Cape Verde				
Central African Republic				
Chad				
Chile				
Colombia				
Comoros				
Congo				
Costa Rica				
Cote d'Ivoire				
Croatia				
Cuba				
Cyprus				
Czech Republic				
Denmark				
Djibouti				
Dominica				
Dominican Republic				
DR Congo				
Ecuador				
Egypt				
El Salvador				
Equatorial Guinea				
Eritrea				
Estonia				
Ethiopia				
Fiji				
France				
Gabon				
Gambia				
Georgia				
Germany				
Ghana				
Greece				
Grenada				
Guatemala				
Guinea				
Guinea-Bissau				
Guyana				
Haiti				
Honduras				
Hungary				
Iceland				
Indonesia				
Iran				
Iraq				
Ireland				
Israel				
Italy				

$ Additional economic costs due to climate change (million USD PPP) - yearly average

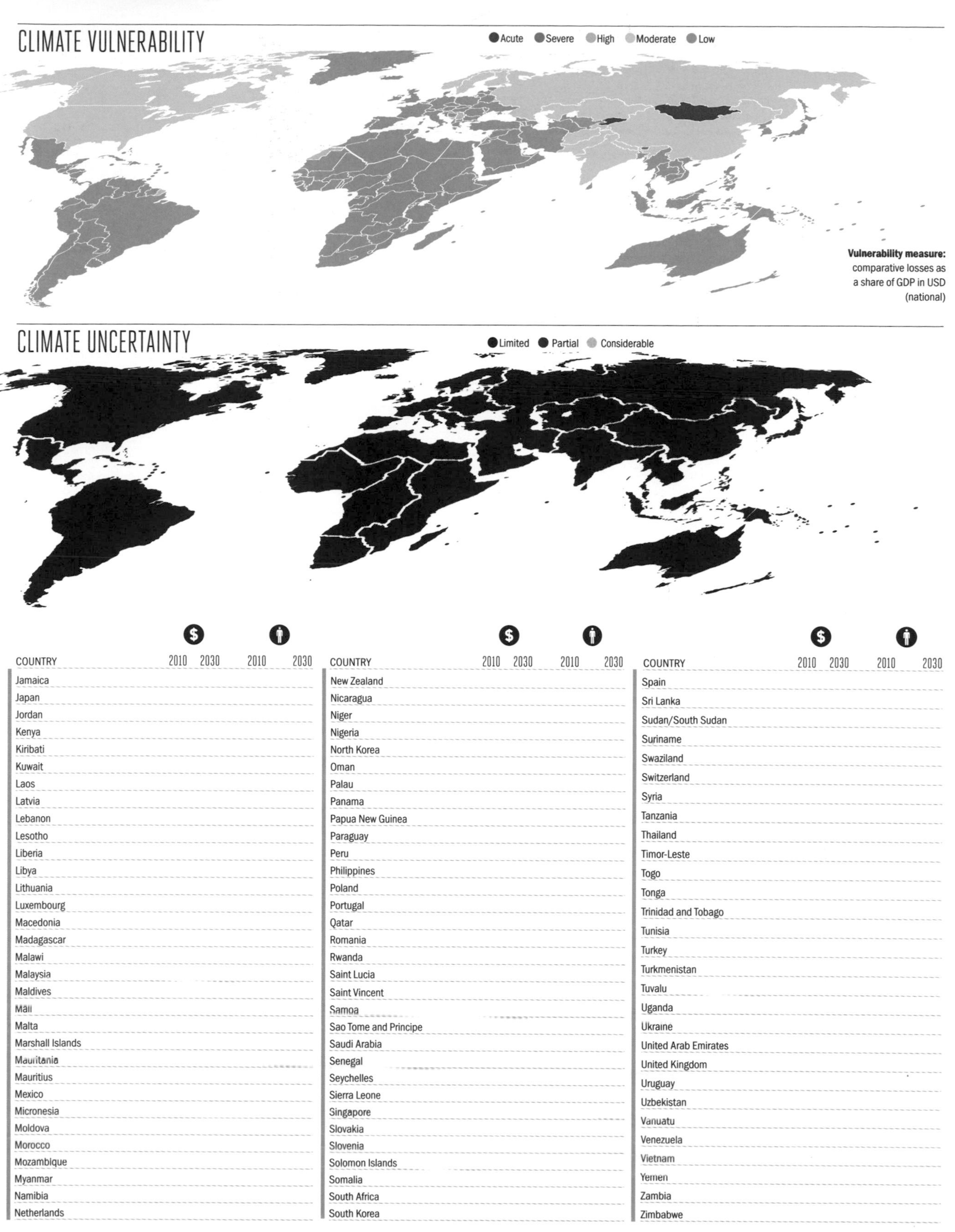

COUNTRY	$ 2010	$ 2030	2010	2030
Jamaica				
Japan				
Jordan				
Kenya				
Kiribati				
Kuwait				
Laos				
Latvia				
Lebanon				
Lesotho				
Liberia				
Libya				
Lithuania				
Luxembourg				
Macedonia				
Madagascar				
Malawi				
Malaysia				
Maldives				
Mali				
Malta				
Marshall Islands				
Mauritania				
Mauritius				
Mexico				
Micronesia				
Moldova				
Morocco				
Mozambique				
Myanmar				
Namibia				
Netherlands				

COUNTRY	$ 2010	$ 2030	2010	2030
New Zealand				
Nicaragua				
Niger				
Nigeria				
North Korea				
Oman				
Palau				
Panama				
Papua New Guinea				
Paraguay				
Peru				
Philippines				
Poland				
Portugal				
Qatar				
Romania				
Rwanda				
Saint Lucia				
Saint Vincent				
Samoa				
Sao Tome and Principe				
Saudi Arabia				
Senegal				
Seychelles				
Sierra Leone				
Singapore				
Slovakia				
Slovenia				
Solomon Islands				
Somalia				
South Africa				
South Korea				

COUNTRY	$ 2010	$ 2030	2010	2030
Spain				
Sri Lanka				
Sudan/South Sudan				
Suriname				
Swaziland				
Switzerland				
Syria				
Tanzania				
Thailand				
Timor-Leste				
Togo				
Tonga				
Trinidad and Tobago				
Tunisia				
Turkey				
Turkmenistan				
Tuvalu				
Uganda				
Ukraine				
United Arab Emirates				
United Kingdom				
Uruguay				
Uzbekistan				
Vanuatu				
Venezuela				
Vietnam				
Yemen				
Zambia				
Zimbabwe				

Additional persons affected due to climate change - yearly average

SEA-LEVEL RISE

ESTIMATES GLOBAL CLIMATE IMPACT

2010 EFFECT TODAY

USD **LOSS** PER YEAR **85 BILLION**

2030 EFFECT TOMORROW

USD **LOSS** PER YEAR **550 BILLION**

ECONOMIC IMPACT

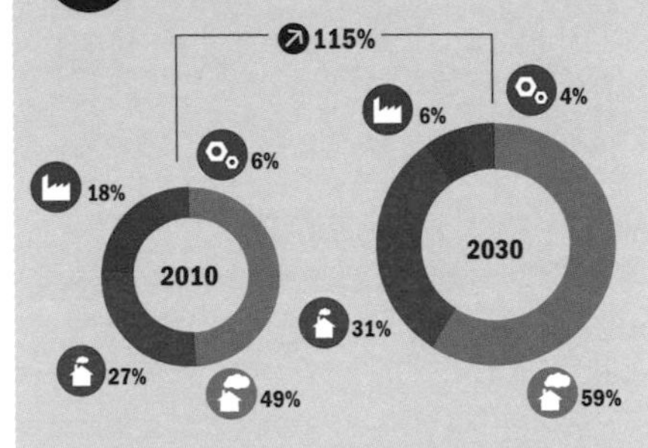

- Melting of the polar ice sheets and mountain ice and glaciers is increasing the amount of water supplied to the oceans, causing sea-levels to rise relative to land
- The oceans heat up together with the atmosphere as the planet warms, and in so doing expand, leading to a greater and growing sea-level rise effect
- The rate of global sea-level rise is gradual—currently about 1cm every three years—but the effects are so comprehensive that its costs are already large-scale and growing
- Tackling sea-level rise is a monumental challenge and will significantly inhibit development in coastal areas attempting to stem growing damage

RELATIVE IMPACT

2010

$$$$$$$$$ 90 | $ 2 2030

HOTSPOTS

2010	$	2030
15,000	**CHINA**	150,000
4,000	**VIETNAM**	40,000
4,500	**INDIA**	30,000
4,500	**ARGENTINA**	25,000
1,250	**BANGLADESH**	20,000

GEOPOLITICAL VULNERABILITY

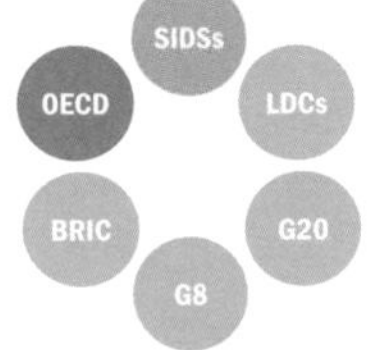

$ Economic Cost (2010 PPP non-discounted)
Developing Country Low Emitters | Developed
Developing Country High Emitters | Other Industrialized

$ = Losses per 1,000 USD of GDP

Change in relation to overall global population and/or GDP

$ = Millions of USD (2010 PPP non-discounted)

Sea-level rise resulting from climate change has the potential to threaten the survival of whole nations, such as low-lying Maldives in the Indian Ocean, of which 80% are one metre or less above sea level; their highest elevation is a sand dune 4 metres above sea-level (Maldives MEEW, 2007). Low-elevation coastal zones, however, are common around the world (CReSIS, 2012). In general, where there is inhabited coastline, there will be vulnerability and economic and social impacts. Sea-level rise is therefore one of the most significant economic effects of climate change. For countries with a substantial proportion of the population and economy situated within reach of the shorefront at low elevation, the impacts of sea-level rise are a constant and crippling economic cost. Scientists have asserted that climate change will "shrink nations and change world maps" (Hansen, 2006).

CLIMATE MECHANISM

As the planet warms and the temperature rises, heat is melting glaciers and ice on land around the world, including the polar ice caps (Olsen et al., 2011). All of the world's glaciers have been in long-term retreat or have already disappeared (NSIDC, 2008). Arctic sea ice used to cover over 7 million square kilometres during the height of summer. As this report went to publication, sea ice was at a record low, close to 3 million km² in the Arctic Sea (NSIDC, 2012). Much of the heat in the atmosphere is also absorbed by the oceans, which release it back into the atmosphere (Hansen et al., 2005). In the meantime, as the oceans absorb more and more heat, they expand in accordance with the basic laws of physics. Viewed from land, this so-called "thermal expansion" is also a significant contributor to sea-level rise (RSNZ, 2010). Overall, sea-level rise is currently about 3mm per year, or 3cm a decade (NASA Climate, 2012). Current estimations point to increases in that rate, with several experts recently estimating a possible maximum of two or more metres of sea-level rise by the end of the century (Pfeffer et al., 2008; Grinstead et al., 2009; Füssel, 2012).

Sea-level rise not only leads to coastal erosion and flooding, it also increases risks from storm surges and seasonal high tides. It can unfavourably increase the salinity of river ways and brackish aquaculture production ponds, contaminate coastal groundwater sources with salt, and damage agricultural production through gradual salt intrusion into the surrounding soil (Nicholls and Cazenave, 2010; Füssel, 2012).

IMPACTS

The global impact of climate-driven sea-level rise on the world's coastlines is estimated to cost 85 billion dollars a year today, increasing to over 500 billion dollars a year by 2030, with a doubling of costs as a share of GDP over this period.

China suffers the largest impact today at 15 billion dollars a year, set to grow to almost 150 billion dollars a year in losses by 2030, reaching 0.3% of China's projected GDP. By 2030, more than 15 countries will experience annual losses around or in excess of 10 billion dollars, including developing countries such as Bangladesh, Indonesia, or Vietnam, as well as developed countries such as the US and South Korea.

Worst affected by share of GDP are small island states, especially in the Pacific, and several coastal African countries. For a handful of countries—the Marshall Islands, Guinea-Bissau, the Solomon Islands, and Kiribati—costs could represent as much as 20% or more of GDP in 2030.

In general, lower-income and least developed countries, especially small island developing states, dominate the ranks of those most vulnerable to the effects of climate-related sea-level rise, with serious implications for human development progress in these areas.

THE BROADER CONTEXt

Coastal erosion and geological subsidence, or the sinking of land due to earth plate tectonics and associated factors, are completely natural phenomena which are part of the basic geological processes sustaining the planet. When land surfaces are lowered near the sea, the result is indistinguishable from sea-level rise, when viewed from a local perspective (Törnqvist et al., 2008).

Likewise, several issues related to the human presence in the environment have serious effects for coastal erosion. Groundwater pumping for irrigation or municipal/industrial purposes near shorelines can cause land to subside or become lower in relation to the sea (Larson et al., 2001). Coastal defences or port structures and other built infrastructure can alter or deflect sea currents and lead to serious erosion in adjacent

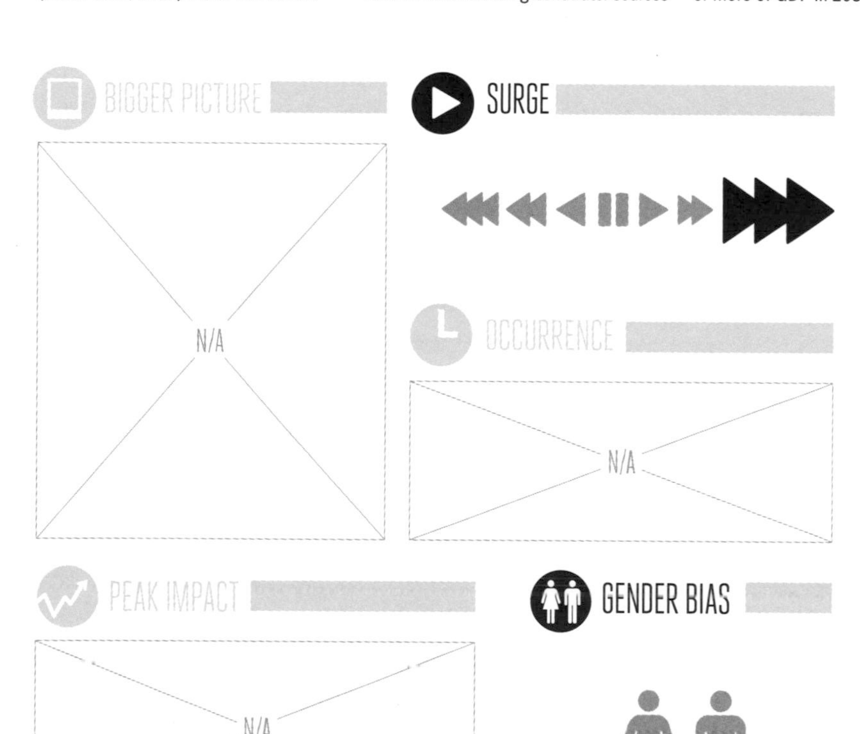

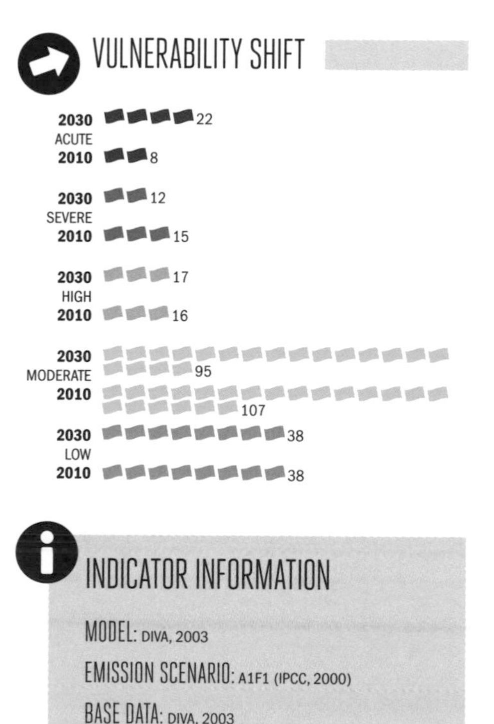

INDICATOR INFORMATION

MODEL: DIVA, 2003

EMISSION SCENARIO: A1F1 (IPCC, 2000)

BASE DATA: DIVA, 2003

= 5 countries (rounded)

Acute Severe High Moderate Low

coastal areas (Appeaning Addo and Labri, 2009). Destruction of coastal ecosystems, such as mangrove forests, reduces coastal integrity and triggers erosion (Wilkinson and Salvat, 2012). In river estuaries, upstream dams for irrigation or in some cases hydro energy can be detrimental to the delta downstream, if river flow is reduced (due to diverted water), or if sediment that would otherwise have flowed to the sea is retained (Ly, 1980; Yang et al., 2005; Boateng, 2009; Baran, 2010; Fredén, 2011).

VULNERABILITIES AND WIDER OUTCOMES

Length of coastline is not the main determinant of vulnerability to sea-level rise. Vulnerability is more closely related to the relative value of land in coastal areas, reflecting the concentration of populations and productive sectors of the economy under stress. It is also closely relates to topography and geology: with current rates of sea-level rise, steep rocky coastlines are much less cause for concern than low-lying, sand-based atolls or river estuaries. Vulnerabilities can be higher, depending on whether or not adjacent communities build coastal defences, which can alter wave dynamics and exacerbate erosion in nearby zones (Appeaning Addo and Labri, 2009). This will pose an important challenge for international adaptation responses along contiguous coastlines under threat, as was illustrated in this report's Ghana country study.

As mentioned earlier, unsustainable resource use, such as water withdrawals that lead to subsidence or the destruction of mangrove forests, only heightens vulnerabilities.

Where populations rely on ground water for irrigation or drinking water, particularly in small islands, salt intrusion is a further serious concern (Werner and Simmons, 2009). Lower-income communities generally cannot marshal the resources needed to protect against the effects of sea-level rise, and so must suffer the consequences of not adapting: loss of land, contamination of water sources, and growing dangers from extreme weather. As is highlighted in both the Ghana and Vietnam country studies in this report, international assistance is most often required to support adaptation. Furthermore, subsistence farmers who may not have their land submerged may see production decrease due to gradual salt intrusion into soils. These effects frustrate poverty reduction efforts in affected areas and drive rural-urban migration (Dasgupta et al., 2009).

RESPONSES

Four different types of approaches can be combined in a variety of ways: 1) coastal defences, whether "hard" through infrastructure defences (gyrones, polders, sea walls, dykes) or "soft", such as sand-banking, ecosystem, or a combination of these; 2) addressing human activities that aggravate sea-level rise, from intensive farming to ground water pumping for irrigation, or upstream dams in delta areas; 3) support programmes for affected communities, such as rainwater harvesting programmes; and 4), retreat or land sacrifices, including relocation and abandonment.

If the value of the land is deemed less than the costs of protecting it, then land is most likely to be let go (DIVA, 2003). However, if communities are involved, they would normally need support to obtain new property and/or migrate and resettle elsewhere (Warner et al., 2009). As mentioned earlier, reducing upstream irrigation loads, and retrofitting dam infrastructure to allow more water and sediment to flow downstream can help counteract localized sea-level rise.

THE INDICATOR

The indictor is deemed robust for several reasons: first, the science is firm on the increase in sea levels over time around the world, as recognized by the IPCC (IPCC, 2007). Second, there is relatively low uncertainty compared to other areas of climate change regarding the scale and rates of change between different models in the near term (Rahmstorf, 2009). Third, the indicator is built on a high-resolution global model (DIVA, 2003). Improvements in the estimation of the complex set of costs involved across countries and in the actual model resolution, now 75km segments, could nevertheless further improve the analysis going forward.

ESTIMATES COUNTRY-LEVEL IMPACT

	$		Persons			
COUNTRY	2010	2030	2010	2030	2010	2030
ACUTE						
Bahamas	300	4,000	90	100	90	200
Eritrea	150	650	10	15	20	55
Gambia	150	750	80	100	40	100
Guinea-Bissau	400	2,250	150	200	50	150
Guyana	200	1,000	150	150	15	40
Kiribati	90	550	80	85	100	250
Liberia	80	400			30	75
Madagascar	850	4,000	100	200	45	100
Maldives	150	900	250	300		
Marshall Islands	90	550	50	55	1	1
Mauritania	250	1,500	15	20	350	900
Micronesia	30	200	15	15		
Mozambique	1,000	5,250	3,250	4,750	100	300
Namibia	10	5,250	1	1	850	2,000
Palau	10	60	5	5	1	1
Papua New Guinea	550	3,250	150	150	550	1,500
Sao Tome and Principe	15	80				
Sierra Leone	200	1,000	45	65	35	85
Solomon Islands	300	1,750	60	65	10	20
Somalia	750	3,750	75	100	45	150
Tuvalu	1	10	5	5		
Vanuatu	100	700	15	20	1	1
SEVERE						
Belize	70	400	20	25	25	40
Cape Verde	40	200	45	65	1	1
Comoros	25	150	20	30		
Fiji	150	800	50	55	10	25
Guinea	250	1,500	5	10	45	100
Iceland	350	700	30	35	40	150
Myanmar	1,750	9,500	2,250	2,500	350	1,250
Nicaragua	400	2,250	15	20	40	100
North Korea	1,750	10,000	1,250	1,250	10	30
Samoa	20	150	15	15		
Timor-Leste	95	600	25		1	
Tonga	20	100	70	75	1	1
HIGH						
Antigua and Barbuda	10	70	55	70	1	1
Argentina	4,500	25,000	650	800	150	300
Bangladesh	1,250	20,000	40,000	45,000	200	450
Cambodia	250	1,750	20	25	20	45
Djibouti	25	150	60	85		1
Dominica	15	95	55	75		1
Estonia	250	1,250	10	10	60	200
Gabon	400	2,000	15	25	150	200
Grenada	15	80	20	25	1	1
Haiti	100	650	100	150	5	15
Honduras	250	1,500	50	65	200	500
Panama	300	2,000	90	100	150	400
Saint Vincent	10	70	20	25		
Senegal	200	1,250	350	550	35	75
Suriname	70	400	80	95	40	100
Uruguay	500	3,250	150	200	5	10
Vietnam	4,000	40,000	20,000	25,000	150	300
MODERATE						
Albania	40	200	45	50	5	5
Algeria	95	550	450	600	40	70
Angola	100	650	550	800	400	950
Australia	800	1,500	2,250	2,250	2,500	7,250
Bahrain	35	95	150	250		1
Barbados	10	35	30	35	1	1
Belgium	350	25	2,250	2,250	10	15
Benin	25	150			60	85
Bosnia and Herzegovina	1	5				
Brazil	3,250	20,000	6,750	8,250	850	2,500
Brunei	50	100	100	150	5	10
Bulgaria	30	150	10	10		
Cameroon	100	850	1,250	1,750	45	100
Canada	1,500	3,500	900	1,000	700	3,000
Chile	550	2,750	400	500	2,000	4,500
China	15,000	150,000	40,000	45,000	250	350
Colombia	350	2,250	400	450	350	600
Congo	30	150	100	150	5	5
Costa Rica	90	650	10	15	55	100
Cote d,Ivoire	150	750			10	25
Croatia	150	700	20	20	25	35
Cuba	550	3,000	350	450	1,500	3,500
Cyprus	20	45	20	20		1
Denmark	550	1,000	1,000	1,250	100	250
Dominican Republic	100	700	30	35	150	300
DR Congo	15	75	1	1	20	50
Ecuador	150	1,000	450	500	400	900
Egypt	1,500	10,000	2,250	3,250	200	450
El Salvador	55	300	50	60	5	15
Equatorial Guinea	50	250			25	60
Finland	85	150	250	250	15	50
France	700	1,250	2,750	2,750	100	150
Georgia	60	300	65	70	50	100
Germany	1,000	1,750	2,750	3,000	85	150
Ghana	200	850			15	35
Greece	250	500	300	350	30	50
Guatemala	60	400	35	45	10	20
India	4,500	30,000	30,000	35,000	450	1,000
Indonesia	2,750	15,000	15,000	15,000	2,000	4,500
Iran	350	2,000	100	150	200	400
Iraq	20	150	250	350	1	1

$ Additional economic costs due to climate change (million USD PPP) - yearly average

Additional persons affected due to climate change - yearly average

CLIMATE VULNERABILITY

Acute · Severe · High · Moderate · Low

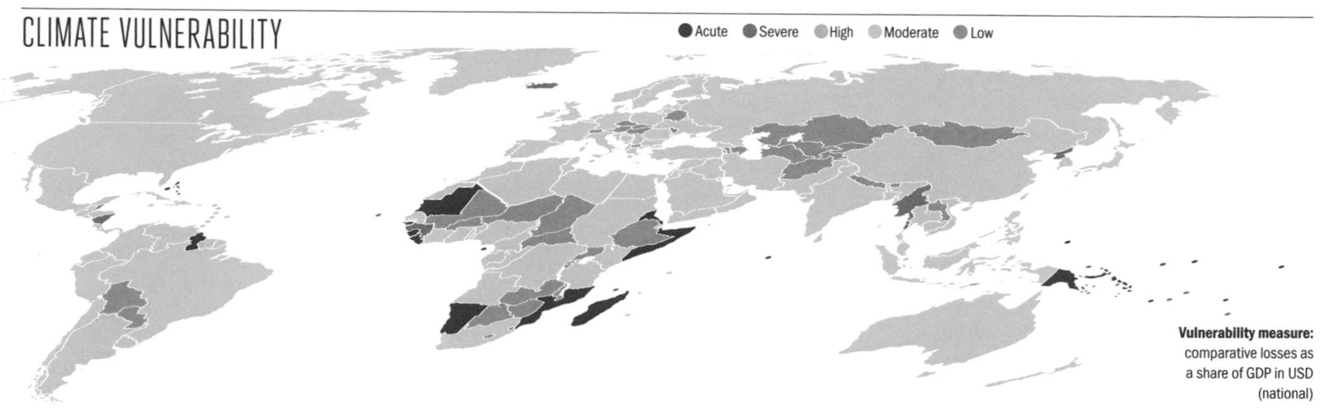

Vulnerability measure: comparative losses as a share of GDP in USD (national)

CLIMATE UNCERTAINTY

Limited · Partial · Considerable

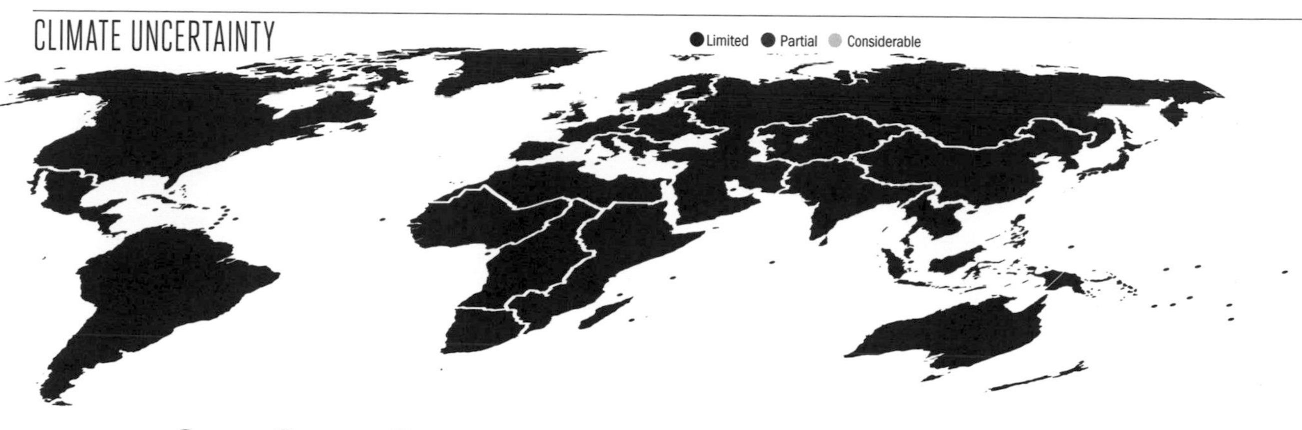

	$					
COUNTRY	2010	2030	2010	2030	2010	2030
Ireland	250	500	300	300	5	10
Israel	10	40	10	15	1	1
Italy	250	550	1,250	1,500	30	50
Jamaica	75	450	20	25	75	95
Japan	950	2,000	6,000	6,250	50	80
Jordan	1	5				
Kenya	200	900	200	300	20	60
Kuwait	55	500	100	150	5	15
Latvia	90	400	55	60	1	5
Lebanon	15	95	150	200		
Libya	200	1,000	80	100	90	250
Lithuania	40	200	30	35	1	10
Malaysia	900	5,750	2,250	2,500	250	450
Malta	1	5	25	30		
Mauritius	20	100			1	1
Mexico	2,250	15,000	1,250	1,750	1,000	2,000
Morocco	250	1,750	1,250	1,750	15	30
Netherlands	1,250	1,250	15,000	15,000	20	25
New Zealand	200	400	600	650	450	1,250
Nigeria	500	2,500	160	200	750	2,000
Norway	500	1,250	250	250	25	75
Oman	100	600	35	45	10	20
Pakistan	500	2,750	1,000	1,250	100	250
Peru	150	1,000	350	450	60	80
Philippines	850	4,750	3,500	4,000	350	850
Poland	200	850	200	200	15	35
Portugal	100	200	400	400	25	40
Qatar	45	250	60	85		1
Romania	80	400	150	150	90	200
Russia	3,000	10,000	1,750	1,750	400	1,000
Saint Lucia	10	60	15	15		
Saudi Arabia	300	1,500	75	100	40	90

	$					
COUNTRY	2010	2030	2010	2030	2010	2030
Seychelles	15	60	20	25	10	25
Singapore	10	55	600	700		
Slovenia	1	5	1	1		
South Africa	600	3,000	100	200	65	200
South Korea	2,500	10,000	2,500	2,500	10	15
Spain	200	450	1,000	1,250	35	65
Sri Lanka	150	1,000	800	1,000	45	75
Sudan/South Sudan	50	300	1	1	10	30
Sweden	150	300	550	600	5	10
Syria	10	65	10	15		
Tanzania	200	1,250	1,500	2,000	25	70
Thailand	1,500	6,750	5,250	6,250	65	150
Togo	10	55			10	25
Trinidad and Tobago	50	300	65	80	1	1
Tunisia	500	2,750	500	700	20	45
Turkey	300	750	850	1,250	55	85
Ukraine	1,000	5,250	2,000	2,250	45	95
United Arab Emirates	50	250	20	30	1	5
United Kingdom	1,500	2,750	5,000	5,250	100	300
United States	4,250	9,000	10,000	15,000	10,000	25,000
Venezuela	850	5,000	1,000	1,250	200	400
Yemen	150	1,250	70	100	45	150
LOW						
Afghanistan						
Armenia						
Austria						
Azerbaijan						
Belarus						
Bhutan						
Bolivia						
Botswana						
Burkina Faso						

	$					
COUNTRY	2010	2030	2010	2030	2010	2030
Burundi						
Central African Republic						
Chad						
Czech Republic						
Ethiopia						
Hungary						
Kazakhstan						
Kyrgyzstan						
Laos						
Lesotho						
Luxembourg						
Macedonia						
Malawi						
Mali						
Moldova						
Mongolia						
Nepal						
Niger						
Paraguay						
Rwanda						
Slovakia						
Swaziland						
Switzerland						
Tajikistan						
Turkmenistan						
Uganda						
Uzbekistan						
Zambia						
Zimbabwe						

Additional land lost due climate change (km^3) - yearly average

WATER

ESTIMATES GLOBAL CLIMATE IMPACT

2010 EFFECT TODAY

USD LOSS PER YEAR **15** BILLION

2030 EFFECT TOMORROW

USD LOSS PER YEAR **15** BILLION

ECONOMIC IMPACT

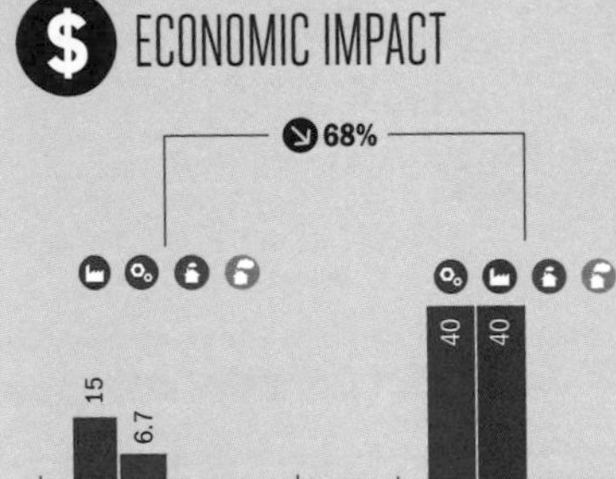

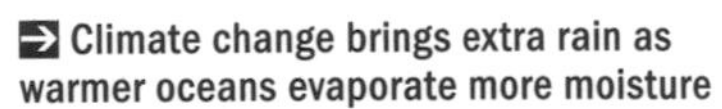

- Climate change brings extra rain as warmer oceans evaporate more moisture
- Water resources will not increase everywhere: in places more rain may not keep pace with strong heat
- Longer, hotter summers deplete water resources but melting glaciers can cause short-term surges
- Where less or more water is made available to countries already facing chronic water scarcity, losses or gains match heightened marginal water supply costs
- Adapting to impacts of climate change on water is feasible in most cases, but in highly arid regions, solutions may prove too costly

RELATIVE IMPACT

HOTSPOTS

2010		2030
4,000	MEXICO	30,000
9,000	FRANCE	25,000
5,000	GERMANY	15,000
4,750	SPAIN	15,000
1,250	CZECH REPUBLIC	9,000

GEOPOLITICAL VULNERABILITY

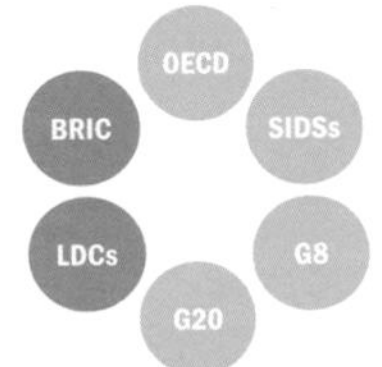

Economic Cost (2010 PPP non-discounted)
Developing Country Low Emitters
Developed
Developing Country High Emitters
Other Industrialized

$ = Losses per 10,000 USD of GDP

Change in relation to overall global population and/or GDP

Water is an important input to the full range of economic activities and is therefore a crucial natural resource with market value (Morrison et al., 2009). Rainfall is highly uncertain (Blöschl and Montanari, 2010). Two global climate change projections could show mirror opposites for a region like Brazil: one dry and the other wet (Murray et al., 2012). A full ensemble of IPCC models was used to predict water supply change presented here (Nohara et al., 2006). But selecting only some models as opposed to others would likely have produced a different set of results. Some regions are uncertain whether they will be dry (such as Southern and Eastern Europe and North Africa) or wet (North America, East Asia). Others are completely unsure about what the future holds (Australasia, South America). In this assessment, roughly half of all countries are expected to either gain or have a no impact. The other half will suffer losses. Water is supplied according to specific local conditions at the market price (McKinsey & Company, 2009). However, the price of water varies widely around the world, from more than 8 dollars per m3 in Denmark to less than 8 cents/m3 in parts of India (GWI, 2008). Generally speaking, water costs a larger share of income in most developed than in developing countries. As a result, climate change is contributing to a worsening of water availability in the Mediterranean basin, and generating a large share of estimated global losses.

CLIMATE MECHANISM

Climate change increases rainfall globally, since the planet's water cycle accelerates as it warms (Huntington, 2006). As temperature increases, so does the overall moisture content of the air and rain falls back to ground levels (Allen and Ingram, 2002). More moisture in the air from the world's oceans is the main contributor to the water cycle's acceleration (Syed et al., 2010). However, much of the additional rain falls in the far north or south (Nohara et al., 2006).

Recent evidence shows that rainfall has already declined in the tropics and increased significantly in the far north and south (Helm et al., 2010). Even where more rainfall occurs, if evaporation rates are high due to greatly increased temperature, a loss of water availability can result (Chu et al., 2009). Long-term decline in the world's glaciers and longer drier summers also aggravate water scarcity in certain areas and lead to near-term surges in flows elsewhere before declining again (NSIDC, 2008; Immerzeel et al., 2012; Marengo et al., 2011; Olefs et al., 2009). Economic impacts will cause the greatest challenges where water scarcity and the cost of water are already high (Morrison et al., 2009).

IMPACTS

The effect of climate change on water scarcity is already estimated to cost affected countries 45 million dollars a year. However, 30 billion dollars in yearly gains in water resources in countries experiencing increasing water availability mean a net global loss of 15 billion dollars a year. This net global loss is stable at 15 billion dollars a year to 2030 and declines by three times as a share of global GDP. By 2030, affected countries will incur 200 billion dollars in yearly losses, which are almost entirely offset by similar levels of gains in other countries.

The bulk of losses is estimated to affect wealthy European countries, such as France, Germany, Spain, and Italy. Mexico and Turkey are also expected to experience high losses in absolute terms. Canada, China, Japan, India, and Russia are estimated here to recoup the largest gains.

Southern and Eastern European countries are estimated to be worst affected relative to GDP, along with a number of Central American countries, such as Belize and Panama.

The impacts represent a possible outcome of highly unpredictable rainfall and should be treated with caution, especially for countries in sub-regions with considerable uncertainty about the direction of change (wet or dry).

On a global level, the results could be considered more robust since different hydrological regimes will invariably favour some and disfavour others in terms of water availability.

THE BROADER CONTEXT

The world is experiencing a growing water crisis. Between 2010 and 2030, global water demand is expected to increase by around 40%, requiring an additional 3 trillion m3 of water, as compared with a total global demand of only 4.5 trillion m3 today, without accounting for the possible impacts of climate change (McKinsey & Company, 2009). This increase is driven largely by population increases and economic

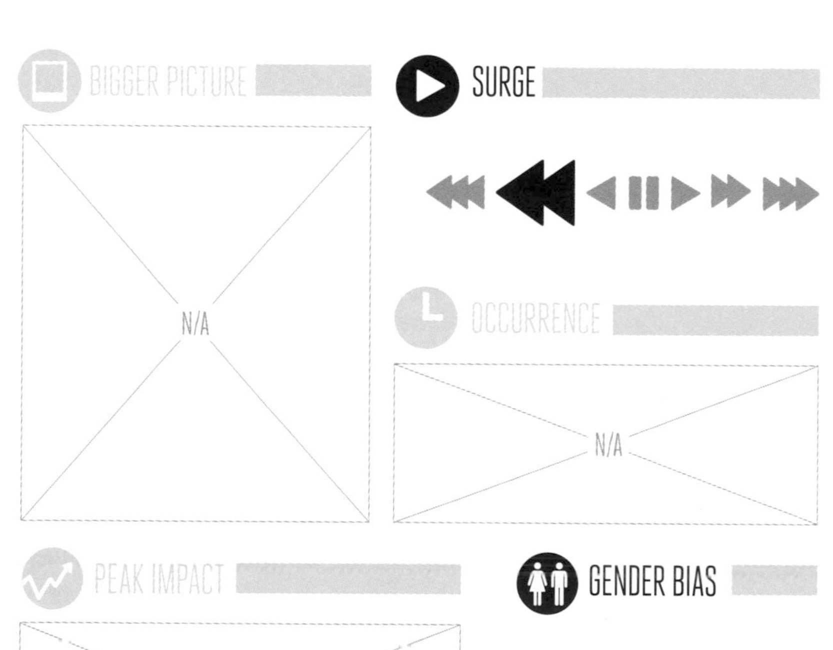

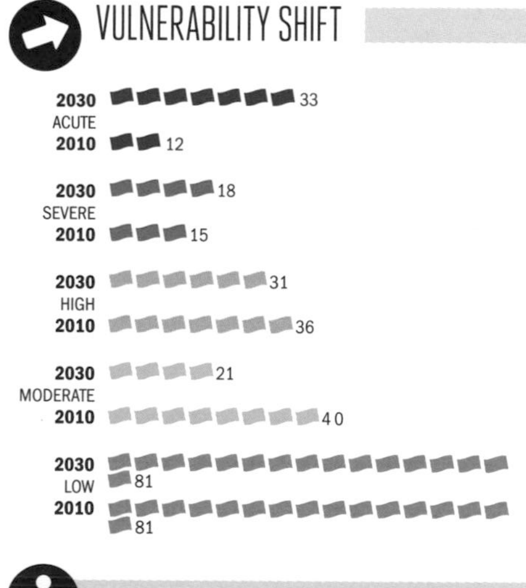

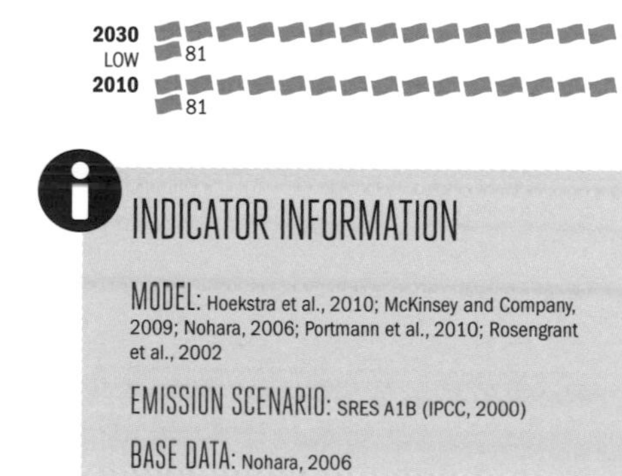

INDICATOR INFORMATION
MODEL: Hoekstra et al., 2010; McKinsey and Company, 2009; Nohara, 2006; Portmann et al., 2010; Rosengrant et al., 2002
EMISSION SCENARIO: SRES A1B (IPCC, 2000)
BASE DATA: Nohara, 2006

= 5 countries (rounded)

Acute Severe High Moderate Low

growth, which brings greater industry demand for water. Over half of the water gap is expected to be met through infrastructure and other changes which deviate from business-as-usual approaches to water. Unless countries develop more sophisticated responses to dealing with the water supply, the expense of closing this gap, while technically possible, will become increasingly cost-prohibitive, because of the steep cost of generating water to compensate for the water scarcity in an economy.

VULNERABILITIES AND WIDER OUTCOMES

Pollution, over-grazing, deforestation, and other environmentally unsustainable practices can all exacerbate water scarcity (Economy, 2010). Farmers who must rely on rainfall alone and who cannot afford or get access to irrigation are highly vulnerable to falling water availability. Water insecurity can lead to food insecurity in marginalized communities and to a lack of water for sanitation and drinking, leading to further negative health consequences, or even violence and conflict (Ludi, 2009; Raleigh, 2010).

Economies heavily reliant on agriculture, responsible for about 70% of global water demand, are also more vulnerable to water stress (FAO AQUASTAT, 2012).

RESPONSES

Managing water often requires large-scale investment that can have an important impact on longer-term development prospects (Aerts and Droogers in Kabat et al. (eds.), 2009). Planning for the wrong outcome is costly. Where uncertainty is high, it is therefore vital that responses are appropriate for a wide range of possible outcomes, i.e., a wet or a dry future (Dessai et al., 2009). However, planning for different outcomes can add significantly to the costs of adaptation. Five broad response areas are central to effective water management: 1) Enhancing catchment capacity or access to supplies, through reservoirs or wells for instance; 2) There is wide scope for improving water efficiency in many contexts (Wallace, 2000), from micro-irrigation, to improved drainage and re-use of water, lining canals and limiting water leakage, as well as the cultivation of more water-efficient crops (Rodríguez Díaz et al., 2007; Wilby and Dessai, 2010; Elliot et al., 2011); 3) Supporting improved institutional environments to enable communities to make and implement effective decisions is critical (Rogers and Hall, 2003); 4) The vulnerability of communities to water stress can also be reduced, whether for socio-economic reasons (e.g., subsistence farmers), pollution, land degradation, or deforestation (Sullivan, 2011; Kiparsky et al., 2012; Epule et al., 2012; Postel and Thompson, 2005); 5) GHG emission reductions do not instantaneously slow or accelerate the hydrological cycle, but will limit the extent of changes in water availability due to climate change in the long term (Wu et al., 2010; Arnell et al., 2011).

THE INDICATOR

The indicator measures costs of changes in the re-supply of water resources due to temperature and precipitation changes caused by climate change (Nohara et al., 2006). It considers agricultural, domestic/municipal and industrial demand and country or region-specific marginal water costs (Rosengrant at al., 2002; McKinsey & Company, 2009). A key limitation not controlled for is that while climate change may increase water availability over a year, if it does not fall when water demand peaks in the absence of adequate catchment, reservoir and irrigation facilities, water scarcity may still increase. It has been estimated that around 20% of areas experiencing increased water could also experience an increase in water scarcity, including India, Northern China, and Europe (Yamamoto et al., 2012). Since the indicator is aggregating the country-level picture of change, it is possible that increases in water availability for some parts of a country are not compensating fully for decreases in water availability elsewhere.

ESTIMATES COUNTRY-LEVEL IMPACT

	$		💧	
COUNTRY	2010	2030	2010	2030
ACUTE				
Armenia	70	500	0.25	0.50
Austria	2,000	6,000	1	1
Belarus	400	2,500	0.50	1
Belize	35	250		0.25
Bolivia	350	2,500	1	1
Bulgaria	600	4,000	1	1
Costa Rica	150	1,000	0.50	0.75
Croatia	700	4,750	0.50	1
Czech Republic	1,250	9,000	0.75	1
El Salvador	150	1,000	0.00	
France	9,000	25,000	5	10
Georgia	200	1,250	0.75	1
Greece	900	2,750	0.50	1
Guatemala	150	1,250	0.75	1
Guyana	15	100		
Honduras	80	650	0.75	1
Hungary	500	3,500	0.75	1
Kyrgyzstan	40	300	0.75	1
Lesotho	10	65	0.50	0.75
Macedonia	100	850	0.25	0.50
Malta	40	100		
Mexico	4,000	30,000	20	35
Moldova	30	200	0.25	0.50
Nicaragua	75	600	1	1
Panama	200	1,250	0.75	1
Romania	1,000	6,750	1	5
Slovakia	700	5,000	0.50	1
Slovenia	400	2,750	0.25	0.50
Spain	4,750	15,000	5	5
Switzerland	800	2,250	0.50	1
Tajikistan	45	300	0.75	1
Ukraine	1,000	7,000	1	5
Zimbabwe	30	200	1	5
SEVERE				
Albania	35	250	0.25	0.50
Antigua and Barbuda	1	20		
Bahamas	15	100		
Barbados	10	70		
Bosnia and Herzegovina	40	300		0.25
Chile	400	3,250	1	5
Cote d,Ivoire	45	300	1	5
Cuba	150	1,250		
Dominica	1	10		
Dominican Republic	100	950		
Germany	5,000	15,000	1	5
Grenada	1	15		
Haiti	15	100		
Jamaica	35	250		
Saint Lucia	1	20		
Saint Vincent	1	15		
Swaziland	10	70		0.25
Turkey	1,750	5,500	10	20
HIGH				
Afghanistan	35	250	1	5
Angola	70	450	1	1
Australia	750	2,000	0.50	1
Azerbaijan	100	800	0.25	0.50
Belgium	350	1,000	0.25	0.50
Benin	10	75	0.25	0.75
Botswana	20	100		0.25
Fiji	1	20		
Guinea	10	60	0.25	0.75
Italy	2,250	6,750	1	5
Kiribati		1		
Luxembourg	50	150		
Mali	15	95	0.75	1
Marshall Islands		1		
Mauritania	5	40	0.25	0.25
Micronesia		1		
Namibia	10	55		0.25
Palau		1		
Poland	900	6,250	1	1
Portugal	250	700	0.25	0.25
Samoa	1	5		
Solomon Islands	1	5		
South Africa	550	3,500	5	5
Suriname	1	15		
Togo	5	30	0.25	0.50
Tonga	1	5		
Trinidad and Tobago	15	150		0.25
Tuvalu				
Uzbekistan	40	300	0.50	1
Vanuatu	1	5		
Venezuela	350	2,750	1	5
MODERATE				
Algeria	15	95		0.25
Burkina Faso	1	15		0.25
Cape Verde	1	5		
Cyprus	5	15		
Egypt	1	15		
Gambia	1	5		
Ghana	10	55	0.25	0.25
Iran	300	2,250	1	1
Iraq	5	55	0.25	0.25
Israel	10	65		

$ Additional economic costs due to climate change (million USD PPP) - yearly average

CLIMATE VULNERABILITY

● Acute ● Severe ● High ● Moderate ● Low

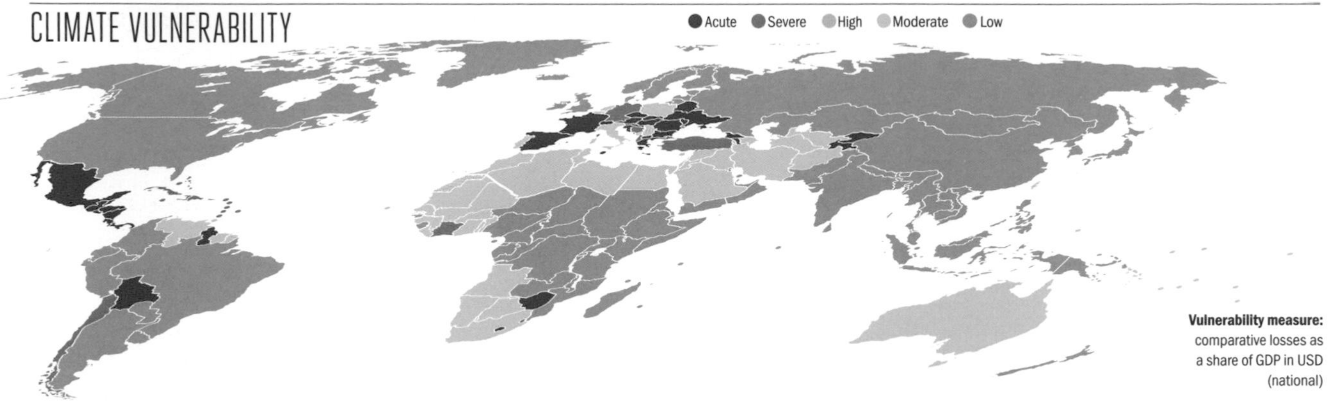

Vulnerability measure: comparative losses as a share of GDP in USD (national)

CLIMATE UNCERTAINTY

● Limited ● Partial ● Considerable

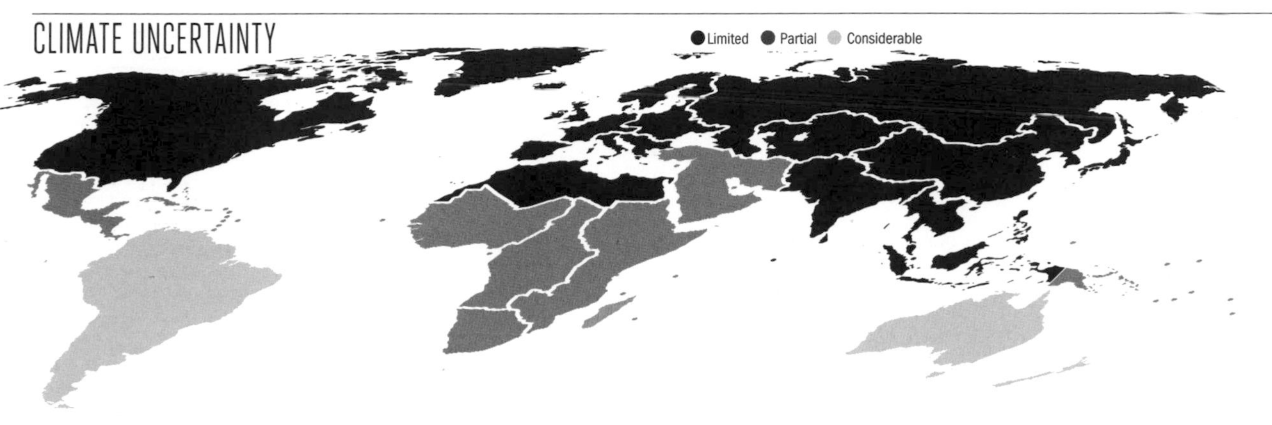

COUNTRY	$ 2010	$ 2030	💧 2010	💧 2030
Jordan	1	10		
Lebanon	1	10		
Liberia	1	1		
Libya	1	5		
Morocco	10	70		0.25
Netherlands	150	500		0.25
Saudi Arabia	20	150		0.25
Senegal	1	5		
Syria	10	65		0.25
Tunisia	1	15		
Turkmenistan	10	75		0.25
LOW				
Argentina	-150	-1,250	-0.25	-0.50
Bahrain	-1	-5		
Bangladesh	-25	-200	-0.50	-1
Bhutan	-85	-700	-0.50	-1
Brazil	-1,250	-10,000	-5	-10
Brunei	-55	-450		-0.25
Burundi	-1	-10	-0.25	-0.25
Cambodia	-15	-150	-0.25	-0.50
Cameroon	-35	-250	-0.75	-1
Canada	-2,500	-7,250	-1	-1
Central African Republic	-5	-25	-0.25	-0.50
Chad	-25	-150	-0.50	-1
China	-5,750	-60,000	-30	-55
Colombia	-250	-2,000	-1	-5
Comoros	-1	-1		
Congo	-5	-50		-0.25
Denmark	-65	-200		
Djibouti	-1	-5		
DR Congo	-20	-100	-1	-5
Ecuador	-750	-5,500	-1	-5
Equatorial Guinea	-5	-35		
Eritrea				
Estonia	-100	-800	-0.25	-0.50
Ethiopia	-100	-650	-5	-5
Finland	-1,000	-3,000	-0.75	-1
Gabon	-1	-10		
Guinea-Bissau		-1		
Iceland	-25	-70		
India	-2,000	-15,000	-15	-35
Indonesia	-950	-7,500	-10	-20
Ireland	-250	-700	-0.25	-0.25
Japan	-4,250	-10,000	-1	-5
Kazakhstan	-50	-350	-0.25	-0.25
Kenya	-65	-400	-1	-5
Kuwait		-1		
Laos	-70	-750	-1	-1
Latvia	-55	-350		-0.25
Lithuania	-20	-150		
Madagascar	-1	-5		
Malawi	-1	-15		-0.25
Malaysia	-800	-6,000	-1	-5
Maldives	-10	-60		
Mauritius	-10	-65		
Mongolia	-1	-10		
Mozambique	-1	-5		
Myanmar	-75	-600	-1	-5
Nepal	-25	-200	-1	-1
New Zealand	80	-250		-0.25
Niger	-10	-55	-0.50	-1
Nigeria	-65	-400	-1	-1
North Korea	-20	-200	-0.50	-1
Norway	-1,250	-4,000	-0.75	-1
Oman	-25	-200		-0.25
Pakistan	-10	-60		-0.25
Papua New Guinea	-100	-850	-5	-5
Paraguay	-25	-200	-0.25	-0.50
Peru	-200	-1,500	-1	-1
Philippines	-45	-350	-0.50	-1
Qatar	-10	-55		
Russia	-2,500	-15,000	-5	-10
Rwanda	-5	-40	-0.25	-0.50
Sao Tome and Principe		-1		
Seychelles	-1	-5		
Sierra Leone		-1		
Singapore	-250	-2,000		
Somalia	-5	-40	-0.50	-1
South Korea	-85	-650	-0.25	-0.50
Sri Lanka	-1	-20		
Sudan/South Sudan	-40	-300	-1	-1
Sweden	-1,500	-4,500	-1	1
Tanzania	-200	-1,250	-5	-10
Thailand	-300	-2,250	-1	-5
Timor-Leste	-5	-35		
Uganda	70	-450	-1	-5
United Arab Emirates	-15	-150		
United Kingdom	-1,250	-4,000	-0.75	-1
United States	-1,250	-4,000	-1	-1
Uruguay	-10	-70		
Vietnam	-100	-1,000	-1	-1
Yemen	-10	-60	-0.25	-0.25
Zambia	-1	-5		

💧 Additional water losses/gains due to climate change (km^3) - yearly average

COSTS

2010
23 BILLION

2030
106 BILLION

HEALTH IMPACT

DIARRHEAL INFECTIONS

HEAT & COLD ILLNESSES

HUNGER

MALARIA & VECTOR-BORNE

MENINGITIS

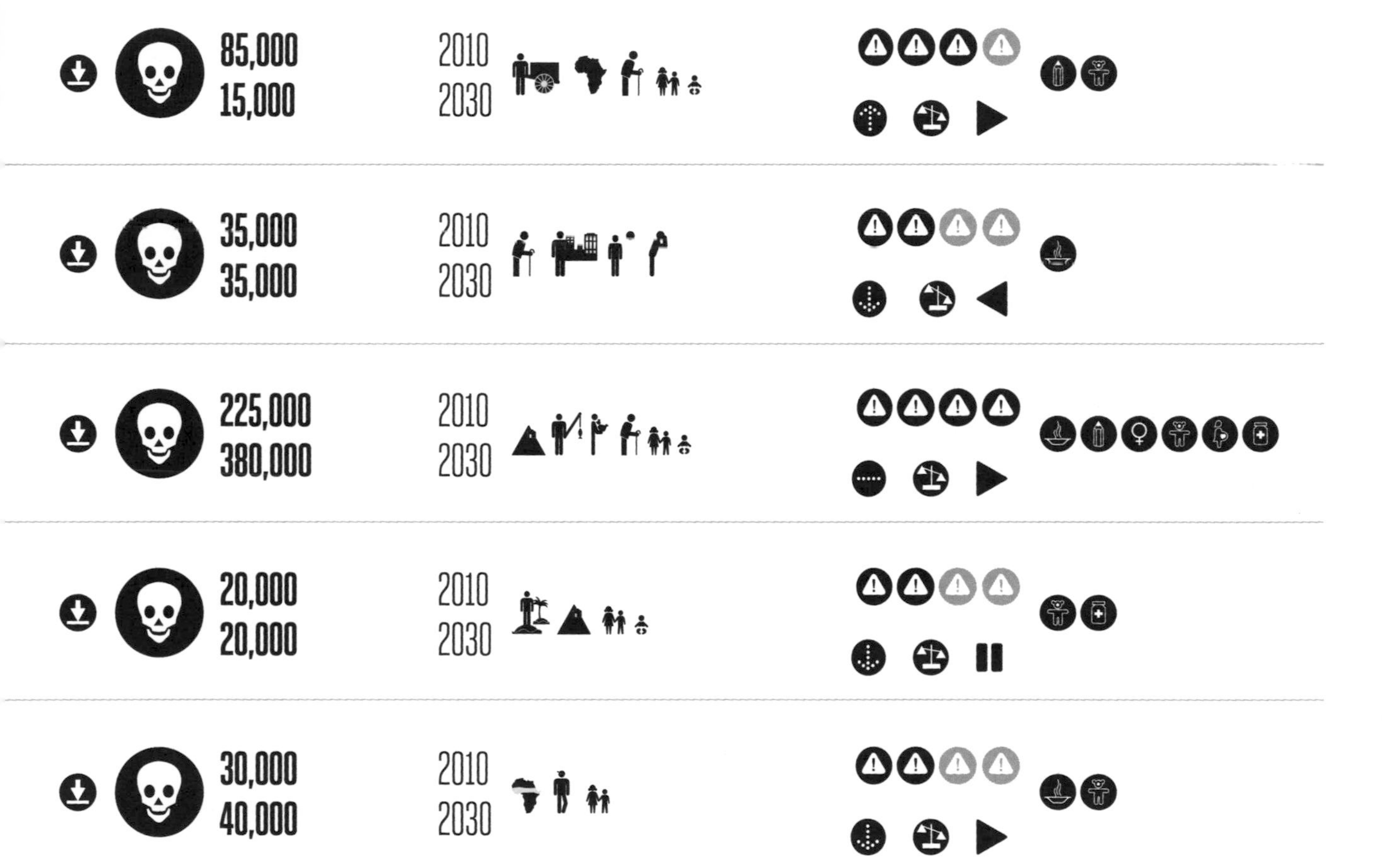
85,000
15,000
2010
2030
35,000
35,000
2010
2030
225,000
380,000
2010
2030
20,000
20,000
2010
2030
30,000
40,000
2010
2030

DIARRHEAL INFECTIONS

ESTIMATES GLOBAL CLIMATE IMPACT

2010 EFFECT TODAY

DEATHS PER YEAR **85,000**

2030 EFFECT TOMORROW

DEATHS PER YEAR **150,000**

MORTALITY IMPACT

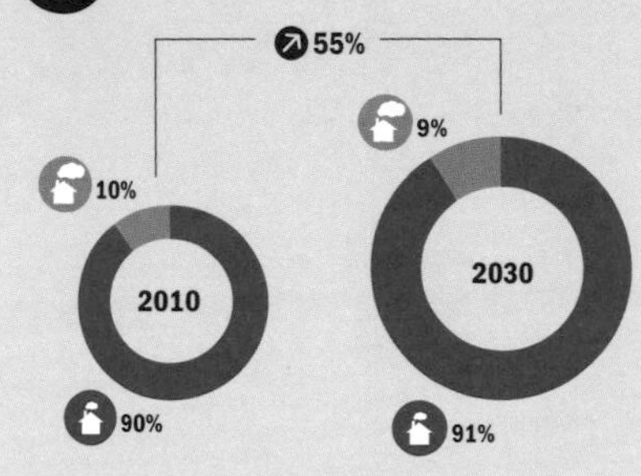

- Diarrheal disease is one of the leading causes of preventable death in developing countries, especially among children and infants
- Today, diarrheal diseases kill 2.5 million people per year globally
- Germs causing these infections favour warmer environments; as the planet heats, the risks of diarrheal diseases will worsen unless counteracting measures are taken

RELATIVE IMPACT

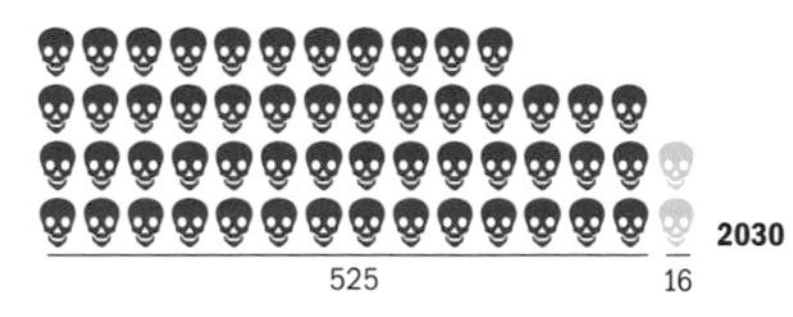

HOTSPOTS

2010		2030
40,000	INDIA	85,000
6,750	NIGERIA	9,250
3,250	PAKISTAN	9,250
3,500	ETHIOPIA	6,500
3,500	DR CONGO	6,500

GEOPOLITICAL VULNERABILITY

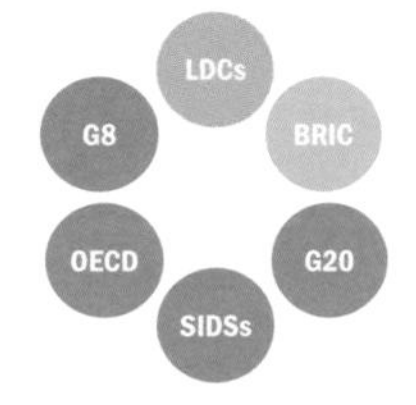

Deaths

Developing Country Low Emitters

Developing Country High Emitters

Developed

Other Industrialized

= Deaths per 10 million

Change in relation to overall global population and/or GDP

Diarrheal infections are one of the world's top communicable disease groups globally by overall death toll (WHO, 1999; WHO BDD, 2011). Food spoils more quickly and water contamination accelerates at higher temperatures, with the result that diarrheal infection rates may be 3–4 times higher in the summer than in the winter. Too much water, from flooding and contamination, or too little water, causing difficulties in treating/rehydrating the ill, are also problematic (WHO, 2009). Diarrheal disease influenced by climate change is a major concern for developing countries because risks are simply higher: inadequate refrigeration, difficult access to plumbed water in homes, or sanitation, such as basic toilet facilities (Bilenko et al, 1999; WHO, 2004; Ashbolt, 2004). In order to save lives and steadily reduce the prevalence of these diseases, simple interventions from vaccines to breastfeeding can prevent death. Systemic improvements in water, sanitation and hygiene are necessary for a more comprehensive reduction in risks (Jamison et al. (eds.), 2006).

CLIMATE MECHANISM

Several climate parameters affect diarrheal diseases from the level of infectious agents (bacteria, pathogen and viruses) through to population level practices. Direct observation of the effects of rising temperatures on infectious agents shows increases in disease replication rates and survival duration (WHO, 2004). Temperature changes also affect hospitalizations rates, with noticeable percentage increases in patient admissions as temperatures rise above normal levels (Checkley et al., 2000). Diarrheal diseases are transmitted via the fecal-oral route through food, water, human contact, or contact with objects such as cups (Dennehy, 2000). Key types of infectious diarrhea include cholera and rotavirus. Other factors such as humidity and rainfall also influence diarrhea. For instance, extremely low rainfall can force people in developing countries to make more use of polluted waters, while too much rain can contaminate unpolluted waters (Hunter, 2003; Ashbolt, 2004). Diarrheal diseases are also affected by malnutrition rates, which are influenced by climate change. This relationship is studied under "Hunger" (WHO, 2004).

IMPACTS

Owing to general temperature increase, the current impact of climate change on diarrheal diseases is estimated to lead to over 80,000 additional deaths per year in developing countries. Each year, over 100 million people are estimated to be affected by diarrheal diseases resulting from climate change.
By 2030, these impacts will increase to over 150,000 deaths proportionate to the future global population, taking into account expected evolutions in the disease in relation to socio-economic development, unless measures are taken to counteract them. Over 200 million people could be affected by 2030.
Africa is by far the region worst affected by diarrheal disease as result of the effects of climate change, with more than a dozen countries estimated to be experiencing similarly extreme levels of impact. Some parts of Asia, particularly, Afghanistan, Pakistan, and India are also particularly vulnerable.
In general, low-income and least developed countries are significantly worse off than middle income countries. No significant impact is expected for developed countries, but primarily because of a higher level of public awareness, and not because people in those countries are invulnerable (WHO, 2004; Bentham, 1997).

THE BROADER CONTEXT

While many preventable diseases in developing countries are seeing reductions in prevalence or declines in growth rates, diarrheal diseases have expanded rapidly since the year 2000, with nearly three quarters of a million additional deaths worldwide by 2010 (Mathers and Loncar, 2006; WHO BDD, 2011). However, different regions have evolved in different ways. In the last 10 years, Africa has worsened considerably, while East Asia has markedly diminished its burden of suffering from diarrheal disease.

VULNERABILITIES AND WIDER OUTCOMES

Less than 1% of diarrheal disease deaths occur in developed countries. Lower-income countries with already significant burdens of diarrheal infections will face serious challenges in combating the disease as temperatures continue to rise, since the same preconditions prevail. Prevalence of diarrhea is closely linked

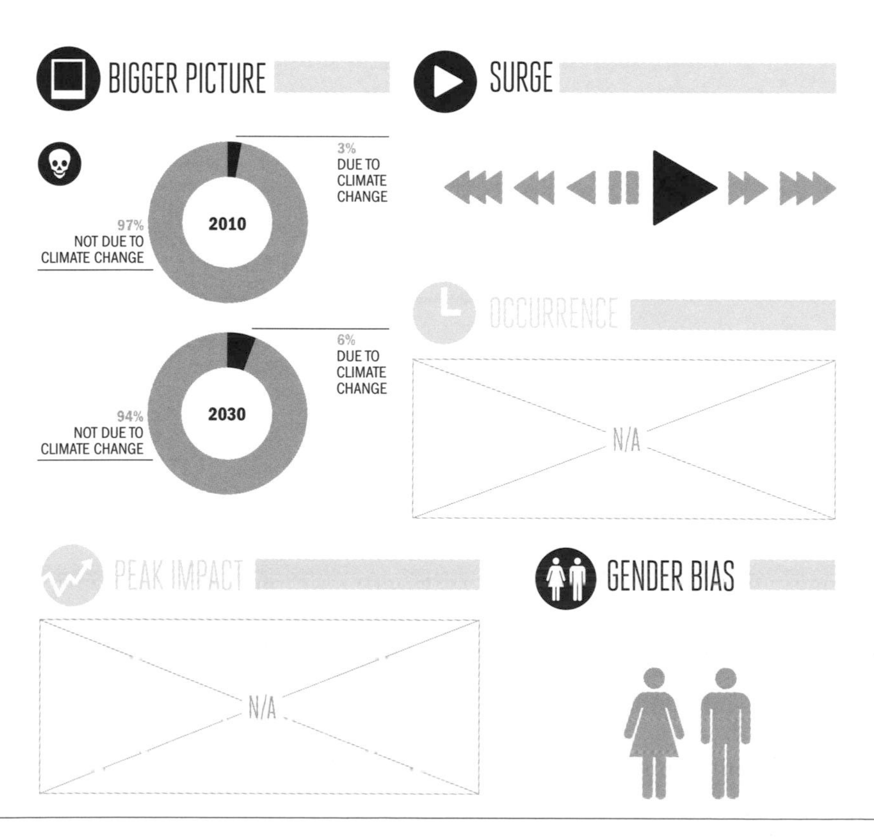

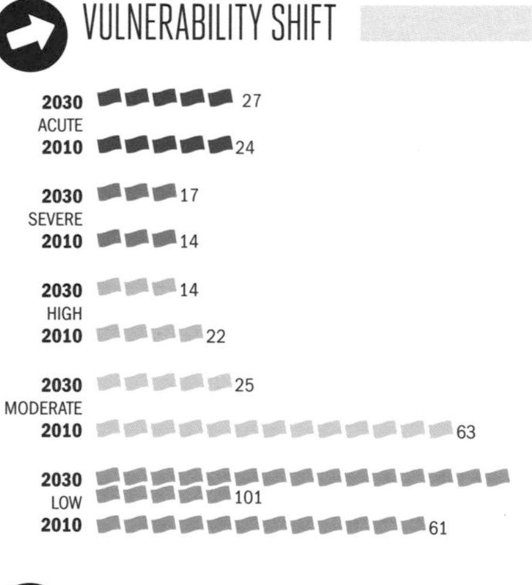

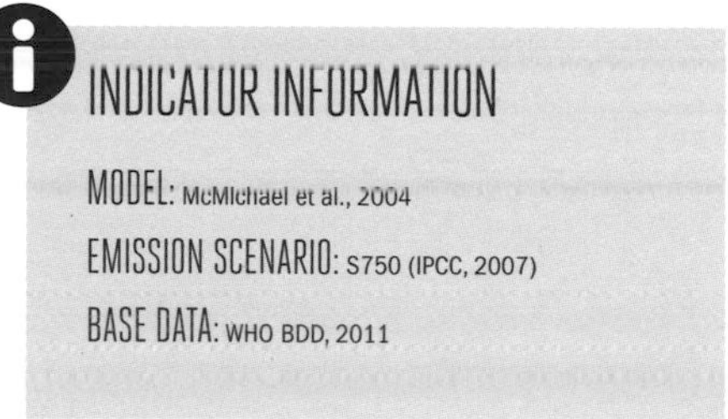

= 5 countries (rounded)

Acute Severe High Moderate Low

to income levels for two reasons: 1) the main vulnerabilities relate to sanitation and by association, hygiene, whereby certain minimum standards in higher-income countries are enough to greatly reduce infection rates; and 2) deaths from diarrhea are easily preventable, especially among infants and toddlers, but only when either medical treatment or clean water are accessible and awareness about treatments is widespread; this is, unfortunately, not the case in many least developed contexts (Ashbolt, 2004; Jamison et al. (eds.), 2006).

While children make up more than half of the death toll, the millions who do survive what may often be repeated illnesses can, in many cases, be left with long-term cognitive impairments (Niehaus et al., 2002). Combined economic and social costs constitute a serious impediment to development progress for the world's poorest communities. With respect to the Millennium Development Goals, 2 (universal education) and 4 (child health) are particularly affected.

RESPONSES

Reponses are needed at the treatment and prevention level. In terms of treatment, simple water and salt, called "oral rehydration" solutions (ORS) cost next to nothing and can prevent death from extreme dehydration, the most common trigger of diarrheal mortality. In terms of prevention, access to clean water and basic sanitation are the central concerns (WHO, 2009). In this context, four sets of strategies are commonplace: 1) vaccination, especially against rotavirus and to a lesser extent cholera, has the potential to save up to half a million lives each year; 2) child breastfeeding programmes which limit the transmission of infections through food and water to infants; 3) sanitation improvements, in the form of improved water sources for houses or small communities, construction of wells, and improved waste and latrine systems; and 4) education programmes, which target awareness about the other three areas and which promote personal hygiene through the use of soap and other simple measures (Jamison et al. (eds.), 2006).

THE INDICATOR

The indicator is deemed robust, particularly because of its reliance on temperature—among the most certain of climate effects—as the parameter for estimating a climate effect and because of the quality of the global health database compiled by the WHO on which the estimates are based (WHO BDD, 2011). Nevertheless, a number of improvements could be envisioned: for example, the WHO modelled the global effect on the basis of two detailed studies, which could benefit from further expansion into different areas, particularly detailed analysis of climate change effects on diarrhea in Africa (WHO, 2004). Moreover, the model does not take into account factors other than temperature, such as humidity and rainfall, nor does it take into account effects for developed countries which, while potentially low in terms of mortality, could be high in terms of the number of illnesses; one study identified a 9% increase in food poisoning causing diarrhea in the UK for every one degree increase in temperature (Bentham, 1997).

ESTIMATES COUNTRY-LEVEL IMPACT

COUNTRY	2010	2030	2010	2030
ACUTE				
Afghanistan	2,000	4,000	2,500	5,000
Angola	1,250	1,750	7,750	10,000
Benin	350	450	400	550
Burkina Faso	900	1,250	1,000	1,500
Burundi	400	750	500	900
Cameroon	900	1,250	1,250	1,500
Central African Republic	150	250	200	350
Chad	900	1,250	1,000	1,500
Cote d'Ivoire	550	950	650	1,250
DR Congo	3,500	6,500	4,500	8,000
Equatorial Guinea	25	35	200	300
Ethiopia	3,500	6,500	4,500	8,250
Ghana	900	1,250	1,250	1,500
Guinea	400	550	500	700
Guinea-Bissau	100	150	150	200
India	40,000	85,000	50,000	100,000
Malawi	450	800	550	1,000
Mali	950	1,250	1,250	1,750
Niger	1,000	1,500	1,250	1,750
Nigeria	6,750	9,250	8,250	10,000
Pakistan	3,250	9,250	4,000	10,000
Rwanda	350	650	450	850
Sierra Leone	350	450	400	550
Somalia	550	1,000	700	1,250
South Africa	1,000	2,000	9,000	15,000
Uganda	1,000	2,000	1,250	2,500
Zambia	400	750	500	950
SEVERE				
Bhutan	10	20	10	25
Comoros	20	30	25	35
Congo	80	150	100	200
Djibouti	15	25	85	150
Eritrea	85	150	100	200
Gambia	45	65	60	80
Kenya	800	1,500	1,000	1,750
Lesotho	25	45	30	55
Liberia	150	200	200	250
Madagascar	500	700	600	850
Mauritania	100	150	150	200
Mozambique	550	950	650	1,250
Senegal	300	400	400	500
Sudan/South Sudan	850	1,500	1,000	2,000
Swaziland	15	30	100	200
Tanzania	1,000	2,000	1,250	2,250
Togo	150	250	200	300
HIGH				
Algeria	350	500	2,250	3,000
Bangladesh	1,250	2,250	1,500	2,750
Botswana	15	25	100	200
Cape Verde	5	5	25	35
Gabon	20	30	200	250
Guatemala	150	150	850	800
Haiti	150	100	200	150
Iraq	300	850	1,750	5,000
Myanmar	550	1,000	650	1,250
Namibia	15	25	85	150
Nepal	300	550	350	650
Sao Tome and Principe	1	5	1	5
Yemen	400	850	500	1,000
Zimbabwe	150	250	150	300
MODERATE				
Albania	1	1	5	1
Armenia	1	1	5	5
Azerbaijan	15	10	95	55
Bolivia	80	70	450	450
Bosnia and Herzegovina			1	
Bulgaria	1		1	1
Ecuador	15	15	100	80
Egypt	95	150	550	1,000
Georgia	1	1	15	5
Kyrgyzstan	15	5	15	10
Macedonia			1	1
Maldives		1	1	5
Mauritius	1	1	5	10
Morocco	150	250	850	1,500
Nicaragua	15	15	15	15
North Korea	60	100	75	150
Peru	45	35	250	200
Poland	1	1	10	5
Romania	1	1	5	1
Seychelles			1	1
Slovakia			1	1
Tajikistan	45	25	60	30
Turkey	25	15	250	150
Turkmenistan	20	15	100	85
Uzbekistan	55	35	70	45
LOW				
Antigua and Barbuda				
Argentina				
Australia				
Austria				
Bahamas				
Bahrain			1	
Barbados				
Belarus				

Additional mortality due to climate change - yearly average

CLIMATE VULNERABILITY

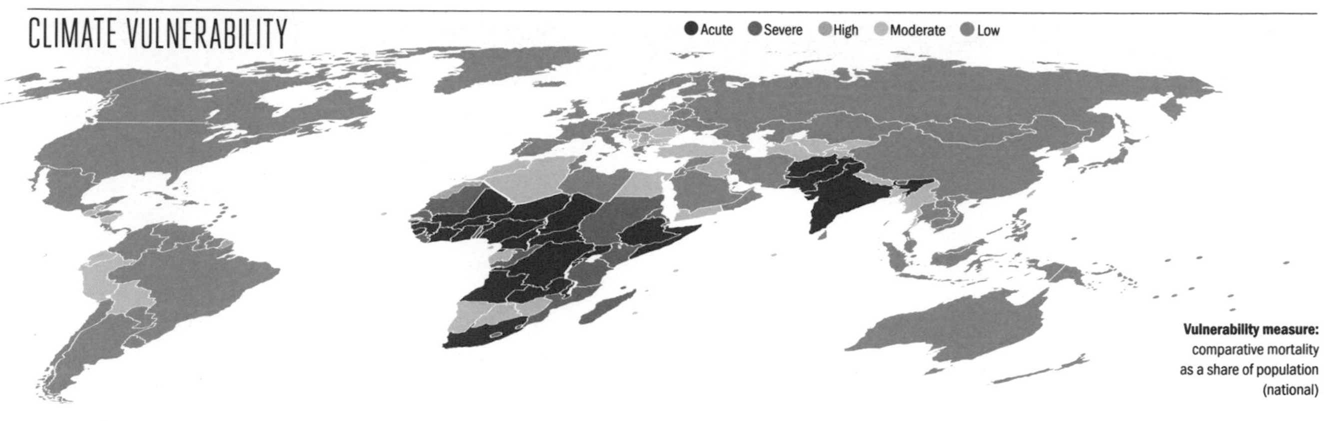

Vulnerability measure: comparative mortality as a share of population (national)

CLIMATE UNCERTAINTY

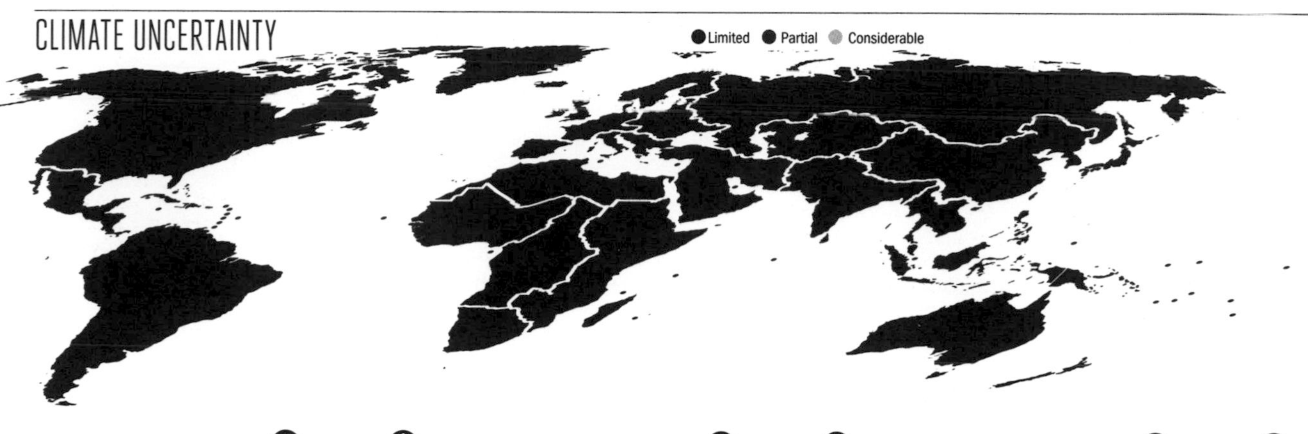

COUNTRY	2010 (deaths)	2030 (deaths)	2010 (persons)	2030 (persons)
Belgium				
Belize				
Brazil				
Brunei				
Cambodia	100		150	
Canada				
Chile				
China	550		3,000	
Colombia				
Costa Rica				
Croatia				
Cuba				
Cyprus			1	
Czech Republic				
Denmark				
Dominica				
Dominican Republic				
El Salvador				
Estonia				
Fiji	1		10	
Finland				
France				
Germany				
Greece				
Grenada				
Guyana				
Honduras				
Hungary			1	
Iceland				
Indonesia				
Iran	100		600	
Ireland				

COUNTRY	2010 (deaths)	2030 (deaths)	2010 (persons)	2030 (persons)
Israel				
Italy				
Jamaica				
Japan				
Jordan	5		25	
Kazakhstan	1		15	
Kiribati	1		5	
Kuwait			1	
Laos	35		45	
Latvia				
Lebanon	1		10	
Libya	5		30	
Lithuania				
Luxembourg				
Malaysia	5		55	
Malta				
Marshall Islands			1	
Mexico				
Micronesia			1	
Moldova				
Mongolia	5		5	
Netherlands				
New Zealand				
Norway				
Oman	1		10	
Palau				
Panama				
Papua New Guinea	30		35	
Paraguay				
Philippines	200		1,250	
Portugal				
Qatar			1	

COUNTRY	2010 (deaths)	2030 (deaths)	2010 (persons)	2030 (persons)
Russia	5		45	
Saint Lucia				
Saint Vincent				
Samoa			1	
Saudi Arabia	15		250	
Singapore				
Slovenia				
Solomon Islands	1		1	
South Korea	5		55	
Spain				
Sri Lanka				
Suriname				
Sweden				
Switzerland				
Syria	15		85	
Thailand				
Timor-Leste				
Tonga			1	
Trinidad and Tobago				
Tunisia	10		55	
Tuvalu				
Ukraine	1		6	
United Arab Emirates			1	
United Kingdom				
United States				
Uruguay				
Vanuatu			1	
Venezuela				
Vietnam	90		100	

Additional persons affected due to climate change (thousands) - yearly average change

HEAT & COLD ILLNESSES

ESTIMATES GLOBAL CLIMATE IMPACT

2010 EFFECT TODAY

DEATHS PER YEAR **35,000**

2030 EFFECT TOMORROW

DEATHS PER YEAR **35,000**

MORTALITY IMPACT

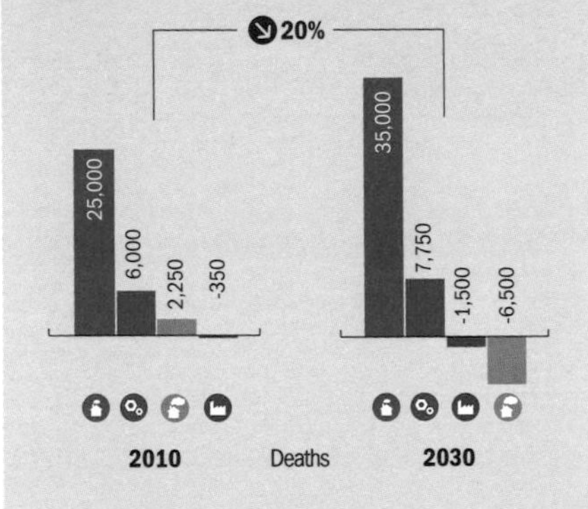

- Extreme heat is dangerous, entails high risks for the elderly, sufferers of chronic cardiovascular and respiratory diseases, and may increase skin cancer rates
- Shorter and less harsh winters alleviate dangers for the same risk groups and reduce the incidence of flu-like illnesses
- Some developed countries are estimated to experience modest health gains, as winters become less severe on average
- Effective responses to heat and cold illnesses benefit from a restricted high-risk group, concentrated on the elderly and chronic disease sufferers, while skin cancer risk is more diffuse in the population

RELATIVE IMPACT

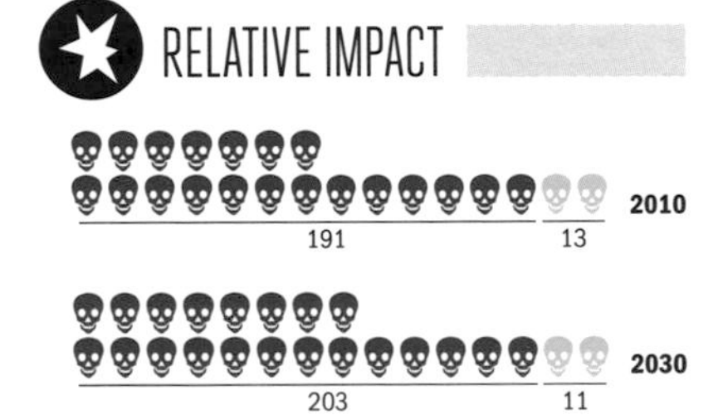

HOTSPOTS

2010	Country	2030
10,000	INDIA	10,000
3,000	NIGERIA	4,250
2,250	RUSSIA	3,000
2,000	UKRAINE	2,250
1,750	BANGLADESH	2,000

GEOPOLITICAL VULNERABILITY

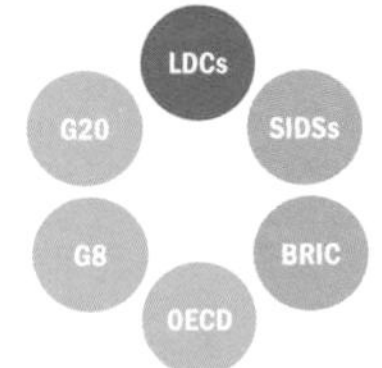

 Deaths

 Developing Country Low Emitters

 Developed

Developing Country High Emitters

Other Industrialized

 = Deaths per 10 million

Change in relation to overall global population and/or GDP

  = Millions of USD (2010 PPP non-discounted)

Changes in the average levels and the extremities of heat and cold affect health. Increases in hospitalization and mortality rates are particularly evident for those suffering from chronic disease during heat waves (Michelozzi et al., 2009). Vulnerabilities to extreme hot and cold exist both in developed and developing countries and involve cardiovascular and respiratory diseases, skin cancer, and influenza-like illnesses, with both positive and negative effects. In tropical developing countries, exposure to heat is higher, especially since air conditioning, being linked to income, is less prevalent (Isaac and van Vuuren, 2009). Nor do tropical countries reap any of the potential benefits of shorter, warmer winters. While cooler, wealthy countries are likely to see improved health outcomes, experts have argued that even in developed countries, heat-related deaths may be greater than any gains from milder winters (McMichael et al., 2006). In Europe for example, 2003 was the hottest summer in some 500 years and left an estimated death toll of approximately 35,000–70,000 additional deaths (Patz et al., 2005; Robine et al., 2008). Scientists have argued the extent to which such extreme heat waves would be unlikely without climate change (Hansen et al., 2012). Reponses to the challenge benefit from clearly delineated groups among chronic disease sufferers. Skin cancer risk is much more generalized and presents a growing challenging for the promotion of safe behavioural adjustments for communities at risk (Bharath and Turner, 2009).

CLIMATE MECHANISM

Warm spells and heat waves have become more common and extreme, cold spells less so (IPCC, 2007). Because heat causes sweating, which removes water from the blood, high temperatures "thicken" blood, causing heart attacks or strokes (Solonin and Katsyuba, 2003). Sufferers of chronic respiratory illnesses, such as chronic obstructive pulmonary disease are also under additional stress during periods of high heat, but reduced stress in cold extremes. The elderly are another major risk group, due in part to impaired body temperature regulation (Lin et al., 2009; Gosling et al., 2009). Populations are thought to gradually acclimatize to increasing heat up to a point, a process for which the elderly are poorly equipped to handle; however, the speed of heat increase is outstripping the capacity to acclimatize (Kennedy and Munce, 2003; Kjellstrom, 2009b). Skin cancer rates are expected to be affected by behavioural change—as people in colder climates spend more time outdoors as the planet warms, increasing the carcinogenicity of UV radiation—and by the delay or speed of recovery of the ozone layer, due to temperature effects in the upper atmosphere (Bharath and Turner, 2009; Gilchrest et al., 1999; Waugh et al., 2009). In some regions, ozone recovery is speeded up through climate change; in others, the recovery is slowed. Finally, influenza-like illnesses, in particular pneumonia, respond in complex ways to weather, but are generally more prevalent at lower temperatures, i.e., during winter, with climate change reducing the risks (van Noort et al., 2012).

IMPACTS

The global impact of climate change on heat and cold-related illnesses is estimated at 35,000 additional deaths a year in 2010, with one million more people affected than would have been the case without climate change. The net figure includes approximately 45,000 deaths, mainly in developing countries, and close to 10,000 deaths avoided in developed countries, which are expected to see a net positive effect.

The worst affected countries are mainly developing countries of Africa and Asia, but include Russia and several Commonwealth of Independent States countries where chronic disease burdens are very high. The largest total effects occur in India, with over 10,000 deaths per year. Very high total impacts are also seen in countries such as Nigeria, Russia, the Ukraine, Bangladesh, and DR Congo.

The death toll is expected to remain relatively stable through to 2030, with mortality increasing to 55,000 people, but with avoided deaths also doubling from 10,000 to 20,000 over the same time period.

THE BROADER CONTEXT

The types of illnesses, particularly non-communicable illnesses, that are most affected by extreme heat and cold fluctuations are widely prevalent in both developed and developing countries. The incidence of cardiovascular and chronic respiratory diseases as well as skin cancer have increased in the last decade, while respiratory, including influenza-like diseases have declined (WHO BDD, 2000 and 2011).

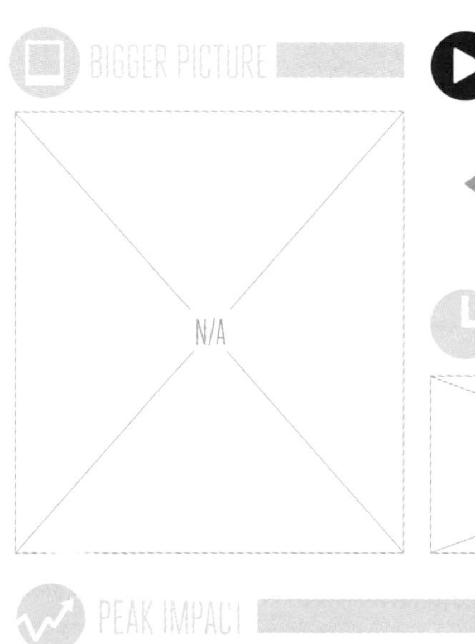

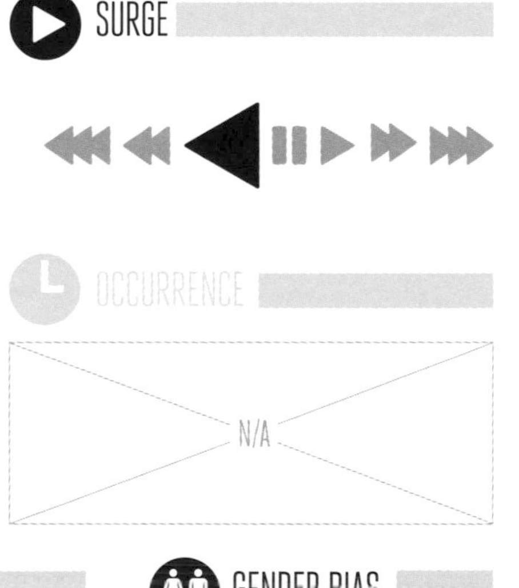

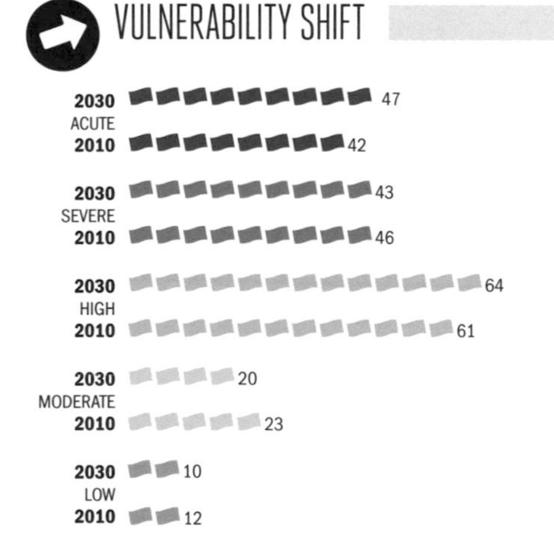

PEAK IMPACT

N/A

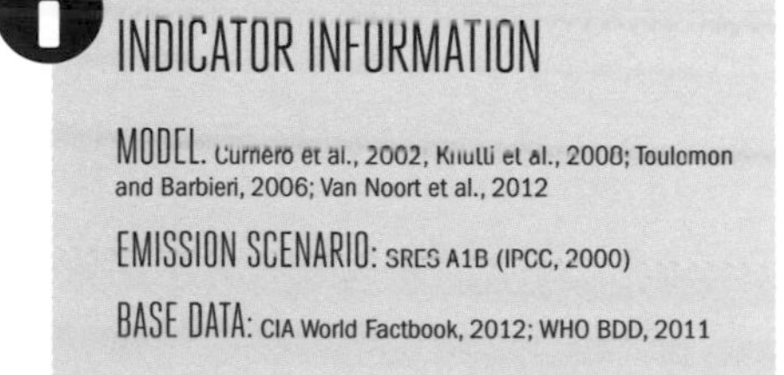

INDICATOR INFORMATION

MODEL: Curriero et al., 2002, Knutti et al., 2008; Toulomon and Barbieri, 2006; Van Noort et al., 2012

EMISSION SCENARIO: SRES A1B (IPCC, 2000)

BASE DATA: CIA World Factbook, 2012; WHO BDD, 2011

= 5 countries (rounded)

Acute Severe High Moderate Low

VULNERABILITIES AND WIDER OUTCOMES

Elderly populations are at the greatest risk by far, with two-thirds of all mortality in persons of 70 years of age, and over 80% of all mortality in persons over 60.

Countries with higher relative burdens of cardiovascular risk and chronic respiratory diseases have higher levels of vulnerability. Those same sufferers are less at risk of disease aggravation during milder winters; so geography is key: those in cold countries will benefit, while those in warmer countries will suffer more. Heat stress effects are deemed also to be stronger in tropical regions where temperatures are already elevated, air conditioning and insulation less prevalent, and outdoor work more common (Kovats and Hajat, 2008; Kjellstrom, 2009b). Since most developing countries fall in this category, there are negative implications for poverty reduction and development. Cities are more vulnerable, because they exaggerate extreme heat through the well-known heat island effect (Campbell-Lendrum and Corvalán, 2007).

More frequent and severe hot periods with sudden impacts will contribute to temporary capacity overloads on the health systems of affected areas, which may lead to further degradations in health services, with still additional negative health outcomes (Frumkin et al., 2007; Gosling et al., 2009). The well-being and health of outdoor workers especially in hot countries is also seriously jeopardized (Kjellstrom et al., 2009b).

RESPONSES

Responses include a variety of measures from preventative (pre-summer) health assessments, early-warning procedures for heat spells, and behaviour adjustments, such as increasing fluid intake, adjusting medication, and avoiding midday heat, as well as increasing climate-controlled indoor cooling or heightened vigilance of high risk patients. Longer-term measures might include changes to building design and housing, improved institutional care for the elderly, and stricter controls on urban air pollution, which seriously exacerbates the heat effects of the summer hot spells (Kovats and Hajat, 2008; Ayres et al., 2009).

THE INDICATOR

The indicator measures the impact of new heat or cold patterns on cardiovascular and respiratory diseases, skin cancer, and influenza-like illnesses (Curriero et al., 2002; Bharath and Turner, 2009; Hill et al., 2010; van Noort et al., 2012). Baseline mortality is drawn from World Health Organization disease data (WHO BDD, 2011). The indicator has corrected for the so-called "harvesting effect"– i.e., climate change merely shifts the timing of mortality, as opposed to triggering it, given the high share of morality in already high-risk groups. Baseline research from a wider set of countries studies would help improve the analysis, although the basic mechanisms of heat stress are understood to be broadly similar from country to country (Suchday et al., 2006). While the temperature effect is highly certain, other weather effects, such as humidity, which plays a key role, are more unpredictable. The complex interplay of disease and climate parameters for influenza-like illnesses is particularly difficult to map.

ESTIMATES COUNTRY-LEVEL IMPACT

COUNTRY	2010	2030	2010	2030
ACUTE				
Armenia	75	85	400	-1,250
Belarus	250	300	6,000	6,750
Bosnia and Herzegovina	50	85	1,000	1,500
Bulgaria	200	200	2,000	-250
Burundi	150	200	6,250	9,250
Cameroon	350	450	15,000	20,000
Central African Republic	95	150	4,000	5,500
Chad	250	400	10,000	15,000
Comoros	10	15	450	700
Congo	70	100	3,000	5,000
Cote d'Ivoire	350	450	15,000	20,000
Croatia	55	75	650	-300
Cuba	150	150	5,000	4,750
DR Congo	1,250	2,000	50,000	85,000
Equatorial Guinea	15	20	550	850
Estonia	20	25	700	750
Gabon	25	40	1,250	1,750
Georgia	65	100	1,750	3,000
Germany	700	1,250	80,000	150,000
Greece	150	200	15,000	20,000
Guinea	150	250	6,750	10,000
Guinea-Bissau	25	40	1,250	1,750
Haiti	200	250	8,750	10,000
Honduras	150	150	3,750	4,750
Hungary	100	200	4,000	5,250
Italy	600	850	60,000	95,000
Latvia	45	60	1,500	1,750
Lesotho	40	35	1,750	1,500
Liberia	75	150	3,250	5,750
Lithuania	10	55	-600	300
Macedonia	45	60	950	1,250
Malawi	250	400	10,000	15,000
Marshall Islands	1	1	40	50
Moldova	55	75	1,500	950
Mozambique	400	550	15,000	20,000
Namibia	40	55	1,250	1,500
Nigeria	3,000	4,250	100,000	150,000
Romania	300	400	150	-6,000
Russia	2,250	3,000	75,000	90,000
Seychelles	1	1	65	95
Somalia	150	250	5,750	10,000
Suriname	10	10	350	350
Swaziland	25	30	800	900
Tuvalu			5	5
Ukraine	2,000	2,250	55,000	60,000
Zambia	250	400	10,000	15,000
Zimbabwe	200	250	8,250	10,000
SEVERE				
Angola	200	300	5,250	9,000
Antigua and Barbuda	1	1	40	40
Australia	100	250	8,000	20,000
Austria	30	85	3,000	8,750
Bangladesh	1,750	2,000	70,000	85,000
Barbados	5	1	150	100
Benin	90	150	3,750	5,750
Bolivia	100	150	3,250	4,250
Brazil	1,750	2,000	50,000	55,000
Burkina Faso	150	250	6,000	10,000
Djibouti	10	10	300	350
Dominica	1	1	35	35
Dominican Republic	150	150	4,000	4,250
El Salvador	55	65	1,500	2,000
Eritrea	45	65	1,750	2,750
Ethiopia	750	1,250	30,000	50,000
Fiji	10	10	250	250
Finland	30	70	3,000	6,750
Gambia	20	25	750	1,000
Grenada	1	1	50	50
Guyana	10	5	250	200
India	10,000	10,000	500,000	500,000
Kenya	350	450	15,000	20,000
Kyrgyzstan	60	75	1,000	-600
Madagascar	200	350	9,000	15,000
Mauritania	30	45	1,250	2,000
Myanmar	600	650	25,000	30,000
New Zealand	20	50	1,500	3,750
Niger	150	250	5,500	9,750
North Korea	150	300	7,250	10,000
Poland	250	350	-3,000	-15,000
Rwanda	100	150	5,250	7,250
Saint Vincent	1	1	55	55
Samoa	1	1	55	65
Sao Tome and Principe	1	5	85	150
Senegal	100	150	4,500	6,500
Sierra Leone	75	100	3,000	4,750
Sudan/South Sudan	600	850	25,000	35,000
Sweden	45	90	5,500	10,000
Tanzania	350	550	15,000	20,000
Togo	55	80	2,250	3,250
Tonga	1	1	30	35
Yemen	200	450	8,250	20,000
HIGH				
Afghanistan	250	400	10,000	15,000
Albania	5	20	-1,500	-3,250
Algeria	150	200	4,750	5,750

Additional mortality due to climate change - yearly average

CLIMATE VULNERABILITY

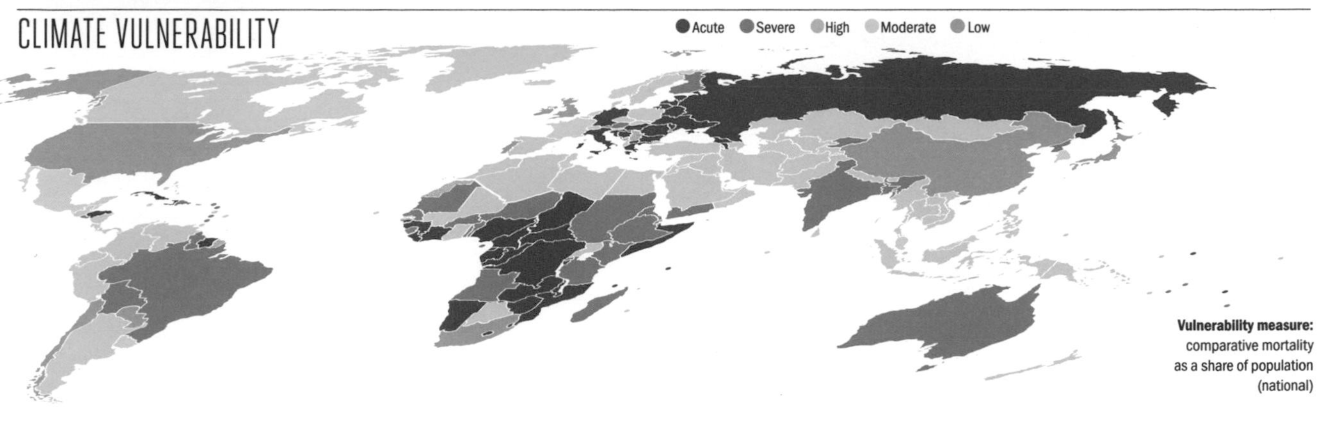

CLIMATE UNCERTAINTY

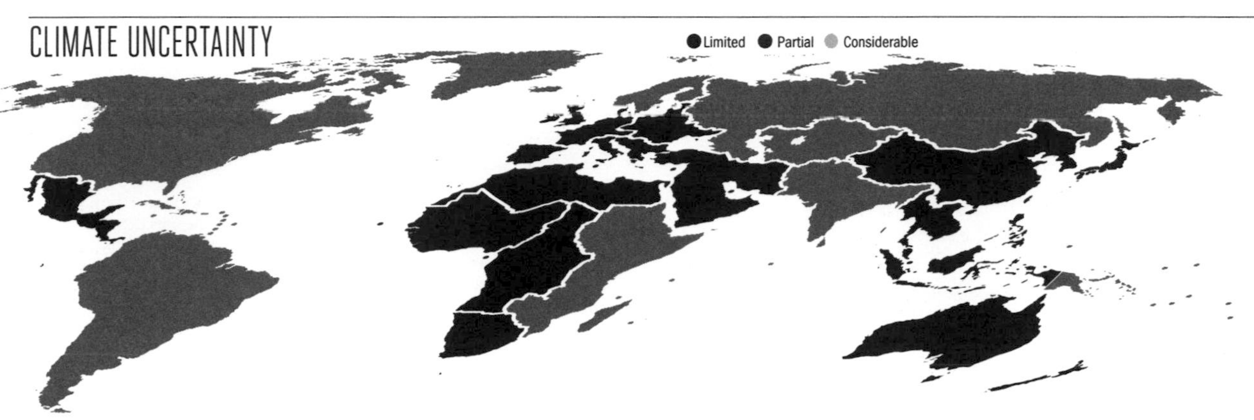

COUNTRY	2010 (deaths)	2030 (deaths)	2010 (persons affected)	2030 (persons affected)
Argentina	300	250	-9,750	-45,000
Azerbaijan	25	65	-2,250	-5,000
Belize	1	1	85	100
Bhutan	5	10	250	400
Botswana	15	15	650	700
Brunei	1	1	100	150
Cambodia	100	150	5,000	5,500
Canada	75	200	10,000	25,000
Cape Verde	5	5	95	100
Colombia	300	350	8,750	10,000
Costa Rica	20	25	850	1,000
Cyprus	5	10	600	900
Czech Republic	30	70	-3,000	-5,250
Denmark	15	30	2,500	5,250
Ecuador	60	70	1,750	2,000
Egypt	450	500	10,000	15,000
Ghana	200	250	8,250	10,000
Guatemala	90	100	2,500	3,500
Indonesia	1,250	1,250	35,000	35,000
Iran	250	300	7,250	8,750
Iraq	100	150	3,500	4,750
Israel	30	35	2,750	3,000
Jamaica	15	15	400	400
Kazakhstan	15	85	-8,000	-15,000
Kiribati	1	1	20	25
Laos	45	50	2,000	2,000
Lebanon	35	40	1,500	1,750
Libya	20	30	1,000	1,250
Luxembourg	1	1	100	400
Maldives	1	1	25	40
Mali	80	150	3,500	5,500
Mauritius	5	5	200	300
Micronesia	1	1	30	35
Mongolia	15	10	100	-700
Morocco	100	150	3,500	4,000
Nepal	250	300	9,500	15,000
Nicaragua	40	55	1,750	2,250
Oman	10	15	350	650
Pakistan	1,250	1,750	55,000	75,000
Palau			10	10
Panama	15	20	750	800
Papua New Guinea	60	80	2,500	3,500
Peru	100	150	3,500	4,000
Philippines	700	800	20,000	25,000
Saint Lucia	1	1	70	65
Saudi Arabia	75	150	7,250	10,000
Singapore	25	25	2,250	2,500
Slovakia	40	40	-1,000	-3,500
Slovenia	5	10	900	1,500
Solomon Islands	5	5	150	200
Spain	250	300	30,000	45,000
Sri Lanka	90	150	2,750	3,750
Switzerland	15	40	2,000	5,250
Thailand	200	350	5,250	9,750
Trinidad and Tobago	5	5	300	250
Turkey	250	500	10,000	20,000
Uganda	250	500	10,000	20,000
Uzbekistan	200	300	2,500	-1,500
Vanuatu	1	1	50	70
Venezuela	150	150	6,250	7,250
Vietnam	450	350	20,000	15,000
MODERATE				
Bahamas	1	1	40	70
Bahrain	1	1	150	150
Belgium	20	20	5,500	9,250
France	20	150	10,000	30,000
Iceland		1	50	150
Jordan	10	10	200	300
Kuwait	5	5	350	450
Malaysia	1	65	40	3,000
Malta			200	350
Mexico	150	95	5,500	4,250
Netherlands	-10	1	3,000	8,500
Norway	5	10	1,250	2,750
Qatar	1	1	70	70
South Korea	-1	30	5,000	15,000
Syria	10	10	300	300
Tajikistan	45	20	-1,000	-7,250
Tunisia	1	30	75	900
Turkmenistan	25	5	-4,500	-15,000
United Arab Emirates	5	1	300	250
Uruguay	20	10	-1,750	-5,000
LOW				
Chile	-20	-70	-9,250	-25,000
China	-5,500	-15,000	-500,000	-1,000,000
Ireland	-15	-15	-250	900
Japan	-850	-1,750	20,000	50,000
Paraguay	-5	-25	-3,000	-9,000
Portugal	-15	-60	5,250	7,750
South Africa	-300	-1,250	-100,000	-200,000
Timor Leste				
United Kingdom	-55	-200	25,000	40,000
United States	-1,500	-3,250	-100,000	-250,000

Additional persons affected due to climate change - yearly average

HUNGER

ESTIMATES GLOBAL CLIMATE IMPACT

2010 EFFECT TODAY

DEATHS PER YEAR **225,000**

2030 EFFECT TOMORROW

DEATHS PER YEAR **380,000**

MORTALITY IMPACT

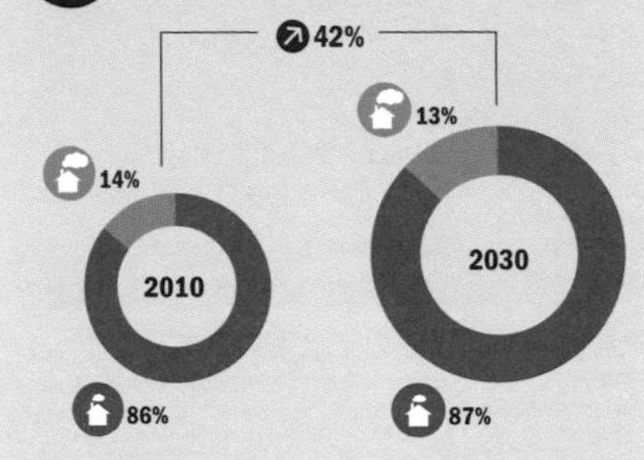

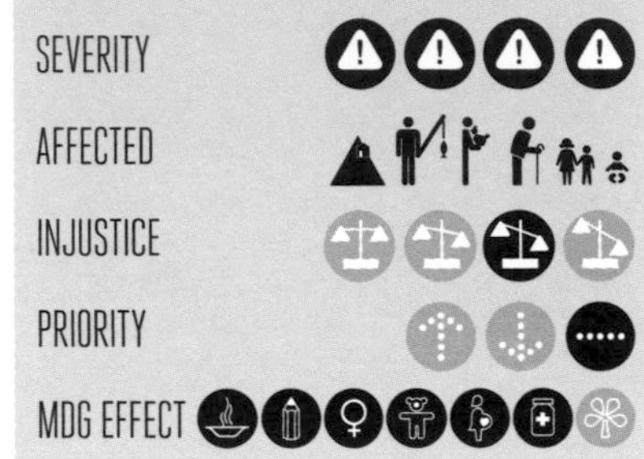

- 200,000 deaths each year and over 200 million people affected are estimated to suffer from food insecurity as a result of climate change in lower-income countries
- Half of all such deaths are of children and infants in the world's poorest communities, the group least responsible for climate change
- Although hunger is among the most preventable causes of human death, there are no quick fixes to the 850 million people facing hunger today
- There are major ongoing food emergencies and famine facing populations in the Horn of Africa and the Sahel

RELATIVE IMPACT

HOTSPOTS

2010		2030
100,000	**INDIA**	250,000
10,000	**PAKISTAN**	25,000
9,750	**BANGLADESH**	15,000
10,000	**NIGERIA**	10,000
7,500	**INDONESIA**	10,000

GEOPOLITICAL VULNERABILITY

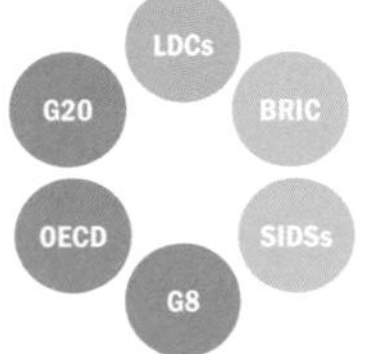

Deaths
Developing Country Low Emitters
Developing Country High Emitters
Developed
Other Industrialized
= Deaths per million
Change in relation to overall global population and/or GDP

Fifteen percent of all human beings are undernourished and 850 million people are prevented from active lives as a result of hunger (FAO, 2011). The Millennium Development Goal (MDG) target for reducing hunger has remained static since the early 1990s in all the world's developing regions. Despite enormous increases in wealth over the last two decades, the world has made almost no progress on hunger and its roots in the most extreme forms of poverty. A humanitarian food emergency continues in the Sahel and the Horn of Africa (HPN, 2012; Oxfam, 2012; CARE, 2012). Scientists are agreed that extreme heat and drought are key triggers of famine (Hansen et al., 2012; Glanz (ed.), 1987). The combined effects of climate change on agricultural production on land, rivers, coastal zones, and oceans reduces disposable incomes and food availability for the world's poorest, especially in those communities with the least resources to adjust and diversify activities in the face of warmer and more extreme weather (Nelson et al., 2009; Allison et al., 2009). When people are hungry for prolonged periods, they not only suffer illness and potentially death as a result of acute nutritional imbalances, but may also become seriously predisposed to illness and death from other diseases, such as pneumonia, diarrheal infections, malaria, and measles, dramatically expanding the death toll that is attributable to hunger (WHO, 2004).

CLIMATE MECHANISM

The effects of climate change on agriculture and fisheries are well covered in other sections of this report and extensively examined in the scientific, development, and humanitarian literature (IPCC, 2007; UNDP, 2007; World Bank, 2010). Rising heat, increasing variability, overabundance, or absence of rainfall, flooding, drought, disease and insect infestations are real threats to agricultural communities around the world (Parry et al., 2004; Gregory et al., 2009). Coastal areas are endangered by the rise in sea levels and the depletion of fish populations (Dasgupta et al., 2009; Allison et al., 2009). Increasing temperatures are making it difficult for subsistence farmers to accomplish the same amount of work in a given day and leave them few options other than to go hungry when food availability and/or incomes fall below critical levels (Kjellstrom et al., 2009b). Communities outside of the subsistence spectrum are much better able to adjust to the effects of climate change and minimize losses.

IMPACTS

The global impact of climate change on rates of hunger causes more than 200,000 deaths each year, half of which are among children in low-income countries. This implies that over 200 million people each year are affected by hunger as a result of climate change. Anticipated increases in socio-economic development should continue to reduce the global burden of malnutrition deaths into the future (Mathers and Loncar, 2005). However, unless actions are taken by 2030, nearly 400,000 lives could be lost each year, and the number of people affected could exceed 400 million. Lower-income developing countries of Africa and Asia are worst affected, with Sub-Saharan Africa, least developed, and land-locked developing countries dominating the list of those hit hardest. However, even as the scale of the problem expands, researchers project a decrease in the number of countries suffering the most acute effects, resulting from expected socio-economic development over the next 20 years. India suffers more than half of all the hunger effects of climate change, with an estimated climate change-aggravated death toll in excess of 100,000 people yearly. Bangladesh, Indonesia, Nigeria, and Pakistan are also heavily affected.

THE BROADER CONTEXT

Poverty is declining. Although serious progress has been made on the MDGs, despite the array of challenges faced, the important goal for hunger is not among the success stories (UN, 2012). More than 2 million children die each year solely as a result of undernutrition (WHO, 2009). The number of people living with hunger has been stable for decades and remains undiminished by the opposing forces of rapidly expanding income and population growth. Food prices adjusted to inflation were at their highest in the 1960s and 1970s, declining until around 2000, at which point they have continued to rise, culminating in current new highs (FAO, 2011).

VULNERABILITIES AND WIDER OUTCOMES

The world's poorest groups spend virtually all their income on food,

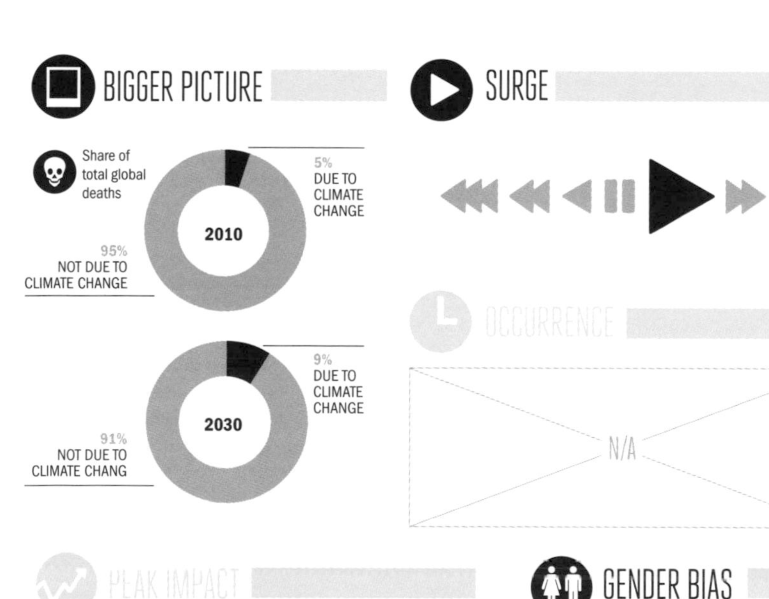

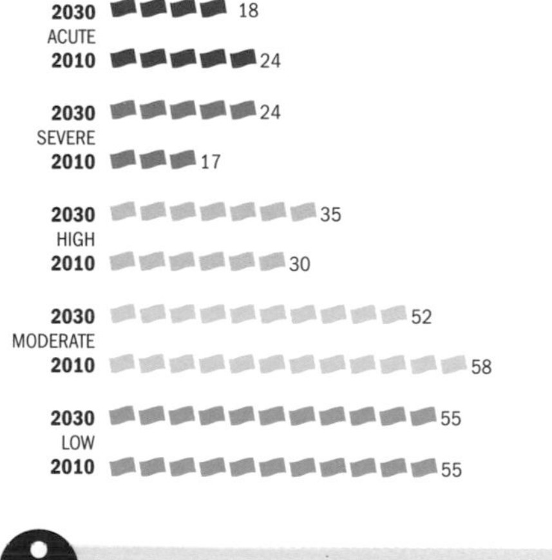

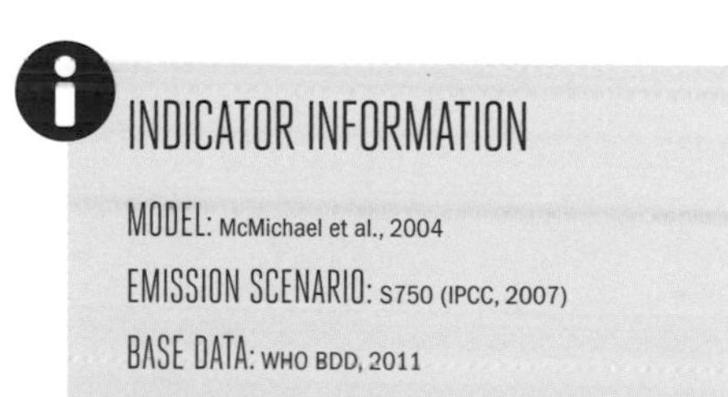

● Acute ● Severe ● High ● Moderate ● Low

making them more vulnerable to shifts in food prices. Issues affecting food prices include fuel oil, food preferences, population and income growth, trade regulations, extreme weather, and macroeconomic sensitivities in commodity markets, to name a few (FAO, 2011). Welfare is most compromised when affected communities are less able to take autonomous action in response to additional pressures from climate change. By far the worst off are subsistence, small-scale farmers, and fishermen in developing countries (Morton, 2007; Nelson et al., 2009). Hunger stalls development progress. This can be understood through analysis of the effects that sickness and death from hunger have across the full spectrum of the MDGs. First, Goal 1, aimed at eradicating hunger itself. Goal 2, aimed at universalizing primary education is affected, since school attendance rates are lowest in communities with the highest levels of malnutrition; this, in turn, affects Goal 3 (gender equality), since it prevents girls from beginning school (Glewwe and Jacoby, 1993; UN, 2012). Goal 4, which aims to reduce child mortality is affected, since hunger is a vicious killer of children and infants under 5—around 50% of all mortality). The close interlinkages between malnutrition, child and maternal health also imply serious effects for maternal health (Goal 5) (Black et al., 2008). Finally, progress towards MDG Goal 6, aiming to significantly reduce HIV/AIDS, malaria and other diseases is also threatened, since a majority of deaths from hunger occur as a result of diseases for which low weight is a key risk factor, especially malaria, pneumonia, diarrheal diseases, and measles (WHO, 2004).

RESPONSES

First and foremost is the humanitarian imperative to intervene and avert highly preventable deaths as a result of hunger aggravated by climate change (Parry et al., 2009). The inability of the international community to defuse the simultaneous and ongoing Horn of Africa and Sahelean food crises is a testament to the lack of preparedness and the inadequacy of contemporary responses to food security emergencies (Oxfam, 2012; CARE, 2012).

There is no vaccine for hunger. Decades of development commitments and foreign aid have not eradicated global hunger. Trade conditions continue to disfavour equitable food availability for many of the world's poor, and the World Trade Organization negotiations offer faint hope for the world's most vulnerable groups despite the solutions proposed (FAO, 2011; Moser and Rose, 2012; Priyadarshi, 2009).

Development programmes, it is hoped, will become more effective (Brown and Funk, 2009). The Ghana country study in this report emphasizes what steps must be taken to counteract the pressure on the disposable income of food-stressed families and communities. Without these sensible steps, it will be challenging to adopt and sustain the wide range of sensible technical or social protection measures which could limit risks, through insurance policies, new seed and fertilizer purchases, or investments in irrigation infrastructure, capital, and financial resources (Parry et al., 2009). Possibilities for expanding the purchasing power of the most vulnerable communities could be created through the promotion of small-scale agricultural industries that increase options for farmers to access and sell their goods in global supply chains. It is possible to enable rural communities currently locked out of global markets to benefit from higher food prices, rather than, as net importers of food, to suffer from them (Swinnen and Squicciarinim, 2012).

THE INDICATOR

The indicator measures the risk for malnutrition and disease for which low-weight is a principal risk factor as a result of global climate change (WHO, 2004). It relies on the latest global health data updated by the World Health Organization (WHO BDD, 2011). Scientists and the IPCC have recognized the challenges of hunger in the context of climate change. In addition to socio-economic considerations, which add layers of complexity and potential error, the many uncertainties related to impacts on agriculture apply to hunger. Nevertheless, the scientific community is virtually unanimous that lower-income groups are profoundly affected by the impacts of climate change on agriculture (Loetze-Campen et al. in Edenhofer et al., 2012). The indicator could have benefitted from the use of updated emission scenarios than those upon which the base model is built. The base model includes carbon fertilization, which is otherwise considered a "carbon" issue in this report.

ESTIMATES COUNTRY-LEVEL IMPACT

COUNTRY	2010	2030	2010	2030
ACUTE				
Afghanistan	5,750	7,500	5,000	6,500
Bangladesh	9,750	15,000	10,000	15,000
Bhutan	60	150	65	150
Burkina Faso	1,750	1,750	800	850
Cameroon	1,500	1,750	750	800
Central African Republic	250	400	150	250
Chad	1,250	1,500	650	700
DR Congo	4,750	7,500	3,000	4,750
Guinea-Bissau	200	200	85	90
Haiti	600	800	750	1,000
India	100,000	250,000	150,000	250,000
Myanmar	5,250	7,750	5,750	8,500
Nepal	2,000	2,500	2,000	2,750
North Korea	1,750	2,500	2,000	2,750
Pakistan	10,000	25,000	9,750	20,000
Sierra Leone	650	700	300	350
Somalia	1,750	2,000	1,500	1,750
Sudan/South Sudan	3,250	4,000	2,750	3,500
SEVERE				
Angola	1,750	2,000	850	900
Benin	600	650	300	300
Bolivia	300	650	400	850
Burundi	400	600	250	400
Cote d'Ivoire	850	1,250	550	850
Djibouti	40	50	35	45
Equatorial Guinea	50	50	25	25
Ethiopia	3,250	5,250	2,000	3,250
Gambia	85	90	40	45
Guatemala	500	1,000	650	1,500
Guinea	800	850	400	400
Indonesia	7,500	10,000	9,500	15,000
Iraq	850	2,000	750	1,750
Liberia	250	250	100	150
Malawi	650	1,000	400	650
Mali	1,250	1,500	650	700
Mozambique	1,000	1,750	650	1,000
Niger	1,500	1,750	750	800
Nigeria	10,000	10,000	5,250	5,500
South Africa	1,250	1,750	700	1,250
Tanzania	1,500	2,500	950	1,500
Timor-Leste	35	50	35	55
Uganda	1,500	2,250	850	1,250
Zambia	600	900	350	550
HIGH				
Algeria	550	600	250	300
Cambodia	200	300	900	1,250
Comoros	35	35	15	20
Congo	150	200	80	150
Dominican Republic	100	200	250	450
Ecuador	200	350	250	450
El Salvador	75	150	150	350
Eritrea	85	150	50	80
Gabon	40	45	20	20
Ghana	900	950	450	450
Guyana	10	15	25	30
Honduras	80	150	200	350
Jamaica	35	65	85	150
Kenya	800	1,250	500	750
Laos	85	100	350	500
Lesotho	30	50	20	30
Madagascar	600	650	300	300
Maldives	5	10	5	10
Marshall Islands	1	1	1	5
Mauritania	150	150	75	75
Mexico	1,000	1,750	2,250	4,000
Morocco	500	600	450	500
Namibia	30	45	20	30
Nicaragua	70	150	90	200
Papua New Guinea	95	200	450	900
Peru	650	1,250	800	1,500
Rwanda	350	550	200	350
Sao Tome and Principe	5	5	1	1
Senegal	550	550	250	250
Sri Lanka	200	350	250	450
Swaziland	20	35	15	20
Thailand	1,000	1,500	1,250	2,000
Togo	250	300	150	150
Yemen	1,250	1,500	1,000	1,500
Zimbabwe	250	400	150	250
MODERATE				
Antigua and Barbuda	1	1	1	1
Argentina	300	500	650	1,250
Bahamas	1	1	1	5
Bahrain	1	1	5	5
Barbados	1	1	5	5
Belize	1	5	5	10
Botswana	15	25	10	15
Brazil	1,250	2,500	3,000	5,500
Cape Verde	5	5	5	5
Chile	85	150	200	350
China	1,750	2,750	7,500	10,000
Colombia	250	450	500	950
Costa Rica	5	10	15	25
Cyprus	1	1	5	10
Dominica	1	1	1	1

Additional mortality due to climate change - yearly average

CLIMATE VULNERABILITY

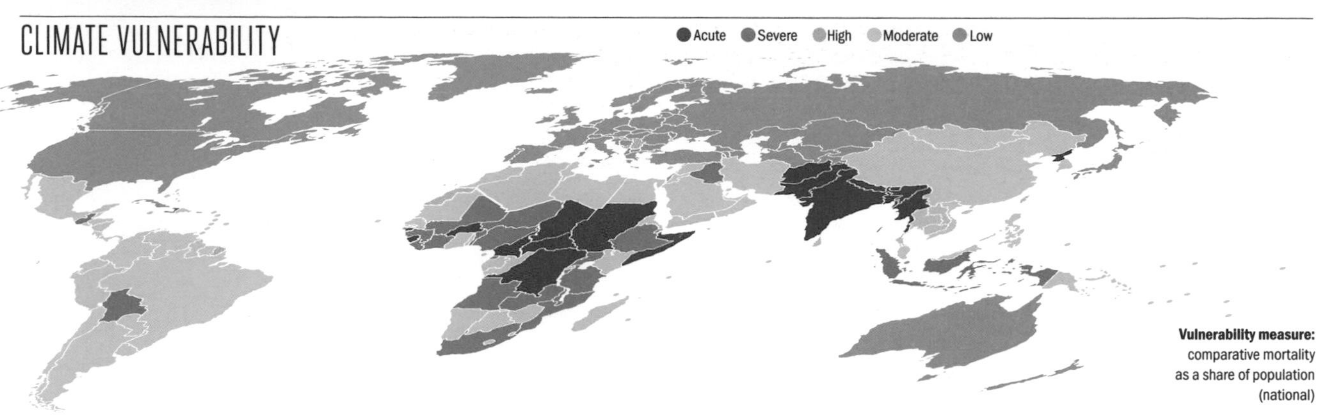

Vulnerability measure: comparative mortality as a share of population (national)

CLIMATE UNCERTAINTY

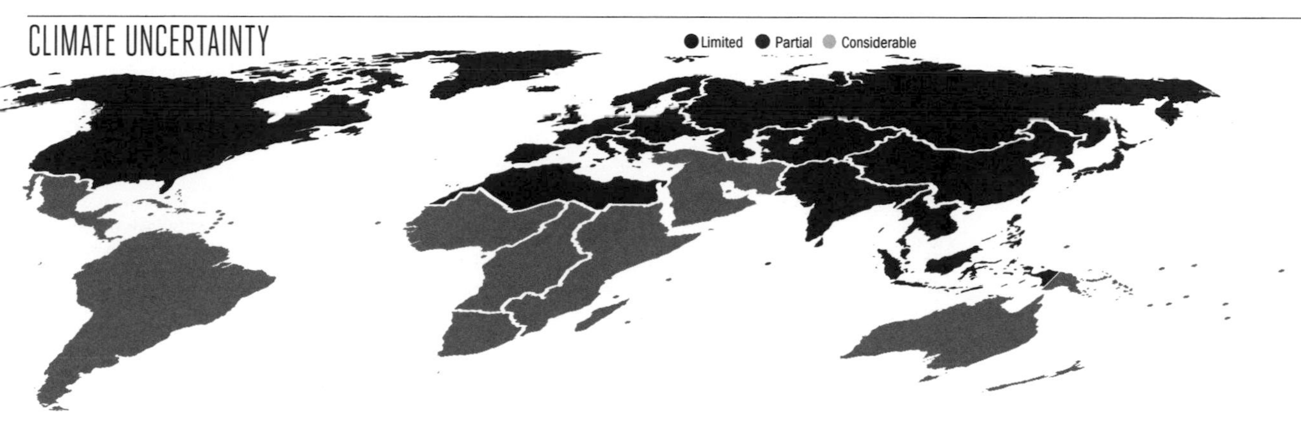

COUNTRY	2010	2030	2010	2030
Egypt	600	750	550	650
Fiji	5	5	15	25
Grenada	1	1	1	1
Iran	200	400	900	1,750
Jordan	20	45	85	200
Kiribati	1	1	5	5
Kuwait	1	5	10	15
Lebanon	5	15	30	55
Libya	15	20	70	80
Malaysia	75	100	350	450
Mauritius	5	5	1	1
Micronesia	1	1	5	5
Mongolia	5	15	35	60
Oman	1	5	5	20
Palau				1
Panama	20	35	50	85
Paraguay	40	90	95	200
Philippines	550	700	2,250	3,250
Qatar		1	1	1
Saint Lucia	1	1	1	1
Saint Vincent	1	1	1	5
Samoa	1	1	5	10
Saudi Arabia	55	150	250	550
Seychelles	1	1	1	1
Solomon Islands	5	5	15	20
South Korea	55	90	250	400
Suriname	1	5	5	10
Syria	50	100	200	450
Tonga	1	1	1	5
Trinidad and Tobago	5	10	15	25
Tunisia	75	85	300	350
Tuvalu				1
United Arab Emirates	5	10	20	35
Uruguay	25	40	55	90
Vanuatu	1	1	5	10
Venezuela	90	150	200	400
Vietnam	200	250	850	1,250
LOW				
Albania				
Armenia				
Australia				
Austria				
Azerbaijan				
Belarus				
Belgium				
Bosnia and Herzegovina				
Brunei				
Bulgaria				
Canada				
Croatia				
Cuba				
Czech Republic				
Denmark				
Estonia				
Finland				
France				
Georgia				
Germany				
Greece				
Hungary				
Iceland				
Ireland				
Israel				
Italy				
Japan				
Kazakhstan				
Kyrgyzstan				
Latvia				
Lithuania				
Luxembourg				
Macedonia				
Malta				
Moldova				
Netherlands				
New Zealand				
Norway				
Poland				
Portugal				
Romania				
Russia				
Singapore				
Slovakia				
Slovenia				
Spain				
Sweden				
Switzerland				
Tajikistan				
Turkey				
Turkmenistan				
Ukraine				
United Kingdom				
United States				
Uzbekistan				

Additional persons affected due to climate change (thousands) - yearly average

MALARIA & VECTOR-BORNE

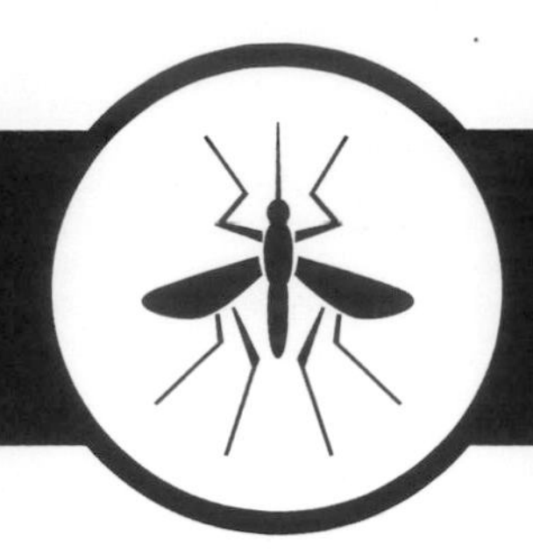

ESTIMATES GLOBAL CLIMATE IMPACT

2010 EFFECT TODAY

DEATHS PER YEAR **20,000**

2030 EFFECT TOMORROW

DEATHS PER YEAR **20,000**

MORTALITY IMPACT

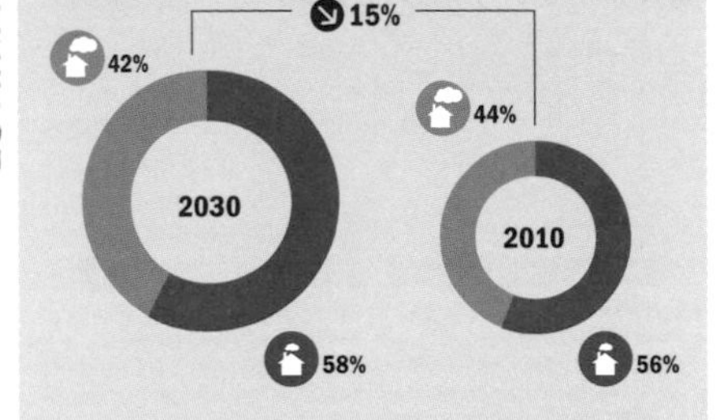

- Malaria is a large-scale cause of illness, with over 90% of child deaths in tropical regions, in particular in Africa and the Pacific
- Malaria and other vector-borne diseases have declined over the last decade, as a result of poverty reduction and anti-malaria programmes
- Vector-borne diseases are sensitive to climate; as climate becomes warmer and wetter, changes to their prevalence will slow and complicate efforts aimed at eradication
- Fighting vector-borne diseases is highly cost effective; minimizing vulnerability requires action to reduce or eradicate prevalence and increase the resilience of populations affected

RELATIVE IMPACT

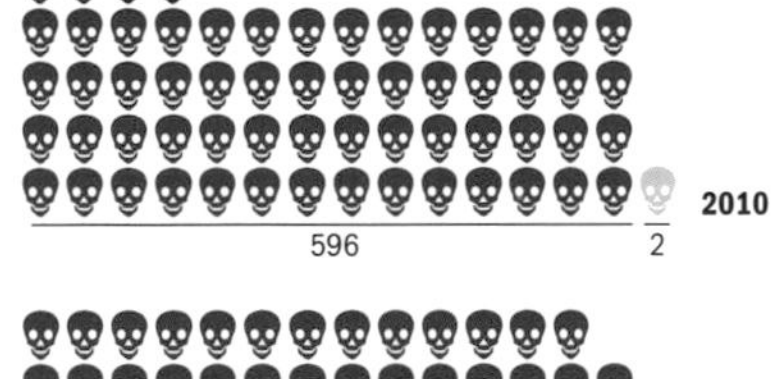

HOTSPOTS

2010		2030
6,000	DR CONGO	5,750
1,750	MOZAMBIQUE	1,750
1,750	TANZANIA	1,750
1,500	UGANDA	1,500
2,250	NIGERIA	1,250

GEOPOLITICAL VULNERABILITY

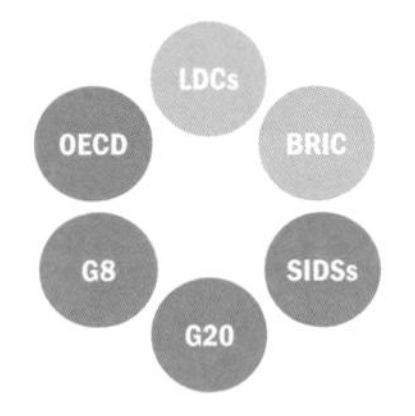

Deaths
Developing Country Low Emitters
Developing Country High Emitters
Developed
Other Industrialized

= Deaths per 10 million

Change in relation to overall global population and/or GDP

A major cause of illness in developing countries, climate change will worsen the burden of vector-borne diseases, although it is difficult to predict with any precision the areas that will be worst affected (IPCC, 2007). Countries that already have serious malaria burdens should expect to see an aggravation of these diseases, due to increasing temperatures and other climate-related phenomena. Such aggravations will be offset to some degree through anticipated socio-economic development in the predominantly lower-income countries in which these diseases are most prevalent (Mathers and Loncar, 2005). But vector-borne outbreaks are also re-occurring in places where they have long been absent: a yellow fever epidemic in Uganda in 2010 was the first in 20 years (Rosenberg and Beard, 2011). As climate change brings warmer weather to colder places, the range of vector-borne disease is also shifting from the tropics, and to higher altitudes, as insects and other vectors roam further afield. In the US for instance, Leishmaniasis, a vector-borne disease originating in Mexico and Texas has begun to shift further north (González et al., 2010). Communities now linked by globalization are also becoming exposed to higher risks, as illustrated for instance by a colony of yellow fever mosquitoes recently found in Holland (Enserink, 2010). Successful international programmes fighting these diseases should be reinforced in areas of particular risk, in order to safeguard against set-backs due to climate change in the fight to eradicate malaria and control other deadly vector-borne diseases (WHO and RBMP, 2010).

CLIMATE MECHANISM

Climate change is understood to enable the shift in vector-borne diseases like malaria, dengue, and yellow fever in several ways. As mountainous areas warm up for instance, vectors, such as mosquitos, would reach higher altitudes and increase exposure to disease in zones adjacent to affected areas; the same can be said of higher latitudes at the boundaries of current areas of infection. Transmission conditions and seasons are likely to expand in warm areas where rainfall used to be too low to support vectors, but now will increase. Temperature changes affect incubation rates and, together with range changes, increase the amount of time people are exposed to insect bites (Jetten and Focks, 1997). However, transmission could also decline, due either to a drop in rainfall and temperature peaks—beyond which diseases like malaria cannot thrive—or due to very high rainfall that washes away insect larvae (WHO, 2004 and 2011). At a smaller scale, temperatures also influence the survival rates of mosquitoes (Martens et al., 1999). As was pointed out in the Ghana country study in this report, climate change also affects human behaviour, as, for instance, when people sleep outside on the hottest nights without mosquito net protection, significantly increasing their risk of contracting vector-borne diseases.

IMPACTS

The impact of climate change on the key vector-borne diseases of malaria, dengue fever and yellow fever is estimated to be over 20,000 deaths a year today, with 6 million people affected.

Fourteen African and Pacific island countries are estimated to suffer Acute and Severe levels of vulnerability to the effects of climate change on vector-borne disease; most of these countries are land-locked developing countries, such as the Central African Republic or Zambia, or small island developing states, such as the Solomon Islands. The greatest total effects are estimated to occur in the DR Congo, with nearly 6,000 additional deaths due to vector-borne diseases in 2010. Five other countries also suffer large scale effects in the thousands: Nigeria, Mozambique, Tanzania, Uganda, and Côte d'Ivoire. By 2030, the effect of climate change on malaria is expected not to change since it is expected that there will be continued large-scale reductions in the prevalence of malaria, due mainly to economic growth over this 20-year period. In fact, as a proportion of population, malaria is estimated to decrease as a concern under these assumptions.

THE BROADER CONTEXT

According to the World Health Organization, malaria has undergone a major reduction in its overall prevalence in the last decade, falling from 1.2 million deaths in 2000 to 0.8 million deaths in 2008. However, most of the reduction occurred in the first years of the decade: over the four-year period between 2004 and 2008, there was a reduction of only 60,000 deaths (WHO BDD, 2000 and 2011). However, even at lowered rates of death, malaria

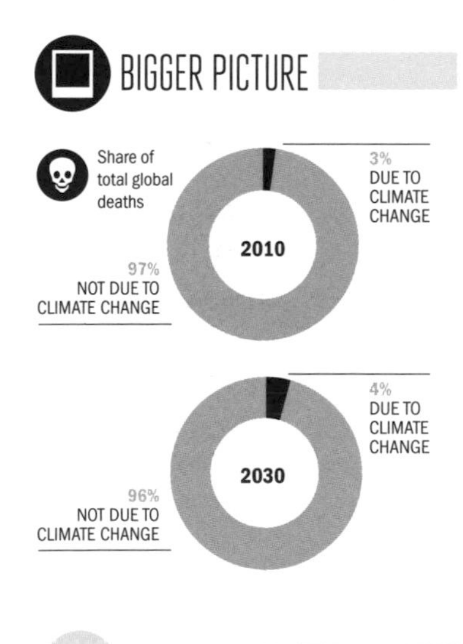

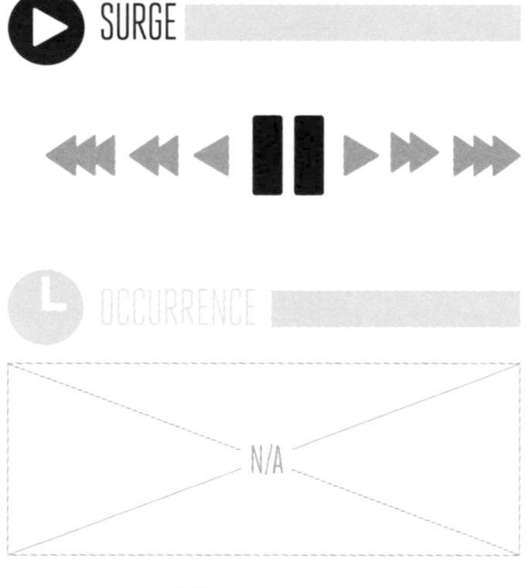

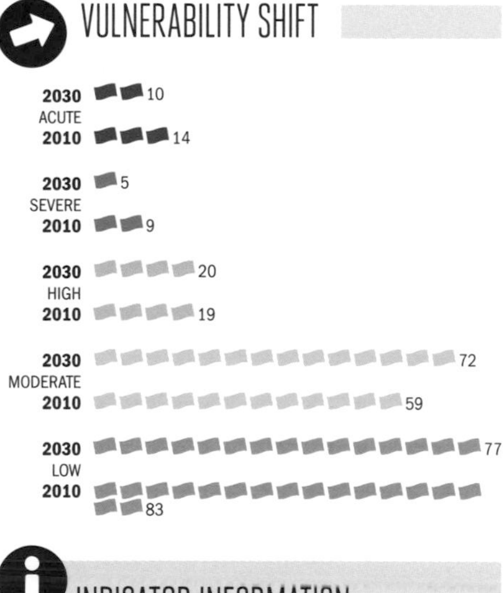

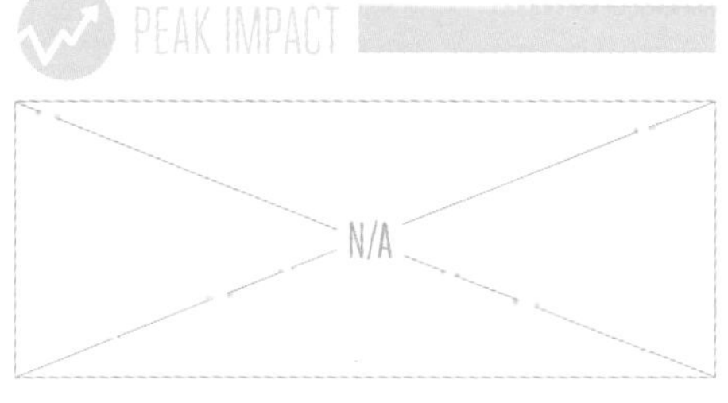

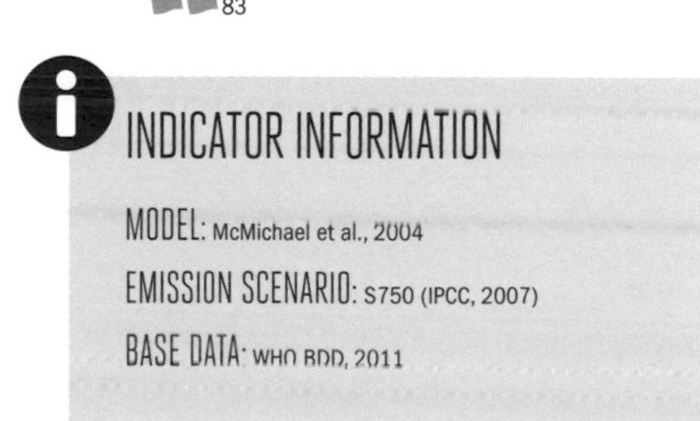

= 5 countries (rounded)

Acute Severe High Moderate Low

is considered one of the largest global contributors to sickness. Interpretations of the scale of the disease also vary dramatically, with some estimating more than 5 billion clinical episodes that resemble, and could be characterized as, malaria occurring in endemic areas annually (DCPP, 2006). Other factors, such as economic growth, will likely compensate for increased risks due to climate change, but they will also slow efforts to eradicate these diseases (Reiter, 2001).

Given that climate-aggravated malaria is highly prevalent in impoverished rural communities, delaying efforts to eradicate the disease will also delay development progress. As people in the affected communities also have a high propensity to migrate, malaria could also be carried to new areas, generating epidemics (Haleset al., 2000).

VULNERABILITIES AND WIDER OUTCOMES

Experts have identified various determinants of malaria and vector-borne diseases. Environmental conditions play an important role, such as high temperatures, high rainfall, and humidity, together with pools of still, sun-drenched water (WHO, 2009). Social vulnerabilities include the level of education enabling people to take preventative measures, such as draining mosquito ponds, or address environmental predispositions to disease (Garg et al., 2009). Finally, poverty seriously inhibits access to medicine, vaccines, and preventative measures, such as insecticides and bed nets (Breman, 2001).
Given that some 6 million people are affected, the economic productivity of those worst hit communities is jeopardized. For example, when members of rural, subsistence families lose working hours because of illness, their already minimal disposable income will be threatened further. The Ghana country study in this report illustrated how in malaria-infested areas, people were often ill several times in a given year. One study has showed how a 10% reduction in malaria is associated with a 0.3% increase in economic growth (Gallup and Sachs, 2001). With over 90% of the death toll assessed here affecting children under 15, a greater challenge faces those making efforts to improve child health, such as through attainment of Millennium Development Goal 4 for reducing child mortality.

RESPONSES

Responses are numerous and comprise preventative and treatment-type actions. Drugs and vaccines through national or region-specific immunization programmes (for dengue and yellow fever, not malaria), insecticide-treated bed nets, use of pesticides outdoors, insecticide for personal use and indoors, and civil engineering projects to drain malaria breeding sites are all key components of the anti-malaria and vector-borne response toolkit. Access to affordable health services, including through low-cost health insurance, is also critical for the speedy diagnosis and treatment of disease. Education and awareness can also help to raise the level of preventative responses and encourage health services to be sought soon after the onset of symptoms. Aside from civil infrastructure projects, vector-borne disease control is considered to be highly cost effective (DCPP, 2006).

THE INDICATOR

The indicator measures the effect of climate change on malaria, dengue fever, and yellow fever, based on World Health Organization research and data (WHO, 2004; WHO BDD, 2011). The climate change effect on malaria is used as a proxy for dengue and yellow fever, since research suggests similar mechanics apply (Epstein, 2001; Hales et al., 2002). Uncertainties in climate parameters, particularly rainfall, environmental, and socio-economic factors call into question the reliability of all estimations. The indicator is also conservative from the perspective that it does not take into account a variety of other vector-borne diseases, whose prevalence may also be significantly influenced by climate change, such as viral encephalitis, schistosomiasis, leishmaniasis, Lyme disease, and onchocerciasis (WHO, 2003).

ESTIMATES COUNTRY-LEVEL IMPACT

COUNTRY	2010	2030	2010	2030
ACUTE				
Central African Republic	400	400	100,000	100,000
Congo	200	200	55,000	55,000
Cote d'Ivoire	1,250	1,250	300,000	300,000
DR Congo	6,000	5,750	1,500,000	1,500,000
Malawi	600	600	150,000	150,000
Mozambique	1,750	1,750	500,000	450,000
Papua New Guinea	400	850	100,000	250,000
Tanzania	1,750	1,750	450,000	450,000
Uganda	1,500	1,500	400,000	400,000
Zambia	600	600	150,000	150,000
SEVERE				
Solomon Islands	20	15	5,250	4,500
Somalia	200	200	50,000	60,000
Sudan/South Sudan	750	950	200,000	300,000
Vanuatu	1	5	1,250	2,500
Zimbabwe	250	250	65,000	60,000
HIGH				
Benin	95	60	25,000	20,000
Bolivia	60	150	35,000	70,000
Burkina Faso	350	200	90,000	50,000
Burundi	150	150	40,000	40,000
Cambodia	90	90	25,000	30,000
Cameroon	250	150	65,000	40,000
Chad	250	150	65,000	35,000
Guinea	200	100	50,000	35,000
Guinea-Bissau	30	20	8,500	4,750
Guyana	1	5	800	1,250
Kenya	250	250	65,000	70,000
Kiribati	1	1	150	350
Laos	40	50	15,000	20,000
Namibia	30	30	10,000	10,000

COUNTRY	2010	2030	2010	2030
Niger	250	150	70,000	40,000
Nigeria	2,250	1,250	600,000	400,000
Peru	100	200	60,000	100,000
Philippines	450	900	250,000	500,000
Rwanda	70	65	20,000	20,000
Sierra Leone	150	75	35,000	20,000
MODERATE				
Afghanistan	10	15	2,750	6,000
Algeria			5	5
Angola	150	90	65,000	35,000
Bangladesh		45		15,000
Barbados			5	15
Bhutan				100
Botswana	1	1	400	400
Brazil	100	250	55,000	100,000
Canada			100	150
Cape Verde			5	1
China	50	80	25,000	45,000
Colombia	45	100	25,000	55,000
Comoros	5	1	1,000	550
Costa Rica			20	55
Djibouti	1	1	350	400
Dominica			10	15
Dominican Republic	10	20	5,250	10,000
Ecuador	10	20	5,500	10,000
Egypt	10	10	4,250	5,000
El Salvador	1	5	900	2,000
Equatorial Guinea	5	5	2,750	1,500
Eritrea	1	1	450	450
Ethiopia	400	400	100,000	100,000
Fiji	1	1	350	550
Gabon	5	5	2,250	1,500

COUNTRY	2010	2030	2010	2030
Gambia	15	10	4,000	2,250
Ghana	100	65	30,000	20,000
Guatemala	1	5	800	1,750
Haiti	35	45	10,000	20,000
Honduras	5	10	2,500	6,000
India		300		95,000
Iraq			5	15
Jamaica			5	5
Japan			100	150
Kazakhstan			80	150
Lesotho			25	35
Liberia	40	25	10,000	6,750
Madagascar	15	10	4,250	2,250
Malaysia	30	50	10,000	20,000
Maldives				75
Mali	150	90	45,000	25,000
Marshall Islands			65	150
Mauritania	10	5	3,000	1,750
Mexico	1	5	700	1,500
Micronesia			45	95
Moldova			35	65
Morocco			1	5
Myanmar		85		25,000
Nepal		1		450
Nicaragua	1	5	800	1,750
Pakistan	100	400	40,000	100,000
Palau			5	10
Panama			1	1
Paraguay			1	5
Russia	1	1	300	450
Samoa		1	150	300
Sao Tome and Principe			40	20

Additional mortality due to climate change - yearly average

CLIMATE VULNERABILITY

CLIMATE UNCERTAINTY

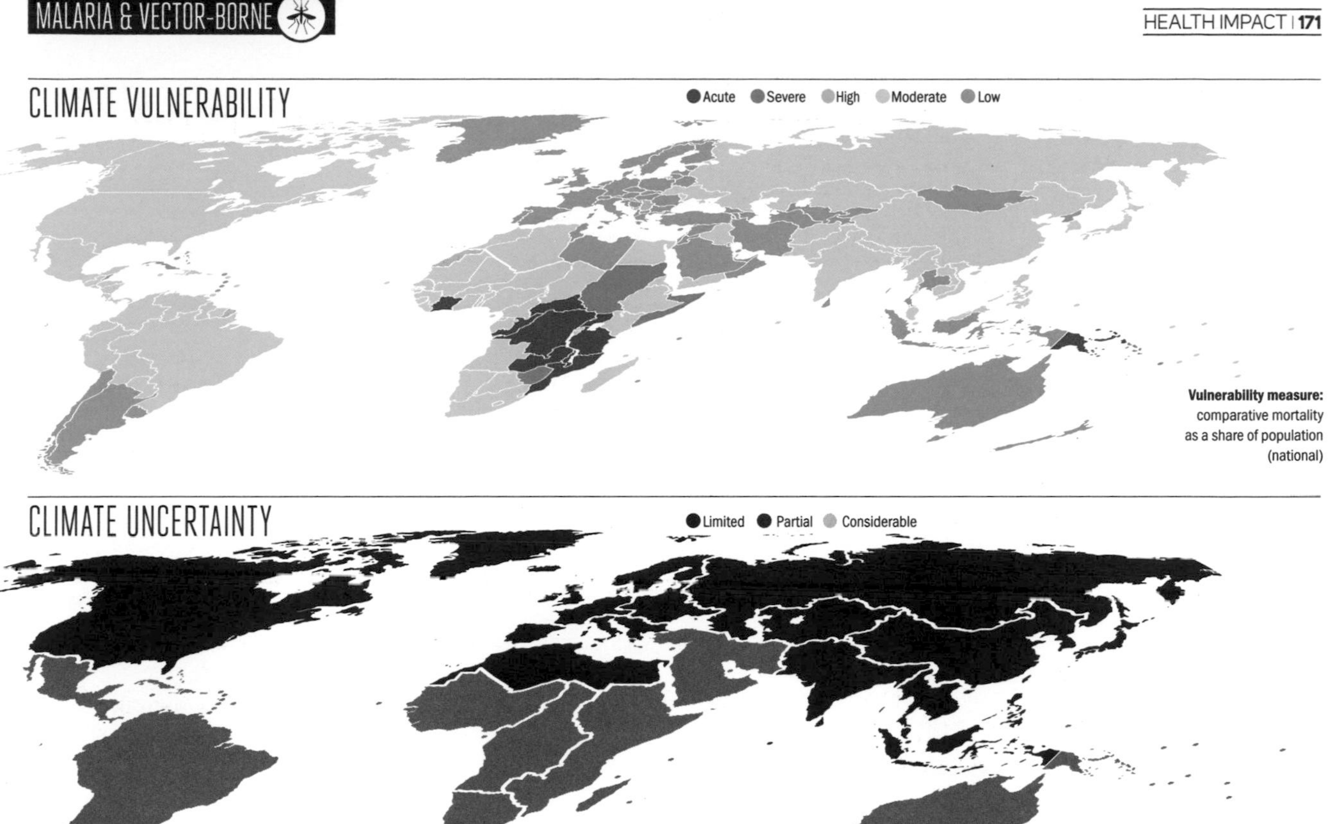

COUNTRY	2010	2030	2010	2030
Senegal	100	65	30,000	20,000
Singapore	1	1	250	300
South Africa	5	5	2,000	2,000
South Korea	1	1	350	600
Suriname	1	1	500	1,000
Swaziland			75	75
Togo	40	25	10,000	6,250
Tonga		1	85	200
Trinidad and Tobago			20	40
Tuvalu			5	5
Ukraine	1	1	200	300
United States	1	1	600	1,000
Venezuela	15	30	5,250	15,000
Vietnam	40	55	15,000	25,000
Yemen	80	95	20,000	25,000
LOW				
Albania				
Antigua and Barbuda				
Argentina				
Armenia				
Australia				
Austria				
Azerbaijan				
Bahamas				
Bahrain				
Belarus				
Belgium				
Belize				
Bosnia and Herzegovina				
Brunei				
Bulgaria				
Chile				
Croatia				
Cuba				
Cyprus				
Czech Republic				
Denmark				
Estonia				
Finland				
France				
Georgia				
Germany				
Greece				
Grenada				
Hungary				
Iceland				
Indonesia				
Iran				
Ireland				
Israel				
Italy				
Jordan				
Kuwait				
Kyrgyzstan				
Latvia				
Lebanon				
Libya				
Lithuania				
Luxembourg				
Macedonia				
Malta				
Mauritius				
Mongolia				
Netherlands				
New Zealand				
North Korea				
Norway				
Oman				
Poland				
Portugal				
Qatar				
Romania				
Saint Lucia				
Saint Vincent				
Saudi Arabia				
Seychelles				
Slovakia				
Slovenia				
Spain				
Sri Lanka				
Sweden				
Switzerland				
Syria				
Tajikistan				
Thailand				
Timor-Leste				
Tunisia				
Turkey				
Turkmenistan				
United Arab Emirates				
United Kingdom				
Uruguay				
Uzbekistan				

Additional persons affected due to climate change - yearly average

MENINGITIS

ESTIMATES GLOBAL CLIMATE IMPACT

2010 EFFECT TODAY

DEATHS PER YEAR **30,000**

2030 EFFECT TOMORROW

DEATHS PER YEAR **40,000**

MORTALITY IMPACT

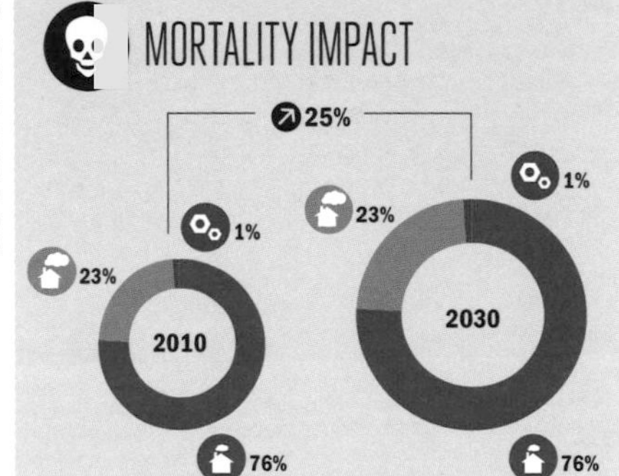

- Meningitis is growing worldwide and claims around 350,000 lives a year
- Humidity levels, wind, and dust are linked to outbreaks of the disease, factors actively influenced by climate change
- A "meningitis belt" stretches across northern Sub-Saharan Africa from Senegal to Ethiopia, sharing dusty and dry conditions, favouring meningitis
- Vaccines exist, but hundreds of millions of people living in risk areas around the world create a serious challenge for mass immunization
- Broader vulnerability measures, such as health education campaigns and improved sanitation will also be crucial

RELATIVE IMPACT

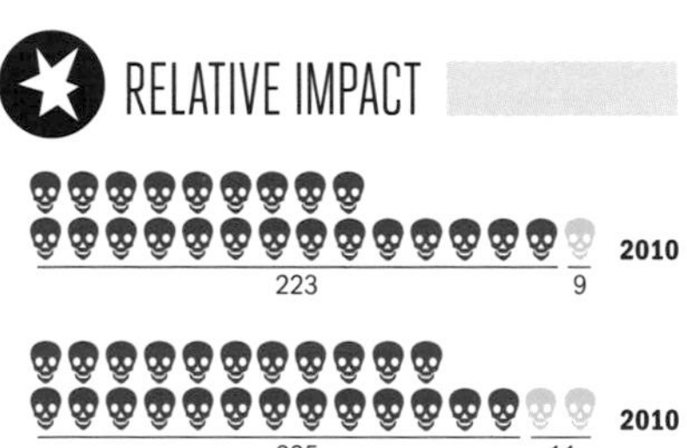

HOTSPOTS

2010 — 2030

2010		2030
6,500	INDIA	8,000
3,500	NIGERIA	5,250
2,000	DR CONGO	3,750
2,000	ETHIOPIA	3,000
800	TANZANIA	1,250

GEOPOLITICAL VULNERABILITY

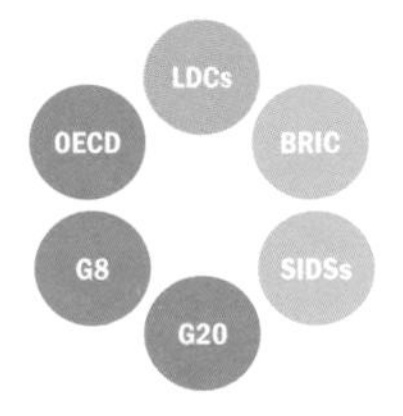

Deaths
Developing Country Low Emitters
Developing Country High Emitters
Developed
Other Industrialized

= Deaths per 10 million

Change in relation to overall global population and/or GDP

Meningitis is a lethal and greatly feared disease in affected areas, because of the rapid onset of symptoms and serious risk of mortality, as well as high rates of infection—as many as 1 per 1,000 in parts of the African Sahel (Adamo et al., 2011). With mortality having more than doubled since the year 2000 and risks escalating as a result of climate change, mass inoculation is an attractive and life-saving component of any response to this growing challenge. However, beyond tackling the disease itself, it is also critical to address underlying vulnerabilities, such as over-grazing, soil degradation, deforestation, and the lack of adequate sanitation.

CLIMATE MECHANISM

The fact that meningococcal meningitis is largely a seasonal disease indicates the extent to which its prevalence is determined by weather-related parameters directly affected by climate change. Models that attempt to recreate meningitis epidemics show a high degree of success when calibrated with climate and environmental parameters. Meningitis epidemics are more likely to occur during the hottest, driest periods which are accompanied by high dust content in the air, and thus most likely to abate with the onset of the rainy season (Molesworth et al., 2006). The bacteria which causes meningitis is spread from person to person through coughing and sneezing, much like influenza or the common cold, and can be spread through poor sanitation (WHO, 2011; Schonning and Stenström, 2004).
Bacteria can be present in a significant proportion of a population in areas affected by meningitis, but still remain benign.
Dust is a key trigger, because it damages the tissues of the nose and throat, facilitating the passage of pathogenic meningitis bacteria into the bloodstream (Thomson et al., 2009).
Climate change affects both weather (heat, humidity, wind) and the environment (extent of vegetation or desertification) and can increase heat, dust, and wind, resulting in exposure and creating peaks of meningitis (Patz et al., 1996; Sultan et al., 2005). Climate change intensifies those factors that most determine meningitis outbreaks, particularly humidity (drought) and dust levels for areas that will become more arid (Sheffield and Wood, 2008; Prospero and Lamb, 2003).

IMPACTS

The global impact of climate change on meningitis is estimated to cause around 20,000 deaths a year in 2010, with 50,000 people affected. Some 30 countries are acutely vulnerable to the impact of climate change on meningitis exclusively in Africa, both inside and beyond the meningitis belt.
Least developed and landlocked countries of Africa are significantly more vulnerable than countries with even marginally higher levels of development. The largest impacts are estimated to occur in India, with nearly 7,000 deaths, and in Nigeria, the DR Congo, and Ethiopia, each of which is estimated to have an annual death toll in the thousands.
As incidence of the disease is rapidly increasing, it is expected to moderately expand through to 2030 and increase proportionate to population growth, claiming over 40,000 a year by 2030 with 80,000 people affected each year.

THE BROADER CONTEXT

Meningitis underwent explosive growth in the first decade of the 21st century, doubling from just over 150,000 deaths in 2000, to well over 350,000 deaths a year by 2008—this in spite of a dramatic increase in economic development during that period. Meningitis is one of the few communicable diseases to have rapidly expanded in the past decade (WHO BDD, 2011).

VULNERABILITIES AND WIDER OUTCOMES

Pockets of environmental vulnerability to meningitis exist around the world, but outside of Africa, India makes up a large share of the remainder of the global burden of the disease. Environmental predispositions to meningitis are exacerbated through land degradation, such as deforestation, over-irrigation, and over-grazing—effects that also generate the dry and dusty conditions that are most favourable to meningitis (Nicholson et al., 1998). The incidence of meningitis is also closely related to cramped living conditions and poor sanitation, inadequate hygiene and access to water, since infection is carried through human contact, coughing, and sneezing (WHO, 2011). Levels of awareness and education can affect understanding of the disease and largely determine the measures taken by individuals to prevent contracting the

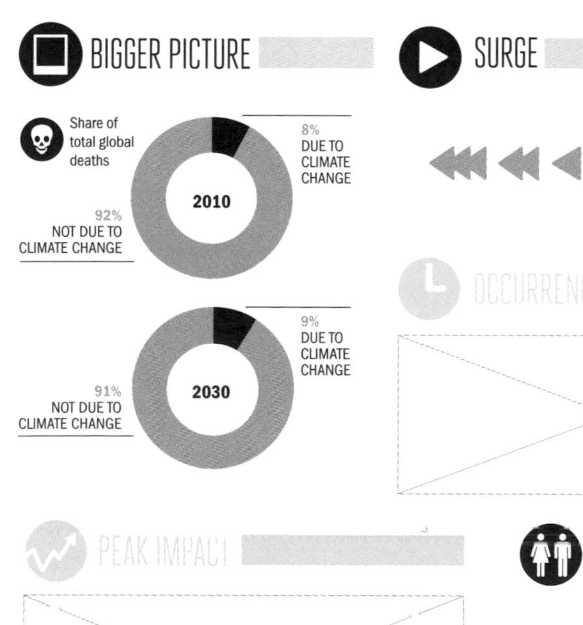

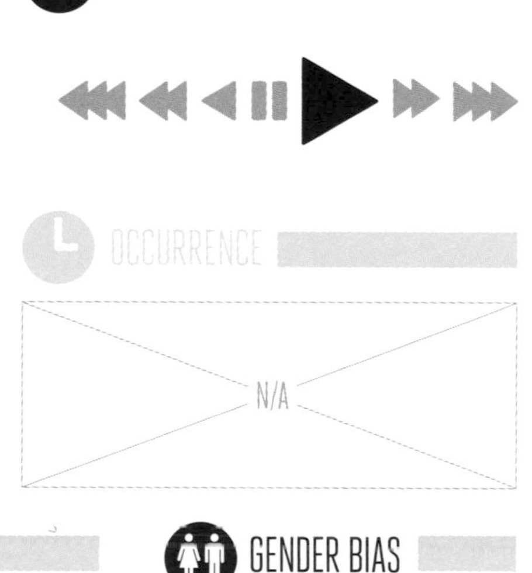

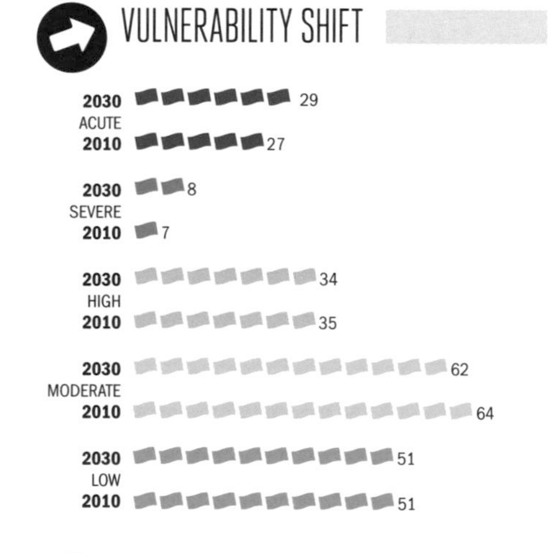

PEAK IMPACT

N/A

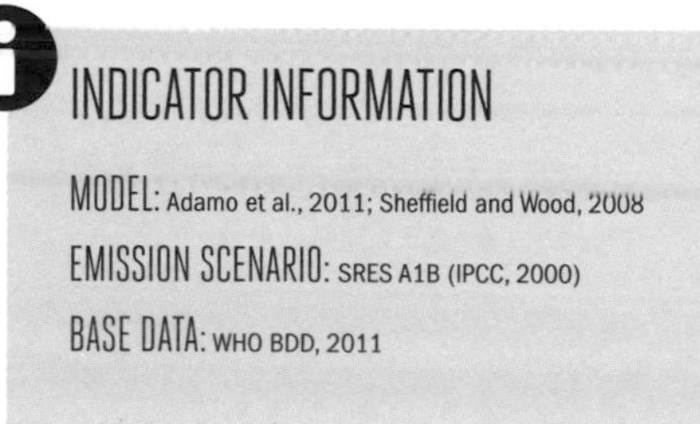

INDICATOR INFORMATION
MODEL: Adamo et al., 2011; Sheffield and Wood, 2008
EMISSION SCENARIO: SRES A1B (IPCC, 2000)
BASE DATA: WHO BDD, 2011

= 5 countries (rounded)

Acute Severe High Moderate Low

disease (Nutbeam, 2000).
Given the high prevalence of meningitis among some of the world's poorest communities, the impact of climate change on the disease is a serious concern for human development progress (Arora, 2001). More tangibly, the increasing prevalence of meningitis with its high death rate among children—around two-thirds of all mortality—limits progress in lag regions towards the achievement of Millennium Development Goal 4, which aims to tangibly reduce child mortality (WHO BDD, 2011).

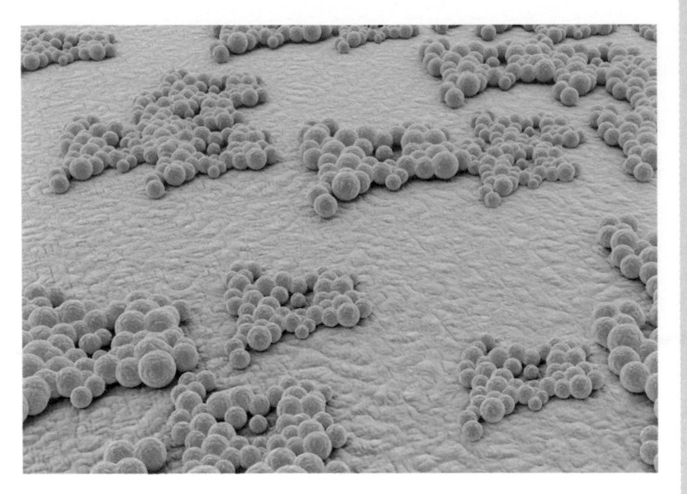

RESPONSES

Meningitis is one of the few major deadly infectious diseases affecting developing countries for which several effective vaccines already exist. Immunization is a particularly cost effective response. There are now several success stories in the fight against meningitis, where programmes have managed to significantly reduce the burden of the disease (Kshirsagar et al., 2007; LaForce and Okwo-Bele, 2011).
Given the large scale of the populations at risk—in Africa alone comparable to the entire population of the US—full breadth vaccination becomes prohibitively expensive, even using the lowest-cost solutions available. For this reason, response strategies to meningitis outbreaks have favoured early warning monitoring and vaccine interventions at the community level, when outbreaks of meningitis exceed a certain threshold (LaForce et al., 2007). Although newer, more effective meningitis vaccines are currently being disseminated in affected zones of the Sahel which promise to dramatically reduce the incidence of meningitis, it could take a full decade to provide them for the required numbers (Thomson et al., 2009).
Improving sanitation and living conditions, promoting education and awareness, and tackling environmental issues, including overgrazing, deforestation and land degradation will address the underlying causes of meningitis, in addition to ensuring the other well known benefits of such actions (DCPP, 2006; Nutbeam, 2000; Donohoe, 2003).

THE INDICATOR

The indicator is a simple model that relates the incidence of meningitis to the incidence of drought. Global changes in the frequency of drought were linked to a meningitis risk model and population density, the indicator being highly sensitive to the latter, since close human contact is a major vulnerability driver for meningitis outbreaks (Sheffield and Wood, 2007; Adamo et al., 2011). The indicator then draws on the main WHO database to estimate how the current burden of meningitis evolves as drought incidence changes (WHO, 2011; WHO BDD, 2011). Uncertainty in relation to the climate effect is present due to the unpredictability of future rainfall patterns, a determining factor of drought.

ESTIMATES COUNTRY-LEVEL IMPACT

COUNTRY	2010	2030	2010	2030
ACUTE				
Afghanistan	500	850	850	1,250
Angola	500	900	1,250	2,500
Benin	250	350	350	600
Burkina Faso	300	600	500	950
Burundi	200	300	300	500
Cameroon	500	700	800	1,250
Central African Republic	90	150	150	200
Chad	300	550	500	850
Comoros	15	25	25	35
Cote d,Ivoire	450	600	700	1,000
DR Congo	2,000	3,750	3,250	6,000
Equatorial Guinea	15	25	50	85
Ethiopia	2,000	3,000	3,250	5,000
Guinea	250	400	400	600
Guinea-Bissau	65	100	100	150
Haiti	200	300	350	500
Liberia	90	150	150	300
Malawi	400	650	650	1,000
Mali	250	400	400	650
Mozambique	400	550	600	900
Niger	450	800	700	1,250
Nigeria	3,500	5,250	5,500	8,750
Rwanda	150	250	250	400
Sierra Leone	150	300	300	450
Somalia	150	250	250	450
South Africa	700	700	2,250	2,250
Tanzania	800	1,250	1,250	2,000
Uganda	500	900	800	1,500
Zambia	250	400	400	600
SEVERE				
Bhutan	5	10	10	15
Congo	40	75	65	100
Gambia	15	25	30	40
Madagascar	200	300	300	500
Mauritania	45	75	70	100
Sao Tome and Principe	1	1	1	5
Swaziland	10	10	25	35
Togo	65	100	100	150
HIGH				
Algeria	150	200	350	550
Armenia	10	10	20	25
Bangladesh	600	800	950	1,250
Bolivia	45	75	150	200
Botswana	15	15	45	55
Cambodia	100	150	200	250
Cape Verde	1	5	5	10
Djibouti	5	5	10	15
Eritrea	25	35	40	60
Gabon	10	15	35	55
Ghana	95	150	150	200
Guatemala	50	90	150	250
Honduras	20	35	55	90
India	6,500	8,000	10,000	15,000
Iraq	150	250	400	700
Kenya	200	300	350	450
Kyrgyzstan	20	30	35	50
Laos	50	65	80	100
Lesotho	15	20	30	30
Mongolia	10	10	15	15
Myanmar	250	300	400	500
Namibia	10	15	25	40
Nepal	100	200	200	300
North Korea	90	100	150	150
Pakistan	700	1,000	1,250	1,750
Senegal	100	150	150	250
Sudan/South Sudan	350	550	550	900
Tajikistan	55	80	85	150
Timor-Leste	5	5	10	10
Tunisia	45	60	100	150
Turkmenistan	25	35	60	95
Uzbekistan	90	150	150	200
Yemen	150	300	200	500
Zimbabwe	85	100	150	200
MODERATE				
Antigua and Barbuda				
Argentina	40	55	150	200
Azerbaijan	20	25	55	70
Bahamas			1	1
Bahrain	1	1	5	10
Barbados			1	1
Belize			1	1
Brazil	200	300	550	750
Brunei			1	1
Chile	10	15	35	50
China	800	850	2,000	2,250
Colombia	55	75	150	200
Costa Rica	5	5	10	15
Cuba	5	5	15	20
Cyprus			1	1
Dominica				
Dominican Republic	15	20	40	60
Ecuador	20	30	55	80
Egypt	200	300	500	800
El Salvador	10	15	30	45
Georgia	5	5	15	15

Additional mortality due to climate change - yearly average

CLIMATE VULNERABILITY

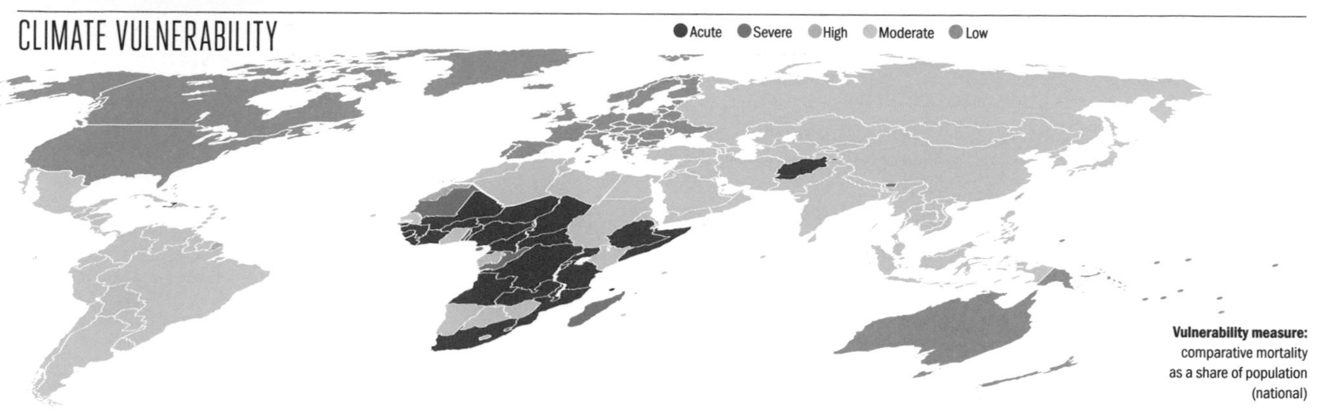

CLIMATE UNCERTAINTY

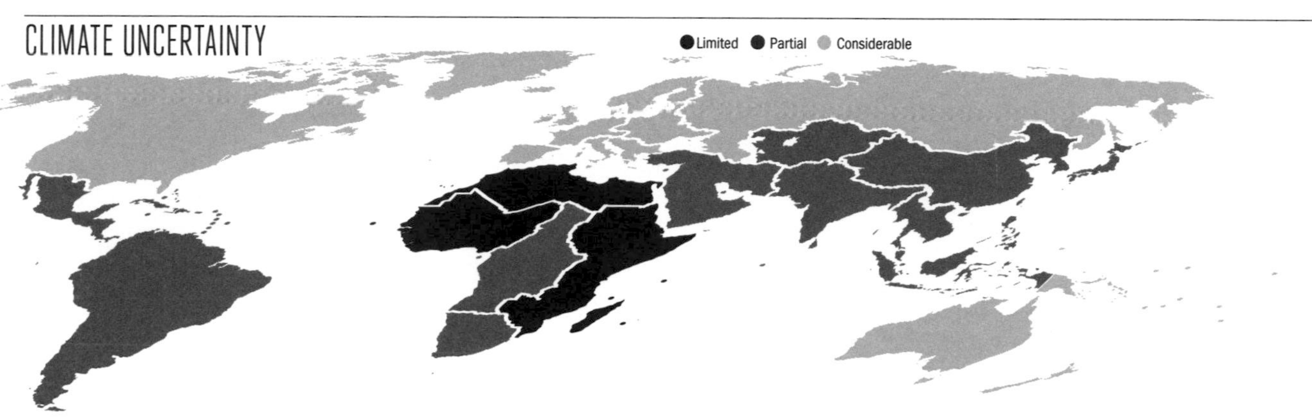

COUNTRY	2010	2030	2010	2030
Grenada				1
Guyana	1	1	1	1
Indonesia	550	650	1,500	1,750
Iran	65	90	150	250
Israel	1	5	25	35
Jamaica	5	10	15	20
Japan	25	25	250	250
Jordan	10	15	25	40
Kazakhstan	40	45	100	100
Kuwait	1	1	5	10
Lebanon	5	5	15	25
Libya	5	10	20	25
Malaysia	10	15	30	40
Maldives	1	1	1	1
Mauritius	1	1	5	5
Mexico	30	45	100	150
Morocco	40	55	100	150
Nicaragua	15	20	20	35
Oman	1	1	1	5
Panama	5	5	10	20
Paraguay	15	25	40	65
Peru	55	75	150	200
Philippines	200	250	500	650
Qatar			1	1
Russia	200	200	650	650
Saint Lucia			1	1
Saint Vincent				
Saudi Arabia	15	25	150	300
Seychelles			1	1
Singapore	1	1	5	5
South Korea	5	5	45	50
Sri Lanka	25	25	65	75

COUNTRY	2010	2030	2010	2030
Suriname	1	1	5	5
Syria	30	50	80	150
Thailand	40	50	100	150
Trinidad and Tobago	1	1	5	5
Turkey	100	150	350	450
United Arab Emirates	5	5	30	45
Uruguay	1	5	10	10
Venezuela	25	40	85	100
Vietnam	70	85	100	150
LOW				
Albania				
Australia				
Austria				
Belarus				
Belgium				
Bosnia and Herzegovina				
Bulgaria				
Canada				
Croatia				
Czech Republic				
Denmark				
Estonia				
Fiji				
Finland				
France				
Germany				
Greece				
Hungary				
Iceland				
Ireland				
Italy				
Kiribati				

COUNTRY	2010	2030	2010	2030
Latvia				
Lithuania				
Luxembourg				
Macedonia				
Malta				
Marshall Islands				
Micronesia				
Moldova				
Netherlands				
New Zealand				
Norway				
Palau				
Papua New Guinea				
Poland				
Portugal				
Romania				
Samoa				
Slovakia				
Slovenia				
Solomon Islands				
Spain				
Sweden				
Switzerland				
Tonga				
Tuvalu				
Ukraine				
United Kingdom				
United States				
Vanuatu				

Additional persons affected due to climate change (thousands) - yearly average

INDUSTRY STRESS

AGRICULTURE

FISHERIES

FORESTRY

HYDRO ENERGY

TOURISM

TRANSPORT

50 BILLION LOSS
350 BILLION LOSS
2010
2030
15 BILLION LOSS
150 BILLION LOSS
2010
2030
5 BILLION LOSS
45 BILLION LOSS
2010
2030
5 BILLION GAIN
25 BILLION GAIN
2010
2030
NIL
NIL
2010
2030
1 BILLION LOSS
5 BILLION LOSS
2010
2030

AGRICULTURE

ESTIMATES GLOBAL CLIMATE IMPACT

2010 EFFECT TODAY

$ USD LOSS PER YEAR **50 BILLION**

2030 EFFECT TOMORROW

$ USD LOSS PER YEAR **350 BILLION**

ECONOMIC IMPACT

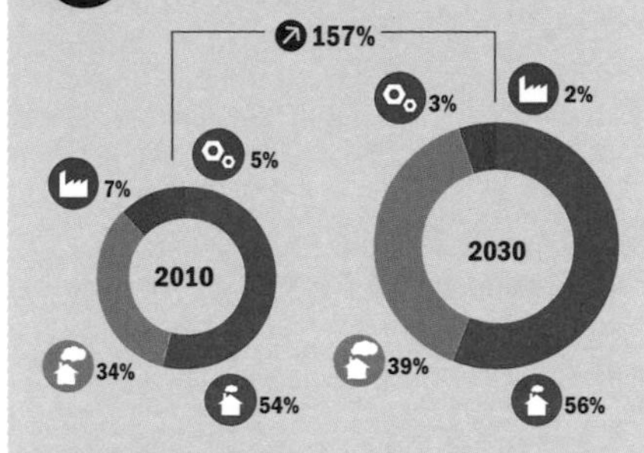

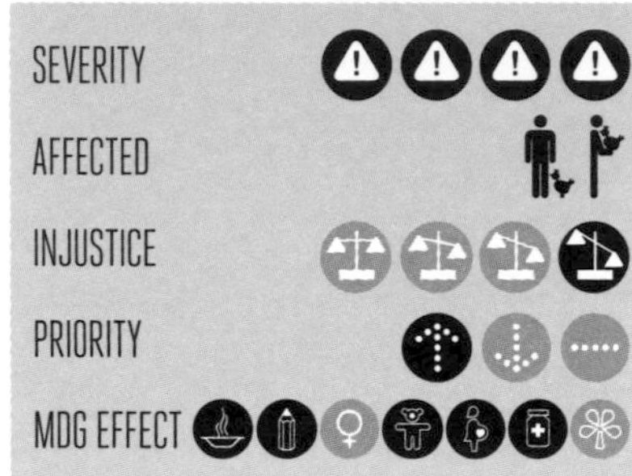

- Land-based agriculture is the sector worst affected by climate change, while global demand for food and agricultural products is booming
- Africa is most vulnerable, but several large Asian economies, small islands, and parts of Latin America also suffer
- The worst-affected economies have the highest shares of agricultural workers, so impacts will likely worsen national unemployment
- Adaptation responses abound, but technical solutions are not viable where farmers lack the means to take measures or finance them
- Extreme effects on rural subsistence farmers clearly delays human development, causing new food emergencies

RELATIVE IMPACT

$$$$$$$$ $ 2010 — 80 / 3

$$$$$$$$$ $ 2030 — 84 / 6

HOTSPOTS

2010	$	2030
15,000	INDIA	100,000
5,500	CHINA	55,000
1,500	PAKISTAN	15,000
1,250	THAILAND	10,000
1,250	INDONESIA	9,500

GEOPOLITICAL VULNERABILITY

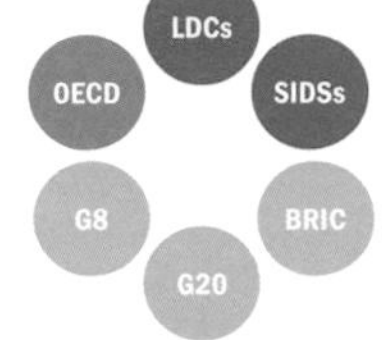

$ Economic Cost (2010 PPP non-discounted)
Developing Country Low Emitters
Developed
Developing Country High Emitters
Other Industrialized

$ = Losses per 10,000 USD of GDP

Change in relation to overall global population and/or GDP

$ = Millions of USD (2010 PPP non-discounted)

Agriculture was one of the first sectors widely recognized to be heavily affected by climate change (IPCC, 1990; Cline, 1992). Agriculture is one of the most significant and best studied impacts of climate change assessed in the Monitor, and for many, the best known (Nordhaus and Boyer, 1999). Within regions and countries, some will be affected, while others will benefit (Bindi and Olesen, 2011). Climate change will have a particularly serious impact on farmers with limited possibilities for adapting to shifts in climate, e.g., by planting different varieties of plants and implementing new irrigation techniques (Kurukulasuriya et al., 2006; Easterling in Hillel and Rosenzweig (eds.), 2011). Agricultural losses from climate change harm subsistence farmers whose insufficient income or capital reserves prevent them from taking steps to adapt to weather change (IPCC, 2007). In developing countries with economies still heavily reliant on agriculture, the negative effects for this sector are estimated to be severe and widespread (World Bank Data, 2012). The research undertaken as a part of the Monitor's development underscored the importance of empowering vulnerable farmers to generate more value for their products in order to break the vicious spiral of poverty (see in particular the Ghana country study).

CLIMATE MECHANISM

Climate change increases heat stress and evaporation, and aggravates drought (Hansen et al., 2007). While many of these also change in relation to natural weather phenomena such as El Niño, recent evidence suggests a shift to more extreme warm weather conditions (Jung et al., 2010; Hansen et al., 2012). Climate change is altering the pattern of rainfall, which may become more or less abundant or more erratic (Kharin et al., 2007). Rainfall shifts can damage those crops and livestock, which are less suited to the changing weather or susceptible to disease or declining yield. Agricultural losses can be measured when climate deviates from optimal growing conditions, resulting in lower yield per acre (Cline, 2007). Gradual changes can be compounded by more extreme weather, especially large-scale floods (Mueller and Quisumbing, 2011).

IMPACTS

Globally, climate change is already estimated to cause 50 billion dollars a year in agricultural losses, around 90% of which occur in developing countries, since the sector accounts for between just 1-5% of GDP in most developed countries. However, costs are still relatively small in most countries, except for a small handful of the most vulnerable, some of whom are already estimated to lose 1-2% of GDP. Low-income and least developed countries are more vulnerable and suffer the most extreme effects, creating serious concern for food security. Regionally, Sub-Saharan Africa is singled out, Central, East, and West Africa most seriously. Latin America, the Pacific, and parts of Asia also have elevated levels of vulnerability. India and China are currently estimated to suffer the greatest share of the total impact, each with 2010 losses estimated at over 5 billion dollars a year. A small fraction of countries are expected to experience any gains in the agricultural sector in the near future. The scale of effect jumps rapidly over the course of 20 years from less than 0.1% of global income in 2010, more than doubling as a share of global GDP to about 0.2% in 2030, or over 350 billion dollars in yearly losses. However, the rate of increase in damage is declining: as the share of global output in service and industrial sectors grows, agriculture is expected to continue to lose importance—in line with the expansion of industrialization over the next 20 years (OECD, 2012).

THE BROADER CONTEXT

The agricultural sector is also struggling to meet the food demands of growing and wealthier populations (FAOSTAT, 2012; Friedman, 2009). But climate change is preventing the sector from meeting this demand, as indicated by both scientific research and statistical analysis (Cline, 2007). It will also lower the comparative advantage of agriculture-based, lower-income economies, with effects estimated to be especially severe for Africa (Nelson et al., 2009; Tol, 2011). Nevertheless, carbon fertilization—through which high concentrations of CO_2 in the atmosphere might improve plant productivity and agricultural outputs—is understood by researchers to outweigh losses due to climate change at least early on (Mendelsohn in Griffin (ed.), 2003). This effect is accounted for in the Carbon section of the Monitor; where large-scale

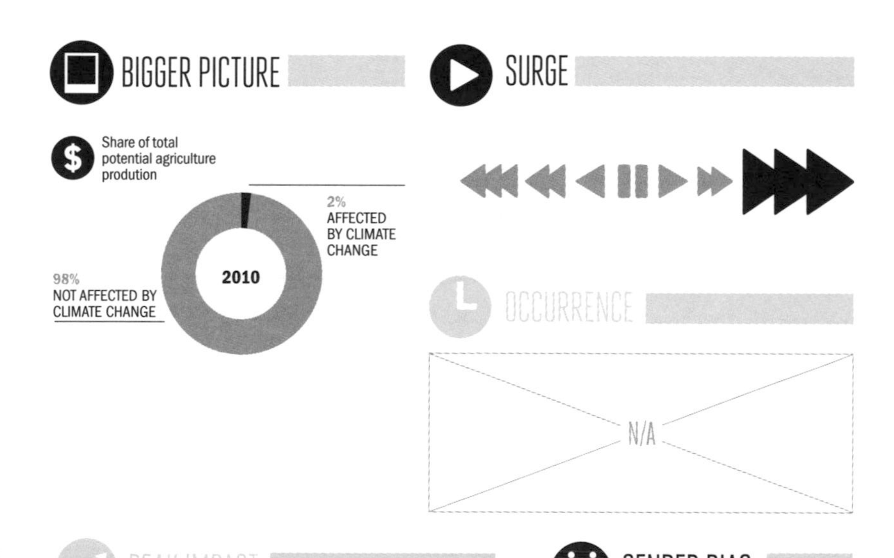

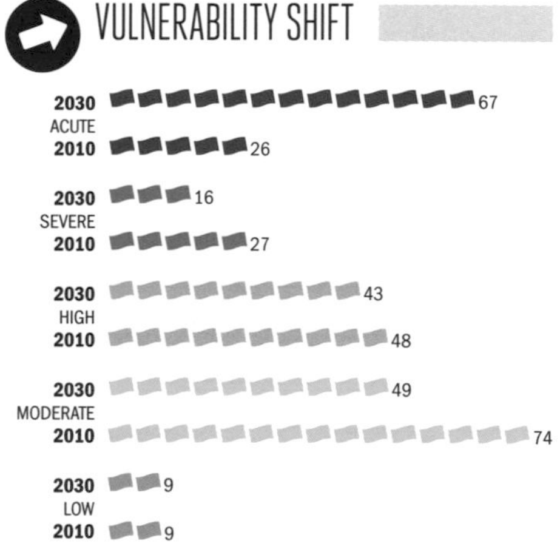

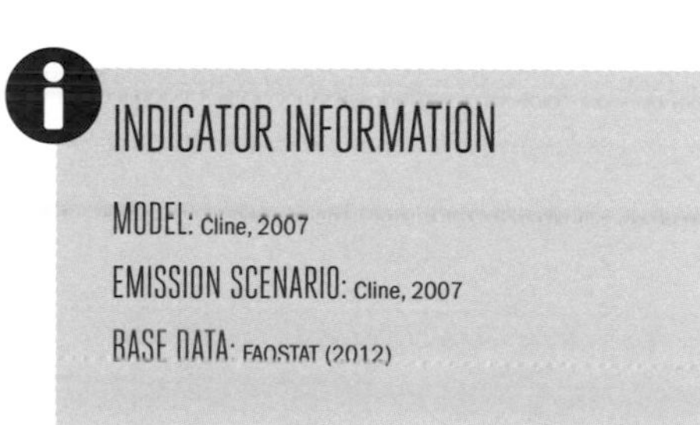

= 5 countries (rounded)

Acute Severe High Moderate Low

benefits are estimated by the IPCC to be possible, they never outweigh the costs of climate change estimated here (IPCC, 2007). Recent research has been cautious about the practical realisation of these benefits (Ainsworth et al., 2008; Leaky et al., 2009). A World Bank study recently suggested that a high carbon fertilization effect would reduce adaptation costs by less than 10% (World Bank, 2010).

VULNERABILITIES AND WIDER OUTCOMES

Underscoring the vulnerability of developing countries, especially the least developed, is the significance at the national level of the size and composition of the agricultural sector in terms of output and workforce.
One of the few advantages that small-scale farmers have over large commercial operators is the ability to adjust crop varieties or experiment more readily with different crops. Agricultural companies that practice large-scale mono-cropping may suffer correspondingly large losses, if climate conditions shifted to the disadvantage of the chosen crops (Brondizio and Moran, 2008). Countries that rely heavily on just one or two cash crops face similar concerns, as is highlighted in the Ghana country study in this report. Poor environmental protection also increases vulnerability, such as when biodiversity losses inhibit resistance to invasive species (Castree et al. (eds.), 2009). In general, rainfed-only agriculture is much more vulnerable than irrigated land (Kurukulasuriya et al., 2006). Communities reliant on subsistence farming are dangerously vulnerable, as global warming accelerates; the World Health Organization has estimated climate change to be a major driver of contemporary malnutrition (WHO, 2004). These health effects are measured in the Health Impact section of the Monitor.
Climate change is a major risk for food insecurity, since a number of the world's food-insecure regions are expected to experience the most severe climate shocks (Lobell et al., 2008). Indeed, climate effects on agriculture harm development, since they diminish the disposable incomes of communities already struggling to achieve gains (UNDP, 2007). They also drive the seasonal rural-urban migration of young adults, as shown by the Ghana country study.

RESPONSES

The vast literature on the impact of climate change on agriculture cannot be summarized here. All societies are understood to be "adaptive," but communities differ considerably in this capacity (Adger et al., 2003; Dixon et al., 2003). Response options vary widely, including from large-scale or micro irrigation infrastructure, to index-based weather insurance, new/hybrid seeds, and education/rural extension programmes. The involvement of local communities in the design of adaptation measures is advised, so that initiatives are feasible and practical (Smit and Wandel, 2006). The Monitor's country studies emphasize that where farmers cannot afford to take measures, efforts should focus on increasing capacity for investment and enabling local products to access more lucrative global supply chains and markets. Farmers with growing incomes could make better use of parallel extension schemes that offer appropriate adaptation options. Development plans that promote biodiversity and crop and livestock diversification will also lower vulnerability to plant and animal disease. Macroeconomic risks can only be offset by ensuring steady growth of less sensitive industrial and service sectors.

THE INDICATOR

This Indicator relies on a recent and comprehensive global review of agricultural impacts of climate change that combines a wealth of experience from a range of methods and models (Cline, 2007). The difficulties in predicting rainfall accurately make some regions more uncertain about agriculture outcomes. Carbon fertilization or other effects related to atmospheric pollutants are not considered here. The Monitor accounts for the effect under Agriculture in the Carbon section of this report.

ESTIMATES COUNTRY-LEVEL IMPACT

COUNTRY	$ 2010	$ 2030
ACUTE		
Afghanistan	85	700
Antigua and Barbuda	5	45
Bahamas	45	350
Belize	10	75
Benin	90	600
Bhutan	10	100
Bolivia	150	1,250
Brunei	75	650
Burkina Faso	70	450
Burundi	60	400
Cambodia	100	1,500
Cameroon	200	1,250
Cape Verde	5	45
Central African Republic	50	350
Chad	60	400
Congo	50	350
Cote d'Ivoire	150	900
Djibouti	10	70
Dominica	5	25
Eritrea	15	85
Ethiopia	450	3,000
Gabon	300	2,000
Gambia	15	100
Ghana	200	1,500
Grenada	5	35
Guinea	150	900
Guinea-Bissau	15	100
Haiti	35	300
India	15,000	100,000
Jamaica	250	2,000
Kiribati	1	20
Laos	90	1,000
Liberia	15	100
Madagascar	100	800
Malawi	150	1,000
Mali	150	1,000
Marshall Islands	1	15
Mauritania	40	250
Micronesia	5	30
Mozambique	100	800
Nepal	150	1,250
Nicaragua	55	450
Niger	65	450
Pakistan	1,500	15,000
Palau	1	10
Papua New Guinea	45	350
Paraguay	150	1,250
Rwanda	100	750
Saint Lucia	5	50
Saint Vincent	5	30
Samoa	5	30
Sao Tome and Principe	1	15
Senegal	250	1,750
Sierra Leone	30	200
Solomon Islands	5	60
Somalia	35	250
Sudan/South Sudan	650	5,000
Swaziland	15	100
Tanzania	350	2,500
Timor-Leste	10	80
Togo	55	400
Tonga	5	25
Tuvalu		1
Uganda	150	1,000
Vanuatu	5	40
Zambia	85	600
Zimbabwe	75	500
SEVERE		
Bangladesh	650	5,500
Costa Rica	100	850
Cuba	250	2,000
DR Congo	60	400
Ecuador	200	1,500
Fiji	10	75
Honduras	75	600
Lesotho	10	55
Morocco	400	3,000
Myanmar	200	1,500
Nigeria	900	6,250
Seychelles	5	30
Thailand	1,250	10,000
Uzbekistan	200	1,500
Vietnam	550	6,000
Yemen	100	800
HIGH		
Albania	15	100
Algeria	300	2,250
Angola	150	1,000
Argentina	550	4,500
Bahrain	25	200
Barbados	5	45
Colombia	300	2,500
Comoros	1	5
Dominican Republic	150	1,000
El Salvador	60	500

$ Additional economic costs due to climate change (million USD PPP) - yearly average

CLIMATE VULNERABILITY

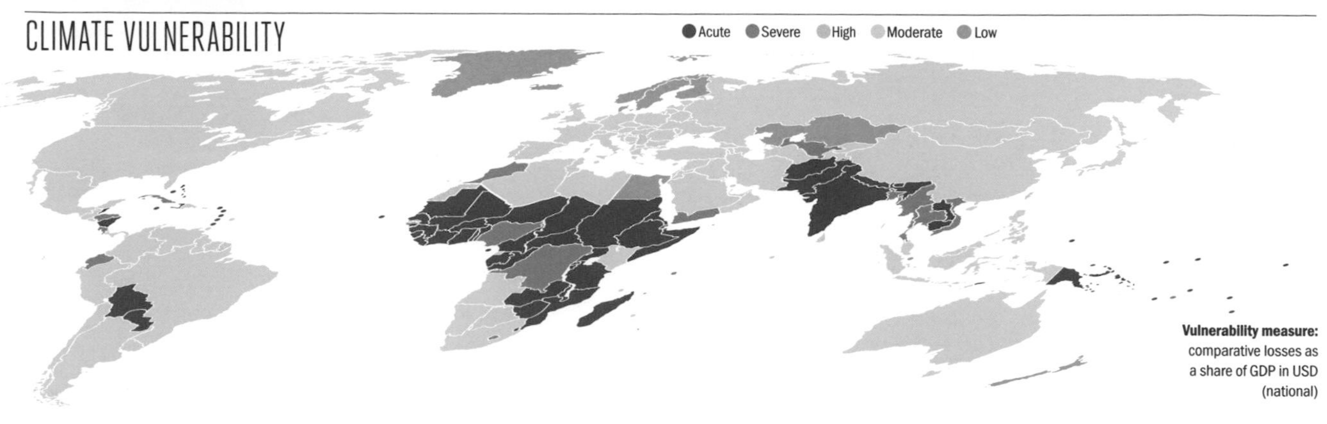

Vulnerability measure: comparative losses as a share of GDP in USD (national)

CLIMATE UNCERTAINTY

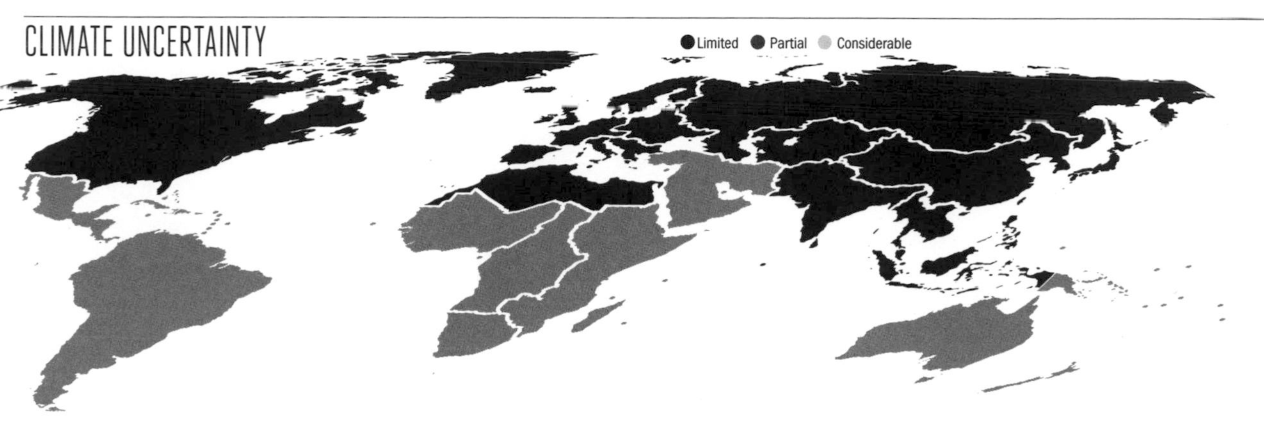

COUNTRY	2010	2030
Georgia	15	100
Guatemala	100	850
Guyana	5	55
Indonesia	1,250	9,500
Iran	1,250	8,750
Iraq	150	1,000
Jordan	20	150
Kenya	60	400
Kuwait	95	750
Kyrgyzstan	15	100
Lebanon	70	550
Libya	150	1,000
Macedonia	15	100
Malaysia	500	4,000
Maldives	1	25
Mauritius	25	200
Mexico	1,250	7,750
Moldova	15	90
Namibia	10	80
Oman	60	500
Peru	250	2,000
Philippines	550	4,500
South Africa	550	3,750
Sri Lanka	100	900
Suriname	5	35
Syria	90	700
Tajikistan	15	100
Tunisia	150	1,000
Turkey	1,250	3,000
Turkmenistan	40	300
United Arab Emirates	200	1,500
Uruguay	30	250
Venezuela	350	2,750
MODERATE		
Armenia	5	45
Australia	450	1,000
Austria	15	35
Azerbaijan	25	200
Belarus	55	400
Belgium	35	85
Bosnia and Herzegovina	10	90
Botswana	1	10
Brazil	900	6,750
Bulgaria	40	250
Canada	35	80
Chile	150	800
China	5,500	55,000
Croatia	25	150
Cyprus	1	1
Czech Republic	25	100
Equatorial Guinea	5	50
Estonia	5	20
France	300	700
Germany	90	200
Greece	200	450
Hungary	30	150
Ireland	1	5
Israel	80	450
Italy	300	650
Japan	450	1,000
Latvia	5	30
Lithuania	15	100
Luxembourg		1
Malta		1
Mongolia	1	15
Netherlands	50	100
North Korea	10	100
Panama	20	150
Poland	90	500
Portugal	65	150
Qatar	1	10
Romania	100	800
Russia	400	2,750
Saudi Arabia	100	950
Slovakia	10	50
Slovenia	5	30
South Korea	550	3,250
Spain	350	850
Switzerland	10	25
Trinidad and Tobago	10	75
Ukraine	150	1,250
United Kingdom	60	150
United States	1,000	2,500
LOW		
Denmark	-25	-60
Egypt	350	2,750
Finland	-15	-35
Iceland		-1
Kazakhstan	-55	-400
New Zealand	-5	-10
Norway	-5	-15
Singapore		
Sweden	-20	-40

FISHERIES

ESTIMATES GLOBAL CLIMATE IMPACT

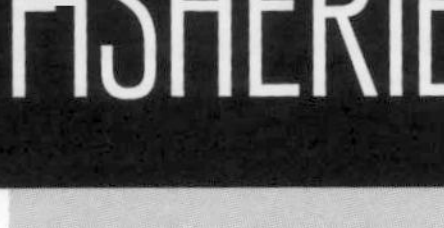

2010 EFFECT TODAY

USD LOSS PER YEAR **15** BILLION

2030 EFFECT TOMORROW

USD LOSS PER YEAR **150** BILLION

ECONOMIC IMPACT

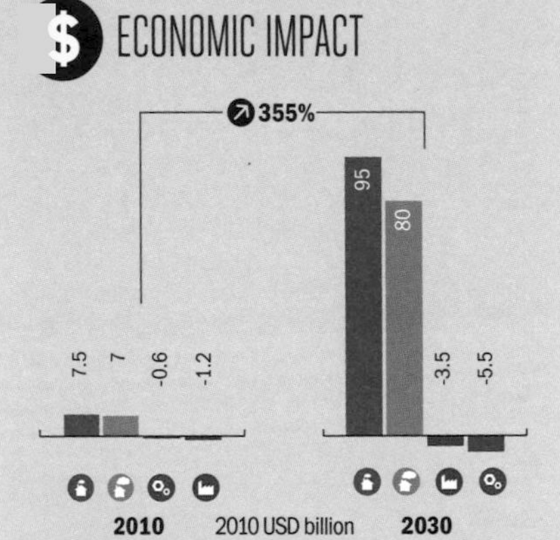

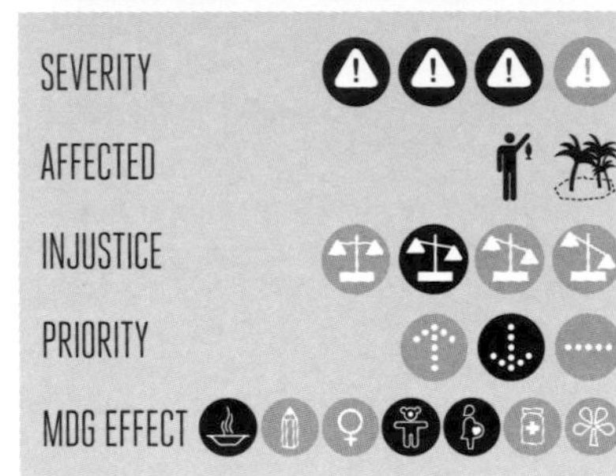

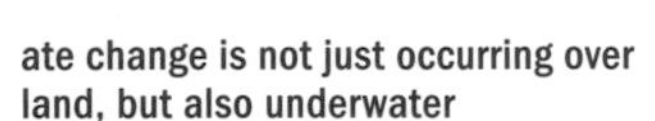

ate change is not just occurring over land, but also underwater

- Water temperature also rises as the planet heats up
- Over 1,000 commercially exploited fish species live in specific aquatic zones already affected: the location of their preferred waters shift as the tropics reach temperatures with no analogue to existing fish habitats and as cooler seas disappear
- Falling fish stocks will affect food security and human development in low-income fishing communities
- Increasing the sustainability of fishing operations and enhancing marine conservation zones may alleviate these strains

RELATIVE IMPACT

$$$$$$$$$$ $ 2010
98 | 2

$$$$
$$$$$$$$$$ $ 2030
135 | 3

HOTSPOTS

2010 $ 2030

2010	Country	2030
1,500	VIETNAM	25,000
1,500	CHINA	15,000
1,250	PERU	15,000
700	THAILAND	8,500
650	INDONESIA	7,750

GEOPOLITICAL VULNERABILITY

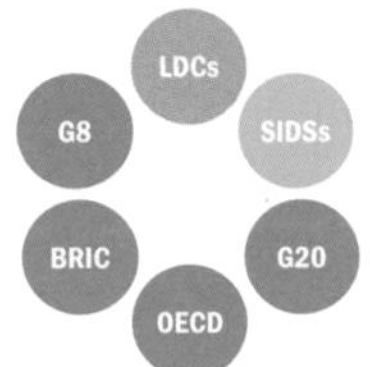

$ Economic Cost (2010 PPP non-discounted)
Developing Country Low Emitters
Developed
Developing Country High Emitters
Other Industrialized

= Losses per 10,000 USD of GDP

Change in relation to overall global population and/or GDP

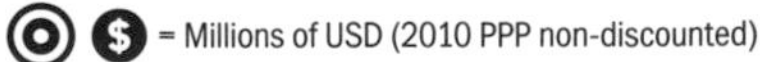
= Millions of USD (2010 PPP non-discounted)

As climate change warms the world's oceans, seas, lakes. and rivers, it is fundamentally changing the marine habitat, forcing fish to migrate or perish (Perry et al., 2005; Ficke et al., 2007; Rijnsdorp et al., 2009; Last et al., 2010; Cheung et al., 2011; Engelhard, 2011). Some far northern or southern zones may experience improved stocks as sea ice recedes and fish from the hottest waters seek relative cool (Hiddink and Hofstede, 2008). Declines brought about by climate change will only increase over time as temperature rise accelerates (Cheung et al., 2009). The world's fish stocks are in large-scale, long-term decline, with the ocean fish catch now half what it was 50 years ago due to an increase in commercial catch boats and unsustainable fishing (FAO, 2007; Watson et al., 2012). Climate change is the most significant driver of global marine ecosystem decline (Halpern et al., 2008). Responding effectively is challenging, since the international cooperation and regulations required are notoriously difficult to conclude, monitor, and enforce (Barkin in Dinar (ed.), 2011). In developing countries hard hit by declining fish stocks, food security and livelihoods are at risk (Srinivasan et al., 2010).

CLIMATE MECHANISM

Water temperature is a defining element of fish habitat (Hoegh-Guldberg and Bruno, 2010). Fish have low tolerance for thermal extremes (Pörtner and Rainer Knust, 2007). Part of the sea-level rise from climate change is caused by the thermal expansion of the seas as they warm (Domingues et al., 2008). As equatorial waters undergo unprecedented temperature increases beyond familiar heat thresholds for fish, the total available range of habitats is disappearing (Cheung et al., 2009). Nutrients are also declining in the warmest waters and reefs suffer as well (Brander, 2007; Munday et al., 2008). Considering the range of interconnected factors involved, from biological processes to changes in ocean current, the types of shocks that could occur in oceans which cover more than 70% of the planet's surface may be underestimated (Harley et al., 2006). The increase in temperature in polar waters shrinks the range of cold-water fish habitats towards the finite limit of the poles. Only the Arctic and southern oceans are compensating species loss by providing new ranges for an invasion of fish from other regions. Nearer the equator, decline will be permanent (Cheung et al., 2009). Inland, similar processes are underway, although with little or no scope for fish migration, depletion could be faster and more permanent (Ficke et al., 2007).

IMPACTS

The current cost of climate change on the fisheries sector is estimated to be about 10 billion dollars a year. By 2030, the impact is expected to more than triple its share as a cost of global GDP, when estimated losses will be over 160 billion dollars per year.

The Pacific, South and Southeast Asia, and Africa, especially West Africa, are the regions worst hit by fishery sector losses due to climate change. Vietnam and China are estimated to suffer the greatest losses, with current impacts estimated to be in excess of 1 billion dollars per year. Vietnam could experience losses in excess of 20 billion dollars per year by 2030. Bangladesh, Indonesia, Myanmar, Morocco, Peru, and Thailand are also experiencing large-scale losses.

The countries with the most severe impacts relative to GDP include small island countries in the Pacific, such as Vanuatu, Tuvalu, or Micronesia; in the Indian Ocean, the Seychelles; and parts of West Africa, such as Sierra Leone and Gambia. By 2030, losses for these countries all exceed 4% of GDP. As traditional livelihoods are eroded, developing countries are worst affected, including a number of least developed countries and small island developing states, raising serious concerns for food security and poverty reduction efforts. Only a handful of countries are expected to gain from the large-scale ecosystem shift, with the largest share attributed to Norway, Russia, and Iceland, and with total gains not exceeding 15 billion dollars in 2030.

THE BROADER CONTEXT

Global fish catch is on a trend toward predictable long-term expansion owing to increases in aquaculture production (Brander, 2007). Global fish stocks, on the other hand, are experiencing a predictable long-term decline, as the number of commercial fishing craft has increased ten-fold since the 1950s, and 25-fold in Asia (Watson et al., 2012). Experts have estimated that marine fisheries declined by 40% between 1970 and 2007 (Hutchings et al., 2010). With or without climate change, global fisheries are endangered (Halpern et al., 2008). Unsustainable fishing

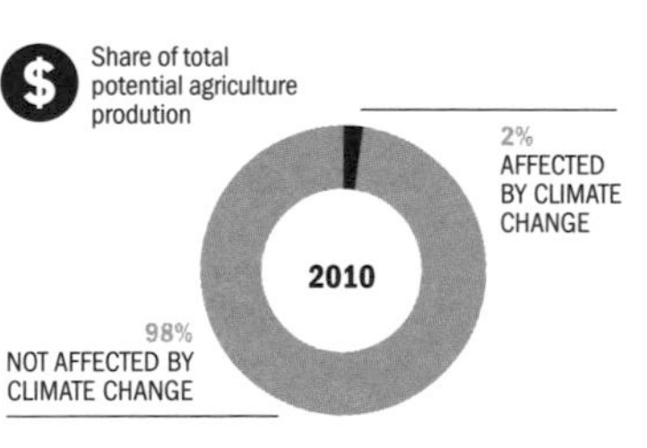

OCCURRENCE

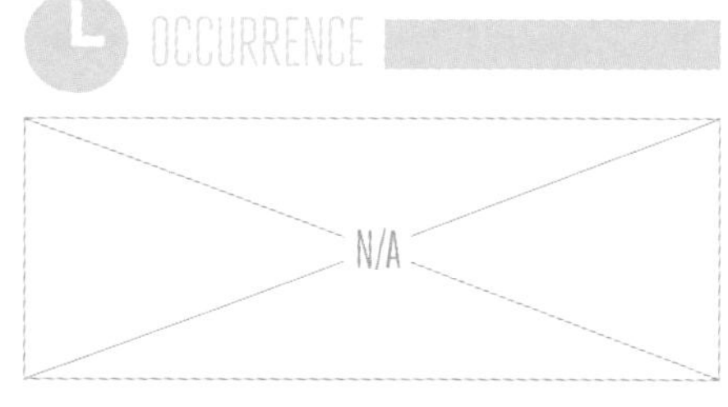

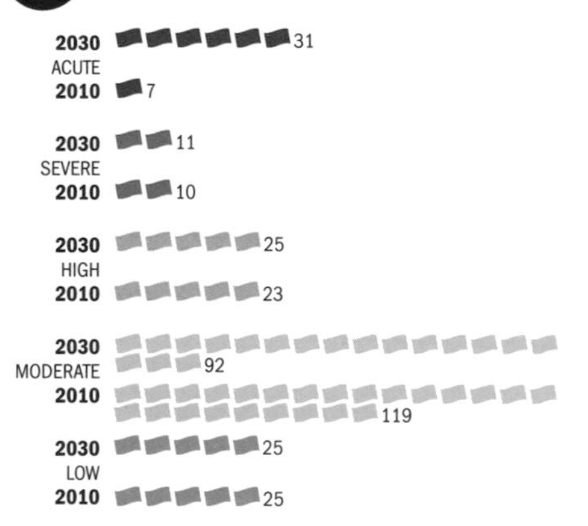

PEAK IMPACT

INDICATOR INFORMATION

MODEL: Cheung et al., 2010; O' Reilly et al., 2003

EMISSION SCENARIO: SRES A1B (IPCC, 2000)

BASE DATA: FAOSTAT (2012)

■ = 5 countries (rounded)

● Acute ● Severe ● High ● Moderate ● Low

and environmentally unsound fishing practices, such as poison dumping, use of narrow-gauge nets that capture immature fish, bottom-dragging, and illegal fishing are important factors in the decline (Gray, 1997; Agnew et al., 2009; FAO, 2012). Bringing these practices under control will be key to responding to climate change-related fishery impacts.

VULNERABILITIES AND WIDER OUTCOMES

Countries with the highest levels of vulnerability are heavily dominated by lower-income nations which depend to a larger extent on fisheries as a share of GDP and are located in highly exposed latitudes or in particular geographical configurations, such as those near to closed water bodies (Allison et al., 2009). Effects will be most severe for subsistence or near-subsistence fisherfolk and fish-reliant communities, both coastal and inland (Srinivasan et al., 2010). The impacts of climate change on the fishing sector will therefore have significant effects on food security and human development progress and will likely feed migration trends (IOM, 2008; Le Manach et al., 2012).

RESPONSES

Responses concern three main types of fish zones where managed (aquaculture) and unmanaged (commercial) fishing are practised, including oceanic marine fish stocks, inland lake or river fish, and brackish or semi-salt waters.
In marine and inland environments, sustainable fisheries management will be key. This can include the strict setting and implementing of fishing quotas, net size restrictions, poison bans, and control of waters from exploitation, including by foreign fishing interests (Grieve and Short, 2007; FAO, 2007). When catch size reductions are unavoidable, compensatory measures can be implemented to ensure that there is no loss in community welfare; efforts can also be made to diversify livelihoods (Sumaila and Cheung, 2010). The establishment, expansion, and conservation of fish sanctuaries can also play an important role in sustaining or even increasing the resilience of stressed aquatic ecosystems (Gray, 1997).
In brackish environments and in all managed fishing regimes, the quality of otherwise high-risk hatchery production is vital. Post-larvae fish or shrimp carrying disease as they leave hatcheries have the potential to contaminate whole aquaculture farms or systems in an area. Therefore, system-wide quality controls, from hatcheries through nurseries to pre-marketing grow-out ponds, will improve end-to-end resilience and resistance to disease. Here, water temperature is a principal environmental factor (Gilad et al., 2003).
As with agriculture, affected fisherfolk, if given access to higher levels of disposable income and diversified livelihoods, will have more scope for autonomous action (Teh et al., 2008). With surging global demand for food products, more benefits could be gained through strategies that increase the portion of the global value chain enjoyed by small-scale fisherfolk, as highlighted in the Ghana country study in this report. One example is the promotion of local light industrial processing, such as freezing and packaging works for marketing local fish products through global supply chains.

THE INDICATOR

The indicator relies on a global high resolution bio-climate study that maps the change in preferred water climates due to global warming for over a thousand key commercial species, as compared to their current habitats (Cheung et al., 2010). The main limitation is that the inland aspect of the indicator relies on a study carried out in one area (O'Reilly et al., 2003). Ocean temperature changes are fairly well studied and understood and the economic data from the UN Food and Agriculture Organization is comprehensive and accurate, all of which contributes to the robustness of the indicator (Domingues et al., 2008; FAOSTAT, 2012). Economic data on various segments of global fishery production could have been of a higher standard for the purpose of this analysis.

ESTIMATES COUNTRY-LEVEL IMPACT

COUNTRY	$ 2010	$ 2030
ACUTE		
Bangladesh	500	7,750
Benin	25	350
Burundi	15	200
Cambodia	150	3,000
Central African Republic	10	150
DR Congo	150	1,750
Ecuador	300	3,250
Gambia	45	450
Ghana	200	2,250
Guinea	55	550
Guyana	25	300
Madagascar	65	700
Malawi	60	900
Mali	60	850
Micronesia	15	150
Morocco	650	7,250
Mozambique	65	700
Myanmar	600	7,500
Oman	200	2,000
Palau	1	5
Papua New Guinea	95	1,250
Peru	1,250	15,000
Samoa	5	40
Senegal	90	950
Seychelles	70	700
Sierra Leone	65	650
Tuvalu	1	15
Uganda	200	3,000
Vanuatu	80	950
Vietnam	1,500	25,000
Zambia	35	500

COUNTRY	$ 2010	$ 2030
SEVERE		
Cameroon	70	850
Chile	850	6,500
Kenya	90	1,250
Kiribati	1	10
Liberia	1	25
Namibia	30	300
Niger	15	200
Panama	85	1,000
Sri Lanka	150	2,000
Suriname	10	100
Togo	10	150
HIGH		
Angola	80	800
Bahrain	20	200
Belize	1	20
Burkina Faso	10	150
Cote d,Ivoire	20	200
Fiji	5	65
Gabon	20	200
Grenada	1	10
Indonesia	650	7,750
Iran	450	5,000
Laos	5	150
Malaysia	500	5,750
Nicaragua	15	200
Nigeria	300	3,750
North Korea	20	300
Philippines	450	5,000
Solomon Islands	1	20
South Africa	300	3,000
Sudan/South Sudan	40	650

COUNTRY	$ 2010	$ 2030
Tanzania	20	300
Thailand	700	8,500
Tonga	1	10
Tunisia	90	1,000
Uruguay	30	350
Zimbabwe	5	70
MODERATE		
Albania	1	20
Algeria	30	350
Argentina	80	950
Armenia		1
Austria		
Azerbaijan		5
Bahamas	1	35
Belarus	1	5
Belgium	1	5
Bhutan		1
Bolivia	5	65
Bosnia and Herzegovina	1	10
Brazil	55	500
Brunei	1	30
Bulgaria	1	25
China	1,500	15,000
Colombia	40	500
Congo	1	20
Costa Rica	5	55
Croatia	5	65
Cuba	5	35
Cyprus	1	5
Czech Republic	1	10
Denmark	35	100
Dominica		1

$ Additional economic costs due to climate change (million USD PPP) - yearly average

CLIMATE VULNERABILITY

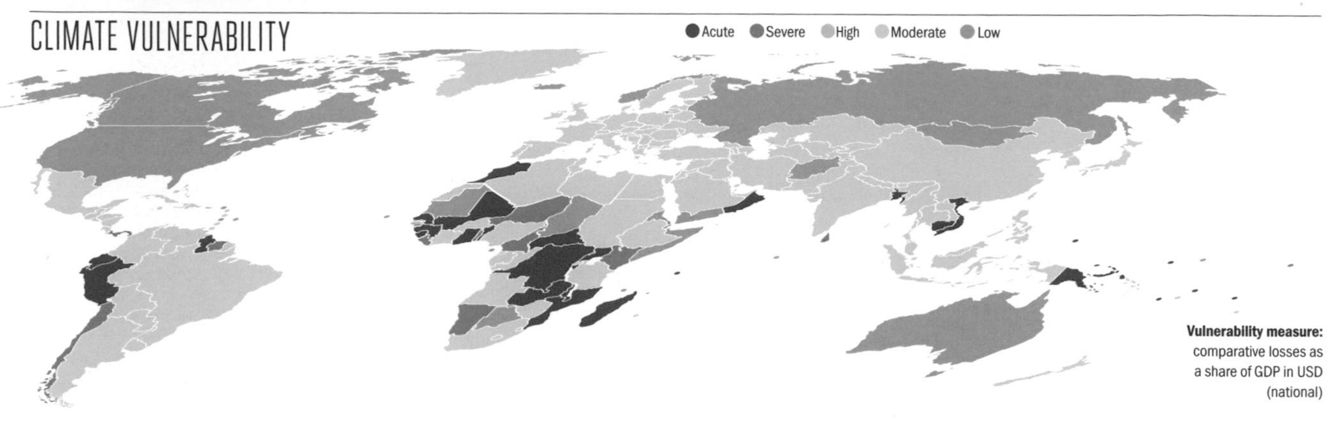

Vulnerability measure: comparative losses as a share of GDP in USD (national)

CLIMATE UNCERTAINTY

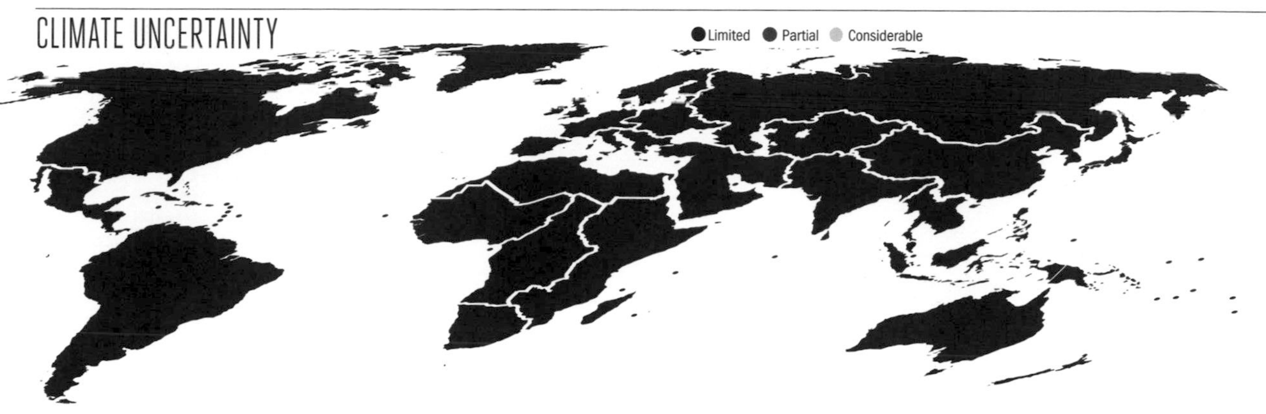

COUNTRY	2010	2030
Dominican Republic	5	65
Egypt	150	2,250
El Salvador	5	85
Equatorial Guinea	1	25
Estonia	15	90
Ethiopia	15	200
Finland	15	55
France	30	90
Georgia	10	95
Germany	15	55
Greece	10	25
Guatemala	5	85
Haiti	1	15
Honduras	5	65
Hungary	1	15
India	650	6,000
Iraq	20	250
Ireland		
Israel	1	15
Italy	20	60
Jamaica	5	65
Japan	200	600
Jordan		5
Kazakhstan	5	85
Kuwait	5	40
Kyrgyzstan		
Latvia	15	150
Lebanon	5	35
Lesotho		
Libya	25	300
Lithuania	15	150
Macedonia		1

COUNTRY	2010	2030
Malta		1
Mauritius	5	55
Mexico	100	950
Moldova		5
Nepal	5	75
Netherlands	15	45
New Zealand	30	90
Pakistan	100	1,250
Paraguay		5
Poland	25	200
Portugal	20	60
Qatar	10	150
Romania	1	10
Rwanda	5	55
Saint Lucia	1	10
Saudi Arabia	85	950
Singapore	1	10
Slovakia	1	5
Slovenia		1
South Korea	200	1,750
Spain	35	100
Swaziland		
Sweden	10	25
Switzerland		1
Syria	5	80
Tajikistan		1
Timor-Leste		5
Trinidad and Tobago	1	25
Turkey	400	1,250
Turkmenistan	5	65
Ukraine	55	600
United Arab Emirates	40	450

COUNTRY	2010	2030
United Kingdom	1	1
Uzbekistan	1	10
Venezuela	65	800
LOW		
Afghanistan		
Antigua and Barbuda		
Australia	-10	-25
Barbados		
Botswana		
Canada	-45	-100
Cape Verde		
Chad		
Comoros		
Djibouti		
Eritrea		
Guinea-Bissau		
Iceland	-350	-1,000
Luxembourg		
Maldives		
Marshall Islands		
Mauritania		
Mongolia		
Norway	-900	-2,750
Russia	-1,250	-8,250
Saint Vincent		
Sao Tome and Principe		
Somalia		
United States	-300	-1,000
Yemen		

FORESTRY

ESTIMATES GLOBAL CLIMATE IMPACT

2010 EFFECT TODAY

USD **LOSS** PER YEAR **5 BILLION**

2030 EFFECT TOMORROW

USD **LOSS** PER YEAR **45 BILLION**

ECONOMIC IMPACT

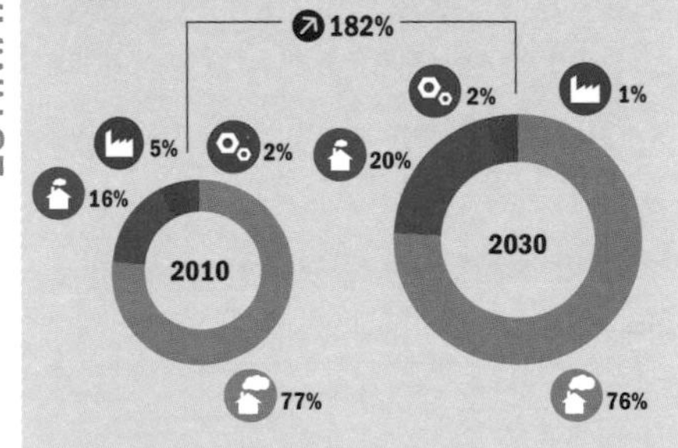

- Climate change is shifting the world's climate zones as the planet warms
- As this occurs, commercial and native tree stands are becoming stranded in climate zones with less than optimal growing conditions
- Many forests are suffering from invasive species, more extreme weather, and flooding, further compounding stresses
- As a result, forests in all regions of the world are in decline or a state of flux, although gains in forest area and growth are evident in some regions
- Reversing the large-scale, rampant deforestation of recent decades would help to attenuate new losses due to climate change

RELATIVE IMPACT

$$$$$$$$$$$$$$$$ $ 2010

154 | 3

$$$$$$$$$$
$$$$$$$$$$$$$$$$ $ 2030

260 | 3

HOTSPOTS

2010	$	2030
2,500	**BRAZIL**	20,000
1,000	**MEXICO**	7,750
450	**ANGOLA**	4,500
400	**VENEZUELA**	4,500
400	**BOLIVIA**	4,250

GEOPOLITICAL VULNERABILITY

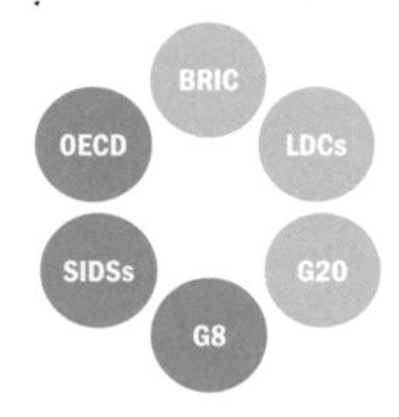

$ Economic Cost (2010 PPP non-discounted)
Developing Country Low Emitters
Developed
Developing Country High Emitters
Other Industrialized

$ = Losses per 100,000 USD of GDP

Change in relation to overall global population and/or GDP

$ = Millions of USD (2010 PPP non-discounted)

Forests cover nearly one-third of the world's land surface, and both commercial and native forests nearly everywhere are affected by the changing climate (Shvidenko et al. in Hassan et al. (eds.), 2005; Bolte et al., 2009). The potential for large-scale tree diebacks and loss of vegetation and forest biodiversity is considered significant. As the planet warms, climate zones are shifting, with stationary forests now in inhospitable conditions, triggering rapid decline and widespread tree mortality, although in some cases forests may be expanding into new areas (Gonzalez et al., 2010). The permanence of forests presents a unique challenge in terms of long-term planning and management, such as substituting tree varieties, although this is not a concern for seasonal crop-based agriculture. Communities that rely on forestry in threatened zones, including indigenous groups, are particularly at risk. If empowered through knowledge, resources, and legal support, these same communities can play a key role in helping forests to adapt. Forests are also a vital carbon sink, helping to contain GHG emissions, which widespread tree mortality counteracts (Kurz et al., 2008).

CLIMATE MECHANISM

Heat stress, increased propensity to drought and flooding, all consistent with climate change, can damage tree growth and forest stands (Allen et al., 2009; Lewis et al., 2011; Kramer et al., 2008). Growing risks from fires, pests, and disease are also of concern (Kurz et al., 2008). Above all, it is the shift taking place in forest habitats that outpaces the ability of stationary forests to naturally adapt (Shvidenko et al. in Hassan et al. (eds.), 2005; Bonan, 2008). Particularly affected are those tropical zones already at the maximum heat threshold, which will see further reductions in their viability as rainfall decreases. Boreal forests established at high altitudes or forest stands on permanently frozen land also risk the inevitable disappearance of their natural habitat as warming increases. Elsewhere forests have been observed, and are expected, to grow faster (McMahon et al., 2010).

IMPACTS

The impact of climate change on the world's commercial and native forests is currently estimated to incur annual losses of around 5 billion dollars, increasing by 2030 to around 45 billion dollars or triple the cost as a share of global GDP.

Brazil and Mexico incur the largest overall losses at around 10-20 billion dollars a year in 2030. A number of lower-income countries such as Angola, Central African Republic, Timor Leste and Zambia suffer the most severe effects as a share of GDP. Other South America countries, such as Bolivia, Chile, Colombia, Paraguay, and Venezuela are all also estimated to experience large-scale impacts.

In general, developing countries on all continents are significantly affected. Among developed countries, Australia and Canada stand out, as well as those in Southern Europe, while Russia incurs the largest scale losses among industrialized nations.

The negative effects are quite widespread, with around 50 countries showing vulnerability levels of high or above. Around 20 countries experience gains that are mainly small in scale, with the exception of Argentina, whose gains are already significant, reaching almost 10 billion dollars a year in 2030.

THE BROADER CONTEXT

The Forestry sector is relatively stable, with increasing value but fluctuating production over the last decade (FAOSTAT, 2012). Demand for forest products of all kinds including timber is expected to increase significantly over the coming decade. Illegal logging and deforestation, especially of native forests, remains a serious and widespread concern, with rates estimated at about 10 million hectares per year—an area larger than Greece—although in parts of Europe and North America in particular reforestation is significant (Shvidenko et al. in Hassan et al. (eds.), 2005).

VULNERABILITIES AND WIDER OUTCOMES

The size of forests as an economic sector and their land area constitute the main components of structural vulnerability for countries in the affected zones. In 2005, 25 countries were estimated to have no remaining forest cover; other countries have less than 10% of forest cover remaining. High rates of deforestation clearly also accentuate vulnerability by diminishing local bio-capacity to withstand changes and increasing risks of invasive pests, flooding, drought, and irrigation-driven water stress (Shvidenko et al. in

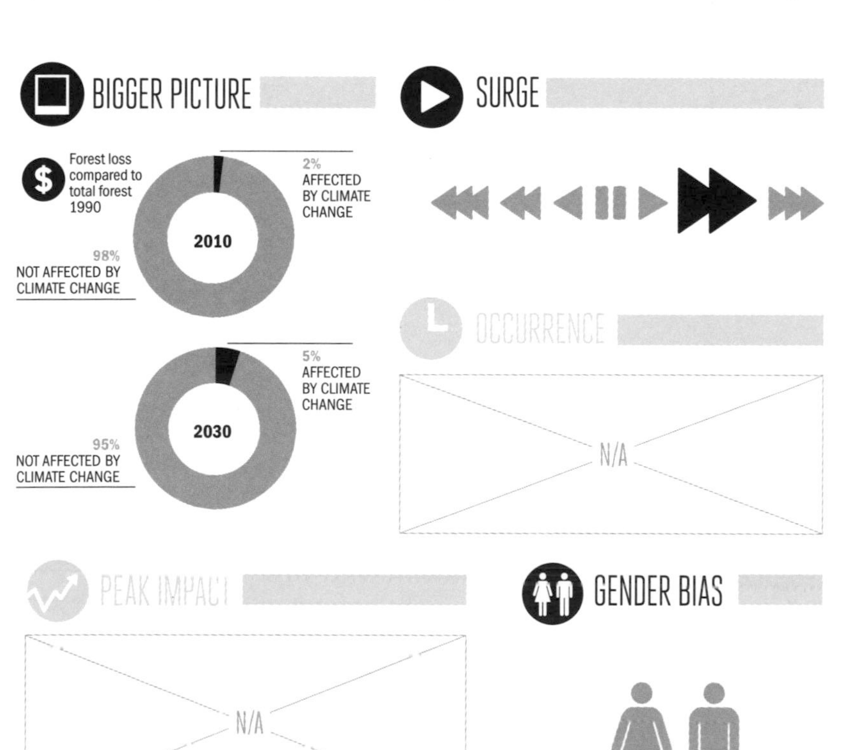

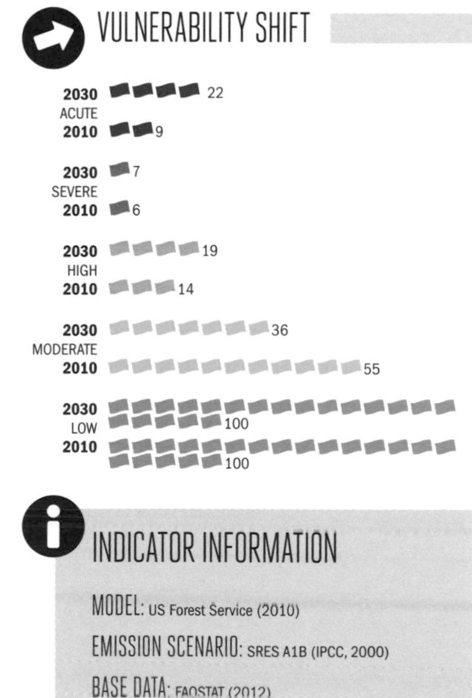

= 5 countries (rounded)

Acute Severe High Moderate Low

Hassan et al. (eds.), 2005; Bolte et al., 2009). Vegetation vulnerability is widespread globally, with forest stands at risk on every continent and in almost all regions, and with Boreal conifer and tropical broadleaf forests equally threatened (Gonzalez et al., 2010). Reliance on forests for market and non-market benefits, from water to biodiversity to wildlife or plant products, is highest among lower-income groups. Forest-based or forest-reliant indigenous groups are also heavily dependent on the health of local forest stands (Munasinghe, 1993; Salick and Byg, 2007). Accordingly, lower-income countries and countries with significant indigenous groups have accentuated vulnerability to the impact of climate change on forests. The loss of vital ecological services as forests die back or decline is a major concern for human development (SCBD, 2009).

RESPONSES

Despite the challenges presented, numerous responses can be foreseen to stem forest decline as a result of climate change or other man-made factors. Stand substitution with more suitable tree varieties can occur progressively; however, the substitution options for the hottest and driest tropical zones are much more limited than elsewhere. Planting, harvesting and thinning regimes and schedules can be adjusted in accordance with altered local conditions (Bolte et al., 2009). Expanding primary forest conservation, particularly in high-risk developing countries, is a priority, but requires increasing capacity to implement that will depend in many cases on foreign assistance (Lee and Jetz, 2008). Additional adaptation strategies may include the establishment and management of biodiversity corridors that reinforce self-supporting connections between forest and non-forest ecosystems (Tabarelli et al., 2010). Pest management could be considered in some managed forest situations. Community forest programmes that support local groups in taking a more proactive involvement in forest conservation and management or sustainable agroforestry projects have the potential to yield double dividends for the environment and development (Hella and Zavaleta, 2009). This could be extended to specific support to indigenous communities (Salick and Byg, 2007). Finally, strong environmental governance, especially if it is community-based, is also key to protecting forest ecosystems, including threats from illegal or condoned deforestation (Baltodano et al., (eds.), 2008). Payment for ecosystem services has met with success in some countries for preserving and enhancing forest ecosystems, Costa Rica being a prime example (Pagiola, 2006).

THE INDICATOR

The indicator considers the scale of estimated shifts in the location and area of different forest biomes due to climate change (Gonzalez et al, 2010). Forestry and biodiversity losses are well recognized in climate science, and are closely linked to significant temperature changes (IPCC, 2007). A key limitation is the valuation method for forests of commercial and non-commercial types, including all varieties of trees in every continent. To simplify the problem, generic values are used for topical and non-tropical forest stands, including bundled biodiversity values (Costanza et al., 2007).

ESTIMATES COUNTRY-LEVEL IMPACT

COUNTRY	$ 2010	$ 2030
ACUTE		
Angola	450	4,500
Benin	20	200
Bolivia	400	4,250
Brazil	2,500	20,000
Central African Republic	5	75
Chile	300	2,000
Dominica	1	10
Dominican Republic	55	600
DR Congo	15	150
Guinea	10	100
Honduras	25	300
Laos	5	100
Mexico	1,000	7,750
Mozambique	75	700
Myanmar	50	600
Nicaragua	10	150
Panama	35	400
Paraguay	100	1,250
Tanzania	35	350
Timor-Leste	20	250
Venezuela	400	4,500
Zambia	150	1,500
SEVERE		
Cambodia	10	150
Cote d,Ivoire	10	100
Cuba	40	450
Ghana	15	150
Saint Lucia	1	5
Saint Vincent		5
Sierra Leone	1	10
HIGH		
Antigua and Barbuda		1
Australia	100	300
Bulgaria	10	100
Cameroon	10	90
Canada	150	500
Colombia	80	900
Congo	1	20
Costa Rica	10	150
El Salvador	5	75
Georgia	1	20
Grenada		5
Guatemala	10	150
Macedonia	5	35
Madagascar	1	25
Malawi	1	10
Mongolia	1	30
Sudan/South Sudan	10	100
Thailand	100	1,500
Togo	1	10
MODERATE		
Albania		1
Armenia	1	5
Azerbaijan	1	25
Barbados		1
China	60	650
Croatia		
France	30	90
Greece	10	25
Haiti	1	5
Iceland		
India	10	80
Indonesia	30	350
Ireland	1	1
Italy	15	50
Kazakhstan	5	75
Kenya	5	30
Kyrgyzstan	1	5
Lesotho		
Morocco	5	75
Nepal		1
Nigeria	25	200
North Korea	1	5
Pakistan	1	15
Philippines	1	30
Portugal	5	20
Russia	150	850
South Korea	1	15
Spain	35	100
Sri Lanka	1	15
Sweden	10	25
Switzerland	1	1
Tajikistan		1
Turkey	5	20
Ukraine	1	10
United Kingdom	5	10
Vietnam	1	20
LOW		
Afghanistan		
Algeria		
Argentina	-950	-10,000
Austria	-1	-10
Bahamas		
Bahrain		
Bangladesh		-1

$ Additional economic costs due to climate change (million USD PPP) - yearly average

CLIMATE VULNERABILITY

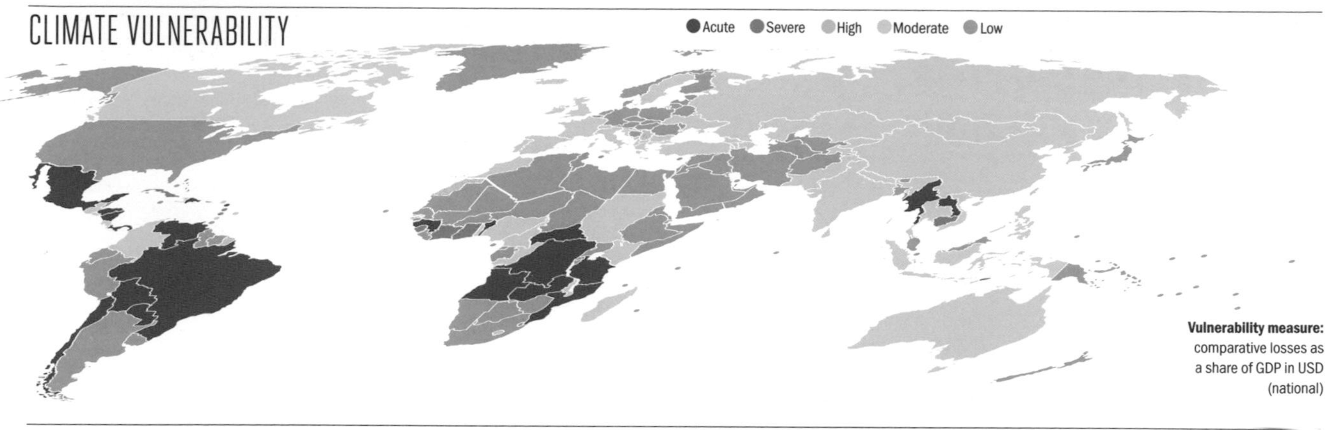

CLIMATE UNCERTAINTY

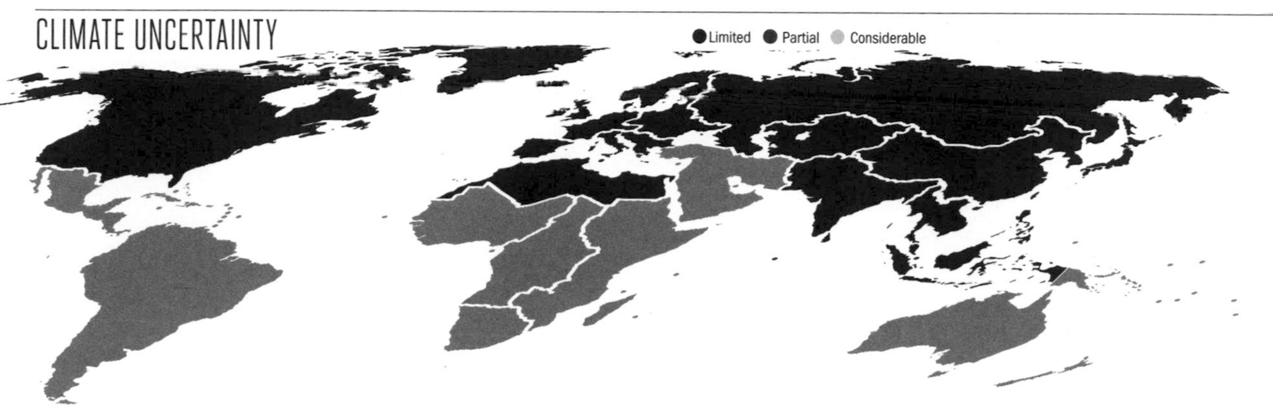

COUNTRY	2010 ($)	2030 ($)
Belarus	-1	-15
Belgium		
Belize		
Bhutan		
Bosnia and Herzegovina		
Botswana		
Brunei		
Burkina Faso		
Burundi		
Cape Verde		
Chad		
Comoros		
Cyprus		
Czech Republic		
Denmark		
Djibouti		
Ecuador	-40	-500
Egypt		
Equatorial Guinea		
Eritrea		
Estonia		-1
Ethiopia		
Fiji		
Finland	-5	-15
Gabon		
Gambia		
Germany	-1	-10
Guinea-Bissau		
Guyana		
Hungary	-1	-10
Iran		
Iraq		
Israel		
Jamaica		
Japan	-10	-30
Jordan		
Kiribati		
Kuwait		
Latvia		
Lebanon		
Liberia		
Libya		
Lithuania	-1	-5
Luxembourg		
Malaysia		
Maldives		
Mali		
Malta		
Marshall Islands		
Mauritania		
Mauritius		
Micronesia		
Moldova		
Namibia		
Netherlands		
New Zealand		
Niger		
Norway	-1	-5
Oman		
Palau		
Papua New Guinea		
Peru	-70	-800
Poland	-5	-40
Qatar		
Romania		-1
Rwanda		
Samoa		
Sao Tome and Principe		
Saudi Arabia		
Senegal		
Seychelles		
Singapore		
Slovakia		
Slovenia		
Solomon Islands		
Somalia		
South Africa	-5	-60
Suriname		
Swaziland		
Syria		
Tonga		
Trinidad and Tobago		
Tunisia		
Turkmenistan		
Tuvalu		
Uganda	1	10
United Arab Emirates		
United States	-90	-300
Uruguay	-5	-80
Uzbekistan		
Vanuatu		
Yemen		
Zimbabwe		

HYDRO ENERGY

ESTIMATES GLOBAL CLIMATE IMPACT

2010 EFFECT TODAY

USD GAIN PER YEAR **5 BILLION**

2030 EFFECT TOMORROW

USD GAIN PER YEAR **25 BILLION**

ECONOMIC IMPACT

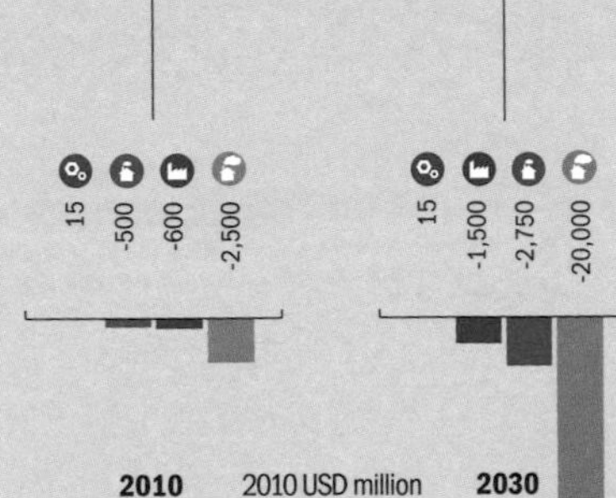

- The world will benefit from increasing hydro energy wealth as climate change brings more rain to many places
- Some regions will be heavily affected by localized reductions in rainfall and a corresponding loss of energy potential for existing hydropower installations
- Additional hydro energy capacity can already be foreseen in zones where there is high certainty of more useable rainfall, especially in high latitudes
- The negative effects of hydro energy can be offset by measures such as expanding reservoirs to increase water holding capacity in affected zones, and through a forward-looking diversification of energy supply

RELATIVE IMPACT

$$$$$$ $ 2010 — 54 / 2

$$$$$$$$ $ 2030 — 72 / 3

HOTSPOTS

2010	$	2030
150	UKRAINE	800
30	ROMANIA	250
85	TURKEY	250
25	IRAN	150
35	ITALY	100

GEOPOLITICAL VULNERABILITY

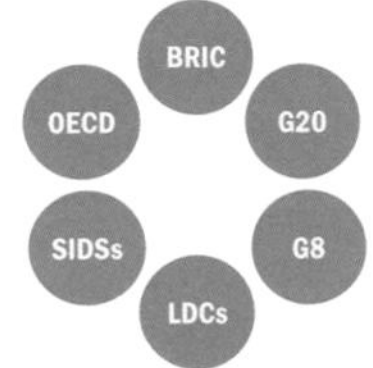

$ Economic Cost (2010 PPP non-discounted)

Developing Country Low Emitters — Developed

Developing Country High Emitters — Other Industrialized

 = Losses per 100,000 USD of GDP

Change in relation to overall global population and/or GDP

Vulnerability of hydropower to climate effects can be high: in Brazil in 2001, intense drought was a key contributor to a "virtual breakdown" of power generation from hydro sources, a dominant energy supply for the country (IPCC, 2012b). Such extreme hydrological events are becoming more common (IPCC, 2007; Hansen et al., 2012). According to the assessment made here, however, fewer than 20 countries would be negatively affected to any significant degree, and many more could benefit. This is because water availability is increasing in many areas of the world as a result of climate change (Bates et al., 2008).

New opportunities will arise over the next 30 years as precipitation increases global hydro energy capacity, and when access to this established clean energy technology will be most needed. Where reductions do occur, they may be severe: a study of nearly 6,000 European hydro stations concluded that 25% reductions in power generation could become a reality for the southern and Mediterranean areas (Lehner et al., 2005). Where the effects are likely to be negative, economies should plan for a diversification to other energy sources, and mitigate the effects of rainfall loss through measures such as reservoir expansion. The intrinsic uncertainty of rainfall will make planning for these large-scale and capital-intensive energy systems difficult (IPCC, 2012b).

CLIMATE MECHANISM

The hydro energy sector has recognized sensitivities to climate change. This is because climate change alters the water cycle of the planet, notably accelerating it and increasing the amount of available rainfall, water, and river flow (Huntington, 2006; Stromberg et al., 2010). However, many countries will not experience an improvement in water availability, but will see declines, as water replenishments fail to keep pace with rising heat (Chu et al., 2009). In the long term, melting glaciers may further increase water scarcity, but in the coming years it is likely to increase water flows (Olefs et al., 2009). All these factors can have an impact on the power generation capacity of hydro energy installations (Lehner et al., 2001; Pereira de Lucena et al., 2009; Hamududu and Killingtveit, 2012). Globally, major rivers are expected to increase in flow or decline depending on local and regional climate conditions—although these are uncertain for many areas (Nohara et al., 2006). Evidence tends to favour an increase in rainfall (or runoff) in the far north and south, and a decrease in tropical regions (Helm et al., 2010).

IMPACTS

Given the still relatively small scale of hydro power installations in the global energy mix—although it is still by far the largest source of renewable energy—the positive effect worldwide is small at around 4 billion dollars in 2010 (US EIA, 2011).

Losses by comparison are estimated at around 0.5 billion dollars.

The worst affected zones are Southern Europe and Central America, while the largest total gains include China, Canada, and the US, subject of course to different degrees of uncertainty linked to rainfall projections to 2030.

Between 2010 and 2030 the estimated effect more than doubles as a proportion of GDP, with around 25 billion dollars in yearly gains by 2030.

The number of worst affected countries has more than doubled, and there is a significant increase in gains among the many countries that are projected to benefit.

THE BROADER CONTEXT

The hydro energy sector has undergone continued expansion in recent decades—although not as rapidly as renewable energy technologies—and is expected to continue to grow as a source of power generation (US EIA, 2011; BP, 2012). Given the large-scale up-front capital investment involved and the long-term shelf life of installations, careful consideration should be given to new investments, particularly since several episodes of decline in water-fed energy supply have already been observed in different areas (IPCC, 2012b). Significant opportunities to support an expansion of hydro energy are emerging in some areas, especially high-latitude regions where there is much greater certainty of increasing rainfall over the next 20 years and beyond (Bates et al., 2008; Helm et al., 2010).

VULNERABILITIES AND WIDER OUTCOMES

Watershed or water catchment capacity in reservoirs is a key contributor to resilience of hydro power installations, since these can stock water during

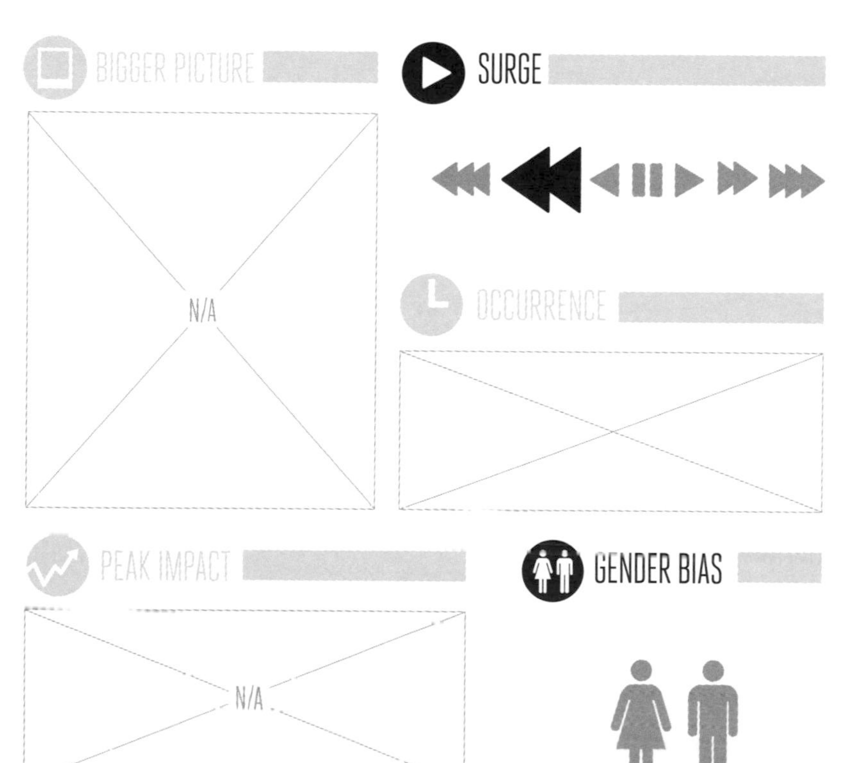

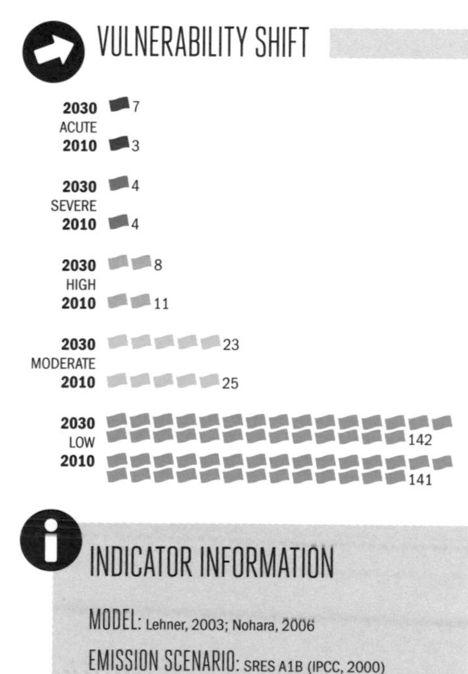

INDICATOR INFORMATION

MODEL: Lehner, 2003; Nohara, 2006

EMISSION SCENARIO: SRES A1B (IPCC, 2000)

BASE DATA: IEA, 2011; Lehner, 2001

= 5 countries (rounded)

Acute Severe High Moderate Low

extended periods of drought, and retain water deposited at inconvenient times of the year and saved for later use (IPCC, 2012b). Hydro installations that are powered only by river flow and not through a reservoir are particularly exposed to diminished rainfall and water runoff, as was pointed out in the Vietnam country study in this report. Whether environmental management is poor or sound may also play a role: for example, Costa Rica, one of the countries worst hit, has begun to reverse its deforestation process, which is expected to result in improved watershed capacity, although only high altitude or mature forests are understood to add to surrounding water supplies (Morse et al., 2009; Postel and Thompson, 2005; Hamilton, 2008). Lower-income countries are relatively well shielded since investment in capital-intensive hydro power installations in these countries has so far been marginal (UNEP Risoe, 2012). Both the Ghana and Vietnam country studies in this report highlight the potential negative effects of hydro installations for coastal erosion, which can compound climate change-induced sea-level rise.

RESPONSES

Where energy potential is set to decline, there are two main response areas: first, undertaking or intensifying measures aimed at improving the supply of water through enhanced watershed catchment and upstream water resource conservation. Increasing forest area and certain types of nature reserves can help build up the water capacity under certain conditions (Postel and Thompson, 2005). Depending on the type of installation, expanding the size of drawing reservoirs to stock more water may also provide a buffer against declining rainfall. In more arid regions, managing upstream water consumption, such as irrigation, may also yield positive results by lessening water withdrawals (Kang et al., 2004). Second, ensure diversification of future energy investments away from hydro power. At the same time, there is a danger that affected economies compensate for lost production in the hydro energy sector through an increase in carbon intensive modes of energy supply. In some major economies, experts have recently been recommending further investment in oil and gas energy generation as a least-cost adaptation option for hydro energy and other renewable energy sources that may be affected by climate change (Pereira de Lucena et al., 2010). Conversely, certain experts have argued that the promotion of hydropower has caused serious environmental damage and should be reconsidered (Haya, 2007).

THE INDICATOR

The indicator maps changes in river discharge in relation to estimated effects of climate change and the corresponding effect on the global hydro-energy potential of existing installations, and draws on International Energy Agency data (Lehner et al., 2001; IEA, 2012b). Key limitations relate to the scale of the information and uncertainty in the direction and magnitude of rainfall changes. The main model is geographically limited to Europe, and effects are extrapolated using river flow information (Nohara et al., 2006). Differences in anticipated changes in rainfall patterns could mean very different outcomes in river discharge and energy potential for those areas where there is less agreement and certainty around the direction of the change (Bates et al., 2008; Hamududu and Killingtveit, 2012).

ESTIMATES COUNTRY-LEVEL IMPACT

COUNTRY	2010	2030
ACUTE		
Albania	10	100
Bosnia and Herzegovina	15	100
Costa Rica	15	100
Honduras	10	70
Macedonia	5	30
Panama	10	80
Ukraine	150	800
SEVERE		
Bulgaria	5	95
Croatia	10	75
Romania	30	250
Syria	20	100
HIGH		
Austria	10	50
El Salvador	5	35
Guatemala	10	55
Haiti	1	5
New Zealand	10	25
Nicaragua	1	10
Slovenia	5	40
Turkey	85	250
MODERATE		
Australia	5	15
Belarus		
Belgium		
Cuba		1
Czech Republic		5
Dominican Republic	1	20
France	25	100
Greece	1	20
Iran	25	150
Iraq	1	15
Israel		1
Italy	35	100
Jamaica	1	1
Jordan		1
Lebanon	1	15
Lithuania		
Moldova		1
Netherlands		
Poland	5	20
Portugal	-1	20
Slovakia	5	35
Spain	10	95
Switzerland	1	30
LOW		
Afghanistan		
Algeria		
Angola	-1	-5
Antigua and Barbuda		
Argentina	-20	-150
Armenia	-1	-15
Azerbaijan	-5	-20
Bahamas		
Bahrain		
Bangladesh	-1	-20
Barbados		
Belize		
Benin		
Bhutan		
Bolivia	-1	-10
Botswana		
Brazil	-150	-750
Brunei		
Burkina Faso		
Burundi		
Cambodia		
Cameroon	-5	-20
Canada	-350	-800
Cape Verde		
Central African Republic		
Chad		
Chile	-10	-60
China	-2,250	-20,000
Colombia	-20	-100
Comoros		
Congo		-1
Cote d,Ivoire	-1	-5
Cyprus		
Denmark		
Djibouti		
Dominica		
DR Congo	-5	-30
Ecuador	-5	-40
Egypt	-15	-95
Equatorial Guinea		
Eritrea		
Estonia		
Ethiopia	-1	-10
Fiji		
Finland	-10	-30
Gabon	-1	-5
Gambia		
Georgia	-15	-75
Germany	-10	-10

$ Additional economic costs due to climate change (million USD PPP) - yearly average

CLIMATE VULNERABILITY

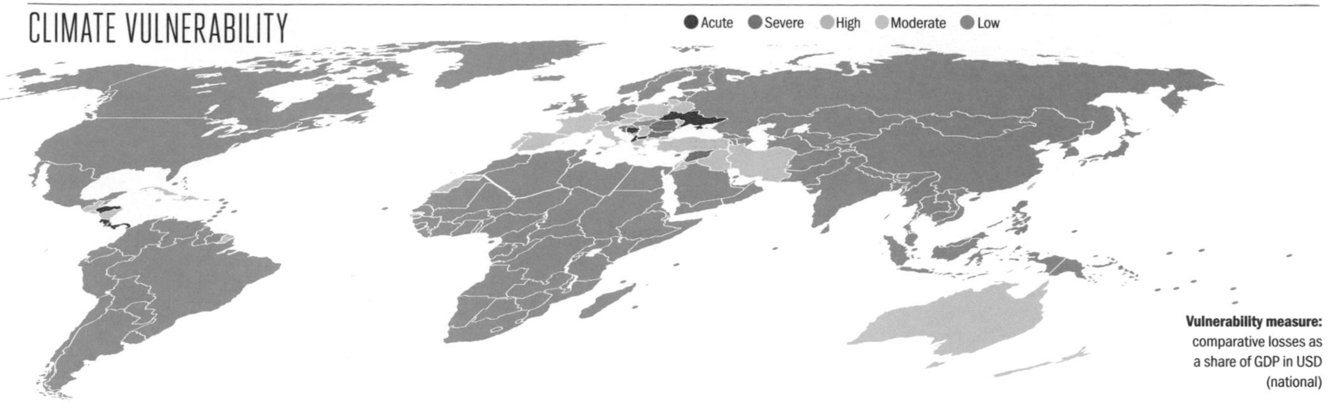

CLIMATE UNCERTAINTY

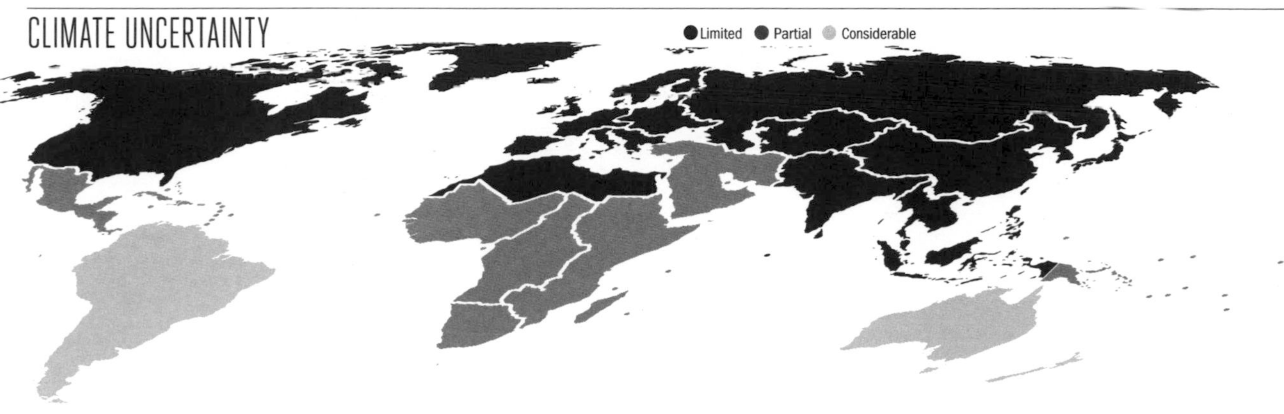

COUNTRY	2010	2030
Ghana	-5	-35
Grenada		
Guinea		
Guinea-Bissau		
Guyana		
Hungary		-1
Iceland	5	-1
India	-250	-1,500
Indonesia	-10	-75
Ireland	-1	-1
Japan	-80	-150
Kazakhstan	-10	-70
Kenya	-1	-5
Kiribati		
Kuwait		
Kyrgyzstan	-40	-250
Laos		
Latvia	-1	-15
Lesotho		
Liberia		
Libya		
Luxembourg		
Madagascar		
Malawi		
Malaysia	-10	-65
Maldives		
Mali		
Malta		
Marshall Islands		
Mauritania		
Mauritius		
Mexico	-60	-350

COUNTRY	2010	2030
Micronesia		
Mongolia		
Morocco	-1	-5
Mozambique	-10	-55
Myanmar	-1	-15
Namibia	-1	-5
Nepal	-5	-30
Niger		
Nigeria	-5	-30
North Korea	-25	-200
Norway	35	-150
Oman		
Pakistan	-55	-350
Palau		
Papua New Guinea		
Paraguay	-40	-250
Peru	-10	-75
Philippines	-10	-75
Qatar		
Russia	-300	-1,500
Rwanda		
Saint Lucia		
Saint Vincent		
Samoa		
Sao Tome and Principe		
Saudi Arabia		
Senegal		
Seychelles		
Sierra Leone		
Singapore		
Solomon Islands		
Somalia		

COUNTRY	2010	2030
South Africa	-1	-5
South Korea	-5	-40
Sri Lanka	-10	-55
Sudan/South Sudan	-1	-5
Suriname		
Swaziland		
Sweden	40	-60
Tajikistan	-45	-250
Tanzania	-1	-15
Thailand	-10	-60
Timor-Leste		
Togo		-1
Tonga		
Trinidad and Tobago		
Tunisia		-1
Turkmenistan		
Tuvalu		
Uganda		
United Arab Emirates		
United Kingdom	-5	-5
United States	-300	-700
Uruguay	-5	-20
Uzbekistan	-15	-90
Vanuatu		
Venezuela	-30	-200
Vietnam	-30	-300
Yemen		
Zambia	-5	-25
Zimbabwe	-1	-15

TOURISM

ESTIMATES GLOBAL CLIMATE IMPACT

2010 EFFECT TODAY

USD LOSS PER YEAR **NIL**

2030 EFFECT TOMORROW

USD LOSS PER YEAR **NIL**

ECONOMIC IMPACT

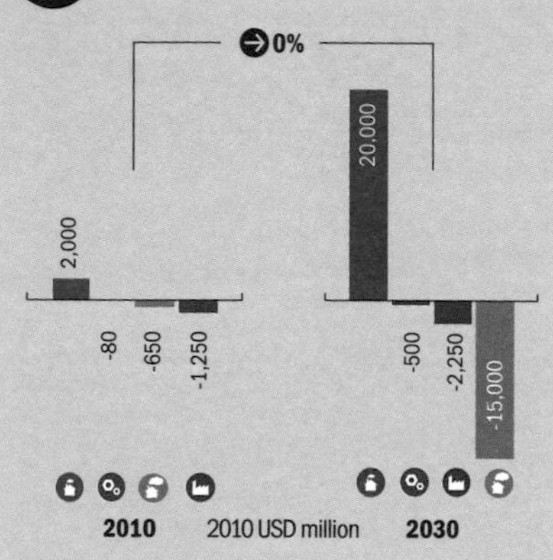

- Impacts will affect tropical beaches and island destinations reliant on seaside and tropical reef tourism and winter sports as low-elevation reefs die and snowfall becomes unreliable
- Extreme and hot weather will affect tourism, but are not yet well understood
- Net global impact of climate change on tourism may not be negative; effects may redistribute tourism revenues among cooler countries with perceived climate advantages
- Adapting to impacts of climate change on tourism is challenging

RELATIVE IMPACT

$$$$$$ $ 2010 — 55 / 1

$$$$$$$ $ 2030 — 67 / 3

HOTSPOTS

2010	$	2030
1,250	INDONESIA	10,000
1,250	MALAYSIA	10,000
800	INDIA	8,000
600	EGYPT	5,000
200	SRI LANKA	1,750

GEOPOLITICAL VULNERABILITY

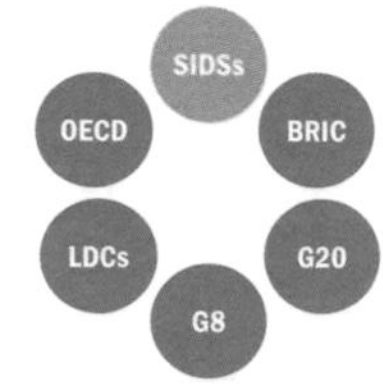

$ Economic Cost (2010 PPP non-discounted)
Developing Country Low Emitters | Developed
Developing Country High Emitters | Other Industrialized

 $ = Losses per 10,000 USD of GDP

Change in relation to overall global population and/or GDP

$ = Millions of USD (2010 PPP non-discounted)

Tourism is clearly a climate-dependent sector. Weather conditions affect business in this sector, and general theory on the impact of climate change on tourism has been understood to favour cooler countries over tropical ones (Wall, 1998; Hamilton et al., 2005; Amelung et al., 2007). Yet there are exceptions: experts have suggested that Switzerland may see half of its ski stations become snow unreliable, with the snow reliability altitude rising from 1,200 metres today to over 1,800 metres, effectively stranding large, profitable, and irreplaceable ski zones (Elsasser and Bürki, 2002). Some economists have put forward evidence that the impact of climate change on tourism might result in an overall loss to global welfare (Berrittella et al., 2004). Tourism is currently a fast growing industry, however, and in the near term it is more likely that any impacts would instead trigger redistribution of tourism revenues away from low- and middle-income tropical coastal resorts to other global destinations, in particular high-income countries, which benefit from more pleasant weather as the planet warms (UNWTO, 2012; Harrison et al., 1999). Experts have been unsure about national outcomes for some countries—such as the tourist magnet France—which are exposed to a range of positive and negative tourism-related concerns (Ceron and Dubois, 2004). The full range of possible effects for tourism is large in scale, given the heavy reliance on outdoor recreation and environmental leisure activities (Jones and Phillips eds., 2011). This assessment is anchored in two relatively well-studied concerns: decline of reef-based and low-elevation winter sports tourism (Steiger, 2011; ECLAC, 2011). In this way, the Monitor's tourism indicator serves to ensure that adequate attention is given by policymakers to the issue of tourism and climate change, despite the lack of comprehensiveness in analysis here, since even through this narrow lens, some countries may experience 1% losses of GDP by 2030.

CLIMATE MECHANISM

The climate effect assessed here examines only the effects for reef-based and mountain tourism. The degradation and bleaching of coral reefs and a decline of tropical fish stocks is a clear consequence of the steady warming of the atmosphere and oceans (Hoegh-Guldberg et al., 2007). Likewise, climate propelled sea-level rise is leading to coastal erosion, affecting beaches and coral reefs (Nicholls and Cazenave, 2010). Cultural heritage sites around the world's coastlines are also affected or threatened by this erosion (UNESCO, 2010). These effects penalize tourism that has flourished in places where there is an abundance of coral for diving and other related pursuits (Uyarra et al., 2005; ECLAC, 2011).

Other clear effects on tourism are a general onset of shorter, milder winters, long-term glacier decline and a snow-line gradually gaining in elevation in mid- to high-latitude regions (Euskirchen et al., 2006; Kelly and Goulden, 2008). These combined effects entail a slight and gradual degradation of mountain resort offerings, especially in low-elevation areas, which in turn can limit revenues in a high-risk industry (Koenigg and Abegg, 1997; Scott, 2003; Steiger, 2011).

IMPACTS

While the global effect is expected to be cost neutral, losses to affected countries are currently estimated at around 5 billion dollars a year, building to over 40 billion dollars, with an almost double share of global GDP in losses by 2030. Small island paradises such as the Bahamas, the Maldives, and Fiji dominate the list of countries most vulnerable to the negative effects of climate change on tourism. More marginal effects will also be felt in traditional skiing destinations, such as Australia, Austria, France, and Switzerland.

By 2030, lost revenue in tourism could cost upwards of 1% of GDP for several of the worst affected small island nations, although the greatest overall losses will be incurred in larger economies such as Egypt, Indonesia, or Malaysia. The effects for winter tourism host countries are expected to be marginal on a national scale, but could be highly unfavourable to mountain communities, which rely on short, peak seasons for the bulk of annual profits. Around 20–30 countries are estimated to experience serious effects; losses are estimated to be redistributed among high-latitude countries where domestic and foreign tourism is expected to improve along with favourable climate change. High-altitude ski resorts may also see surges in demand.

THE BROADER CONTEXT

Tourism is a major growth industry globally, due especially to income and population trends that bolster

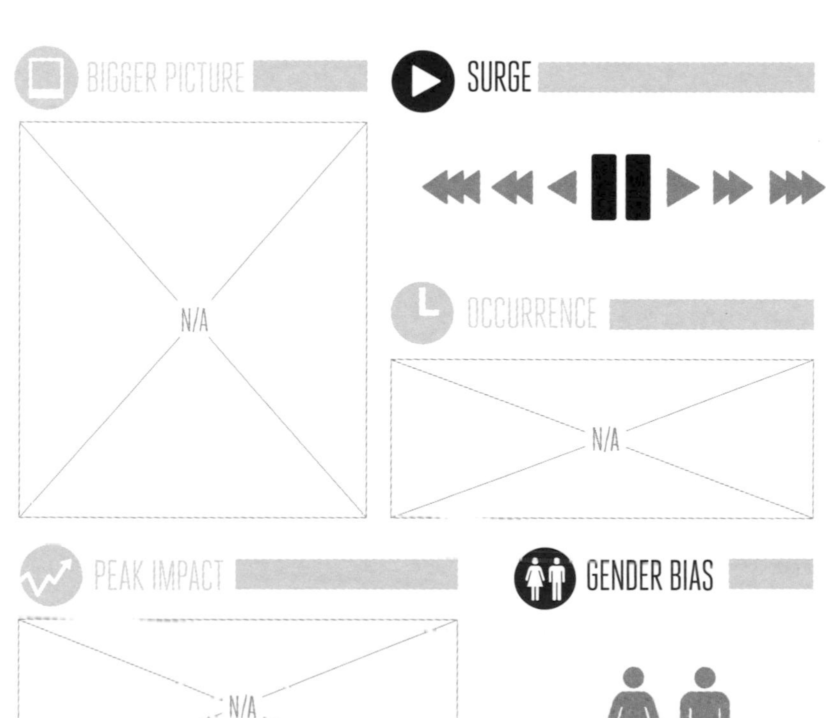

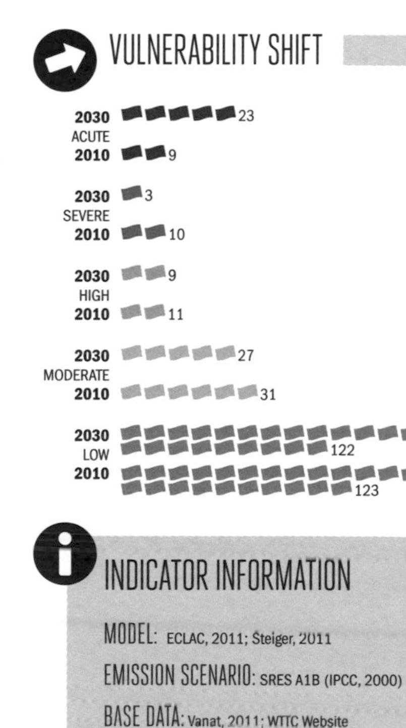

= 5 countries (rounded)

Acute Severe High Moderate Low

the leisure sector (UNWTO, 2012). Given this growth, it is unlikely that any areas will experience significant absolute declines in revenues in the next few years (Hamilton et al., 2005). However, some niches in the industry grow more slowly than others: ski trips to mountain resorts have been stable over the last decade (Vanat, 2011). The broader industry context suggests that countries are more likely to have the growth of their tourism revenue slowed, rather than incur absolute losses, at least in the near term. This assessment represents an estimate of the potential opportunity cost for affected communities.

VULNERABILITIES AND WIDER OUTCOMES

KPMG identified the tourism sector as one of the industries most vulnerable to climate change, especially in light of physical risks, but also as one of the industries least prepared and therefore most likely to incur losses (KPMG, 2008). Geography clearly plays a role in physical risk, given the emphasis some experts have given to winners and losers in the global tourism industry depending on latitude (Amelung et al., 2007). The risks of coastal and mountain dependent tourist zones are also covered above. The size of the tourism sector and the level of its exposure to climate-related risks are the key determinants of vulnerability. Particularly in small island states, tourism is a large-scale revenue generator, whose remote locations allow unique access to a lucrative global market (Uyarra et al., 2005). Long-term sector decline could damage national income prospects and state expenditure on public goods such as schools, since tourism is an important form of public revenue in popular areas (Archabald and Naughton-Treves, 2001; Gooroochurn and Sinclair, 2005).

RESPONSES

In many cases, adaptation will require a diversification of the value offering of affected market segments, diversification away from long-term tourism-based risks where possible, and support or rehabilitation programmes to assist worst affected communities. Overcoming the unpreparedness of the sector to address climate stresses through awareness and education at different levels is of vital importance (Scott, 2011). However, the lack of preparedness of the sector underscores fundamental gaps in current response strategies (Scott et al., 2009). A variety of quite costly coastal conservation measures exist to stem beach and coastland erosion, but are unlikely to render such places more attractive to tourists (Klein et al., 2001). Strong environmental protection and sustainable fishing regulations, along with the promotion and expansion of natural marine reserves or mangrove forests can also help to boost local ecosystem resilience against coral and fish stock decline (Hughes et al., 2003; Corcoran et al., 2007). For low-elevation winter ski spots, relying on energy-intensive snow-making can assist to some degree, but would constitute a paradoxical response to the locally felt effect of global climate change on these vulnerable mountain tourist areas (Dawson et al., 2009). More generally, experts have raised concern about the potential for the tourism sector to become a major contributor to GHG emissions in the coming decades (Scott et al., 2010).

THE INDICATOR

The indicator measures the effects of the loss in tourism revenue potential in tropical seaside resorts and winter ski resorts, based only on two separate studies on the question (Steiger, 2011; ECLAC, 2011). Given the climate factors involved, such as ocean temperatures and the length and temperature of winter ski seasons, the IPCC has been firm on the anticipated effects for the tourism industry (IPCC, 2007). The indicator should still be considered only to address the types of effects countries with a heavy reliance on reef and winter tourism might face. The main limitation is the lack of scope of the indicator, which captures only a fraction of the broader problem.

ESTIMATES COUNTRY-LEVEL IMPACT

COUNTRY	$ 2010	$ 2030
ACUTE		
Antigua and Barbuda	10	100
Bahamas	65	550
Barbados	40	400
Dominica	5	30
Fiji	20	200
Grenada	1	25
Jamaica	100	950
Kiribati	1	10
Malaysia	1,250	10,000
Maldives	15	150
Marshall Islands	1	5
Micronesia	1	15
Palau	1	5
Saint Lucia	10	100
Saint Vincent	5	25
Samoa	5	35
Seychelles	15	100
Solomon Islands	5	45
Sri Lanka	200	1,750
Timor-Leste	5	65
Trinidad and Tobago	100	900
Tuvalu		1
Vanuatu	10	100
SEVERE		
Cuba	150	1,250
Egypt	600	5,000
Indonesia	1,250	10,000
HIGH		
Bahrain	15	150
Belize	1	20
Djibouti	1	15
Madagascar	15	100
Mozambique	10	65
Tanzania	25	200
Tonga	1	5
United Arab Emirates	150	1,500
Yemen	30	250
MODERATE		
Armenia		
Australia	150	400
Austria	55	300
Bosnia and Herzegovina		5
Czech Republic	5	70
Eritrea	1	10
Finland	1	5
France	30	200
Georgia		
Germany	10	70
Haiti	1	25
Hungary	-1	5
India	800	8,000
Italy	15	85
Myanmar	10	95
New Zealand	1	5
Norway	1	15
Papua New Guinea	1	25
Qatar	10	80
Saudi Arabia	100	1,000
Slovakia	5	50
Slovenia	1	25
Spain	5	30
Sudan/South Sudan	10	60
Sweden	1	15
Switzerland	20	90
Turkey		1
LOW		
Afghanistan		
Albania		
Algeria		
Angola		
Argentina	-10	-65
Azerbaijan		
Bangladesh		
Belarus	-1	-20
Belgium	-1	-1
Benin		
Bhutan		
Bolivia		
Botswana		
Brazil		
Brunei		
Bulgaria	-1	-5
Burkina Faso		
Burundi		
Cambodia		
Cameroon		
Canada	-100	-200
Cape Verde		
Central African Republic		
Chad		
Chile	-1	-15
China	-3,500	-40,000
Colombia		
Comoros		
Congo		

$ Additional economic costs due to climate change (million USD PPP) - yearly average

CLIMATE VULNERABILITY

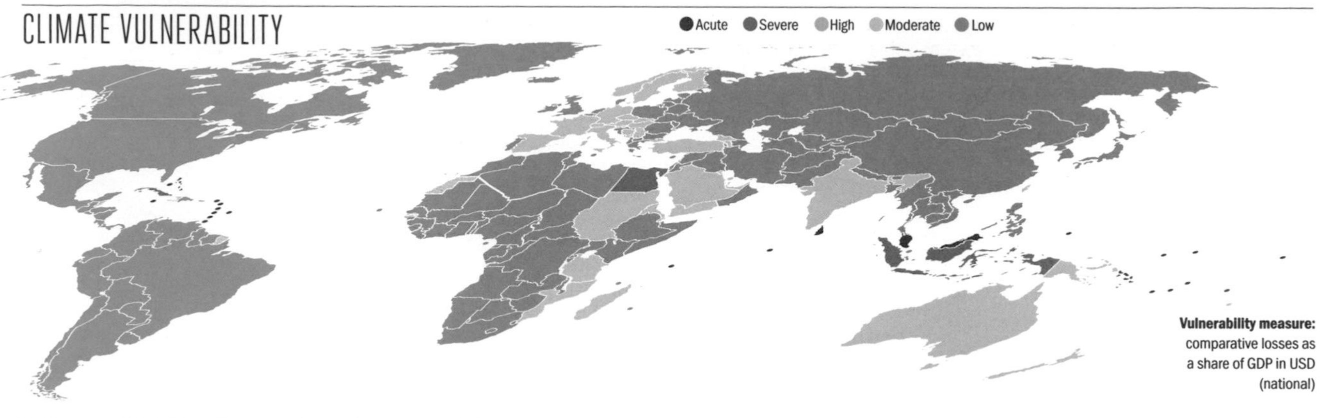

Vulnerability measure: comparative losses as a share of GDP in USD (national)

CLIMATE UNCERTAINTY

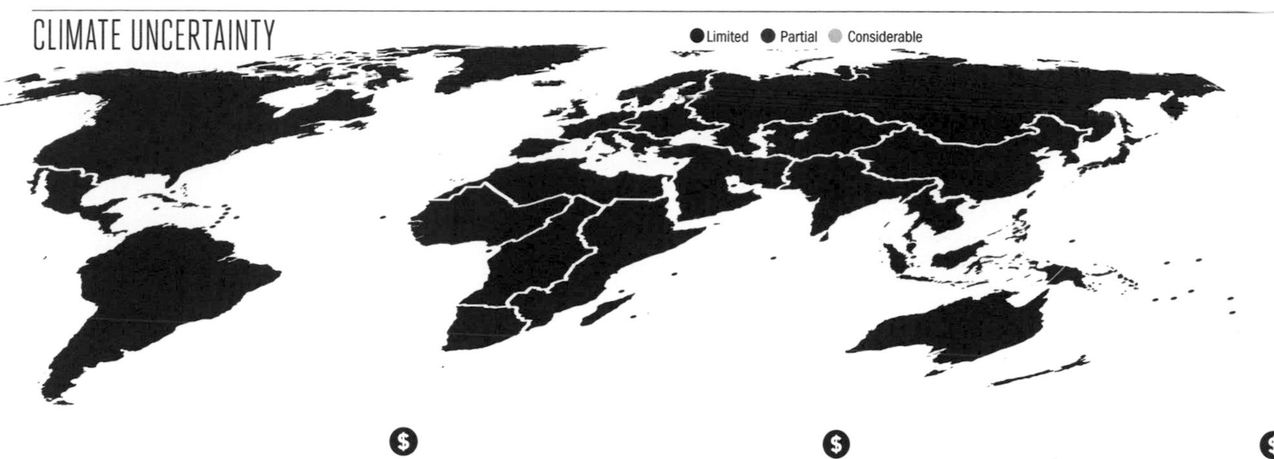

COUNTRY	2010	2030
Costa Rica		
Cote d,Ivoire		
Croatia		
Cyprus		
Denmark	-1	-1
Dominican Republic		
DR Congo		
Ecuador		
El Salvador		
Equatorial Guinea		
Estonia		-1
Ethiopia		
Gabon		
Gambia		
Ghana		
Greece		
Guatemala		
Guinea		
Guinea-Bissau		
Guyana		
Honduras		
Iceland		
Iran		
Iraq		
Ireland	-1	-1
Israel		
Japan	-55	-5
Jordan		
Kazakhstan		
Kenya		
Kuwait		
Kyrgyzstan		

COUNTRY	2010	2030
Laos		
Latvia	-1	-1
Lebanon		
Lesotho		
Liberia		
Libya		
Lithuania	-1	-5
Luxembourg		
Macedonia		
Malawi		
Mali		
Malta		
Mauritania		
Mauritius		
Mexico		
Moldova		-1
Mongolia	-1	-5
Morocco		
Namibia		
Nepal		
Netherlands	-1	-5
Nicaragua		
Niger		
Nigeria		
North Korea	-15	-150
Oman		
Pakistan		
Panama		
Paraguay		
Peru		
Philippines		
Poland	-10	-65

COUNTRY	2010	2030
Portugal		
Romania	-1	-10
Russia	-65	-500
Rwanda		
Sao Tome and Principe		
Senegal		
Sierra Leone		
Singapore		
Somalia		
South Africa	-60	-400
South Korea	-35	-150
Suriname		
Swaziland		
Syria		
Tajikistan		
Thailand		
Togo		
Tunisia		
Turkmenistan		
Uganda		
Ukraine	-5	-35
United Kingdom	5	-15
United States	-1,500	-3,250
Uruguay	-1	-5
Uzbekistan		
Venezuela		
Vietnam		
Zambia		
Zimbabwe		

TRANSPORT

ESTIMATES GLOBAL CLIMATE IMPACT

2010 EFFECT TODAY

USD LOSS PER YEAR **1 BILLION**

2030 EFFECT TOMORROW

USD LOSS PER YEAR **5 BILLION**

ECONOMIC IMPACT

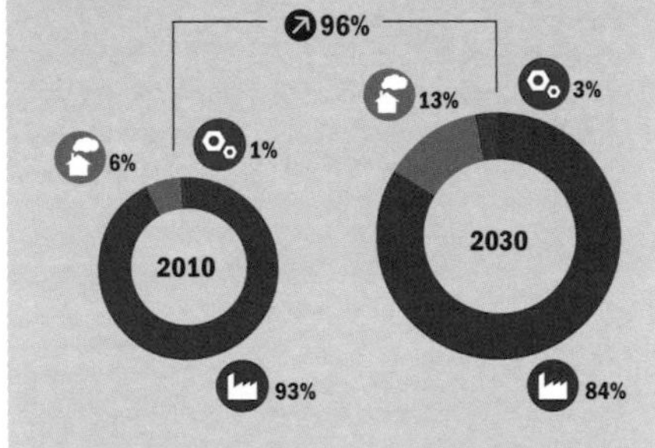

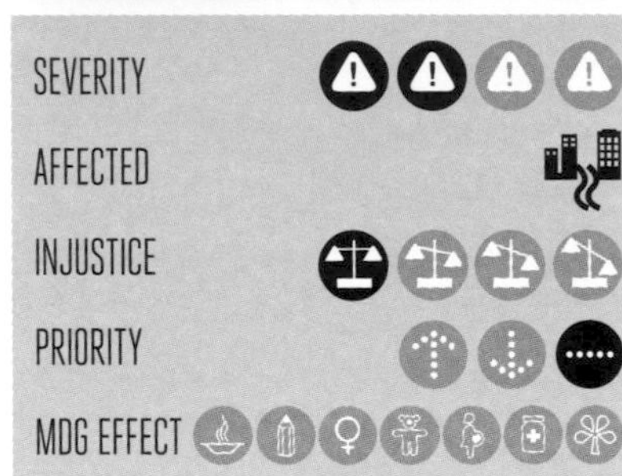

- The impact of climate change on the transport sector is relatively unstudied compared to other areas
- Changes will lead to geographic shifts in volume rather than overall losses
- Apparent net negative effects relate to losses incurred through increasing costs of logistics for inland transport, as some important river levels decline
- These losses are not expected to be offset by gains in transport effectiveness in parts of the world experiencing more flooding of river-ways due to climate change
- Water resource management and conservation are required to limit these effects

RELATIVE IMPACT

$$$$$$$$ $ 2010
77 2

$$$$$$$$$$$$$$$$$$$$ $ 2030
202 4

HOTSPOTS

2010		2030
1,000	USA	5,750
75	MEXICO	950
45	GERMANY	200
35	NETHERLANDS	150
10	ROMANIA	100

GEOPOLITICAL VULNERABILITY

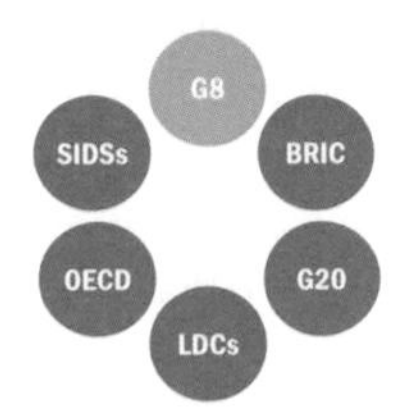

$ Economic Cost (2010 PPP non-discounted)
Developing Country Low Emitters
Developed
Developing Country High Emitters
Other Industrialized

$ = Losses per million USD of GDP

Change in relation to overall global population and/or GDP

Only the impact of climate change on river transport is considered here. Many other negative and positive effects of climate change on the transportation sector are conceivable, but difficult to simulate (Koetse and Rietveld, 2009; Eisenack et al., 2012). Climate change, however, can clearly affect the flow of rivers, increasing or decreasing the rate and volume of water over which goods are transported (Stromberg et al., 2010). A number of the world's waterways are already independently stressed due to infrastructure, pollution, or water withdrawals, which can reduce river flows and make them more vulnerable to climate change impacts (Palmer et al., 2008; Sabater and Tockner, 2010). Climate change has been simulated to have potentially serious negative effects on the river levels of some of the world's most important waterways, including the Danube, the Rhine, and the Rio Grande rivers (Nohara et al., 2006). Lower water levels will continue to increase shipping costs for major global transport conduits affected by river level decline, with potentially significant effects for affected communities—for example, the Rhine carries around 70% of all inland waterway transport of the pre-2004 EU-15 (Jonkeren et al., 2007).

CLIMATE MECHANISM

There are also discernable linkages between river flows and climate factors, such as extreme heat, rainfall, and drought (Kaczmarek et al. (eds.), 1996). Increasing temperatures, the earlier onset of spring, longer, hotter summers, long-term glacial decline, and changes in rainfall patterns, among other effects characteristic of climate change, will have an increasing role in determining water levels in the world's rivers. Increased rainfall and heavy flooding will also affect rivers in some places. However, there is little evidence of any beneficial effect from higher river levels, which are more likely to increase flooding and other risks, since most additional water will fall during the rainy season, when flows and supply are in abundance (Arnell, 2004). When river levels decline, an economic loss arises by affecting the maximum cargo payload that can be transported, or the size of ships transporting goods. The inefficiencies thus created increase shipping costs in a predictable way (Jonkeren et al., 2007).

IMPACTS

Only a handful of countries are affected in any significant way by the impact of climate change on river transportation. This is because large-volume, inland, water-borne transportation is a major economic activity in only a few river basins of the world (UNECE, 2012a). Moreover, only a small number of river basins are currently projected to see continued decline, mainly because in many areas rainfall will increase with climate change (Nohara et al., 2006). The costs of climate change on the transport sector as a result of effects for inland water-borne logistics are currently estimated at 1 billion dollars per year, increasing to over 7 billion dollars by 2030 as the effect intensifies and the overall impact grows as a share of GDP. The bulk of all losses are estimated to be incurred in the United Sates, with European countries along the Rhine and Danube, such as Germany and the Netherlands, as well as Bulgaria and Romania, affected to lesser degrees. Mexico also shows high levels of vulnerability, linked to decline of the Rio Grande.

Caution is suggested with regard to the assessment results, which may underestimate the vulnerabilities of several river basins if rainfall patterns were to evolve differently than expected, based on the research relied upon here.

THE BROADER CONTEXT

Many factors other than climate change—especially water withdrawals from rivers due to growth in agricultural, industrial, and municipal water demand—can play a central role in the level of rivers (Alcamo et al., 2003). Indeed, so-called "basin" closure—the inability of a waterway to meet local water demands for part of the year—currently affects 1.4 billion people in various river basins around the world (Falkenmark and Molden, 2008). Population growth exacerbates these issues when alternate resources are not adequately managed (Vösösmarty et al., 2000; Palmer et al., 2008).

The transportation and logistics sector is a steady growth industry in a globalizing economy, with no expectation of declining demand, except for passenger transportation in some industrialized country settings (US DoT, 2010; Millard-Ball and Schipper, 2011). Therefore, losses are unlikely to lead to unemployment issues, but rather to generate additional costs for communities that have relied on highly efficient inland water-borne transportation, which can be a major economic benefit.

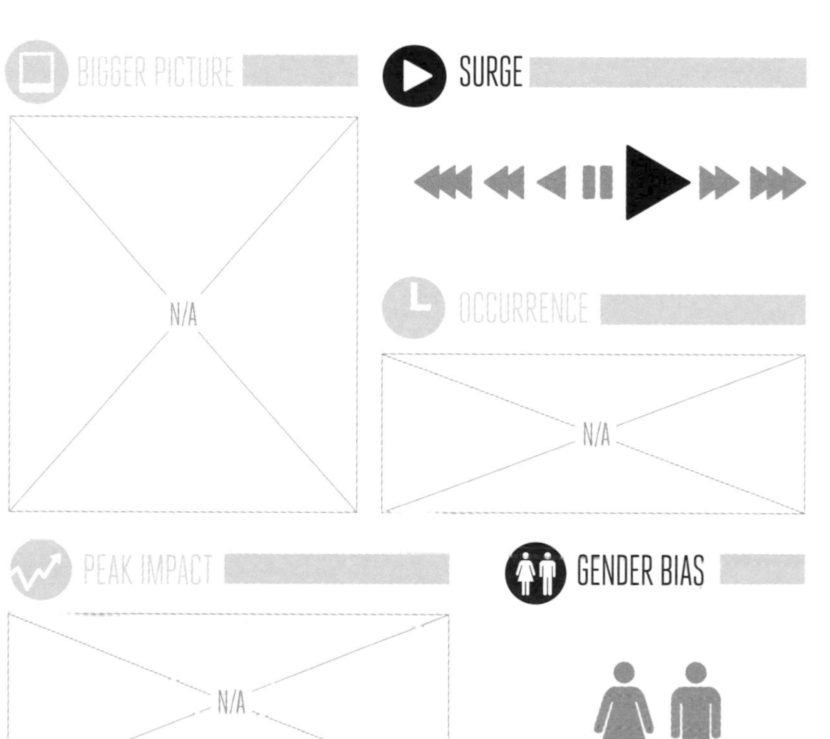

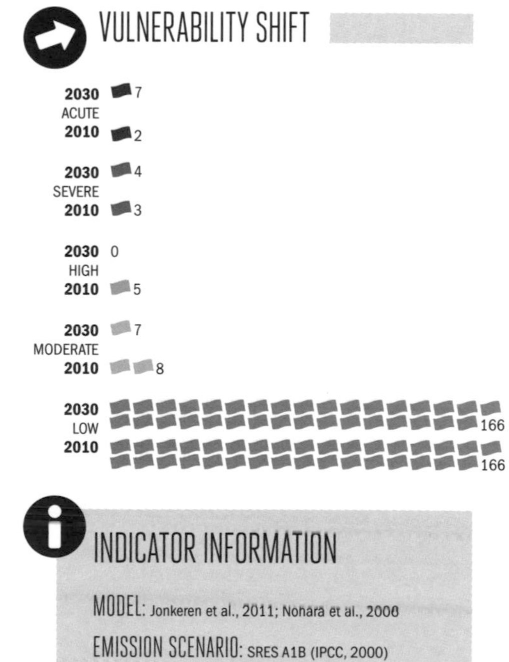

INDICATOR INFORMATION

MODEL: Jonkeren et al., 2011; Nohara et al., 2006

EMISSION SCENARIO: SRES A1B (IPCC, 2000)

BASE DATA: UNECE (2012a)

= 5 countries (rounded)

Acute Severe High Moderate Low

VULNERABILITIES AND WIDER OUTCOMES

In arid regions, water demand for irrigation has an amplified effect on river levels (Kang et al., 2004). Africa may be particularly vulnerable as a result (de Wit and Stankiewicz, 2006). Smaller rivers may also be asymmetrically affected (Pandey et al., 2010). Free-flowing rivers are more resilient than riverways with dams (Palmer et al., 2008). Deforestation or expanded agricultural and industrial activity can further lower resilience to any shocks and river-level decline brought on by climate change (Sahin and Hall, 1996; Conway, 2005). As the effects are currently interpreted, the narrow economic impact is not expected to have many discernable wider outcomes, aside from burdening a handful of countries/communities with additional costs.

RESPONSES

With glacial retreat, growing heat, and rainfall decline out of societal control, responses would likely include some form or combination of water resource management and the enhancement of catchment potential (Palmer et al., 2008; Falkenmar and Molden, 2012). Water resource management could seek to minimize or reduce water withdrawals, especially during high summer or drought periods, as well as increase water re-use and reduce water contaminants from industrial or agricultural sources (Geng et al., 2001; Friedler, 2001; Asano, 2002). Government quotas on irrigation could stimulate broader use of micro-irrigation and other water conservation actions (Pereira et al., 2002; Barret and Wallace, 2011). Water catchment potential can be enhanced through such measures as large-scale forestry expansion and conservation (Sahin and Hall, 1996). Limiting riverine infrastructure also improves resilience (Palmer et al., 2008).

THE INDICATOR

The indicator is considered uncertain and speculative for those countries assessed—provided projections for river flow and levels are accurate (Nohara et al., 2006). The economic effect of river decline relies on a study conducted in the Netherlands, not global research (Jonkeren et al., 2007). But the main limitation of the transport sector indicator relates to its scope, as increasing severity and variability of weather, growing heat stress, and other elements will likely affect the transport industry. Growing tire failure, increased delays and congestion, accidents, and port infrastructure damage have not been studied sufficiently to to build even speculative indicators of global effects (Koetse and Rietveld 2009; Eisenack et al., 2012). The rapid opening of previously inaccessible Arctic passageways will likely benefit, but its dynamics are difficult to ascertain (Macdonald et al., 2005). Additional investigation is needed to better understand the global effects of climate change on the transport sector.

ESTIMATES COUNTRY-LEVEL IMPACT

COUNTRY	$ 2010	$ 2030
ACUTE		
Bulgaria	5	65
Germany	45	200
Mexico	75	950
Netherlands	35	150
Romania	10	100
Switzerland	5	30
United States	1,000	5,750
SEVERE		
Austria	5	15
Croatia	1	10
Hungary	1	25
Slovakia	1	15
MODERATE		
France	5	25
Iraq		
Kazakhstan		
Kyrgyzstan		
Tajikistan		
Turkey		
Uzbekistan		
LOW		
Afghanistan		
Albania		
Algeria		
Angola		
Antigua and Barbuda		
Argentina		
Armenia		
Australia		
Azerbaijan		
Bahamas		

COUNTRY	$ 2010	$ 2030
Bahrain		
Bangladesh		
Barbados		
Belarus		
Belgium		
Belize		
Benin		
Bhutan		
Bolivia		
Bosnia and Herzegovina		
Botswana		
Brazil		
Brunei		
Burkina Faso		
Burundi		
Cambodia		
Cameroon		
Canada		
Cape Verde		
Central African Republic		
Chad		
Chile		
China		
Colombia		
Comoros		
Congo		
Costa Rica		
Cote d'Ivoire		
Cuba		
Cyprus		
Czech Republic		
Denmark		

COUNTRY	$ 2010	$ 2030
Djibouti		
Dominica		
Dominican Republic		
DR Congo		
Ecuador		
Egypt		
El Salvador		
Equatorial Guinea		
Eritrea		
Estonia		
Ethiopia		
Fiji		
Finland		
Gabon		
Gambia		
Georgia		
Ghana		
Greece		
Grenada		
Guatemala		
Guinea		
Guinea-Bissau		
Guyana		
Haiti		
Honduras		
Iceland		
India		
Indonesia		
Iran		
Ireland		
Israel		
Italy		

$ Additional economic costs due to climate change (million USD PPP) - yearly average

CLIMATE VULNERABILITY

CLIMATE UNCERTAINTY

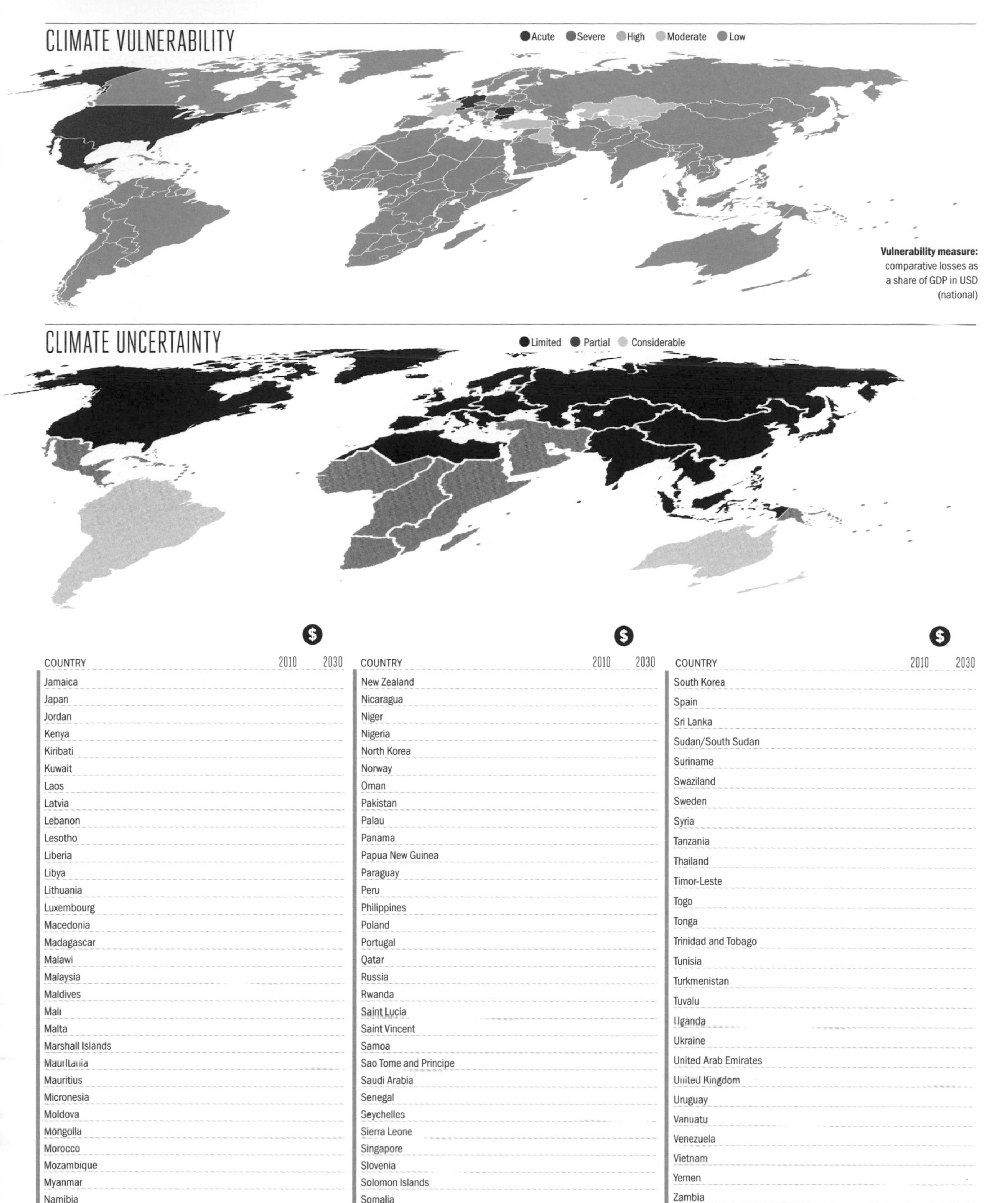

COUNTRY	2010	2030
Jamaica		
Japan		
Jordan		
Kenya		
Kiribati		
Kuwait		
Laos		
Latvia		
Lebanon		
Lesotho		
Liberia		
Libya		
Lithuania		
Luxembourg		
Macedonia		
Madagascar		
Malawi		
Malaysia		
Maldives		
Mali		
Malta		
Marshall Islands		
Mauritania		
Mauritius		
Micronesia		
Moldova		
Mongolia		
Morocco		
Mozambique		
Myanmar		
Namibia		
Nepal		

COUNTRY	2010	2030
New Zealand		
Nicaragua		
Niger		
Nigeria		
North Korea		
Norway		
Oman		
Pakistan		
Palau		
Panama		
Papua New Guinea		
Paraguay		
Peru		
Philippines		
Poland		
Portugal		
Qatar		
Russia		
Rwanda		
Saint Lucia		
Saint Vincent		
Samoa		
Sao Tome and Principe		
Saudi Arabia		
Senegal		
Seychelles		
Sierra Leone		
Singapore		
Slovenia		
Solomon Islands		
Somalia		
South Africa		

COUNTRY	2010	2030
South Korea		
Spain		
Sri Lanka		
Sudan/South Sudan		
Suriname		
Swaziland		
Sweden		
Syria		
Tanzania		
Thailand		
Timor-Leste		
Togo		
Tonga		
Trinidad and Tobago		
Tunisia		
Turkmenistan		
Tuvalu		
Uganda		
Ukraine		
United Arab Emirates		
United Kingdom		
Uruguay		
Vanuatu		
Venezuela		
Vietnam		
Yemen		
Zambia		
Zimbabwe		

COUNTRY
STUDIES

GHANA

COUNTRY STUDIES

GENERAL PURPOSE

1. **FEEDBACK** FOR THE DEVELOPMENT OF THE MONITOR'S METHODOLOGY

2. **EXPLAIN** HOW THE ANALYSIS OF THE MONITOR CAN BE USED IN A NATIONAL SITUATION

3. **SERVE AS A KNOWLEDGE-SHARING MECHANISM** FOR BEST PRACTICE AND CHANGE MANAGEMENT FOR THE BENEFIT OF OTHER VULNERABLE COUNTRIES

4. **PROVIDE AN OUTSIDE SUPPORTING ANALYSIS** OF INTEREST TO NATIONAL POLICY-MAKERS AND DEVELOPMENT PARTNERS

KEY FIGURES	
Population	24,965,816
2012 GDP PPP (Dollars)	
Total	$82,571,000
Per Capita	$3,312
Real Growth	8.8%

ECONOMY	
GDP by Sector	
Primary/Extractive	28.3%
Secondary/Productive	21%
Tertiary/Services	50.7%
Key Sector(s)	Services

SOCIO-ECONOMIC DEVELOPMENT	
Human Development (Rank)	Medium (135th)
Life Expectancy	64.2 years
Annual Population Growth	2.3%
Illiteracy	20.2%
Urban Population	52.2%
Access to Electricity	60.5%
Gender Development	122th
Undernourished Population (2006/08)	5%
Living below poverty line ($1,25/day)	30%
Population without Improved Water Source	15.3%
Official Development Assistance (% of GDP))	6.1%
Public Health Expenditure	6.9%
Public Education Expenditure	5.4%

CLIMATE/GEOGRAPHY	
Climate Zone	Dry and wet tropical
Projected Rainfall Change	20-30% reduction
Tropical Cyclones	No
Desertification	Yes
Low-Elevation Coastal Zone (10m and below)	1%
Forest Cover Change (1990-2008)	30.6%

MIGRATION/DISPLACEMENT	
Emigration Rate	4.5%
Immigrants as Share of Total Population	7.6%
Internally Displaced People	None

	Impact Areas	Indicator	Confidence	Gender Bias	Vulnerability 2010	Vulnerability 2030
CLIMATE		DROUGHT	✓			
		FLOODS & LANDSLIDES	✓	♀		
		STORMS	✓			
		WILDFIRES	✓			
		BIODIVERSITY	✓			
		DESERTIFICATION	✓			
		HEATING & COOLING	✓			
		LABOUR PRODUCTIVITY	✓	♀♂		
		PERMAFROST	✓			
		SEA-LEVEL RISE	✓			
		WATER	✓			
		DIARRHEAL INFECTIONS	✓			
		HEAT & COOL ILLNESSES	✓			
		HUNGER	✓			
		MALARIA & VECTOR BORNE	✓			
		MENINGITIS	✓			
		AGRICULTURE	✓			
		FISHERIES	✓			
		FORESTRY	✓			
		HYDRO ENERGY	✓			
		TOURISM	✓			
		TRANSPORT	✓			
CARBON		OIL SANDS	✓			
		OIL SPILLS	✓			
		BIODIVERSITY	✓			
		CORROSION	✓			
		WATER	✓			
		AIR POLLUTION	✓			
		INDOOR SMOKE	✓	♀		
		OCCUPATIONAL HAZARDS	✓	♂		
		SKIN CANCER	✓			
		AGRICULTURE	✓			
		FISHERIES	✓			
		FORESTRY	✓			

"Unbearable" was a word commonly offered up by residents of rural communities in Ghana visited by the research team, emblematic of their view of the rising heat. Ghana was never a cool country, but an increase in average temperatures of 1 degree Celsius (1.8 degrees Fahrenheit) has been recorded over the past half-century. In comparison to Ghana in the in the 1960s, the effect of this seemingly small change in temperature is striking: there are now 50 more "hot" days and almost 80 "hot" nights every year (McSweeney et al., 2012). In addition to temperature, floods, wind and rain storms, as well as changes in the pattern of rainfall have become serious climate-related concerns for Ghana today (EPA-Ghana, 2011).

Most ecological zones of Ghana are hit by this rapid change in climate with effects already manifested in major sectors of the economy, such as agriculture, fisheries, and forestry, with some of these ramifications triggering severe economic and social decline, especially in rural areas. The success of Ghana is a beacon for Sub-Saharan Africa, which is plagued in many places by extreme poverty, hunger, suffering, conflict, and instability. As this report reaches publication, a humanitarian emergency across the Sahel is ongoing and extending through West Africa with some 20 million people in the grip of a major food crisis (Oxfam, 2012).

All of the drivers of climate change that harm: heat, unpredictable rainfall, changes in the timing and length of the crop season, sea level rise, ocean warming, to name only a few, will only intensify and hasten with each passing decade.

Few developing countries anywhere in the world offer meaningful models for tackling the climate problem at the national level. Even model adaptation options—such as planting medium heat-tolerant maize varieties and delaying sowing dates to minimize climate change impacts—present challenges related to everything from technology transfer to cultural beliefs (Tachie-Obeng et al., 2011). However, delaying investment to attenuate the losses and risks faced by climate change only leads to still higher costs, already estimated at several percentage points of Ghana's GDP.

Climate change and/or the carbon economy are far from being Ghana's only concerns. Indeed, with each climate-related issue, additional social, economic, and environmental problems combine to heighten vulnerabilities and the level of harm generated through the impact of climate change, which itself exacerbates economic, social, and environmental problems.

With limited resources, cost-effective solutions will have to explore the range of competing factors responsible for vulnerability and impact in the context of climate change. It is also an opportunity to revisit and address other longstanding problems, including gender inequality, deforestation, unsustainable fishing, and barriers that limit better use of technologies to drive social and economic activities and enhance resilience. Together with the affected communities, solutions can be found to the current challenges Ghana faces. The average temperature in Ghana has risen by around 1 degree centigrade (1.8° Fahrenheit) since the period from the 1970s to the 2000s. Should Ghana warm by another 3°C (5.5°F) in the 50–60 years to come, the human, economic, and environmental damage will be severe. What happens beyond the next few decades is now in the hands of national policymakers in the world's major economies.

Ghana could harness its successes to date by tackling climate change risks concertedly, and in doing so, not only improve the resistance of its own economy to these effects, but also serve as an inspiration in the coming decades to other countries in the region, which all face similar problems.

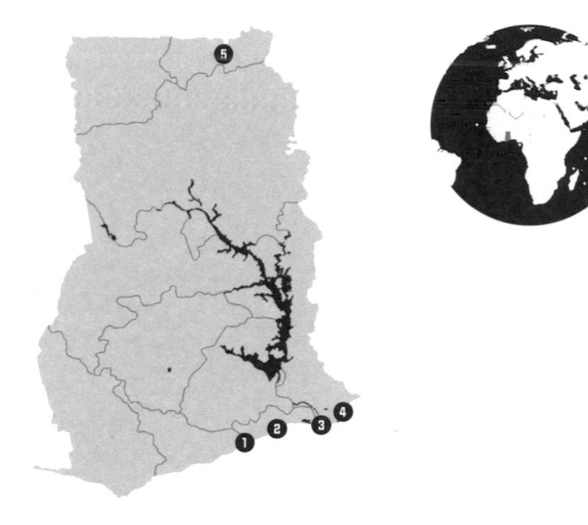

1. ACCRA
2. NEW NINGO
3. ADA FOAH
4. KETA
5. BOLGATANGA

MULTI-DIMENSIONAL CLIMATE VULNERABILITY: **ACUTE**

MULTI-DIMENSIONAL CARBON VULNERABILITY: **MODERATE**

CAPACITY: **RESTRICTED**

POPULATION 2010/2030: **24/32 MILLION**

GDP 2010/2030 (PPP): **65 BILLION/210 BILLION USD**

GDP PER CAPITA 2010/2030 (PPP): **2,650/6,500 USD**

BACKGROUND AND CONTEXT

BACKGROUND AND CONTEXT

With close to 25 million inhabitants, Ghana is a mid-sized and rapidly growing West African country. Now considered a middle-income country (lower-middle income) by the World Bank, Ghana is bordered to the north by Burkina Faso and to the east and west by Togo and Côte d'Ivoire, respectively. Ghana's climate is tropical monsoon, with relatively low-elevation geography, and clear regional differences in climate between the savannah (northern and east coast) and more humid southwestern forested areas along the Gulf of Guinea. Ghana is similar in size to the United Kingdom.

Ghana's real GDP grew at an average of 6% in the first decade of the 21st century and continues with growth for 2012 estimated by the IMF at almost 9% (IMF WEO, 2012). Ghana's per capita income is still very low, at around 3,000 dollars (PPP) or 1,700 US dollars (nominal). Income inequality is also high, with nearly half the urban population living in slums (UN-HABITAT, 2012). Ghana is not considered a Least Developed Country by the United Nations but its capacity is considered to be Restricted, due to comparatively limited human and infrastructure assets, and despite relatively strong government effectiveness. The climate-sensitive agricultural sector still represents around 30% of GDP and employs nearly 60% of the workforce.

Ghana recently discovered large-scale new offshore oil and gas reserves, which are expected to boost national income further in the coming years. Ghana also produces large amounts of cash-yielding cocoa and gold that are mainstays of its economy. Heavy reliance on one type of crop may, however, represent a serious latent but systemic climate risk for Ghana's agricultural sector, were climate change to make plant diseases and pests more prevalent in the humid southern zone where much of the cocoa is grown (Brondizio and Moran, 2008). Nevertheless, continued national economic growth is well assured in the medium term. But whether or not Ghana's climate change policies are effective will be increasingly important in determining the extent and distribution of this growth, and the sustainability of its economic development as currently programmed.

GHG emissions remain very low at 3.2 tons per capita and are not expected to even exceed 3.5 tons per capita by 2020 (Climate Analytics, 2012). Deforestation is at very high rates and currently represents over 40% of total emissions; a little more than a decade ago, the forestry sector was acting as a net carbon sink, not an emitter (EPA-Ghana, 2011). Urban air pollution is beginning to become more serious, but household fuels are a much greater health concern, since indoor firewood stoves are still widely in use. Moreover, 40% of all homes lack access to electricity.

As is the case for many countries in close proximity to the equator, the environmental vulnerability of Ghana is extreme. Ghana is exposed to fisheries impacts, due to rising water temperatures and coastal erosion caused by the rising sea level; in the north, the increase in heat is occurring in a continental climate not restrained by the proximity of the sea. These effects are compounded by floods, drought, wildfires, land degradation, soil erosion, the threat of desertification, and the prevalence of diseases, such as cholera and meningitis. Major cash and staple crops, such cocoa and maize will be affected in growing measure by climatic shifts, including increased temperature, the contraction of cropping seasons and changes in the distribution of rainfall.

In both urban and rural communities, socio-economic vulnerabilities are also extreme. Cities such as Accra have sprawling slums which form hazard-prone zones, exposing populations to unsafe water, restricted sanitation, and deadly flood risks—much of Accra was flooded in 2011, causing significant loss of life. In rural areas, subsistence farming is still widespread, and a lack of basic agricultural inputs and infrastructure, such as irrigation, roads and storage facilities make this group less adaptive to changes in climate.

THE MONITOR'S ASSESSMENT
OVERVIEW / CLIMATE CHANGE

THE MONITOR'S ASSESSMENT
OVERVIEW

Despite its relatively strong economic position in West Africa, Ghana is among the countries most vulnerable to climate change. According to the Monitor, Ghana's economic development will have already been significantly compromised due to changes in the climate that have already taken place.

The multi-dimensional vulnerability of Ghana to climate change is considered in the highest category of Acute, with vulnerability steadily increasing as global and local temperatures rise. Ghana's vulnerability to carbon impacts is considered Moderate and is actually declining, due mainly to the expectation that agriculture might benefit from carbon fertilization as CO_2 levels rise, and because economic development should lead households to adopt less hazardous cooking and heating practices over time.

Both human (Severe) and economic (Acute) vulnerability are very high. Climate change is estimated to claim around 2,000 lives each year in 2010, while carbon-related mortality is at 13,000 deaths per year; each impact is expected to decline slightly by 2030 as a share of overall population, due to anticipated socio-economic gains between now and then. Losses due to climate change are estimated at 4% of GDP in 2010, rising to 9% of GDP in 2030. Carbon losses are stable at approximately 1.5% of GDP.

CLIMATE CHANGE

Following are the most serious climate change impact areas as assessed (for 2010/2030) in order of the scale of GDP losses, from highest to lowest:

- LABOUR PRODUCTIVITY, ACUTE/ACUTE 3.0%/6.1% of GDP
- FISHERIES, HIGH/ACUTE 0.3%/1.1% of GDP
- AGRICULTURE, SEVERE/ACUTE 0.4%/0.7% of GDP
- SEA-LEVEL RISE, MODERATE/MODERATE 0.3%/0.4% of GDP
- BIODIVERSITY, MODERATE/HIGH 0.1%/0.2% of GDP

The most serious health effects are Diarrheal Infections, Hunger, Heat and Cold Illnesses and Meningitis. Heat and Cold Illnesses relate to the impact of heat waves on chronic disease sufferers, particularly the elderly. While mortality rates are not alarmingly high, more than 1 million people are estimated to be affected on average each year, due to the impact of climate change on diarrheal diseases, and over 400,000 people suffer from hunger.

The impacts for Labour and Sea-Level rise carry a relatively high degree of certainty, while other areas are more of an indication, due to the limitations of the models used and agreement on the signal of key changes, such as rainfall.

Other areas of high vulnerability constituting serious concerns for affected communities include Desertification (High) and Drought (High), although these are not as significant in economic terms on a national level. Desertification is nevertheless estimated to already be affecting 75,000 people in Ghana, which could rise to 200,000 people at risk by the year 2030. By 2030, drought could cause 15 million dollars of damage on average each year to farmers, especially small-scale and subsistence farmers with low-resilience to these impacts.

Floods and Landslides have been assessed as a Moderate concern; however, field research demonstrated that flooding is a major and growing concern in both urban and rural areas. For instance, recent large-scale floods in October 2011 inundated large parts of downtown Accra, reportedly killing 14 in the greater

CARBON ECONOMY

NATIONAL RESPONSE
STATUS

CLIMATE FINANCE

Accra region and 33 nationwide, according to Ghana's National Disaster Management Organization (NADMO). The international disaster database records 300 deaths due to floods for the whole of the last two decades since 1990, not including the 2011 floods (CRED/EM-DAT, 2012).
The only positive effect Ghana is estimated to experience on the basis of the Monitor's assessment is a less than 0.1% of GDP boost to Hydro Energy, as a result of small, although uncertain, increases in annual river flow that are projected by some models for this region of the world. Wildfires are a legitimate concern in Ghana and increased aridity and drought in certain areas will increase the likelihood of fires. However, since Ghana is projected to experience some increased rainfall, the final outcome of the role of climate change on wildfires is ambiguous, so vulnerability is assessed as Low.

CARBON ECONOMY

With respect to carbon economy costs, in human terms Indoor Smoke claims an estimated 10,000 lives each year today, followed by over 2,000 deaths associated with urban air pollution. Air Pollution deaths are expected to grow as a share of population to close to 4,000 deaths per year in 2030. However, Indoor Smoke is expected to decline to around 8,000 deaths per year by that time.
In economic terms, the largest carbon impact is to Biodiversity at 1% of GDP in 2010, growing to 2% of GDP by 2030. Health impacts are the next biggest loss to GDP at 0.8% of GDP, declining to 0.4% of GDP by 2030. The agricultural sector is still generally unaffected by pollution, but could benefit from higher CO2 levels, in which case gains are estimated at 0.1% of GDP in 2010 and 0.8% of GDP in 2030. Thus, any current benefits of CO2 fertilization are outweighed three times over by costs related to climate change. By 2030, scientists predict that all of the future impacts of climate change will be compensated by increases in plant growth due to CO_2 fertilization. The very latest research is nevertheless more pessimistic than the Monitor's assessment on the possible extent of such benefits (Ainsworth et al., 2008; Leaky et al., 2009). This result should therefore be treated with much caution. Field research undertaken for the purpose of the Monitor in Ghana identified key agricultural regions already suffering severe stress and fundamental challenges relating to climate-tied shifts carrying serious humanitarian ramifications, including hunger and other diseases. Local research has also documented the climate-related challenges facing core staple crops, such as cocoa and corn (Tachie-Obeng et al., 2011). Carbon fertilization benefits are known not to accrue under stressed conditions (IPCC, 2007). Nonetheless, improving the resilience of Ghana's agricultural sector to climate change would certainly increase its chances of benefitting from any possible positive effects of high CO_2 levels, if they are ever to materialize; either way, adaptation to climate change remains a core priority.
The health related impacts of Indoor Smoke and Air Pollution are considered relatively reliable, whereas Biodiversity and Agriculture should be considered more indicative or less certain.

NATIONAL RESPONSE
STATUS

Policy development on climate change in Ghana is a new and rapidly advancing focus of energy for key government departments with competencies relating to the environment and disaster issues. The government has recognized climate change as a current concern for the country's economic output. It is viewed as a development challenge requiring action to address climate change so as to ensure that national progress is not derailed. This is at the core of ambitions to mainstream climate change into key planning processes at national, regional and district levels, and into the Ghana Shared Growth and Development Agenda. In this spirit, an active consultation process is now underway aiming to develop a National Climate Change Policy. The National Policy has three core objectives: 1) effective adaptation to climate change, 2) social development, and 3) low carbon growth. The government has also identified the following seven pillars which it is planning to build upon in order to achieve those objectives:

- Governance and coordination
- Capacity building
- Research and knowledge management
- Finance
- International cooperation
- Education, communication and public awareness
- Monitoring and reporting

There exists a National Climate Change Committee grouping some 14 government entities together with development partners, including foreign assistance donors. It has been mandated to drive the climate change policy development work forward and is hosted by the Ministry of Environment, Science and Technology. A National Adaptation Strategy for Ghana has been completed following a detailed process of stakeholder inputs from multiple sectors, with the launch scheduled to take place before the end of 2012.
While the policy process is moving in a very promising direction, Ghana still lacks government policies specifically designed for responding to climate change. In particular, at the community level, district development plans viewed did not account for the additional stress resulting from climate change, nor did such plans contain climate change specific response considerations, whether to reduce carbon intensity or to address climate impacts. Nevertheless, several government entities are dealing with climate change issues as a part of their operational mandates and daily concerns, such as the Environmental Protection Agency-Ghana (EPA-Ghana) and the National Disaster Management Organization (NADMO). And there was evidence of active work on the part of government, international, and local non-governmental organizations and foreign assistance partners in many climate change related areas of concern, from coastal defences, to food security, and health and sanitation issues.

CLIMATE FINANCE

In 2010, Ghana received close to 80 million US dollars in public climate change finance from foreign sources, making Ghana the 31st largest recipient that year among developing countries. This amount represented 0.25% of Ghana's GDP— compare this to the amount received by Vietnam (also studied in this report), which represented 0.5% of Vietnamese GDP in 2010. The largest bilateral donors of climate change finance in 2010 were Japan and France, which provided more loans for mitigation finance and only grants for adaptation. The component of those resources targeted to assist Ghana in adapting to the negative effects of climate change made up only about 10% of the total, or 10 million dollars. An order of magnitude increase in climate change finance for adaptation in Ghana would be needed, if a balance with respect to mitigation were to be achieved. Even such levels would likely fall far short of the actual requirement, considering the estimate that climate change already costs Ghana 4% of its GDP.
Deserving of high praise are Ghana's development successes in high rates of real GDP growth and the progress achieved towards the Millennium Development Goals to-date. There is, however, a risk that foreign development partner donors view those achievements and the discovery of important fossil fuel reserves as reasons for withdrawing international support. The research team which visited various regions in connection with this project found that, in certain cases, foreign assistance programmes were already being withdrawn from some of the most vulnerable communities. Climate change impacts

ASSETS

GAPS

are now expected to accelerate very quickly, putting the development gains of Ghana at greater risk, in particular where last-mile efforts to empower the poorest of the poor have not succeeded. Ghana's forthcoming National Adaptation Strategy should provide a vehicle for donors to ensure that adequate support is provided to the country as it seeks to address these serious and growing concerns.

ASSETS

Ghana faces a number of capacity constraints that are commonplace for lower-middle income countries in sub-Saharan Africa. But Ghana also has a number of important assets at its disposal as it gears up to tackle climate change locally:

- *Community Reach:* With the National Disaster Management Organization (NADMO), Ghana has centrally organized government officials or trained volunteers on the ground in every district, if not every village. NADMO volunteers are mobilized and actively working to respond to and reduce risks for communities dealing with climate change and other threats to safety and livelihoods and their responsibilities include advocacy and emergency assistance. Given appropriate strategies and resources, the NADMO apparatus will be invaluable for ensuring that community-level actions are carried out among the most vulnerable groups.
- *Technical Capacity:* the Environmental Protection Agency-Ghana (EPA-Ghana), the lead institution for UNFCCC-related activities, has been establishing important foundations of local expertise on core climate-related concerns, as it serves as the main Country Implementation Institution for the technical coordination of activities on climate change, including specialized working groups and expert climate change study teams, all of which support national policy development and the implementation of climate change project activities.
- *Fiscal Resilience:* Ghana is financially stable with relatively low levels of public debt and surging economic growth. There are significant and important infrastructure investments that Ghana will be making over the next 5 to 10 years as it reinvests its growing wealth back into the economy. Ghana has yet to commit streams of public funds to a formal climate change policy, but should consider allocating some specific levels of resources to its own domestic climate change policies while the economy is strong.
- *Health Insurance:* In all communities visited as a part of the field research for the Monitor, participation rates in local health insurance schemes were very high, with annual fees very affordable, in some cases as little as 5 US dollars (10 Ghanain Cedis). Health insurance did not, however, cover preventative measures, such as insect-repellent infused mosquito nets or vaccinations. Therefore, preventative measures remain a challenge for communities themselves, the government and foreign aid programmes.
- *Indigenous Knowledge:* The long cultural history and traditions of the people of Ghana represents a great wealth of indigenous knowledge relating to the environment. As climate change brings rapid change to that environment, much of this knowledge is not only not obsolete, but has become more important and useful. In one region for instance, crickets, still announced the end of the warm season, even when the timing of the season had shifted considerably. Documenting and disseminating the best of indigenous knowledge to supplement highly technical or costly infrastructure responses to climate change would help to lower costs and improve impact.
- *Sound Policy Environment:* From the capital in Accra to the remote villages of northern Ghana, community leaders, NGOs, entrepreneurs, farmers, experts, and other members of civil society consistently expressed deep concern and interest in climate-related issues. The government is benefitting from the attention and knowledge as a part of the consultative process leading towards the National Climate Change Policy and should continue to promote that interest, which will likely pay dividends in terms of fine-tuned policies and more robust implementation.

GAPS

Ghana still lacks a dedicated climate change policy and never issued a National Adaptation Programme for Action under the UNFCCC since it is not a Least Developed Country. So policy gaps are large for now, but will progressively be filled, as different aspects of the government's policy project come online. Some gaps in the general policy approach can still be identified, and should be reinforced:

- *Leadership:* As evident from the more than one dozen government entities already participating in Ghana's National Climate Change Committee, the challenge of coordinating and ensuring sound implementation of cross-sector challenges is immense. The government has already recognized the need for a dedicated statutory body on climate change to oversee the government response, enhancing coordination and avoiding duplication. However, executive leadership on climate change has been largely absent and does not appear to be a planned component of a climate change body for Ghana. Ghana might do well to take a cue from successful national policy approaches of other vulnerable countries, such as the Philippines or Vietnam, where there is direct involvement of the government executive branch, which issues formal policy directives to all other relevant organs of government.
- *Prioritization:* The research undertaken for the Monitor revealed that the government of Ghana has yet to flag climate change as a key priority area in its formal discussions with leading development partner donors. As such, several donors had the impression that climate change is not a priority for the government. A key step to mobilizing enhanced international support for Ghana's domestic climate change policies is for the government to be unambiguous regarding the importance of the climate policy project for Ghana when interacting with foreign assistance partners.
- *Fragmentation:* Experts also expressed concern over the potential fragmentation of national efforts to address climate change, as wide-ranging initiatives were being pursued in different directions. Fragmentation risks exhausting precious capacities, especially in central government, and favouring project-based pathways over strategic approaches more capable of tackling systemic issues.
- *Reference Scenarios:* Ghana plans to publish national reference scenarios for climate change as part of its National Adaptation Strategy. But to date, it has lacked truly comprehensive and highly specific reference scenarios for all key regions of the country across all main climate parameters, including river flow, rainfall/runoff, temperature, sea-level rise, sea temperatures and acidity, wind, fire risk, flooding, and drought/extreme aridity. For example, scenarios for rainfall cited in the most recent UNFCCC National Communication are at odds with the analyses of some other leading experts, which point to increases not decreases in rain, although seasonal, not annual, declines of rainfall may be extreme, including during growing periods (EPA-Ghana, 2011; McSweeney et al., 2012; Tachie-Obeng et al., 2011). The regular updating and publication of new national reference scenarios is critical for guiding the progressive calibration of adaptation investments as knowledge evolves. Establishing scenarios through wide consultation that all key stakeholders can have confidence in, despite intrinsic uncertainties, is an important component in building strong support for the national response to climate change.
- *Donor Support Group:* There is no formal group involving a wide range of key foreign donors that is operationally

OTHER CHALLENGES AND OPPORTUNITIES

focused on supporting Ghana to develop and implement climate change policies. Best practice from other country experiences such as Vietnam point to the clear value of a donor support group that could add to the policy implementation efforts of Ghana on climate change and help to harmonize aid, avoid overlap and drains on capacity, track progress and results, and ensure that financial commitments match government defined priorities and needs as effectively as possible.

OTHER CHALLENGES AND OPPORTUNITIES

- *Access to Markets and Industry:* All rural areas visited by the research team had in common a near total absence of any local light industry operations aimed at processing and packaging the raw products of farmers and fishermen into finished goods that could be transported to reach non-domestic markets. This led to the paradox of purchasing boxed South African mango juice from a food stall to be consumed under a fully laden local mango tree. In the Gulf of Guinea, fishing boats from China, Japan and Korea plied the waters and sent back home the fruits of Ghanaian seas. Tragic outcomes also resulted: an unusual bumper crop of tomatoes that was left to spoil on the road led some farmers to commit suicide when they realized that their superb crop was unable to reach any market. Yet none of the communities visited had development plans in place to give incentives to local entrepreneurs or to attract Investment to set-up freezing works for seafood, canning facilities for tomatoes, packaging houses for fruit juice, or any other light industrial facilities that would enable farmers to achieve higher prices for their goods, receive more from the commercial value chain, and ultimately increase profits and disposable income.
- *Energy and Carbon Markets:* The abundant heat and sunshine that is now a concern for Ghana as temperatures continue to rise, underscores the existence of a latent wealth of solar energy that is not being harnessed anywhere. Programmes aimed at distributing efficient and clean-burning indoor cooking stoves would not only reduce disease, but also help stem deforestation, land degradation, and desertification, since communities rely heavily on local wood as the primary fuel. Making the most of new opportunities in the renewable energy sector was a major theme expressed in interactions with experts during the research work undertaken as a part of the Monitor's development. Ghana has yet to gain meaningful access to international carbon markets and to the support mechanisms that drive renewable sector growth in other developing countries. With only one project registered with the CDM and a handful of others under development, virtually no investment has yet been leveraged (UNEP Risoe, 2012). Making the most of a potential future forest carbon market (via REDD+) would help reverse the rampant deforestation that caused Ghana's forestry sector to transition from a net carbon sink to a major source of GHG emissions since only the late 1990s (EPA-Ghana, 2011). Public and private sector capacity building would need to be actively fostered in order to break through and stimulate serious progress for Ghana's renewable energy and carbon sink sector.
- *Migration:* Hallmarks of a long-term rural decline whereby traditional livelihoods faced ongoing erosion were evident in many of the communities studied for this edition of the Monitor. Seeing limited opportunities for themselves, young adults were migrating on a seasonal basis to the larger centres, where they seek informal employment. Men or couples whose livelihoods in agriculture or fishing have been compromised were also moving on a more permanent basis, sometimes leaving children behind in the care of elderly relatives or single mothers; these "stranded" homes were reported to be particularly food insecure and vulnerable: if a remittance did not come in a given month for whatever reason, the children would go hungry. The situation is fuelling the rapid urbanization of Ghana's metropolitan centres, were slums have been steadily growing, with settlements often developing in marginal or high-hazard zones, such as river flood plains, creating additional risks. It is difficult to attribute a specific proportion of that migration to climate change. However, the change in climate has had a negative affect on agriculture and fisheries—which determine income levels—and stifles economic activity in mainstay rural sectors. The heat, the extreme and erratic nature of rainfall, the rise in sea-levels, the stress on biodiversity and forests, are all set to increase dramatically in the decades ahead. With it, migration pressures will only increase considerably.
- *Women's and Youth Empowerment:* Ghana is known to have low levels of gender-related development or high degrees of gender inequality that disadvantage women (UNDP, 2007; UNDP, 2011). The research undertaken as a part of the Monitor's development highlighted the extent to which women are currently marginalized from decision making on community issues at multiple levels. Many of the men interviewed as a part of the research conducted autonomously suggested that greater involvement of women would lead to more sensible decision making and community action; it was emphasized that women are more receptive to change. The same issues were understood to also apply to youth. Gender development and inequality in particular are highly correlated to climate change vulnerability according to the Monitor's assessment; this suggests that gains across the full spectrum of gender-related development would reduce levels of vulnerability to climate change, since women are understood to be more vulnerable to climate change in Ghana (EPA-Ghana, 2011). The advent of climate change therefore only strengthens the urgency of overcoming gender equality challenges in Ghana.

NORTHERN GHANA: BOLGATANGA-BONGO-NAVRONGO

The Bolgatanga-Bongo-Navrongo areas of the Upper East Region of northern Ghana is close to the border with Burkina Faso. It is a primary agricultural region, raising livestock and cultivating staples such as rice and millet, market vegetables, and orchard trees. About one million people inhabit the upper east region of Ghana, which covers some 9,000km^2. Northern Ghana is the hottest part of the country, where the so-called "Harmattan" winds blow in from the Sahara desert, and where the increase in heat and the number of hot days and hot nights has been the most extreme. The relentless rise in temperature in the years ahead will also continue to be the most extreme here (McSweeney et al., 2012).

The serious increase in heat the area is experiencing has triggered a downward trend in its core economic sector, agriculture, with negative impacts on the health of the region's population. Key concerns range from extreme flooding, drought, desertification, growing energy needs for cooling, and a declining biodiversity. Concerns were also voiced about the nomadic Fulani herdsmen, who cross from Burkina Faso and are indiscriminately cutting and burning the savannah vegetation and causing other social issues, as their bonds with local farmers are increasingly severed along with rural decline. Occupational heat stress is also endemic, since large numbers of subsistence farmers, anxious to feed their families and unable to work in the relative cool of the night, are obliged to work during the intense heat of the day.

All of these effects have serious social and economic implications: the rapid pace of development that Ghana has experienced in other regions has not been enjoyed by this part of the country: every one of the dozens of people interviewed in different villages and centres across this region insisted that life had become much harder.

Social vulnerabilities were also extreme: no running water or sanitation facilities of any kind in many households, less than 50% of households with electricity or lighting, no cooling units or fans virtually anywhere, too few mosquito nets, very few vehicles, and no insurance for houses damaged by flooding and wind or for crops destroyed in drought or floods.

HEALTH

With a significant share of the population living without electricity, refrigeration, running water, or sanitation facilities, the deleterious effects of climate change on health are a major concern. High rates of all of the main climate sensitive diseases were confirmed: diarrheal diseases such as meningitis, cholera, and malaria. In some areas, a majority of households were considered food insecure. People living without any form of climate control would often sleep outside on the hottest nights and in doing so expose themselves to mosquito bites and vector-borne disease, especially malaria, compounding the climate stresses on their health. One local expert explained that people often suffered malaria two or three times a year. Certain villages were able to report on the number of deaths due to meningitis over the preceding few weeks—accounting for more than 10 fatalities in one village alone. In another village, the funeral procession of a victim made its way past the research team's interview site.

While health insurance is now high—reported to be around 80% coverage—vaccinations against communicable diseases common in the area are not covered by the insurance schemes, even though some vaccination campaigns were also reported to be in effect. School feeding programmes were in place in many areas, with the local government and international NGOs such as the World Food Programme responsible for providing one meal per day. Hunger deaths were understood to occur in remote areas or where children were not able to attend school, and significantly low school attendance rates were confirmed. To prevent malaria, more bed nets were needed, but most local experts stressed that education was needed. People were apparently unaware of the importance of basic safety precautions in everyday life, such as personal hygiene, proper waste disposal, or the need to avoid being exposed out of doors at dusk and dawn when mosquitos are most active. Investment in education campaigns and schools is therefore a priority. Ensuring access to clean water for households was also understood to make a significant difference, as is clear from current international knowledge on the issue (Jamison et al. (eds.), 2006).

SEASON SHIFT

A clear erosion of the agricultural system in the Bolgatanga area was reported and manifest. Local experts reported that key causes of this erosion have been the growing length of the hot dry season—traditionally from November to April—and the contraction of the traditional rainy season—April through October. Although farming is done in both seasons, the rainy season is the mainstay of the harvest. In the dry season, it is only possible to grow crops where there is irrigation, while in the wet season, much of the land is available for cultivation. Thus, the contraction of the growing season lowers overall agricultural potential. Rains that reportedly once began in April are now not beginning until May. The new timing has a number of other consequences: one example provided was that butterflies have been slower to adapt their behaviour to the new season onset and caterpillar larvae now exit the cocoon when crops are at their most vulnerable early stages.

DROUGHT AND DRY SEASON HEAT

The dry season itself is now unbearably hot and even dangerous: people exposed outside in the heat are considerably more susceptible to deadly meningitis. It is more difficult for farmers to produce crops in the dry season, if only because of the extreme

levels of heat stress as they toil in the fields. Moreover, periods of drought are now very severe, since the heat is so much more intense, and crop productivity suffers whenever the heat is not offset by generous and evenly spread rainfall, reported to be rarely the case anymore. Rainfall in Ghana reached its lowest in the 1970s and early 1980s; although it has since increased from 2000, it is still below the 1960 baseline. But it is not keeping pace with the increase in temperature and so the evaporation rate of water for the region is increasing. As a result, rainfed agriculture is undergoing a transition away from optimal growing conditions, resulting in lower plant productivity and yield, while reservoirs that supply irrigation are becoming less efficient. Thus, most people migrate to southern Ghana during the dry season.

EROSION OF LIVELIHOODS

To cope with declining yields, farmers have begun to take measures, such as selling their livestock. Farmers who might have had five or six animals, might now have only one or two—others none at all—and may be worried about how they will cope with another difficult season. Such measures hardly constitute a sound long-term strategy, since the hope for a return to bountiful harvests of days gone by is unlikely, given the projections for climate change to come. Residents recalled times in the past when Bolgatanga area was once the breadbasket of Ghana. It is in this dead-end context that farmers were reported to have committed suicide, when their unusual bumper crop of tomatoes spoiled on the roadside for want of buyers.

These developments have upset the delicate balance of these rural communities. Since farmers now own less livestock, the relationship between farmers and nomadic people who settle in the less fertile surrounding areas has also been compromised. In the past, farmers would entrust the nomadic peoples from Burkina Faso (Fulani herdsmen) with their livestock in return for payment, either in-kind or in the form of farm produce. Thus, the nomadic peoples have also been deprived of a source of income and livelihood, and are now being reported to be engaging in a growing number of criminal acts, such as theft, violence, and other social problems, not to mention destroying and burning savannah vegetation. The decline in livestock has also decreased the availability of local manure and therefore fertilizer, forcing farmers to rely more heavily on imported chemical fertilizers, the price of which has been escalating in recent years, together with the increase in gasoline prices. Finally, the chemical fertilizers available were said to be less effective for water retention than organic alternatives, so of declining utility as heat and water stress grew.

RESPONSES

Although heat is, indeed, rising and will continue to do so, the area is not condemned and could thrive. As mentioned earlier, the critical need is to prioritize local entrepreneurship, so that farmers can have better access to wider markets and higher prices for their goods. In reality, there has actually been only one tomato factory in the region, which apparently suffered from management problems. The skills required to oversee such operations are not yet present in the region, so people from outside have been brought in to run this type of industry. However, farmers were not guaranteed better prices, as the factory exercised a monopoly and would pay only low prices, despite being able to sell goods at much higher rates. Moreover, most farmers have no means to transport their goods to the factory. These problems could be solved by following the successful models of other communities which have already surmounted similar issues (Motiram and Vakulabharanam, 2007; Buse et al., 2008).

A range of other responses could be taken to stem and reverse the steady erosion of rural livelihoods in Bolgatanga. Some promising programmes were ongoing in the promotion of Bolgatanga basket weaving to generate improved livelihood opportunities, especially during the relative downtime of the dry season. Bolgatanga baskets are a unique, indigenous handcraft woven by hand exclusively by women. The activity allows local women to earn respectable incomes, with immediate benefits for the promotion of maternal and child health for participating families. Handicraft activities, from basket weaving to leather goods and pottery, help to diversify the livelihoods and supplement subsistence farming, now increasingly at risk because of climate change.

Enabling the farmers to produce more crops during the dry season would also make a significant difference. There is enough rain over a year to ensure wider irrigation, but there were either not enough dams or reservoirs trapping the rain, or too many of these had silted up and become ineffective. Overhauling and building new dams is far beyond the means of local farmers and even the local government. International support can be extremely useful here—there are already some support programmes for dam rehabilitation, and these provide jobs during construction and beyond, representing a sustainable solution for the community. The same was true for less costly water wells, although it was not reported whether the pumping more water from the groundwater aquifer was sustainable or not. However, many did report that wells had dried up.

Enlarging and linking an existing set of wilderness reserves already under conservation protection could help to strengthen biodiversity, with benefits for natural pest control, as well as water catchment. Local composting using on-site crop waste close to fields, and household food waste in vegetable gardens closer to houses, could help to offset the decrease in local fertilizer.

FLOODING AND THE BAGRÉ DAM

Evidence of excess rainfall is seen in the visible flood damage sustained to earthen buildings and is clearly documented with photographic evidence shown to the research team. One major issue is the release of water following heavy rains from the Bagré Dam in southern Burkina Faso; the area around the dam has experienced increasing rainfall in recent years (ICI, 2010). When the floodgates are opened, large areas of the plains in northern Ghana become inundated with water. The local community is defenceless as the water floods across the plains, unable to penetrate the densely packed, arid soil. Aside from damaging buildings, water that remains for several days destroys any crops that are submerged and increases the risk of malaria by greatly expanding the breeding ground for mosquitoes.

Local experts suggested the problem could be addressed by building better drainage infrastructure, in combination with the construction or rehabilitation of feeder roads—small roads that are a sound investment under any circumstances (Stifel et al., 2012; Kingombe, 2011). Ensuring that waterways are not used for cropping, but for the planting of trees to reinforce embankments was another solution put forward. However, with declining fertility and scope for planting crops elsewhere, the fertile embankments with direct access to water are too attractive for farmers. Cooperation with Burkina Faso on infrastructure solutions that might help to release water gradually following heavy rains had apparently not been addressed.

EAST COAST: VOLTA DELTA

The east coast lies at the southeast extremity of Ghana, close to the border with Togo along the Gulf of Guinea. The researchers visited villages across the Greater Accra and Volta regions of Ghana, as well as Prampram, Ada Foah, and Keta. While the south of Ghana is less hot and more humid than the far north, the southeast coast itself has a dry climate within the coastal savannah zone of Ghana, which, according to EPA-Ghana, is due to "coastal alignment and upwelling of cold water" (EPA-Ghana, 2011). Not that it is cold here: truck drivers complained of more frequent tire and windshield explosions on the hottest days. Parents worried that teachers were becoming less effective in educating their children, as they struggled to work in the growing heat during school hours. The area is mainly a low-lying plain, interspersed with a number of lagoons and tributaries at the delta of the Volta River, which originates in Burkina Faso. It is predominantly a fishing and agrarian community, and the area visited is home to over half a million people (Ghana SS, 2010).
The chief climate change concerns for the southeast coastal areas relate to coastal erosion/sea-level rise, fisheries, agriculture and health. Biodiversity, drought, energy for cooling and water are also concerns. As for much of the country, labour productivity and occupational heat stress are also important issues, and concerns over migration were additionally flagged by local experts, who emphasized a constant drain of men and families out of the area. Fisheries are in long-term decline in the area for a variety of reasons, including over-fishing, but research provides strong evidence for the negative impact on marine ecosystems of both rising sea temperatures and ocean acidity. The Gulf of Guinea is understood to be one of the zones worst hit by rising temperatures (Cheung et al., 2010). Coastal erosion in the area has a long history, with dramatic rates of degradation and residents asserting "several kilometres" of land lost to the sea in certain places around the Volta Delta, where sea defences have not been put in place. The agricultural sector has been affected both by the heat and by salt intrusion and land erosion due to sea-level rise, although large areas of land are irrigated by the Volta River and are more resilient to the growing heat. In health terms, malaria was still a common health problem for residents of the area, and malnutrition was raised as a serious concern. Diarrheal diseases were apparently less prevalent than was the case for northern Ghana, since it was understood that plumbed/improved water sources and sanitation or latrines were more common in the coastal Volta area.

COASTAL EROSION AND SEA-LEVEL RISE

Analysis of Ghana's coastline shows that over the last few decades the eastern coast has eroded at the fastest rate. Rates of annual erosion have been estimated in the range of 1-11 metres per year of land (Ly, 1980; Wiafe 2010; Appeaning Addo et al., 2011). Coastal erosion in the area has been noticeable for over a century, suggesting some degree of natural oscillations in delta growth and loss (Akyeampong, 2001; Oteng-Abbabio et al., 2011). In addition to claiming land and damaging coastal infrastructure, the erosion is also affecting water resources and soil quality from the penetration of salt from the sea as it seeps further inland. It has forced the relocation of residents who have abandoned their homes and properties along the coast and moved inland. Risks are particularly high during elevated seasonal tides or storm tides that can inundate tracts of land and severely damage infrastructure, livelihoods, and endanger lives.
Sea-level rise due to climate change is a significant cause of concern in the coastal erosion of Ghana. However, research has highlighted several other important issues. These include the construction of the Volta/Akosombo hydroelectric dam built in the 1960s, which withholds vital sediments that would otherwise be released into the delta from the Volta River; sediment to the littoral delta has been reduced by 10 times according to some estimates (Boateng, 2009). The erosion processes may have doubled since the building of the dam (Ly, 1980). Given that water flow is now controlled, the natural flooding patterns of the area have also changed and the flood plains now rely on irrigation and a reduced water supply (Corcoran et al., 2007). The hydro dam in itself is a positive response to the causes of climate change as a renewable energy generator, but it also presents a unique dilemma here because the dam exacerbates the consequences of climate change, in particular, sea-level rise erosion.
Other important concerns highlighted include the practice of sand mining and the construction of coastal infrastructure and sea-defences (Oteng-Abbabio et al., 2011; Appeaning Addo and Larbi, 2009). Sand removed from the shorefront obviously accelerates erosion, while the construction of coastal infrastructure affects sea-wave dynamics and concentrates energy on adjacent unprotected areas. Even if the entire Ghanaian coast were protected, Togo and Côte d'Ivoire on either side would be more exposed, since it is hard to imagine the possibility of protecting the entire Gulf of Guinea coastline. Residents and officials in Keta were insistent that the construction of the major seaport at nearby Tema during the early 1960s changed the velocity and energy pattern of the waves, further accelerating coastal erosion. A port further distant, on the border of Togo, was also a source of concern. Clearing and degradation of littoral mangrove forests has made matters even worse. Finally, the local practice of pumping out groundwater via "tube irrigation" was very common, even for fields close to the water's edge. In other parts of the world, irrigation using ground-water has been shown to accelerate land subsidence and perceived sea-level rise (Larson et al., 2001). Similar irrigation techniques were also common in the Mekong delta of Vietnam, also highly vulnerable to sea-level rise and studied in this report. In the context of all these varied and significant concerns, sea-level rise resulting from climate change is a very unwelcome new consideration for a community highly vulnerable and already having great difficulty coping with local coastal erosion. A series of large-scale coastal defences have already been built, and local experts have emphasized the sensible preference of "soft" approaches, such as re-vegetation of sand dunes or beach nourishment, over "hard" infrastructure coastal defence options (Oteng-Abbabio et al., 2011). Little information was obtainable about the feasibility of sediment pass-through retrofits to the Volta/Akosombo hydroelectric dam, although retrofitting options are available and would merit further investigation and investment given the scale of impact manifested (IPCC, 2012b). However, clearly the re-establishment of coastal mangrove forests and providing alternatives to ground-water pumping for irrigation would be less expensive than infrastructure-intensive solutions; for example, one single coastal defence construction near Keta cost 90 million US dollars (Armah, 2005). "Soft" approaches are also likely to cause less, if any, collateral damage. There appeared to be few mechanisms in place to compensate households that lost property and needed to relocate or who are subject to damage. If the sea level rises one or two metres during the 21st century—assuming that climate change is not sufficiently brought under control—the whole situation threatens to become quite dire (IPCC, 2007; RSNZ, 2010; Füssel in Edenhofer et al., 2012).

FISHERIES

Local observations of the rise in sea temperatures and some indications of decline in local marine life match global assessments (Wiafe et al., 2008). The

CLIMATE	2010	2030
Contraction of biological zones (km^2) - yearly average	-3,000	-6,000
Additional land degraded due to climate change (km^2) - yearly average	750	1.500
Additional/reduced energy load due to climate change (GWh) - yearly average	350	900
Additional CO_2 generated/reduced for heating and cooling due to climate change (kt CO_2) - yearly average	60	150
Share of workforce particularly affected by climate change (%) - yearly average	55%	45%
Additional land lost due to climate change (km^3) - yearly average	15	35
Additional water losses/gains due to climate change (km^3) - yearly average	0.25	0.25

CARBON	2010	2030
Volume of water to treat (millions m^3) - yearly aveeage	250	350

community was unanimous that there are simply fewer fish. This applies equally to inland and offshore fish stocks. As with sea-level rise, climate change driven sea temperatures and CO2-related acidification of the oceans are not the only causal factors. As with many other social, economic, and environmental challenges, climate change is rarely, if ever, the only factor causing problems. Population growth increases the number of fishermen, resulting in damaging fish practices, such as the use of small gauge nets or even dynamite, and the practically uncontrolled intensification of large-scale commercial operations has not favoured sustainable management of fish stocks.

Two other climate change-related factors have also worsened the situation for fishermen. More volatile, unpredictable, and extreme weather is a serious safety hazard. Some fishermen cannot swim and the small fishing boats are often at serious risk on this high-energy coastline, especially in the case of fierce, unpredictable storms. Second, the retreat of the shore has pushed the blue-water shelf, where most fishing takes place, further away with each passing decade and add to labour, time, cost, and risks for fishermen in small craft.

Large and heavily equipped foreign fishing boats from China, Japan, and Korea ply the offshore waters of the region for fish that are explored from the port base in nearby Tema directly to Asia. In Keta, however, there is no fish processing industry, such as a freezing works, for packaging the catch of local fishermen. Locals rely only on "middle men" who truck the Keta catch back to Accra. Most of the fish leaving for Accra is sold smoked. Local fishermen stated that the smoking of fish used to be permitted by burning the less useful remains of the once bountiful catch. However, the falling fish harvest means that local trees and forests are instead used for fuel, and this has reportedly exacerbated local deforestation concerns. Moreover, degradation of mangrove forests in the delta—with mangrove wood serving as firewood—damages marine and inland fishery biodiversity in an interlinked vicious cycle (Concoran et al., 2007). Responding to the full range of issues affecting the mainstay fisheries industry of the region is not a straightforward matter. Fishing is still a significant industry for the Ghanaian economy as a whole, and its rapid decline will clearly not add to the wealth and social cohesion of the nation. The only solution currently being explored seriously is the establishment of fish farms, for which a few select pilot projects were taking hold, to the great interest of the local industry. Regulation of foreign commercial fishing was dismissed as "unrealistic" under current circumstances, even if only to limit fish net gauge, so that the smallest fish would escape unharmed while promoting the continual replenishment of stocks. Once again, the preservation of the local mangrove forests represents an obvious positive response, with multiple benefits, even if steps towards implementation are unexplored and doubtful. Yet another avenue to be explored, which could lower the vulnerability of the community through expanded incomes is providing incentives and creating an enabling environment for local entrepreneurs to establish fish processing industries to generate value-added goods with broader market potential. Other options worthy of consideration are certified, sustainable fishing programmes and the establishment of marine reserves.

CONCLUSION

The hallmarks of climate stress are clearly evident in the everyday life and the local environment of Ghana, whether in downtown Accra—recovering from unprecedented floods—or in coastal and northern savannah regions. More areas were not visited, but the National Workshop organized as a part of the research undertaken did highlight several other zones of the country facing still different and significant pressures characteristic of those areas, some of which are also documented in local research (Asante et al., 2010; EPA-Ghana, 2011; Tachie-Obeng et al., 2011). In every case, climate change stress met head-on with local issues not caused by climate change. In Accra, the floods were exacerbated by poor drainage and waste disposal methods. In the Volta delta, coastal infrastructure, unsound irrigation, and the upstream Volta hydro dam compounded one another in a context of growing climate-related sea-level rise. In the northern region of Ghana, local deforestation and savannah burning wove complex interrelationships with the extreme heat and water stress that was eroding the rural livelihoods in an area that in former times was the breadbasket for Ghana. With 50 additional days that could be considered "hot" in every current year, as compared with Ghana's climate in the 1960s, the heat has nevertheless only just begun to increase; a doubling, trebling, or more of the temperature increase is expected over the next 20–30 years, given the inertia of the global climate system (McSweeney et al., 2012; Hansen et al., 2005). Thus, future climate stresses are likely to be extreme and will continue to exploit the economic, social, and environmental weaknesses of Ghana, and retard economic growth and social and human development potential, especially among the poorest communities. However, steps taken by the government are heading in a promising direction, and the success and relative stability of Ghana compared with other countries in the region make it an interesting candidate for a more concerted effort. United with the international community, Ghana has the potential to show the way in tackling the local impacts of climate change as they are increasingly coming to the fore.

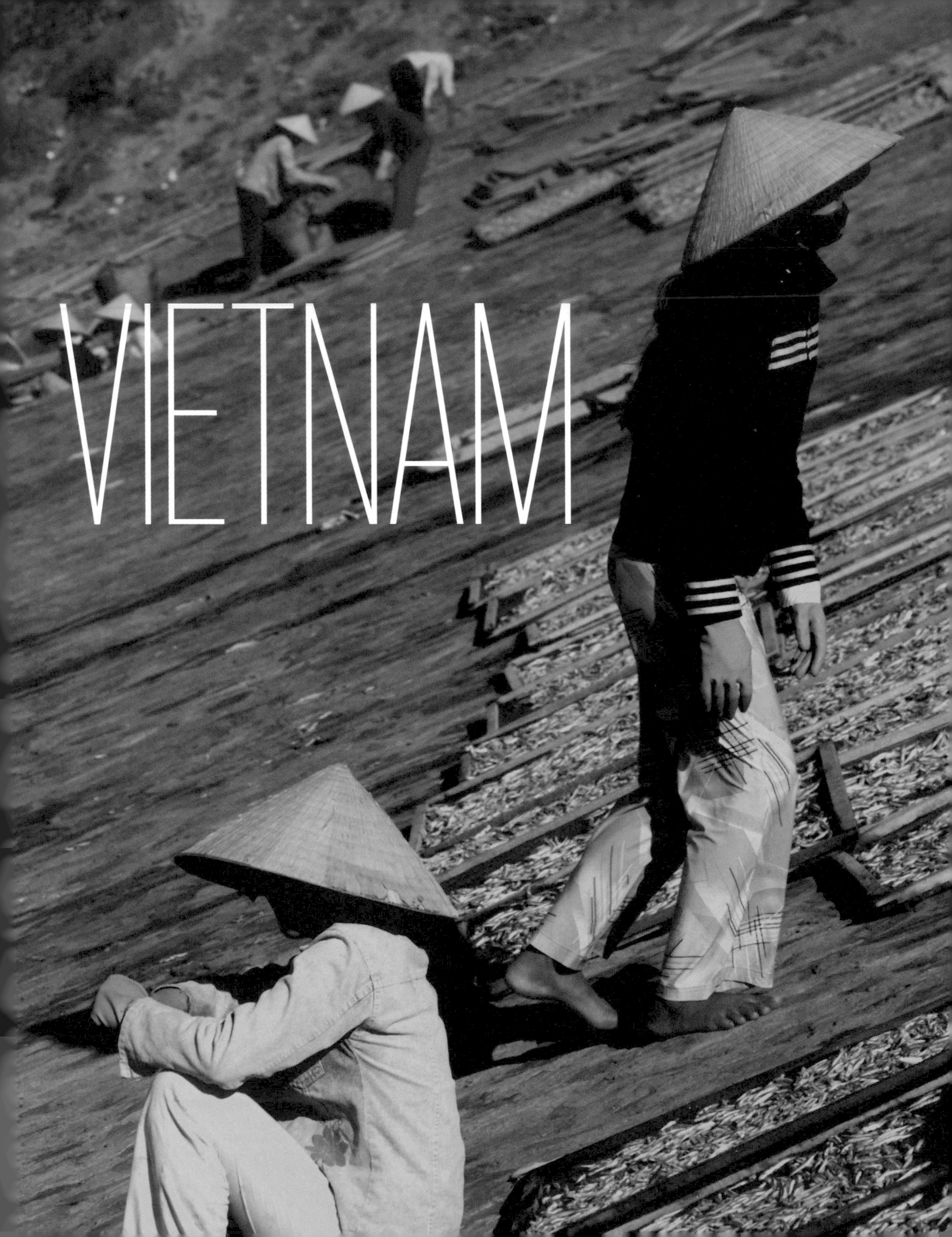

VIETNAM

COUNTRY STUDIES ★

GENERAL PURPOSE

1. **FEEDBACK** FOR THE DEVELOPMENT OF THE MONITOR'S METHODOLOGY

2. **EXPLAIN** HOW THE ANALYSIS OF THE MONITOR CAN BE USED IN A NATIONAL SITUATION

3. **SERVE AS A KNOWLEDGE-SHARING MECHANISM** FOR BEST PRACTICE AND CHANGE MANAGEMENT FOR THE BENEFIT OF OTHER VULNERABLE COUNTRIES

4. **PROVIDE AN OUTSIDE SUPPORTING ANALYSIS** OF INTEREST TO NATIONAL POLICY-MAKERS AND DEVELOPMENT PARTNERS

KEY FIGURES

Population	87,840,000
2009 GDP PPP (Dollars)	
Total	$320,874,000
Per Capita	$3,549
Real Growth	5.6%

ECONOMY

GDP by Sector	
Primary/Extractive	22%
Secondary/Productive	40%
Tertiary/Services	37.7%
Key Sector(s)	Industry

SOCIO-ECONOMIC DEVELOPMENT

Human Development (Rank)	Medium (128th)
Life Expectancy	75.2 years
Annual Population Growth	1%
Illiteracy	3.1%
Urban Population	31%
Access to Electricity	97.6%
Gender Development	48th
Undernourished Population (2006/08)	11%
Living below poverty line ($1,25/day)	13.1%
Population without Improved Water Source	12.2%
Official Development Assistance (% of GDP))	4.4%
Public Health Expenditure	7.2%
Public Education Expenditure	5.3%

CLIMATE/GEOGRAPHY

Climate Zone	Monsoon tropical
Projected Rainfall Change	Likely to increase by 1.0-5.2% and 1.8-10.1%
Tropical Cyclones	Yes (decreasing trend)
Desertification	None
Low-Elevation Coastal Zone (10m and below)	20%
Forest Cover Change (1990-2008)	44.3%

MIGRATION/DISPLACEMENT

Emigration Rate	2.4%
Immigrants as Share of Total Population	0.1%
Internally Displaced People	None

	Impact Areas	Indicator	Confidence	Gender Bias	Vulnerability 2010	Vulnerability 2030
CLIMATE		DROUGHT	✓			
		FLOODS & LANDSLIDES	✓			
		STORMS	✓			
		WILDFIRES	✓			
		BIODIVERSITY	✓			
		DESERTIFICATION	✓			
		HEATING & COOLING	✓			
		LABOUR PRODUCTIVITY	✓			
		PERMAFROST	✓			
		SEA-LEVEL RISE	✓			
		WATER	✓			
		DIARRHEAL INFECTIONS	✓			
		HEAT & COOL ILLNESSES	✓			
		HUNGER	✓			
		MALARIA & VECTOR BORNE	✓			
		MENINGITIS	✓			
		AGRICULTURE	✓			
		FISHERIES	✓			
		FORESTRY	✓			
		HYDRO ENERGY	✓			
		TOURISM	✓			
		TRANSPORT	✓			
CARBON		OIL SANDS	✓			
		OIL SPILLS	✓			
		BIODIVERSITY	✓			
		CORROSION	✓			
		WATER	✓			
		AIR POLLUTION	✓			
		INDOOR SMOKE	✓			
		OCCUPATIONAL HAZARDS	✓			
		SKIN CANCER	✓			
		AGRICULTURE	✓			
		FISHERIES	✓			
		FORESTRY	✓			

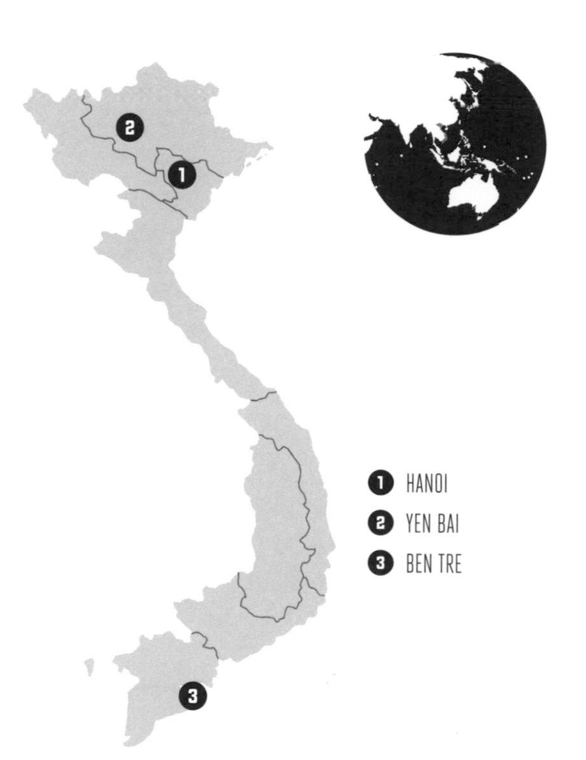

The Monitor research team held a nationally-focused policy workshop in the Vietnamese capital of Hanoi and undertook field research in two provinces: Bến Tre, in the extreme south of Vietnam, at one of the outlet points of the Mekong Delta, and Yen Bái, in the highlands to the north-west of Hanoi in northern Vietnam.

In recent years, Vietnam has consistently been one of the world's fastest growing economies and is an important contributor to global growth (IMF WEO, 2012). Getting climate policy right will enable Vietnam to grow even faster and to accelerate its already impressive strides in reducing poverty and safeguarding the health of its people, as evidenced by the significant progress it has achieved with respect to the Millennium Development Goals (ODI, 2010). Among the countries most vulnerable to the effects of climate change, especially in economic terms, Vietnam also suffers serious health impacts from carbon-intensive urban industrial and transport-related air pollution and, especially in rural and highland areas, hazardous household cooking and heating practices from the indoor burning of wood, coal, and other materials. The full range of climate-related effects is harming last mile efforts to reduce poverty. The government has clearly recognized the benefits of a strong response to climate change and embraced efforts to begin low-carbon transition as a means of increasing competitiveness. It has unequivocally prioritized these steps in its policy directives and foreign relations. As a result, it is taking concrete steps to safeguard and enhance the economic, social, and environmental dividends of its growth. This in itself is a compelling message to the world, given that Vietnam is anticipated to be among the largest economies of the 21st century (O'Neill et al., 2005).

The country's policy stance on climate change is path-breaking for one with low-emissions and limited responsibility for climate change experienced to date. However, new research aggregated for the Monitor's assessment in this report suggests that there is still further scope for enhancing these policies. Nevertheless, the approach adopted serves as an important example of success that other vulnerable countries around the world would be well advised to examine in detail.

 MULTI-DIMENSIONAL CLIMATE VULNERABILITY: **ACUTE** 

 MULTI-DIMENSIONAL CARBON VULNERABILITY: **MODERATE**

CAPACITY: **INTERMEDIARY**

POPULATION 2010/2030: **88/102 MILLION**

GDP 2010/2030 (PPP): **280 BILLION/1.5 TRILLION USD**

GDP PER CAPITA 2010/2030 (PPP): **3,000/14,000 USD**

BACKGROUND AND CONTEXT

BACKGROUND AND CONTEXT

With a population of over 90 million today, Vietnam is a populous and fast-growing lower-middle-income South East Asian country, bordering China to the north and Laos and Cambodia to the west (CIA, 2012). Vietnam is similar in size to Germany or Japan. Its climate is tropical monsoon and varies from warm in the south to cool in parts of the sub-tropical north; its climate also changes depending on elevation in the many mountainous parts of the country.

Although economic growth has been consistently fast in the last decade, GDP per capita is still very low at 3,000 US dollar (PPP), or 1,200 dollars per capita in nominal terms, but could increase ten times by 2030, as anchored in IPCC marker scenarios (IPCC, 2000). The affluent and international urban centres of Hanoi and Ho Chi Minh City contrast with the less developed rural areas with their still excessive poverty levels. A strong education system and human capital, as well as relatively robust institutional governance and infrastructure indicate that Vietnam's capacity is not among the lowest. For similar reasons and due to its population size, the United Nations has never considered Vietnam a Least Developed Country. The country carries relatively high macroeconomic climate risk compared with more advanced economies, since the agricultural sector represents 20% of GDP and employs over half of its workforce. Reducing risks will involve diversification of the labour force into the industrial and service sectors, as well as modernizing farming through irrigation systems.

As the Vietnamese economy experiences sustained high growth, it will be a priority to limit the negative effects of the industrialization process associated with its structural progression to higher income levels. While Vietnam's GHG emissions are low at 3.5 tons per capita and are expected to remain below 4 tons per capita into the 2020s. Vietnam's industrial, urbanizing, power generation, and socio-economic profiles mean have led to high concentrations of fine particles, which are extremely toxic. Moreover, heavy reliance on firewood for domestic cooking and heating poses serious health risks (Climate Analytics, 2012). Despite its strengths, the environmental vulnerability of Vietnam to climate change is extreme. Its mountainous geography and coastal frontage combine with exposure to tropical cyclones (typhoons) and storms which form in the western Pacific Ocean, leaving the country prone to extreme floods, landslides, heavy rainfall, and high winds. The low-lying Mekong delta is one of the largest flood-prone zones of the world. Most of the southern tip of the country, including much of nearby Ho Chi Minh City, are at less than one metre above sea level. Vietnam's tropical climate will continue to heat up, bringing more drought spells and fishery losses as thermal conditions increasingly exceed already elevated historical levels. Social and economic vulnerabilities are also high, especially in remote highland communities. Insurance exists for health care, but is rarely available for farmers, fishing operations or even infrastructure. Electricity grid access is very high for the country as a whole, but in some of the poorest communities, it reaches just over half of all households, where plumbed water sources are also absent and malnutrition rates and the associated stunting of children can be commonplace.

THE MONITOR'S ASSESSMENT
OVERVIEW

On the basis of the Monitor's assessment, the impact of climate change is estimated to have already held back to a significant degree the economic prosperity of Vietnam's fast-growing economy, effects which are estimated here to grow steeply in severity in the next 20 years. Certainly, the top 10% of days and nights previously considered "hot," a key indicator of climate change, has increased in number by 30 and 50 respectively for a given year, as compared with Vietnam's 1960s climate. Both are set to increase even more substantially through to mid-century and potentially beyond (McSweeney et al., 2012).
The multi-dimensional vulnerability of Vietnam to climate change is considered in the highest category of Acute and rising. Vulnerability to the carbon economy is estimated as Moderate and stable. Economic impacts are the main sources of Vietnam's vulnerability, with human or health effects being less extreme in comparison with other countries. Total economic losses are estimated to cost Vietnam 5% of its GDP in net terms in 2010, growing to 11% of GDP by 2030, as the country's vulnerability shifts from Severe to Acute over this period. The economic cost of the carbon economy is estimated at a much lower 0.8% and is set to remain stable relatively through to 2030. However, the human cost of the carbon economy is considered Severe and estimated already to cause over 50,000 deaths per year, increasing to over 60,000 deaths per year by 2030.

CLIMATE CHANGE

The following most serious climate change impact areas are assessed (for 2010/2030) in order of the scale of GDP losses from higher to lower:

- LABOUR PRODUCTIVITY, ACUTE/ACUTE 4.4%/8.6% of GDP
- SEA-LEVEL RISE, HIGH/HIGH 1.5%/2.7% of GDP
- FISHERIES, SEVERE/ACUTE 0.5%/1.0% of GDP
- AGRICULTURE, HIGH/SEVERE 0.2%/0.4%
- HEATING AND COOLING, HIGH/SEVERE 0.1%/0.3% of GDP
- FLOODS AND LANDSLIDES, ACUTE/ACUTE 0.1%/0.1% of GDP
- BIODIVERSITY, MODERATE/MODERATE 0.1%/0.1% of GDP
- DROUGHT, ACUTE/ACUTE 0.1%/0.1% of GDP

The most serious health impacts related to climate change are estimated to be Heat and Cold Illnesses and Hunger. Heat and Cold Illnesses, or mortality among chronic disease sufferers during heat waves, present particularly severe challenges to the elderly, whereas Hunger predominantly concerns young children. While mortality is low in each case, an average of over 800,000 people is estimated to be affected each year by the aggravating effect of climate change on hunger.
The assessment used for Labour Productivity and Sea-level Rise are considered relatively reliable, whereas other main impacts are more indicative or less certain due to the limitations of models relied upon for these indicators. In terms of positive impacts due to climate change assessed here, Vietnam is understood to benefit very slightly from additional water supply as a result of additional rainfall, overcompensating for heightened evaporation as the heat increases. For similar reasons, Vietnam is also estimated to experience a slight decline in aridity in the driest zones which could become more humid. However, these findings are based on global models (or IPCC model ensembles) and their results contrast with Vietnam's own reference scenarios, which project higher rates of evaporation than rainfall, and large declines in rain and river flows during dry spells, which are not always offset by increases in flood flows (Nohara et al., 2006; Hansen et al., 2007; Vietnam MONRE, 2010).

CARBON ECONOMY

Regarding carbon economy cost in human terms, Indoor Smoke is the most serious concern, accounting for just over 40,000 deaths per year in 2010 and similar mortality levels by 2030, as a result of disease from exposure to smoke from indoor fires for cooking and heating. Deaths due to indoor smoke are stable, because despite a fast expanding population, economic growth is expected to see many households adopt cleaner burning fuels and stoves. Air Pollution is estimated to claim 10,000 casualties a year in 2010, rising to over 20,000 deaths per year in 2030 as pollution levels rise. The northern Red River basin around Hanoi has significant, excessive levels of fine air particulates from traffic and industrial emissions which are highly hazardous to human health. The country's current growth pathway would see that worsen as economic growth and industrialization expand (World Bank, 2012; Donkelaar et al., 2010).
In economic terms, the most significant economic losses due to the carbon economy concern Biodiversity (2010/2030: 0.3%/0.6% GDP), Human Health (2010/2030: 0.3%/0.3%) and Fisheries (2010/2030: 0.2%/0.2% GDP). The carbon economy effects for Agriculture constitute a 0.2% loss to GDP in 2010, but are converted into a 0.1% gain to GDP by 2030, due to the expected realization of carbon fertilization benefits for crop productivity. However, this gain to GDP is more than offset by the expected 0.4% of GDP losses due to climate change.
The human health impacts are considered relatively reliable, whereas impacts for Biodiversity, for instance, are considered more indicative. Fisheries impacts are labelled here as speculative, due to the limited scientific research currently available, especially as regards the effects of various pollutants, such as acid rain on key species of fresh or brackish water fish and aquatic life. The acidification of the oceans as it absorbs CO_2 is however a well established area of concern (Sabine and Feely in Reay et al. (eds.), 2007; IPCC, 2007).

NATIONAL RESPONSE
STATUS

Policy development on climate change in Vietnam has been a serious and active field of activity for many years. The 2007/8 "National Target Programme to Respond to Climate Change" (NTP-RCC) carved out the

CLIMATE FINANCE

ASSETS

GAPS

first major national policy framework and committed over 50 million USD of domestic resources to tackling climate change, in particular to respond to the impacts of climate change (Vietnam MONRE, 2008). In 2012, Vietnam launched its "National Climate Change Strategy" (NCCS), which covers a range of vulnerability and low-carbon issues (Vietnam NCCS, 2011). The NCCS is also fundamentally different from the earlier National Target Programme, in that it conveys firm directives of the Executive to all relevant government offices to bear responsibility for implementation. The Strategy outlines the following ten priority task areas for implementation, which provide a useful insight into the foundations of Vietnam's national response to climate change:

1. Disaster preparedness and climate monitoring
2. Food and water security
3. Sea-level rise
4. Protection and sustainable development of forests (carbon sinks and biodiversity)
5. GHG reductions
6. Increase of the role of government
7. Community capacity development
8. Scientific and technological development
9. International cooperation and integration
10. Diversification of financial resources and investment effectiveness

Furthermore, concerted efforts to implement climate change policy at the regional level are also underway, with one of the initial target provinces, Bến Tre, visited as part of the field research for the Monitor.

CLIMATE FINANCE

In 2010, Vietnam attracted the sixth largest volume of international climate change finance among developing countries, totalling over 500 million USD. Only Brazil, Egypt, Kenya, India, and Indonesia received more funds. However, with 200 million USD targeting adaptation, Vietnam was the single largest recipient of Adaptation funds, and has a very balanced allocation of international resources between adaptation and low-carbon investments. These funds represent monies announced by donor governments or multilateral institutions to the main database of the Organization for Economic Co-operation and Development as principally targeting climate change (OECD CRS, 2012). They do not necessarily represent funds supporting the government of Vietnam's climate change policies and programmes, although a share of these funds may, indeed, be applied in this manner. In the case of Vietnam, climate finance is almost exclusively bi-lateral with Japan as the largest climate donor, followed by Germany and France. The split of bilateral funds between loans and grants is almost 90:10, so most of the finance is in the form of concessional loans.

All other factors remaining equal, the high levels of vulnerability in Vietnam and its relatively significant capacity make the country a sensible early priority destination for climate finance. Vietnam is developing a robust climate change policy and implementation model that will be of interest and use to other countries in similar income and vulnerability strata, but which, unlike Vietnam, have farther to go in making progress on building their multi-dimensional capacity for implementation. Despite being the largest contribution worldwide, the 200 million USD of external support for adaptation is well below 0.1% of Vietnam's GDP and therefore pales in comparison to the scale of economic losses estimated at over 5% of GDP in 2010. In ideal circumstances, greatly enhanced international support should be forthcoming to assist Vietnam in dealing with such large-scale impacts. However, given the possible scale of the shortfall and the low-end prospects for large-scale increases in foreign assistance, Vietnam will likely come under increasing pressure to invest available domestic resources in order to preserve the resilience and ensure the ongoing competitiveness of its economy.

ASSETS

Several strong points are notable hallmarks of Vietnam's response to climate change:

- *Strong Executive Leadership:* The clear support of the Prime Minister behind the climate policy project of Vietnam will be essential for meaningful vertical (central, provincial, district/municipal) and horizontal (across multiple ministries/departments) collaboration, necessary to strengthen the country's resilience to climate change and seize key opportunities for low-carbon development.
- *Governance Mechanism:* A clear and comprehensive policy framework and coordination mechanism has been established with executive authority and provides the substantive and operational mechanism with phasing, responsibilities, and financial parameters outlined for implementing Vietnam's climate policy response. The National Workshop held in the context of the country research undertaken highlighted how moving from governance to effective implementation and monitoring is now becoming the overriding challenge for Vietnam.
- *National Reference Scenarios:* Vietnam has regularly updated and communicated national climate change scenarios with a high resolution of sub-national information across a range of key concerns such as rainfall and evaporation, sea-level rise, and others. Clarity on an agreed set of reference scenarios is essential to calibrating policy responses, allocating/prioritizing resources and anchoring expert debate; regular updating is essential, given the fast pace of knowledge development in the field of climate change. In light of this assessment for instance, Vietnam might consider adding sea and pond temperature and acidity reference measures of concern to the fisheries industry, and Wet Bulb Globe Temperature (WBGT) of interest to businesses, occupational safety specialists, and economists.
- *Vibrant National-level Civil Society:* Engaged and concerned groups of academics, non-governmental organizations, international actors, and other civil society actors especially active in the nation's capital are a valuable resource for the Government to draw upon, as it refines and advances its climate change policy project in the years ahead. The group should be fostered and relied upon to support the fine tuning of policy development, implementation, and monitoring.
- *Buoyant International Support:* The Government has clearly indicated to development partners the importance of climate change as a national development priority. International development partner donor governments, such as Japan and France, and international financial institutions including the World Bank have responded by forming a "Support Programme to Respond to Climate Change" (SPRCC) coordination group to assist Vietnam in its development and implementation of climate change policy; an evaluation mechanism fiscal/loan support, including financial resource commitments form a growing share of Vietnam's Official Development Assistance (ODA), all of which promote harmonization, cooperation, action, and results.
- *Public Financial Commitments:* Vietnam has committed substantial government mobilized funds to the project, initially amounting to approximately 50 million USD over a 5–6 year period.
- *Key Sector Effects Addressed:* The existing climate change strategy and policies of Vietnam already address the majority of the key issues, including sea-level rise, agriculture/food and water security, heating and cooling (through urban energy efficiency), as well as disasters, such as flooding and landslides.

GAPS

Some gaps can be identified on the basis of this Monitor's innovative assessment methodology. In 2010, the first Monitor would have identified

OTHER CHALLENGES AND OPPORTUNITIES

very few gaps, testifying to the quickly evolving nature of our understanding of climate change. Gap areas which merit further exploration by stakeholders include:

- *Labour Productivity:* The most significant impact for Vietnam as assessed by the Monitor. It is to be expected that it is not addressed by current policies, since the effect has not been included in any IPCC reports to date (IPCC, 1990, 1995, 2001, and 2007). However, in noting in its 2008 NTP that mines would require more energy for cooling, Vietnam did recognize the important relationship between worker productivity and rising heat (Vietnam MONRE, 2008). Experts also noted ongoing inquiry by the Vietnamese Ministry of Labour – Invalids and Social Affairs (MOLISA) into climate change effects. With nearly half of its workforce currently vulnerable to extreme forms of occupational heat stress, incorporating a response to this large-scale economic impact would be advisable for future climate policy iterations (Kjellstrom et al., 2009a).
- *Fisheries:* The impact of climate change on fisheries was recognized in the 2008 NTP, but has yet to find its way into an operational strategy or response. On the basis of the Monitor's assessment, Vietnam has the largest total losses in the fisheries sector due to climate change of any country in the world. Losses from climate change and the carbon economy are over 0.7% of GDP in 2010, growing to nearly 2% of GDP by 2030. This is in part due to the sheer scale of the country's fishing sector, and the vulnerabilities of its tropical waters and unsustainably managed fish stocks (UoC and Vietnam MPI, 2010). Therefore, building resilience or limiting impacts in the fisheries sector through improved fisheries management would help to reinforce any future climate policies.
- *Low-carbon Objectives:* The current national policy includes increasing energy efficiency across different sectors, carbon sinks through forests and the share of renewable energy in the power generation sector to 5% by 2020 and a modest 11% by 2050. It also involves reducing emissions from agriculture and waste disposal in a comprehensive low-carbon strategy. With carbon economy losses representing 0.8% of GDP and quite significant human impacts particularly due to indoor smoke, providing incentives for the use of clean burning household fuels/stoves and emission reductions that also yield clean air benefits could help Vietnam to maximize the social and economic benefits of low-carbon development. The Clean Development Mechanism (CDM) should continue to be drawn upon in order to maximize low-carbon technology saturation that will increase energy and economic resilience and competitiveness, in additional to their potential health, social and environmental benefits. A "Green Growth" strategy is set to be adopted in 2012, which may provide additional impetus to the work of Vietnam in this area.
- *Regional/Transnational Dimensions:* Vietnam's interests are directly affected by the policies of neighbouring countries. In particular, increased water withdrawals and sediment withholding infrastructure in the upstream Mekong, such as in neighbouring Laos and China, have direct impacts on biodiversity, fisheries, coastal erosion, and saline intrusion in the downstream delta region in Vietnam. Vietnam's national policies could, therefore, consider raising these concerns in the context of the intergovernmental Mekong River Commission, and seeking to stimulate domestic policy responses in other countries that are favourable to its interests.

OTHER CHALLENGES AND OPPORTUNITIES

- *Awareness:* Country research stressed the level of public awareness on the issue of climate change as both a challenge and an opportunity at various levels, national, provincial, and municipal. So much can be achieved through awareness alone, from flood safety to forest protection or farming knowledge, that it was seen as a key priority and features prominently also in the National Strategy. However, explaining complex concepts and responses in terms accessible and meaningful to different communities was seen as a challenge. Wide-ranging media: TV, radio, and the Internet, could provide a range of possibilities for reaching target audiences. Efforts to raise awareness should focus on options for practical action that people can relate to and become involved in implementing.
- *Forestry and Payment for Ecosystem Services/REDD+:* Forest covers almost half of the surface of Vietnam, but land-use conversions, such as wetlands to productive zones for fisheries or agriculture, as well as deforestation and forest degradation, are all clearly at significant levels, as evident from the country's national carbon inventory, where land usage and change (LULUCF) make up 15% of all emissions (Climate Analytics, 2012). Deforestation exacerbates fresh water scarcity, flash flooding and landslides, depletes natural carbon sinks, pollutes the air, and contributes to the erosion of biodiversity, all impacts that drain GDP and inhibit economic growth. The National Strategy aims to stabilize or increase forest cover, but given the macroeconomic risks involved, it may make sense for the Government to give incentives to land holders or local custodians to ensure sustainable forest management through a payment for ecosystem services scheme. Efforts to maximize the potential of the UN deforestation programme (REDD+) should also be prioritized as a central component in future climate strategies.
- *Monitoring and Evaluation:* Policymakers and the climate change community in Hanoi expressed an interest in enhancing monitoring and evaluation efforts in order to promote learning and improve the mobilization and prioritization of resources towards higher impact outcomes. Better criteria for evaluation were seen as vital to ensuring quality control of implementation projects.
- *Safety Nets:* In some of the poorest parts of Vietnam, health services are made available free of charge to the lowest income groups including ethnic minorities, with progressive cost schemes depending on income level for health services or insurance. Emergency teams as state or volunteer services are mobilized for on-the-spot responses to extreme events.
- *State Education System Reach:* Vietnam's public school system is present in every municipality and is a major asset for responding to climate change in vulnerable communities around the country. The potential for expanding awareness and education programmes is high, while schools can also support health monitoring and food security among children, who are a high-risk demographic group.
- *Sustainable Fishing:* Fishing is a large industry, but facing growing concerns about overfishing and fish stock depletion due to unsustainable practices (UoC and Vietnam MPI, 2010). Losses due to climate change could be attenuated in part by improving the sustainability of fishing practices, and in this way the resilience of fish stocks. Enforcing simple regulations on fish net size (large gauge) and promoting sustainable produce certification for fishing operations are just two examples of compelling and simple options for addressing unsustainable fishing.
- *Pollution Controls:* In all regions visited, industrial, domestic and agricultural pollution was highlighted as a major concern. From mining refuse to coal plant slurry, pesticides, domestic sewage and the use of poison to catch fish, water resources were being polluted, with negative effects for fishing, biodiversity, and water availability. The finding implied that increasing resilience to climate-induced water stress could be addressed in part through improved waste management across different sectors.

★

BẾN TRE – MEKONG DELTA

The Mekong delta of Vietnam is almost identical in area and population size to The Netherlands in Europe including the Rhine and Meuse, Schelde Delta, each spanning some 40,000 km² with around 18 million inhabitants. Bến Tre itself is one of a number of low-lying coastal provinces in the area and is heavily dependent on the fishing industry, including intensive aquaculture such as shrimp farming. Hallmark concerns for the area relate to sea-level rise, such as salt intrusion into water and soils, fisheries impacts due to warming waters and to a lesser extent, air pollution. Drought as well as heavy and unpredictable rains were further concerns raised by the community and these are highlighted in the Monitor's assessment. Sea-level rise causes a range of effects, including erosion of sea frontage and isolated flooding especially during record tides when the estuaries of the delta begin to inundate the surrounding land. The most serious current effect, however, relates to the increasing salinity of the waters as the sea pushes further upstream the Mekong. Bến Tre's many downstream waterways are undergoing a transformation as *salty* water progressively replaces previously *fresh* water, ultimately restricting the availability of water for domestic and agricultural purposes, and effectively drying up this coastal community.

RESPONDING TO SEA-LEVEL RISE

Needless to say, the very serious impacts and imminent risks linked to sea-level rise are of great concern. Local adaptation plans aim to gradually transform the Mekong delta into a South-East Asian version of The Netherlands, with a long list of intended actions costing over 100 million dollars in near-term investments for the province of Bến Tre alone, only one of 58 provinces in Vietnam. Although 50-60% of the plan is aimed at crucial infrastructure investments, such as dykes, polders, water supply works and dams, including 65kms of concrete sea walls and coastal defences reminiscent of the Maginot Line, it nevertheless represents a bargain, if compared to the unthinkable costs such enormous infrastructure investments might incur in a developed country. A long-term Mekong Delta "Master Plan" is also under development with the involvement of a Dutch consortium (NWP, 2012). Local officials were open about the fact that investment needs far exceed what the community could conceivably afford to invest, and hoped that 90% of funds would be forthcoming from the international community and the central government. The ability of the community to take on loans to pay for all the intended construction was also severely limited. However, certain projects were reported to be potentially justifiable as loans, in light of the anticipated increases in agricultural production that would result from implementation. This suggests some scope for communities and businesses to pay for construction costs of water infrastructure later on the basis of expanded incomes.

With almost the entire province lying below only one metre above sea-level, the whole area would be underwater by the end of the century according to the mid-point of the IPCC's estimates (IPCC, 2007). Since the last IPCC report, much higher estimates have been consistently put forward, suggesting that the IPCC is at the low-end of possible outcomes (RSNZ, 2010; Füssel in Edenhofer et al. (eds.), 2012). At the moment, however, sea-level rise is a more manageable 2-3mm per year, or 1 cm every 3-5 years (Vietnam MONRE, 2010; NASA Climate, 2012). Given that it is not likely that international resources will ever be made available to fund infrastructure for an expanse of over 60kms of coastline over the next five years, a diversification of the response strategy is likely called for.

In a broader context, it is evident that climate-driven sea-level rise is not the only factor aggravating Bến Tre's water-related concerns. Two important issues are equally worrisome. If adequately addressed, they might well help to alleviate or offset some of the climate-related stress being felt and at a lower cost than solid infrastructure responses.

First, an intensification of agriculture in the area has used water pumped from underground or from canals to meet growing irrigation needs. The water volume removed from local supplies is therefore increasing in a context of growing water scarcity. Increasing heat and drought due to climate change remain a likely exacerbating factor. However, withdrawal of ground water contributes to land subsidence, or sinking land, which heightens inundation vulnerabilities and can result in perceived sea-level rise (Larson et al., 2001).

Rainfall, especially in heavy concentrations, is predicted to increase for much of Vietnam due to climate change, as the Earth's hydrological system is accelerating (Vietnam MONRE, 2010). An alternative to expensive large-scale water generation facilities are low-cost, locally produced water catchment and storage units that harvest rainfall for subsequent use for domestic purposes; however, the available area for artificial catchment would likely fall short of meeting the needs of the agricultural industry.

The second key factor is also linked to the booming agricultural industry of the broader region. From the ocean frontage of Bến Tre back through the Mekong across Vietnam and reaching to the hinterlands of Cambodia, the agricultural boom has been sustained by large-scale irrigation systems that are fed by the Mekong itself. Upstream, not only in Vietnam but also in Cambodia, this is often accomplished through the construction of dams or dikes that help ensure a predictable water supply at specific points. On the whole, however, the Mekong's flow rate may be affected by a large-scale diversion of its water for irrigation (Fredén, 2011). Furthermore, dams built for irrigation purposes also trap riverine sediment upstream, depriving the downstream river delta of crucial alluvial deposits vital to its

CLIMATE ★	2010	2030
Contraction of biological zones (km²) - yearly average	-150	-300
Additional land degraded due to climate change (km²) - yearly average	-3,500	-7,250
Additional/reduced energy load due to climate change (GWh) - yearly average	1,500	6,000
Additional CO_2 generated/reduced for heating and cooling due to climate change (kt CO_2) - yearly average	550	2.500
Share of workforce particularly affected by climate change (%) - yearly average	48%	37%
Additional land lost due to climate change (km³) - yearly average	150	300
Additional water losses/gains due to climate change (km³) - yearly average	-1	-1

CARBON ★	2010	2030
Volume of water to treat (millions m³) - yearly avereage	2,000	3,000

environmental integrity (Baran, 2010; Yang et al., 2005). A slowing river flow might therefore also be responsible for increasing contamination of downstream zones in water with a high salt content as the Mekong's ability to force back oceanic tidal movements is compromised. It is unclear whether or not an expected increase in river flow due to climate change would offset a growing intensification of water withdrawals (Vietnam MONRE, 2010). The retention of sediment also has a further negative impact on marine and freshwater biodiversity and fisheries by reducing the nutrient content of the lower Mekong, as experts confirmed. Nor is does the question concern the suffering of downstream Bến Tre alone. The ecosystem of all parts of the delta system being tightly interlinked, local experts stressed the interdependence of fish movements. With the local biological richness of Bến Tre declining, its ability to serve as a corridor for fish migrations upstream is compromised and is leading to a decline in fish stocks in non-coastal delta provinces. Therefore, there is a strong incentive for inter-provincial cooperation to ensure that common resources are managed effectively and for the benefit of all. However, according to experts, this type of cooperation was still at the exploratory phase.
The upstream provincial university at Can Tho for instance had recently formed "MekongNet," to foster greater understanding and cooperation around shared Mekong river interests.
At a national level, the long-term development objectives of neighbouring Cambodia have direct implications for the prosperity and risks facing the downstream delta communities of Vietnam, such as Bến Tre, Can Tho, and others. Therefore, transnational cooperation on issues affecting the Mekong river are a serious economic, environmental, and livelihood concern for Vietnam—even more so considering the growing array of considerations linked to climate change. Working more actively with the Mekong River Commission, prioritizing the issue in formal bilateral relations with Cambodia and clearly spelling out the concern in future national policies, would constitute steps forward in addressing these challenges.

SUSTAINABLY MANAGING AQUACULTURE AND FISHERIES

Catch fisheries and aquaculture, particularly shrimping, are the dominant industries and sources of livelihood in Bến Tre. Serious exposure of the fisheries industry to climate and carbon risks did not, however, appear to be a major local consideration. And at the same time that the industry is a major income earner, it is also capital intensive and highly risky. If disease breaks out in a shrimp pond, the entire harvest is compromised, and possibly also in the neighbouring ponds. So, while the industry is an important income earner, it is also the sector that incurs frequent losses. No insurance was reported to be available for such high-risk activities as commercial pond shrimping.
Furthermore, experts confirmed that water temperature and acidity (pH) were fundamental concerns for controlled fish or shellfish ponds and directly linked to disease outcomes. Increasing heat and pollution-related water acidity would only heighten the risk of disease. Government intervention appeared to be limited to issuing guidelines during periods of extreme heat, to try and limit the loss of fish or shellfish from farms.
One systemic vulnerability identified for the aquaculture/shrimp industry was the quality of hatcheries. High quality disease-resistant seedlings are bought at extra cost that is hard to justify when a neighbouring pond might purchase the low-cost version and contract and pass on disease anyway. Improving seed supply for shrimp is an important response to this concern: Stricter regulation ensuring highest quality control for all hatcheries could ensure that all farmers use disease resistant seedlings to begin with, reducing

system wide risks and losses. The increased resilience should help offset to some extent the mounting concerns over water temperature and acidity.
In terms of catch fishing, there did not appear to be any serious regulation targeting overfishing and experts referenced the use of poison for fishing and the harmful effect of sewerage and aquaculture pond refuse on free-roaming fish stocks.
Higher prices were reported for fish or shellfish produced under certified sustainable conditions. They provide an economic advantage, which, in most cases, outweighs the extra capital required to ensure compliance with certification schemes, such as MSC. However, many fishermen could not afford the additional financial outlay. With sustainable fishing programmes only beginning to appear, the full possibilities for such programmes were understood to be high. Building the capacity of producers by offering detailed training programmes was seen as an important step for promoting wider adoption of sustainable fishing activities. Financial stimuli or incentives are also likely to be necessary to help operators make the transition to certified operations.
Establishing and enforcing strict regulations on net size (gauge) was another important measure that helped to avoid depletion of young fish stocks and support the sustainable replenishment of fish.
Finally, the preservation of coastal mangrove forests was viewed as an important priority for enhancing biodiversity that could improve the quality and quantity of local fish stocks. Mangrove swamps serve several functions: naturally accreting sediment that stems coastal erosion and warding off sea-level rise and the contamination of coastal water lenses due to salt intrusion. Mangroves also reduce sea-to-land wind speeds during severe storms, and help to limit the damage caused by extreme weather. According to local experts, some preservation zones had been established, but in areas where mangroves were not protected, the forests were in decline, due to a combination of local plundering and coastal stress. There seemed to be few if any arguments for not protecting and seeking to expand the entirety of the remaining mangrove forests. The main driver for degradation of the forests is pressure to enlist more space for agriculture or aquaculture.

★

YEN BÁI – NORTH-WEST HIGHLANDS

Therefore, regulations and monitoring would be required to ensure protection. Yen Bái is a large and relatively populous province in the north-west highland region of Vietnam. It is a heavily forested area with an agriculture-based economy active in the valley zones, with several hydro-energy installations in place. Farmers produce staple crops, such as rice and cassava, and, depending on the zones, cultivate plants ranging from tea to fruit trees, and in certain areas, also raise livestock. The dominant form of energy for cooking and heating is wood and biomass for indoor fires/stoves, with all the health risks that this practice implies.
The area of Yen Bái visited by the project researchers has a very low per capita income and high proportions of minority ethnic groups, living at the socio-economic margin. No specific climate change adaptation plans were in place or under development for that area. However, a number of government-led initiatives address key climate-related vulnerabilities and local officials had participated in workshops on climate change policies as a part of recent provincial and central government initiatives.

SOCIAL VULNERABILITIES

The main climate change risks for the region are extreme weather and shifting climate patterns, with flooding, drought, and agricultural concerns emphasized. Levels of socio-economic vulnerability were very high, with child malnutrition rates and stunting at 10-20% or higher in certain villages. Although mortality was reportedly very low, children and the elderly are the high-risk groups. Some 40% of households were without electricity, and similar levels of households, especially in poorer villages, were without an improved or plumbed water source. Other climate-related health concerns included a recent cholera outbreak in a remote community. However, programmes promoting personal hygiene and other education initiatives had apparently made strides in reducing a variety of health concerns in recent years. In the poorest communities, refrigeration was unusual, and air conditioning was to be found only in upscale restaurants or hotels.

EXTREME WEATHER AND IMPACTS

Experts reported a clear shift in the last 5-7 years in weather patterns. The abruptness and timing of season changes was a hallmark alteration. One school visited by the research team had 60 children absent for reasons of illness, attributed to the sudden arrival of warm weather. Large amounts of stone debris brought downstream in recent flooding were visible in most main waterways. Tractors were in some locations clearing the debris and locals attested to the expense of flood cleanup operations. Prolonged hot and dry spells were widely reported to be more common and had led to livestock and crop losses and reductions in stream-flow during these periods. Higher temperatures were a concern for agriculture and forestry due to water stress and insect and plant disease outbreaks. A hotter climate was forcing farmers to abandon some traditional crops—one form of cabbage was cited as no longer able to grow effectively. Although winters were now shorter and the hot periods of the year longer, the area had also experienced several extreme cold snaps that had caused health concerns and livestock losses, testifying to the volatility of weather in this area. No insurance schemes were available for crop or livestock losses due to such extremes of weather or drought. But public irrigation works were ensuring wider access to reliable water sources and it was hoped these would be further expanded.
A number of government-linked rural extension programmes were operational in the region, assisting farmers to grow new varieties of crops, such as those promising to be more suitable to warmer conditions, and to bring higher yields and higher market prices. However, improved varieties of rice required more attention and technical care from farmers, indicating the importance of access to training and knowledge, as farmers made the shift in their crops and cultivation. The timing of planting and harvesting was cited as particularly important. Weather forecasting information was made readily accessible and was regularly consulted by local farmers, with rural extension officers also promoting the practice.

SCHOOLS AND EDUCATION

Disaster education programmes were being successfully piloted in a number of schools, although the focus was mainly on personal safety, such as avoiding riverbanks during heavy rains. However, environmental and climate issues were set to be introduced in two schools visited, following training sessions for teachers on these issues. Schools were already active in teaching children to help preserve forests, to cultivate climate-resistant vegetables outside their homes as a food supplement, and to follow basic sanitary guidelines. Children from the poorest remote communities were also lodged and fed at the school during term time for minimal fees.
Evidence of behavioural change as a result of these initiatives was cited and teachers confirmed that children also passed on what they learned to their parents and relatives. The importance of education was underscored by the number of houses in some of the lowest-income villages that lacked any improved water source, but did posses colour televisions with satellite dishes. There were also limits to knowledge: hardship was cited as one of the main causes of local forest degradation, since people with no other alternatives would rely as a last resort on the forests by chopping down trees in order to sustain their livelihoods. Teachers suggested that the impact of educational programmes might nevertheless be improved by offering prizes in extra-curricula student competitions on environmental/climate issues; even very low-cost items such as sun caps could make the programmes more attractive, well attended, and broaden results. Schools also worked in close cooperation with health stations monitoring children and their families and alerting and referring sick children who needed early intervention. In several schools, children whose families could not feed them would also receive free meals.

HYDRO-ENERGY

On the basis of the Monitor's assessment, Vietnam is expected to experience modest benefits for its Hydro-Energy sector as a result of higher levels of rainfall. Local experts explained that more dry spells during the hotter seasons would not affect production for energy installations with reservoirs, if annual rainfall (or runoff) were to increase. However, installations without reservoirs which relied instead on a constant stream-flow would be negatively affected. Increasing the immediate water catchment potential and quality of surrounding land could potentially offset any losses. In particular, the high-altitude forests absorb more water (by "cloud catching") and also release it more slowly and regularly, which helps to diminish the severity of droughts (Postel and Thompson, 2005). On the whole, the bulk of hydro energy in Vietnam is being produced from reservoir type installations.
Local hydro-energy producers had also successfully accredited projects with the Clean Development Mechanism (CDM) and were able to confirm that the additional income stream provided by the sale of carbon credits as Certified Emission Reductions (CER) was the determining factor in making the installations commercially viable. Therefore, local entrepreneurs planned to undergo the 1-2 year registration process as a part of all future business

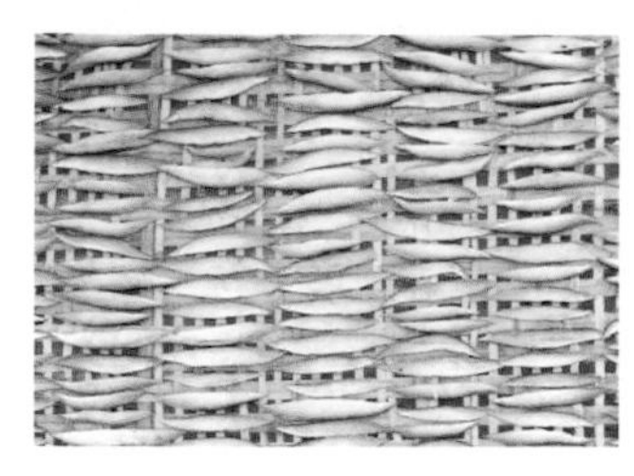

expansion efforts for new energy installations.

TOWARDS COMMUNITY RESILIENCE

A boost to the resilience of Yen Bái as it comes to grips with a warmer and more volatile climate could expand on and reinforce various initiatives already under way as described above. Schools and health stations are active institutions at the centre of the poorest communities doing crucial work but severely lacking in resources. Reinforcing the ability of schools and health centres to deliver social support would likely yield immediate results for the most vulnerable communities. Supporting farmers as they make the transition to higher-yielding, higher-value crops is an ongoing priority, as is the expansion of irrigation works. Preserving, growing and sustainably managing the forests of Yen Bái is also a public good that will reinforce the environmental resilience of the region with positive benefits for farmers and their families, and advantages for hydro-energy installations. The CDM is already being used to support large-scale energy projects in the region. However, CDM projects could also be developed as bundled programmes of activity, in particular to promote the dissemination of clean-burning or low-emission cooking/heating stoves (UNDP, 2011). This would help to address both the indoor smoke health risks and the forest degradation concerns of the region. Local manufacturing of appropriate and low-cost stoves may yield an additional economic dividend. Policymakers may also be interested to consider offering lifeline payments to forest holders or custodians, especially ethnic minority groups for forest stewardship, giving them incentives to preserve and sustainably manage the region's forests.

Finally, the very limited access to either crop/farm and infrastructure insurance or finance for small-scale farmers also merits attention. The government has an interest to increase the transfer of risks to the insurance industry and to expand access to finance in order to support enhanced economic growth. Microfinance and micro-insurance schemes have met with success in other countries in communities of similar income levels, and these could provide inspiration for applying such tools in Yen Bái and other parts of rural Vietnam (Jansson, 2010).

Micro-insurance is of interest for a number of reasons. First and foremost, because communities with the highest levels of vulnerability, such as the subsistence farmers of Yen Bái, risk much more of their livelihoods to extreme weather events than any other segment of the population. Since micro-insurance is by definition affordable and should be offered on a sustainable and equitable business model for all concerned, it offers the prospect of breaking part of the cycle that links poverty so closely to vulnerability (Churchill and Matul, 2012). The fact that health care insurance is widespread, even among the poorest communities in Vietnam demonstrates the viability of the concept for other concerns, particularly in the agricultural context, such as for crops and livestock. If farmers have income protection from year to year, their productivity can be regularized and enhanced. When farmers are insured, they are also more likely to be able to access finance to enhance their yields and income further (Zeller and Sharma, 2000). Ultimately, all this will boost economic growth and public finances, which can, in turn, be reinvested in more sustainable growth and should more than justify any outlay to provide incentives in partnership with competent organizations.

CONCLUSION

Vietnam has made an impressive beginning in tackling climate change, in particular from a government policy perspective. The country serves as a case of interest for other developing countries now considering how to meet the national climate change policy challenge. It has consolidated helpful assistance from foreign partners and, with pilot activities in select provinces, has begun to tackle the larger task of implementing its policies on the ground. As climate change is estimated in the Monitor to cause significant negative externalities for Vietnam, tackling the problem effectively should provide an economic boost for the country. Raising community level awareness, while fostering local sources of knowledge and the people's capacity to engage with climate change and take actions at the community level will enhance their impact. Likewise, focusing on monitoring and evaluating project performance will lead to higher-quality projects and better results.

Vietnam would do well to focus energies on core macroeconomic risks, such as improving resource management in the fisheries sector and responses to labour productivity exposure, as well as promoting ongoing diversification of the economy onto a lower-risk service and industrial sector-orientated footing. Opportunity should also be taken to help those remaining vulnerable communities to become more resilient through programmes such as education campaigns or encouraging the use of agro-insurance. Developing the interlinkages with low-carbon concerns on forestry, wetland or mangrove preservation and indoor household fuel use, and taking advantage of technology transfer and financing through the Clean Development Mechanism will all help to maximize economic, social and environmental benefits. With the anticipated intensification of climate change stresses in the immediate years and decades ahead, early action and investment will surely guarantee the highest dividends.

CARBON

ENVIROMENTAL DISASTERS

5 BILLION LOSS 2010
25 BILLION LOSS 2030

10 BILLION LOSS 2010
40 BILLION LOSS 2030

OIL SANDS

ESTIMATES GLOBAL CARBON IMPACT

2010 EFFECT TODAY

USD **LOSS** PER YEAR **5 BILLION**

2030 EFFECT TOMORROW

USD **LOSS** PER YEAR **25 BILLION**

ECONOMIC IMPACT

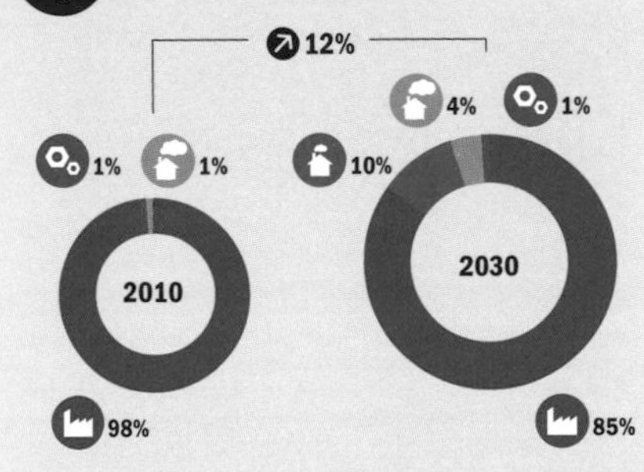

- Oil sands, or tar sands, are an unconventional source of petroleum extracted from an asphalt bitumen sand-like substance With the projected expansion of oil demand over the next twenty years, unconventional fuels, like synthetic crude from oil sands, will make up a significant proportion of the new supply
- Oil sands involve large scale localized ecological damage that is costly to remedy: some environmental damage is thought irreversible
- Oil sand exploitation is highly concentrated with over 90% of all today's production in Canada , although a small number of mainly developing countries also have important reserves

RELATIVE IMPACT

HOTSPOTS

7,250 **CANADA** 20,000

0 **NIGERIA** 1,500

0 **MADAGASCAR** 750

85 **INDONESIA** 600

50 **RUSSIA** 350

GEOPOLITICAL VULNERABILITY

Economic Cost (2010 PPP non-discounted)

Developing Country Low Emitters | Developed

Developing Country High Emitters | Other Industrialized

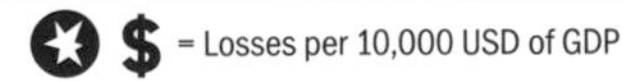
= Losses per 10,000 USD of GDP

= Millions of USD (2010 PPP non-discounted)

Change in relation to overall global population and/or GDP

So-called "unconventional fuels", including oil sand-derived synthetic crude as well as shale oil and gas, make up an increasing share of the global energy mix and are poised to contribute significantly to meeting the surging global demand for fossil fuels expected in the two decades ahead (US EIA, 2011). Unconventional fuels are more costly to extract than ordinary crude oil or natural gas because they involve separating out the hydrocarbon fuels from rocks, sand and other debris. The extraction process is water, energy and emission intensive, and generates large volumes of environmental debris and toxic sludge waste (Severson-Baker and Reynolds, 2005; Tenenbaum, 2009; Giesey et al., 2010). Over 600km2 of land in Canada has now been disturbed by oil sand exploitation with 600 million tons of toxic waste by-products from this process now held in over 100km2 of "slurry" ponds (Reuter et al., 2010). The potential growth in environmental risks is significant: proven recoverable reserves are 300 times today's annual production and bitumen deposits that could become recoverable, given technological advances, lie beneath some 140,000 km2 of land, an area almost the size of Bangladesh (GoA, 2012). The Canadian government aims to make Canada an "Energy Superpower" on the back of its oil sand production. Prime Minister, Stephen Harper, has likened this aspiration to "the building of the pyramids or China's Great Wall. Only bigger" (Canada OPM, 2006). Oil sands are expected to more than double in production scale over the next 20 years, with a handful of countries outside Canada also having important deposits of the resource (CAPP, 2011; World Energy Council, 2010).

HAZARD MECHANISM

There are two main types of oil sands exploitation: open pit mining, which involves digging and excavation of bitumen sands containing oil, and various forms of pumping, termed "in situ" extraction. Both processes involve large quantities of water and often solvents to aid the extraction by increasing the fluidity of otherwise highly dense and viscous bitumen sands (Canada NEB, 1996). In order to access the sands via mining, as much as 75 metres of ground soil including all vegetation, usually boreal forests, is removed. On average some two tons of land is removed per barrel of oil extracted (Reuter et al., 2010). Pumping out bitumen oil in situ involves injecting steam and industrial solvents into the ground before pumping out liquefied bitumen (OSDG, 2009).

Each barrel of oil produced generates eight barrels of waste slurry (so-called "fine tailings") with current production at around 1.5 million barrels of oil a day (Reuter et al., 2010; CAPP, 2011). The refuse slurry generated by extraction is highly acidic and acutely toxic to aquatic life (Allen, 2008). Numerous different types of pollutants from these processes, including cadmium, copper, lead and mercury, have been released into adjacent waterways, exceeding in many cases local concentration guidelines for fresh water in nearby populated areas (Kelly et al., 2010).

To date there has only been minimal reclamation of land to remedy the degradation caused. Experts have estimated that around two thirds of all peatlands damaged by oil sand exploitation would be permanently impaired and irrecoverable (GoA, 2012; Rooney et al., 2012).

If action is not taken to treat open waste ponds, through steps such as "bioremediation", which accelerates natural processes to reduce their toxicity, the environmental damage in terms of human health, water, ecosystems and otherwise, is very likely to exceed any treatment costs (Reuter et al., 2010).

IMPACTS

The environmental impact of oil sands is estimated at over seven billion dollars a year today. As oil sand production is expected to expand, including into other countries, the total environmental costs are set to grow to nearly 25 billion dollars a year in 2030, assuming that much of the world's known reserves have been brought into production (World Energy Council, 2010).

Current and prospective oil sand reserves outside Canada include those found in Angola, China, Congo, Indonesia, Italy, Madagascar, Nigeria, Russia, Trinidad and Tobago and the US. Indonesia, Russia and the US have already commenced small-scale levels of production.

Canada is, and will continue to be, worst affected by the environmental impact of oil sands. By 2030, however, Madagascar, Congo and Nigeria are also expected to suffer significant costs linked to the exploitation of this resource, provided exploitation is carried out. The costs for Canada would grow from seven to 20 billion dollars a year by 2030.

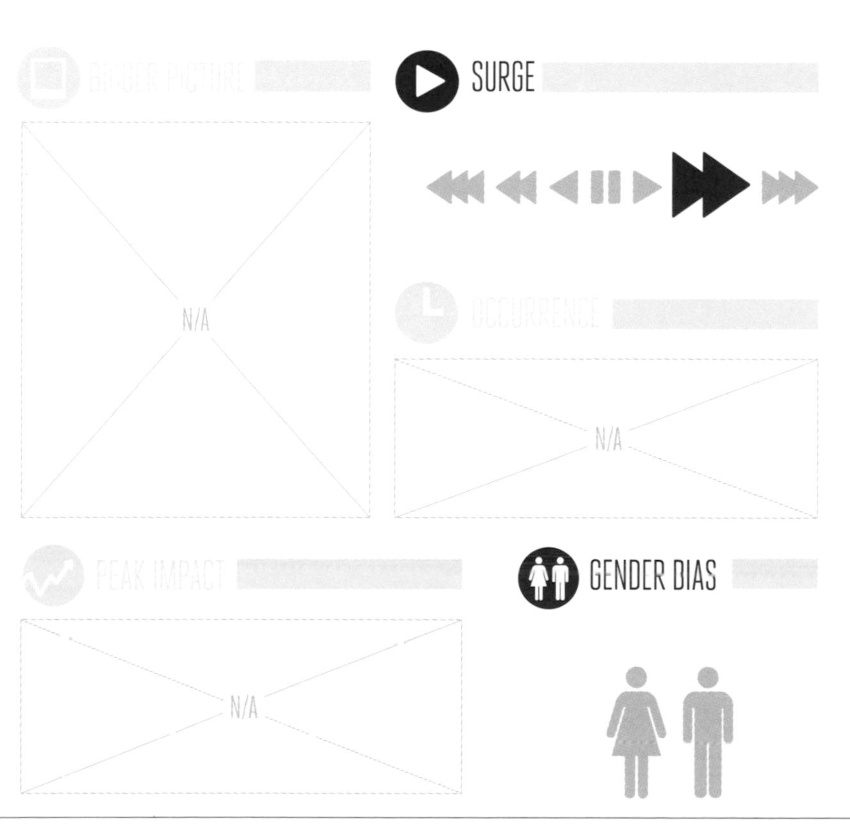

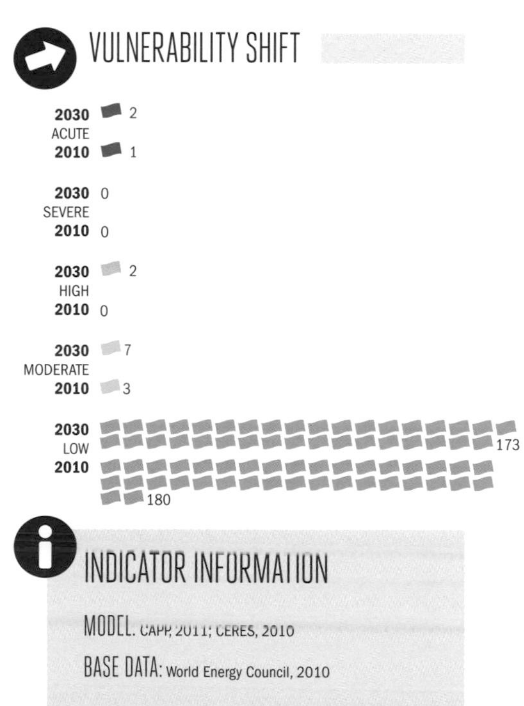

= 5 countries (rounded)

Acute Severe High Moderate Low

THE INDICATOR

The indicator measures the environmental costs of oil sands exploitation by the proxy of measuring the costs of accelerated clean-up, through "bioremediation", of toxic wastes generated. It is assumed that remediation costs are less than or equal to the environmental and health damages that would result if no measures were taken to protect the environment. Currently Canadian oil firms are subject to regulations that could be more forceful in ensuring strict environmental protection measures are complied with: to date the vast majority of toxic waste is untreated (Reuter et al., 2010). Only a small group of countries with significant reserves (four with existing production) are taken into account (World Energy Council, 2010). Environmental "bioremediation" costs per barrel of oil are assumed to be equal for all countries concerned, which could prove an estimation limitation. However, there are few precedents against which to assess the costs.

ESTIMATES COUNTRY-LEVEL IMPACT

COUNTRY	$ 2010	$ 2030	☢ 2010	☢ 2030
ACUTE				
Canada	7,250	20,000	150,000	300,000
Madagascar		750		2,000
HIGH				
Congo		150		650
Nigeria		1,500		5,000
MODERATE				
Angola		150		600
China		95		200
Indonesia	85	600	1,250	2,250
Italy		20		250
Russia	50	350	700	1,250
Trinidad and Tobago		30		100
United States	60	150	1,250	2,250
LOW				
Afghanistan				
Albania				
Algeria				
Antigua and Barbuda				
Argentina				
Armenia				
Australia				
Austria				
Azerbaijan				
Bahamas				
Bahrain				
Bangladesh				
Barbados				
Belarus				
Belgium				
Belize				
Benin				
Bhutan				
Bolivia				
Bosnia and Herzegovina				
Botswana				
Brazil				
Brunei				
Bulgaria				
Burkina Faso				
Burundi				
Cambodia				
Cameroon				
Cape Verde				
Central African Republic				
Chad				
Chile				
Colombia				
Comoros				
Costa Rica				
Cote d,Ivoire				
Croatia				
Cuba				
Cyprus				
Czech Republic				
Denmark				
Djibouti				
Dominica				
Dominican Republic				
DR Congo				
Ecuador				
Egypt				
El Salvador				
Equatorial Guinea				
Eritrea				
Estonia				
Ethiopia				
Fiji				
Finland				
France				
Gabon				
Gambia				
Georgia				
Germany				
Ghana				
Greece				
Grenada				
Guatemala				
Guinea				
Guinea-Bissau				
Guyana				
Haiti				
Honduras				
Hungary				
Iceland				
India				
Iran				
Iraq				
Ireland				
Israel				
Jamaica				
Japan				
Jordan				
Kazakhstan				
Kenya				
Kiribati				

$ Additional economic costs (million USD PPP) - yearly average

CARBON VULNERABILITY

Acute · Severe · High · Moderate · Low

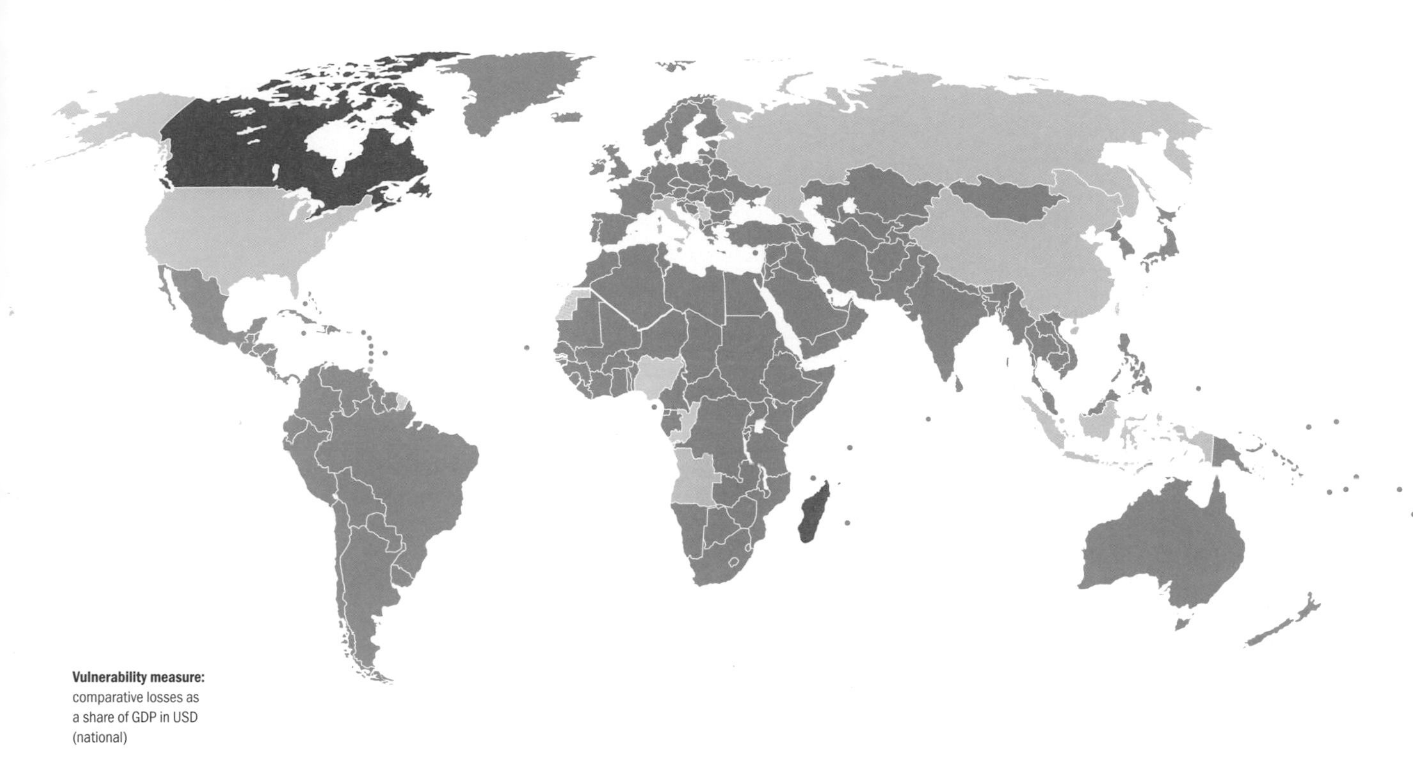

Vulnerability measure: comparative losses as a share of GDP in USD (national)

COUNTRY	$ 2010	$ 2030	☢ 2010	☢ 2030
Kuwait				
Kyrgyzstan				
Laos				
Latvia				
Lebanon				
Lesotho				
Liberia				
Libya				
Lithuania				
Luxembourg				
Macedonia				
Malawi				
Malaysia				
Maldives				
Mali				
Malta				
Marshall Islands				
Mauritania				
Mauritius				
Mexico				
Micronesia				
Moldova				
Mongolia				
Morocco				
Mozambique				
Myanmar				
Namibia				
Nepal				
Netherlands				
New Zealand				
Nicaragua				
Niger				

COUNTRY	$ 2010	$ 2030	☢ 2010	☢ 2030
North Korea				
Norway				
Oman				
Pakistan				
Palau				
Panama				
Papua New Guinea				
Paraguay				
Peru				
Philippines				
Poland				
Portugal				
Qatar				
Romania				
Rwanda				
Saint Lucia				
Saint Vincent				
Samoa				
Sao Tome and Principe				
Saudi Arabia				
Senegal				
Seychelles				
Sierra Leone				
Singapore				
Slovakia				
Slovenia				
Solomon Islands				
Somalia				
South Africa				
South Korea				
Spain				
Sri Lanka				

COUNTRY	$ 2010	$ 2030	☢ 2010	☢ 2030
Sudan/South Sudan				
Suriname				
Swaziland				
Sweden				
Switzerland				
Syria				
Tajikistan				
Tanzania				
Thailand				
Timor-Leste				
Togo				
Tonga				
Tunisia				
Turkey				
Turkmenistan				
Tuvalu				
Uganda				
Ukraine				
United Arab Emirates				
United Kingdom				
Uruguay				
Uzbekistan				
Vanuatu				
Venezuela				
Vietnam				
Yemen				
Zambia				
Zimbabwe				

☢ Tonnes of toxic waste (thousands) - yearly average

OIL SPILLS

ESTIMATES GLOBAL CARBON IMPACT

2010 EFFECT TODAY

USD LOSS PER YEAR **10 BILLION**

2030 EFFECT TOMORROW

USD LOSS PER YEAR **40 BILLION**

ECONOMIC IMPACT

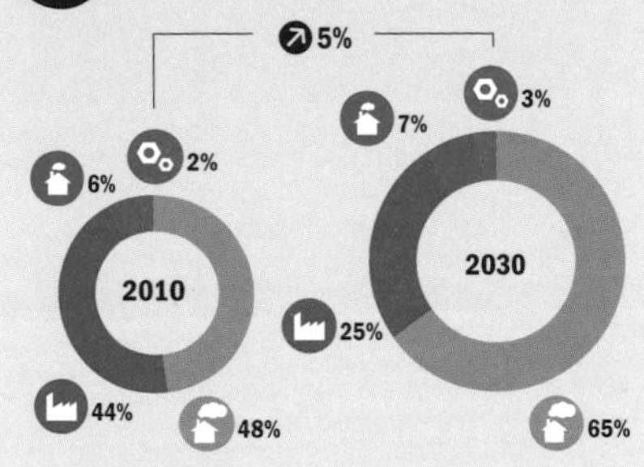

- Oil spills are one of the most graphic manifestations of the environmental risks run by a carbon economy reliant on fossil fuels
- Oil is expected to remain the world's principal fuel well beyond 2030: by then consumption is expected to be some 25% higher than today
- Despite the 2010 Gulf of Mexico disaster an increase in deep-water oil drilling is foreseen as the frontier for new petroleum reserves advances, pushing up against the limits of exploration and exploitation
- The dangers associated with deep-water drilling are expected to cause considerable further increases in the environmental and economic costs of oil spills

RELATIVE IMPACT

HOTSPOTS

2010	$	2030
3,250	KUWAIT	15,000
2,000	SAUDI ARABIA	8,000
3,500	UNITED STATES	6,250
350	ECUADOR	1,500
300	SINGAPORE	1,250

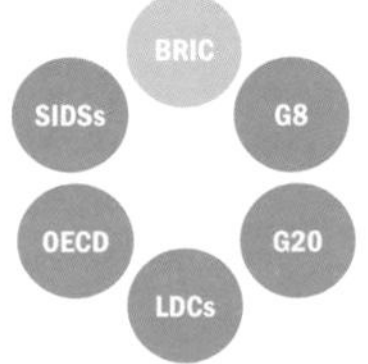

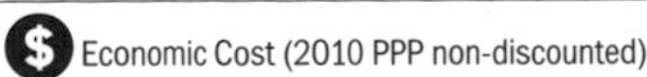

Developing Country Low Emitters | Developed
Developing Country High Emitters | Other Industrialized

$ = Losses per 10,000 USD of GDP

Change in relation to overall global population and/or GDP

$ = Millions of USD (2010 PPP non-discounted)

Improvements in operating safety leading to decreased risks of oil spills in recent decades have occurred in parallel to increases in consumption and new risks associated with deep-water drilling now expected to lead to even greater damage in the years to come in spite of progress made. The April, 2010 BP Gulf of Mexico oil disaster, triggered by an explosion on the ultra deep-water Macondo Well rig, released five million barrels of crude oil into the sea. The unabated stream flowed for months and led to tens of billions of dollars of direct economic damage and profound ecological consequences. Half a year after the spill 32,000 square miles of sea remained closed with much of the American fishing industry unable to operate (Graham and Reilly, 2011). The oil firms themselves and their shareholders also suffered: BP saw its share price fall by more than half in a matter of months and is still to recover as tens of billions of dollars in value were erased forever (Grant, 2010). Analysis has shown that similar incidents cause affected companies roughly 10% losses in market value six months after such accidents (Laguna and Capelle-Blancard, 2010). From 2002 to 2015, deep-water oil exploitation is expected to emerge as a major source of fuel, growing from 2% to around 12% of all global oil production (Douglas-Westwood, 2010). With it the danger of repeats of the Gulf of Mexico disaster will only increase: the risk of abnormal incidents on offshore facilities triples for deep-water oil platforms operating in water depths below 300 metres or 1,000 ft (Cohen, 2011).

HAZARD MECHANISM

The vast majority of oil spills occur in the world's oceans as the principal global energy source – oil – is transported to feed a worldwide demand for a product with highly restricted geographical availability (ERC, 2009; US EIA, 2011). Oil spills occur along global supply chains between key source and destination nodes. When an oil spill occurs there is a predictable and measurable relationship between the amount of surface water contaminated and a corresponding economic loss divided between environmental or biodiversity costs, such as the decimation of birds and other local wildlife populations, socio-economic costs, such as the loss of fishing revenues, and spill response costs, which include the cost of clean-up (Etkin, 2004). The level of economic costs ultimately experienced is determined by factors such as the location of the spills (far offshore, or in a coastal area), the type of oil released into the environment (more viscous and therefore more costly to remove, or vice versa), and environmental conditions prevailing in the days and weeks following the incident (such as ocean currents that disperse or concentrate oil slicks) (McCay, 2004).

IMPACTS

The global impact of oil spills on the world economy is estimated at 12 billion dollars a year today, and is expected to nearly triple to more than 30 billion dollars a year in 2030 but with losses remaining stable as a share of GDP.

On the basis of historical trends in oil spills only a limited number of countries are expected to suffer disproportionately from the growing risk of oil spills. Some 25 countries show globally significant vulnerabilities to oil spills, each either major oil producing or consuming countries, global supply chain nodes like Singapore or neighbouring states. Middle East countries such as Kuwait and Saudi Arabia top the list of those countries most vulnerable to oil spills. The greatest share of effects is estimated to impact Kuwait, Russia, Saudi Arabia and the US, each suffering more than one billion dollars in average annual losses in 2010. These cost estimations are averages, so that one billion dollars of losses in one year might represent a 20 billion dollar loss once every 20 years.

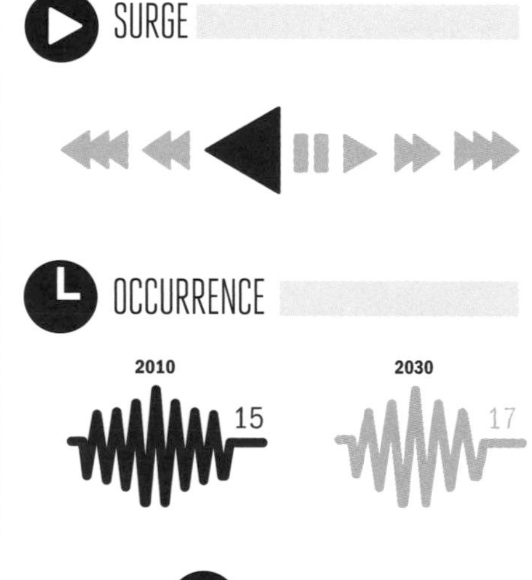

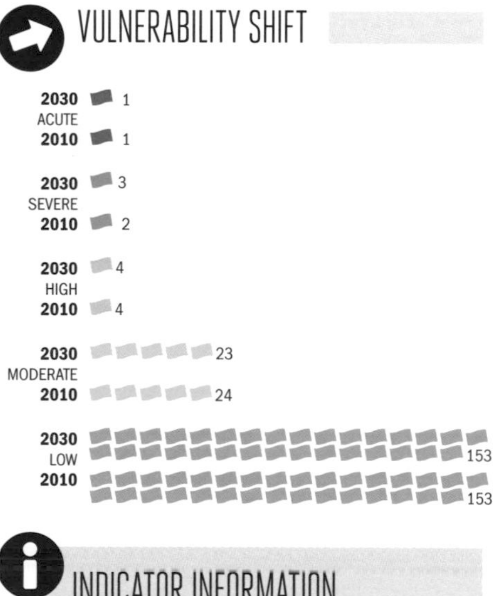

PEAK IMPACT

N/A

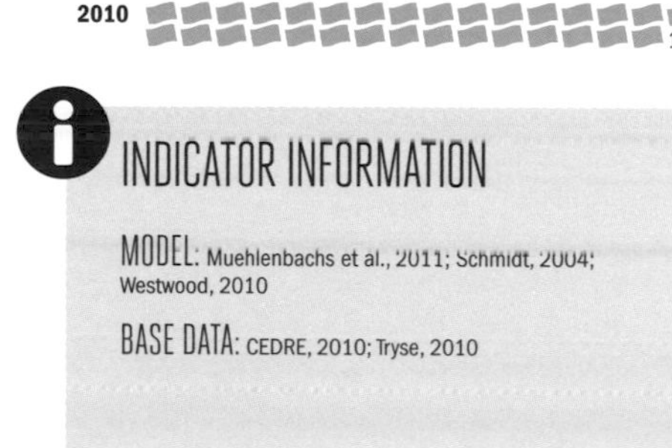

INDICATOR INFORMATION
MODEL: Muehlenbachs et al., 2011; Schmidt, 2004; Westwood, 2010
BASE DATA: CEDRE, 2010; Tryse, 2010

Number of major oil spills per decade (over 10,000 tones of oil spilled)

= 5 countries (rounded)

Acute Severe High Moderate Low

THE INDICATOR

The indicator measures the costs of oil spills in terms of environmental damage and is based on a pooled database of information on global oil spill incidents (Etkin, 2004; Tryse, 2010; CEDRE, 2012; Center for Tankship Excellence, 2012). Costs are assumed to affect countries listed as sites for oil spills in the past, which biases the predicted distribution of oil spill disasters. These might otherwise only be estimated in a semi-random manner, since each oil spill event is unique and random. It also does not take account of shifts in production that could occur over the next 20 years as new countries discover and expand exploitation, in particular of large scale offshore oil reserves: Brazil, for instance, is expected to become the world's fourth largest non-Organisation of Petroleum Exporting Countries (OPEC) supplier of conventional oil by 2035 (US EIA, 2011). Cost estimates of spills have been based on incidents in the US, with costs for other countries determined in relation to GDP.

ESTIMATES COUNTRY-LEVEL IMPACT

COUNTRY	$ 2010	$ 2030	■ 2010	■ 2030
ACUTE				
Kuwait	3,250	15,000	8,250	9,000
SEVERE				
Ecuador	350	1,500	2,750	3,000
Saudi Arabia	2,000	8,000	8,250	9,000
Uzbekistan	250	850	4,250	4,750
HIGH				
Angola	250	850	4,250	4,500
Lebanon	65	250	400	450
Mozambique	20	65	1,250	1,250
Singapore	300	1,250	500	500
MODERATE				
Australia	100	200	550	600
Brazil	5	20	50	55
Canada	20	35	80	85
China	60	350	600	650
France	85	150	400	400
India	1	5	15	15
Ireland	5	5	15	15
Italy	450	750	2,250	2,500
Japan	60	90	300	300
Mexico	5	25	40	45
Nigeria	40	150	1,000	1,250
Norway	20	30	75	85
Pakistan	25	100	450	500
Philippines	1	5	20	20
Russia	300	1,000	1,500	1,750
South Africa	5	10	30	35
South Korea	55	250	150	150
Spain	500	800	2,250	2,500
Ukraine	1	5	10	10
United Arab Emirates	50	200	250	250
United Kingdom	650	1,000	2,500	2,750
United States	3,500	6,250	15,000	15,000
Yemen	10	30	200	200
LOW				
Afghanistan				
Albania				
Algeria				
Antigua and Barbuda				
Argentina				
Armenia				
Austria				
Azerbaijan				
Bahamas				
Bahrain				
Bangladesh				
Barbados				
Belarus				
Belgium				
Belize				
Benin				
Bhutan				
Bolivia				
Bosnia and Herzegovina				
Botswana				
Brunei				
Bulgaria				
Burkina Faso				
Burundi				
Cambodia				
Cameroon				
Cape Verde				
Central African Republic				
Chad				
Chile				
Colombia				
Comoros				
Congo				
Costa Rica				
Cote d,Ivoire				
Croatia				
Cuba				
Cyprus				
Czech Republic				
Denmark				
Djibouti				
Dominica				
Dominican Republic				
DR Congo				
Egypt				
El Salvador				
Equatorial Guinea				
Eritrea				
Estonia				
Ethiopia				
Fiji				
Finland				
Gabon				
Gambia				
Georgia				
Germany				
Ghana				
Greece				
Grenada				
Guatemala				

$ Additional economic costs (million USD PPP) - yearly average

CARBON VULNERABILITY

Acute Severe High Moderate Low

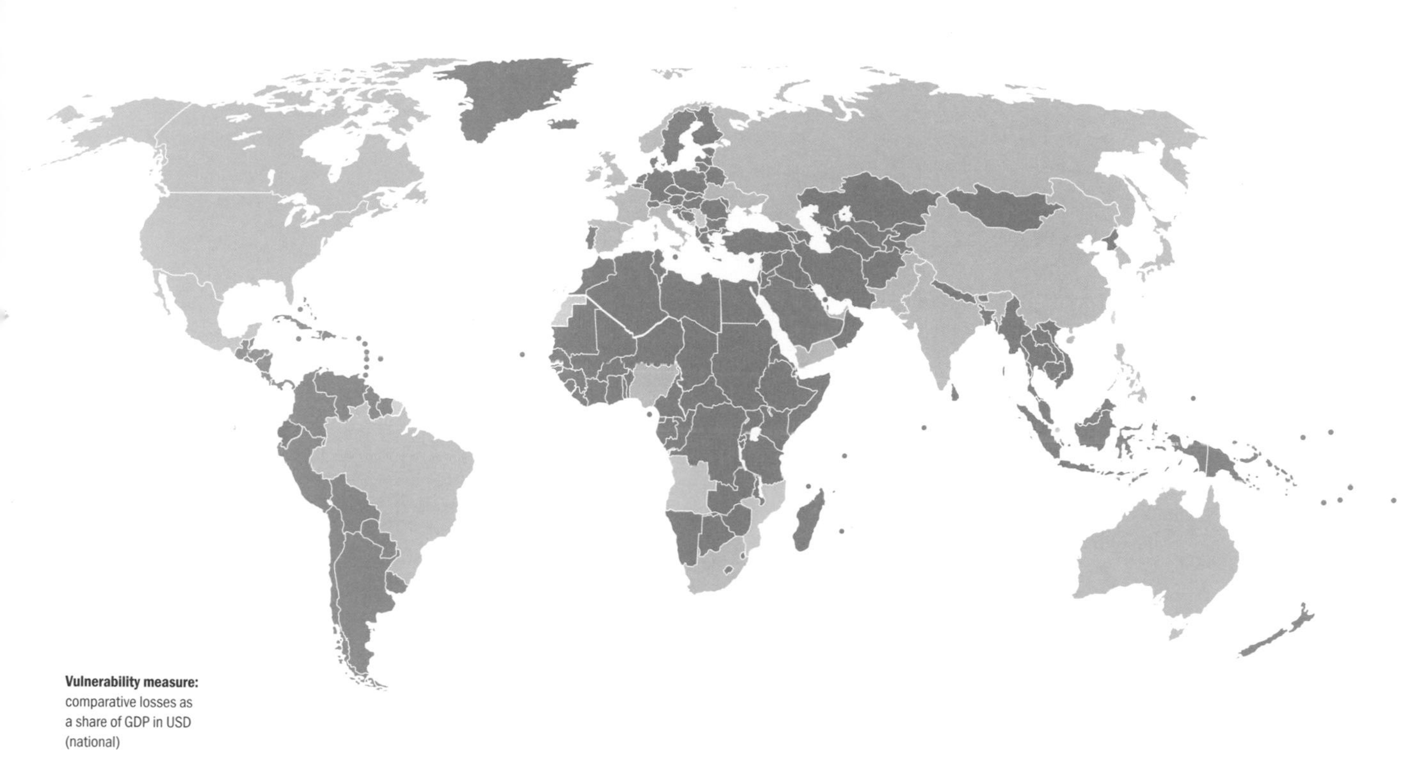

Vulnerability measure: comparative losses as a share of GDP in USD (national)

COUNTRY	$ 2010	$ 2030	Oil 2010	Oil 2030
Guinea				
Guinea-Bissau				
Guyana				
Haiti				
Honduras				
Hungary				
Iceland				
Indonesia				
Iran				
Iraq				
Israel				
Jamaica				
Jordan				
Kazakhstan				
Kenya				
Kiribati				
Kyrgyzstan				
Laos				
Latvia				
Lesotho				
Liberia				
Libya				
Lithuania				
Luxembourg				
Macedonia				
Madagascar				
Malawi				
Malaysia				
Maldives				
Mali				
Malta				
Marshall Islands				

COUNTRY	$ 2010	$ 2030	Oil 2010	Oil 2030
Mauritania				
Mauritius				
Micronesia				
Moldova				
Mongolia				
Morocco				
Myanmar				
Namibia				
Nepal				
Netherlands				
New Zealand				
Nicaragua				
Niger				
North Korea				
Oman				
Palau				
Panama				
Papua New Guinea				
Paraguay				
Peru				
Poland				
Portugal				
Qatar				
Romania				
Rwanda				
Saint Lucia				
Saint Vincent				
Samoa				
Sao Tome and Principe				
Senegal				
Seychelles				
Sierra Leone				

COUNTRY	$ 2010	$ 2030	Oil 2010	Oil 2030
Slovakia				
Slovenia				
Solomon Islands				
Somalia				
Sri Lanka				
Sudan/South Sudan				
Suriname				
Swaziland				
Sweden				
Switzerland				
Syria				
Tajikistan				
Tanzania				
Thailand				
Timor-Leste				
Togo				
Tonga				
Trinidad and Tobago				
Tunisia				
Turkey				
Turkmenistan				
Tuvalu				
Uganda				
Uruguay				
Vanuatu				
Venezuela				
Vietnam				
Zambia				
Zimbabwe				

Gallons of oil spilled (thousands) - yearly average

HABITAT CHANGE

BIODIVERSITY

CORROSION

WATER

300 BILLION LOSS 2010
1,750 BILLION LOSS 2030
1 BILLION LOSS 2010
5 BILLION LOSS 2030
5 BILLION LOSS 2010
10 BILLION LOSS 2030

BIODIVERSITY

ESTIMATES GLOBAL CARBON IMPACT

2010 EFFECT TODAY

USD LOSS PER YEAR **300** BILLION

2030 EFFECT TOMORROW

USD LOSS PER YEAR **1,750** BILLION

ECONOMIC IMPACT

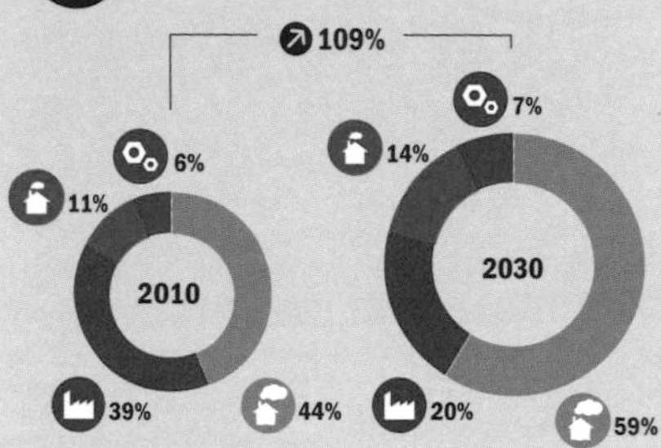

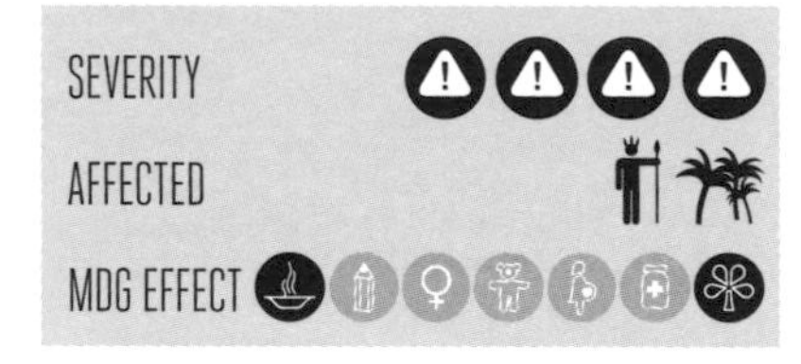

- Natural resources support businesses, communities and economies but are rarely accounted for in company balance sheets or GDP calculations
- Emissions of greenhouse gases, especially toxic ground-level ozone and acid rain, are causing significant losses to biodiversity, much of which will add invisible costs to businesses and economies around the world
- Countries with the richest ecosystems will suffer these effects the most
- Reducing emissions of sulphur and sources of ozone as a priority in the energy, transport and agricultural sectors forms the basis of any plan for stemming these losses

RELATIVE IMPACT

HOTSPOTS

Country	2010	2030
BRAZIL	35,000	300,000
USA	80,000	250,000
CHINA	20,000	200,000
RUSSIA	15,000	100,000
INDONESIA	10,000	90,000

GEOPOLITICAL VULNERABILITY

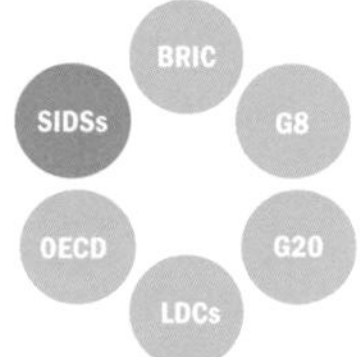

$ Economic Cost (2010 PPP non-discounted)
Developing Country Low Emitters · Developed
Developing Country High Emitters · Other Industrialized

$ = Losses per 1,000 USD of GDP

Change in relation to overall global population and/or GDP

 = Millions of USD (2010 PPP non-discounted)

Global biodiversity is undergoing a period of phenomenal decline across all major land-based and aquatic ecosystems (WWF, 2012). Measured in economic terms the costs of decline in global biodiversity have been estimated at close to seven trillion dollars today, or around 10% of global GDP (UNEP, 2010). This represents the impact of the sum of human activities and changes made to the environment. Carbon economy and GHG emissions that could be eliminated through targeted mitigation efforts are estimated to contribute a modest share of these costs. The effects of climate change further affect biodiversity independently from the direct effects of pollution. Solving climate change will not resolve the biodiversity crisis facing the planet but it will significantly help.

HAZARD MECHANISM

Biodiversity comprises the totality of all genes, species, and ecosystems. When healthy, ecosystems provide so-called ecosystem services to economic systems in abundance: including water catchment, pest control, pollination, air purification, heat regulation, drought stabilization or numerous other values (Mace et al. in Hassan et al. (eds.), 2005). Businesses and communities operating in eco-service abundant areas ultimately reap the benefits through lower operating costs or higher productivity (Costanza et al., 1997; Bayon and Jenkins, 2010). Industrial or transport-related emissions, such as high-sulphur-content acid rain and ground-level ozone, are toxic for plants and have a negative effect on primary productivity, affecting plant growth and health. That negative effect is transferred to the whole ecosystem and damages the abundance and quality of ecosystem services generated. Communities, businesses and economies ultimately suffer these losses through reduced prosperity and returns to investors (UNEP, 2010).

IMPACTS

The global impact of GHG emissions on biodiversity is causing large-scale and widespread losses, estimated at over 290 billion dollars for 2010. As the carbon economy is expected to expand over the next 20 years, these losses will climb to 1.7 trillion dollars by 2030, doubling in scale in proportion to GDP. Around 20 countries are acutely vulnerable to these effects, all tropical developing countries with highly abundant ecosystems in Africa, Latin America and Southeast Asia. The impacts will undermine development, especially since lowest income groups are more dependent on ecosystem services, such as water treatment, pollination and pest control. The greatest overall effects, however, are suffered by the world's most powerful economies: the US, China, Russia and Brazil, each with losses numbering in the tens of billions of dollars. The US is estimated to already suffer 80 billion dollars' worth of lost biodiversity potential in the year 2010.

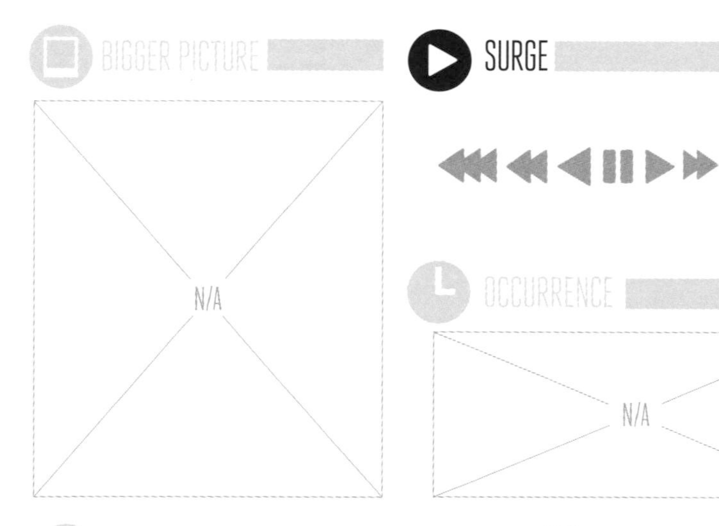

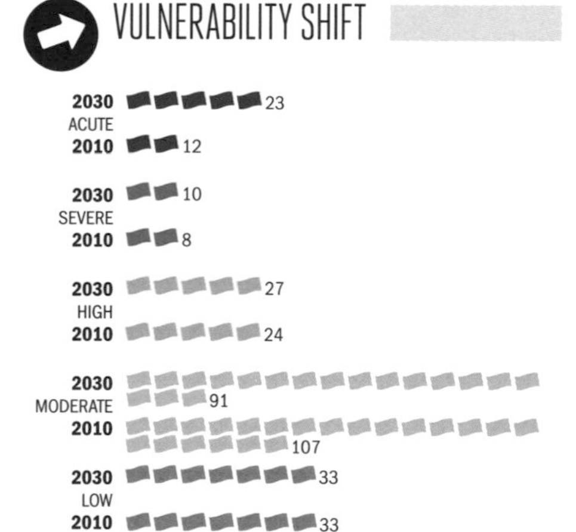

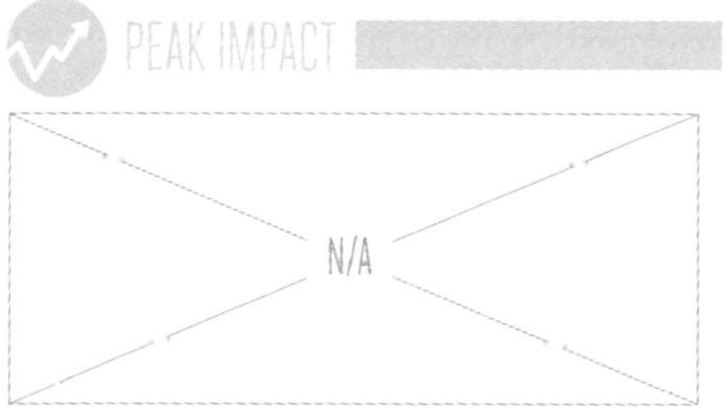

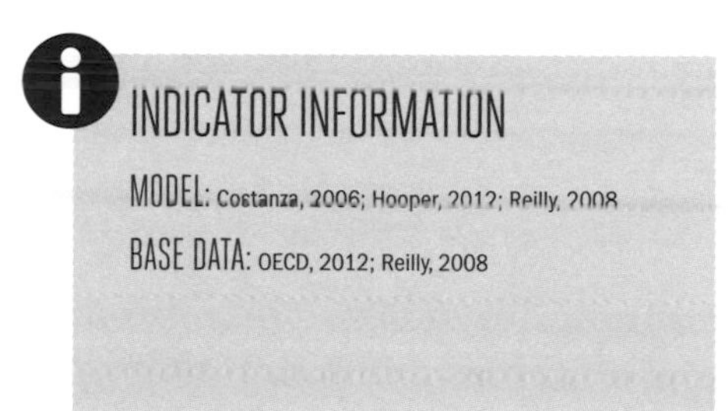

= 5 countries (rounded)

Acute Severe High Moderate Low

THE INDICATOR

The indicator measures losses in biodiversity richness resulting from ground-level ozone toxicity and acid rain and their effect on net primary productivity (Reilly, 2007; Hooper et al., 2012). The change is mapped on the basis of vegetation distribution and translated into losses in ecosystem services value per hectare per year (Costanza et al., 2007). While emissions intensities and projections are fairly reliable, the indicator is very sensitive to changes in the relationship between acid rain and ozone and their effects on primary productivity. Vegetation changes introduce further uncertainty (Ruesch and Gibbs, 2008). Overall however, the large difference between countries currently rich in biodiversity - those countries with the most at stake - and those with comparatively little, is a principal factor in determining vulnerability.

ESTIMATES COUNTRY-LEVEL IMPACT

COUNTRY	$ 2010	$ 2030
ACUTE		
Angola	4,500	30,000
Belize	150	1,000
Bolivia	4,000	30,000
Botswana	600	4,000
Brunei	700	5,500
Cameroon	1,250	7,750
Central African Republic	400	2,500
Congo	1,250	7,250
DR Congo	1,000	6,500
Equatorial Guinea	1,250	7,250
Gabon	5,250	35,000
Guinea	300	2,000
Guinea-Bissau	55	350
Guyana	2,250	15,000
Laos	350	3,750
Liberia	55	350
Nicaragua	400	3,000
Papua New Guinea	1,500	15,000
Paraguay	1,500	10,000
Peru	7,250	55,000
Suriname	1,250	9,000
Timor-Leste	150	1,500
Zambia	600	3,750
SEVERE		
Argentina	9,000	70,000
Bhutan	55	450
Brazil	35,000	300,000
Cote d,Ivoire	700	4,500
Madagascar	250	1,750
Malaysia	7,750	60,000
Mongolia	150	1,750
Mozambique	450	2,750
Panama	700	5,250
Sierra Leone	85	550
HIGH		
Australia	8,500	25,000
Benin	150	950
Cambodia	300	3,500
Canada	10,000	30,000
Chad	100	650
Chile	1,750	15,000
Colombia	5,500	40,000
Comoros	5	25
Costa Rica	250	2,000
Ecuador	1,000	8,000
Finland	850	2,500
Gambia	20	100
Ghana	600	4,000
Guatemala	350	2,750
Honduras	400	3,250
Indonesia	10,000	90,000
Mexico	8,000	60,000
Namibia	150	1,000
New Zealand	1,000	3,000
Philippines	1,750	15,000
Russia	15,000	100,000
Tanzania	500	3,000
Togo	45	300
Uganda	200	1,500
United States	80,000	250,000
Uruguay	200	1,500
Venezuela	4,000	30,000
MODERATE		
Afghanistan	10	65
Albania	30	200
Algeria	60	450
Armenia	15	85
Austria	250	800
Azerbaijan	45	300
Bangladesh	55	400
Belarus	250	1,750
Belgium	55	150
Bosnia and Herzegovina	50	350
Bulgaria	150	1,000
Burkina Faso	15	90
Burundi	1	10
China	20,000	200,000
Croatia	70	500
Cuba	250	1,750
Cyprus	5	15
Czech Republic	100	800
Denmark	55	150
Djibouti		1
Egypt	10	80
El Salvador	200	1,250
Eritrea	1	5
Estonia	35	250
Ethiopia	95	650
France	950	3,000
Georgia	65	450
Germany	750	2,250
Greece	350	1,000
Hungary	95	650
India	2,750	20,000

$ Additional economic costs (million USD PPP) - yearly average

CARBON VULNERABILITY

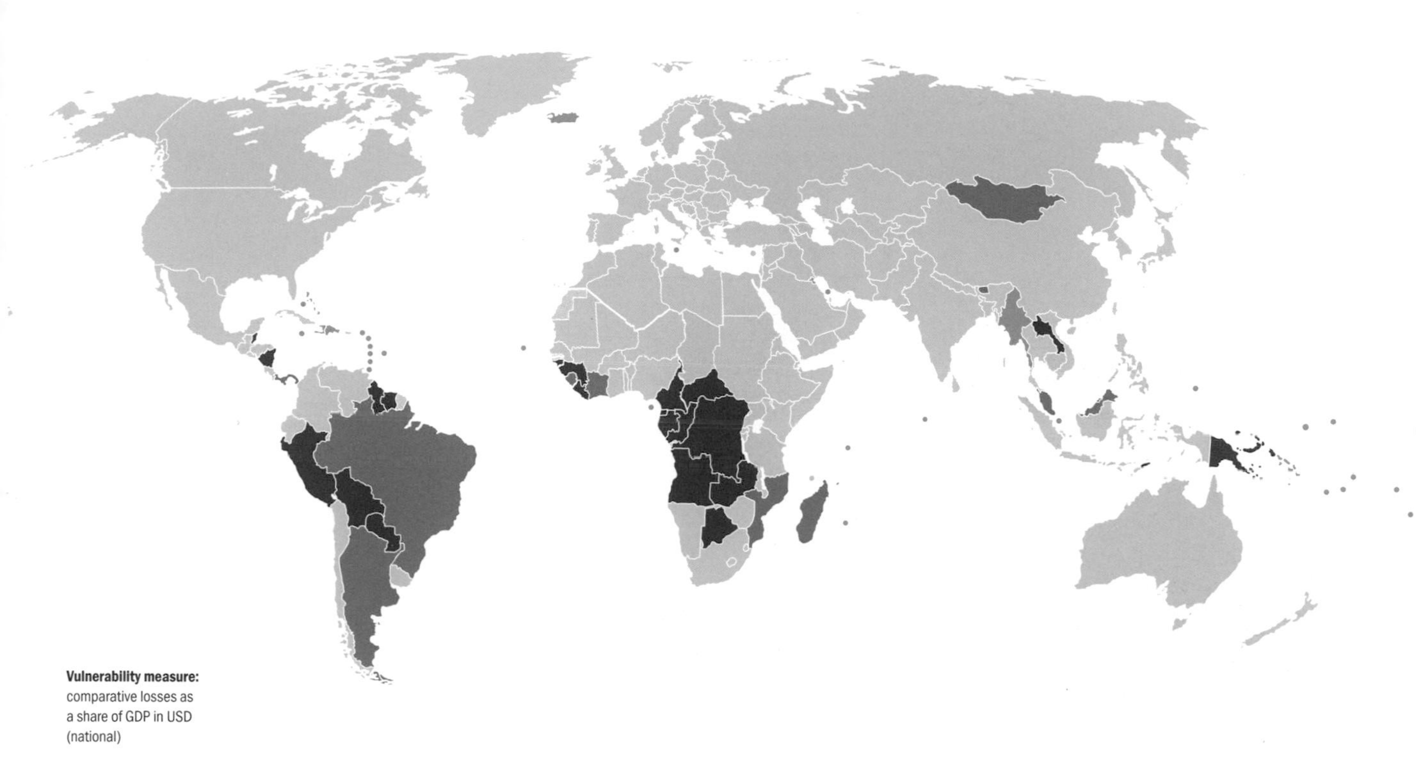

Vulnerability measure: comparative losses as a share of GDP in USD (national)

COUNTRY	2010	2030
Iran	550	4,250
Iraq	10	85
Ireland	100	350
Israel	10	70
Italy	550	1,750
Japan	5,250	15,000
Jordan	1	5
Kazakhstan	350	2,250
Kenya	100	650
Kyrgyzstan	25	150
Latvia	40	300
Lebanon	10	70
Lesotho	5	25
Libya	15	150
Lithuania	65	450
Luxembourg	5	15
Macedonia	35	250
Malawi	35	250
Mali	30	200
Mauritania	10	55
Moldova	10	50
Morocco	35	250
Nepal	150	1,000
Netherlands	45	150
Niger	5	40
Nigeria	900	6,000
North Korea	15	150
Norway	450	1,250
Oman	10	70
Pakistan	100	800
Poland	400	2,750
Portugal	250	750

COUNTRY	2010	2030
Romania	200	1,500
Rwanda	1	15
Saudi Arabia	35	250
Senegal	60	400
Slovakia	100	750
Slovenia	50	350
Somalia	10	50
South Africa	1,500	9,000
South Korea	350	2,750
Spain	1,250	3,500
Sri Lanka	300	2,250
Sudan/South Sudan	40	300
Swaziland	5	45
Sweden	1,000	3,250
Switzerland	85	250
Syria	5	50
Tajikistan	10	70
Thailand	1,750	15,000
Tunisia	20	150
Turkey	650	2,000
Turkmenistan	40	250
Ukraine	350	2,250
United Arab Emirates	5	30
United Kingdom	360	1,000
Uzbekistan	20	150
Vietnam	800	8,750
Yemen	15	100
Zimbabwe	30	200
LOW		
Antigua and Barbuda		
Bahamas		
Bahrain		

COUNTRY	2010	2030
Barbados		
Cape Verde		
Dominica		
Dominican Republic		
Fiji		
Grenada		
Haiti		
Iceland		
Jamaica		
Kiribati		
Kuwait		
Maldives		
Malta		
Marshall Islands		
Mauritius		
Micronesia		
Myanmar		
Palau		
Qatar		
Saint Lucia		
Saint Vincent		
Samoa		
Sao Tome and Principe		
Seychelles		
Singapore		
Solomon Islands		
Tonga		
Trinidad and Tobago		
Tuvalu		
Vanuatu		

CORROSION

ESTIMATES GLOBAL CARBON IMPACT

2010 EFFECT TODAY

USD LOSS PER YEAR **1 BILLION**

2030 EFFECT TOMORROW

USD LOSS PER YEAR **5 BILLION**

ECONOMIC IMPACT

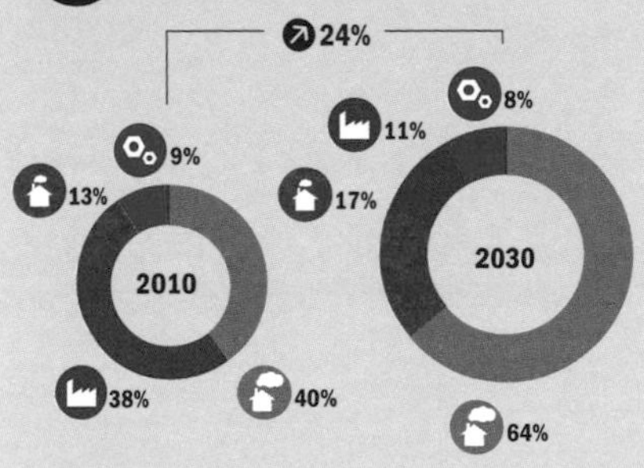

➔ Air pollution from industrial, residential and transport emissions causes costly damage to infrastructure, vehicles and other materials

➔ The corrosion effect is most severe where industrialized or newly-industrializing countries lack controls on harmful emissions such as sulphur dioxide and that rely intensively on coal power generation, an important contributor to acid rain

➔ Affected countries can take inspiration from regulations put into effect in developed countries since the 1990s that have met with considerable success in reducing the amount of acid rain and damages to infrastructure as well as health and the environment

RELATIVE IMPACT

$$$$$$$$$$$$$$$$$$$$$$$$$$$$$$$$$$$$$$ $$$ 2010

361 | 22

$$ $$$ 2030

419 | 22

HOTSPOTS

2010	$	2030
400	CHINA	2,250
100	INDIA	550
80	SOUTH KOREA	450
60	RUSSIA	250
200	UNITED STATES	200

GEOPOLITICAL VULNERABILITY

$ Economic Cost (2010 PPP non-discounted)
Developing Country Low Emitters | Developed
Developing Country High Emitters | Other Industrialized

$ = Losses per 10 million USD of GDP

Change in relation to overall global population and/or GDP

$ = Millions of USD (2010 PPP non-discounted)

Air pollution and the acid rain and smog associated with it accelerate the corrosion of materials and infrastructure, in particular metals. The impact of acid rain is visible on the green streaking of bronze monuments in major metropolitan areas of industrialized countries where it has leached at their protective patina (Bernardi et al., 2009). The US EPA estimated costs to Americans from acid-proofing the paint of automobiles at 60 million dollars a year (US EPA, 2010). In the 1970s, not one government had regulations on air pollution aimed at reducing acid rain. Since the 1990s, however, many governments have implemented regulations that have drastically reduced the environmental impact of the worst forms of acid rain and smog in North America and Europe. Those regulations have cost effectively contributed to clean air in a testament to the economic and social viability of such actions to reduce the impact of pollution (Munton et al. in Young (ed.), 1999; Burns et al., 2011).

It has long been recognized that where newly industrializing and transition economies lack those same regulations, especially where coal combustion is unrestrained, acid rain and smog present a serious challenge (Hart, 1996). These effects of pollution also create major economic concerns for many countries. The World Bank estimated that in 2003 alone corrosion of material and infrastructure due to acid rain cost southern China hundreds of millions of dollars (World Bank, 2005). Places like Nigeria are yet to show any significant impacts, although continued and unregulated industrialization in fast emerging economies can only lead to damages similar to those seen elsewhere (Okafor et al., 2009).

HAZARD MECHANISM

Air pollutants such as sulphur dioxide, nitrogen dioxide and other gases such as ozone derived from industrial, residential and transport emissions, especially coal burning, become corrosive when they dissolve in rain or otherwise come into contact with buildings, cars and other infrastructure. Ordinary water has a pH value of 7, but ordinary rain is more acidic at a pH of 5.6 because of ambient CO_2. Even in the US today, rain rendered more acidic through air pollution can lower pH values to 4.3 (US EPA, 2007). Elevated levels of sulphur dioxide and other harmful pollutants accelerate corrosion of a wide range of metals, which can cause cosmetic and structural damage (Mellanby (ed.), 1988). Corrosion rates in metals such as steel accelerate as exposure time grows and resistance falls (Lin et al., 2011b).

Concrete is also vulnerable to degradation, which raises concerns for the vast new quantities of infrastructure being erected in areas with highly concentrated acid rains such as China (Shah et al., 2000; Jiangang, 2011; Huifang Guo et al., 2012). Historic buildings are often especially vulnerable, in particular when stones with low acidity resistance, such as limestone, have been used in construction (Camuffo, 1992). Infrastructure under ground, such as pipes, can also be damaged if acid rain affects soil pH (Ismail and El Shamy, 2009).

IMPACTS

Globally, the annual cost of damages to materials and infrastructure from acid rain corrosion is estimated to have been 1.5 billion dollars for the year 2010, with that figure expected to grow slightly as a share of GDP to 5 billion dollars a year by 2030.

The countries most severely affected include parts of East and South Asia, Eastern Europe and the Middle East, including China, India, Russia and Bangladesh. China has the largest overall losses, estimated to reach over 2 billion dollars a year by 2030. Other large-scale losses occur in India, South Korea, Russia, the US and Japan.

In general, newly-industrializing and fast-emerging economies as well as transition economies, such as Bulgaria, are particularly vulnerable, while developed countries with emission regulations and lower-income countries with little industry are less affected or unaffected.

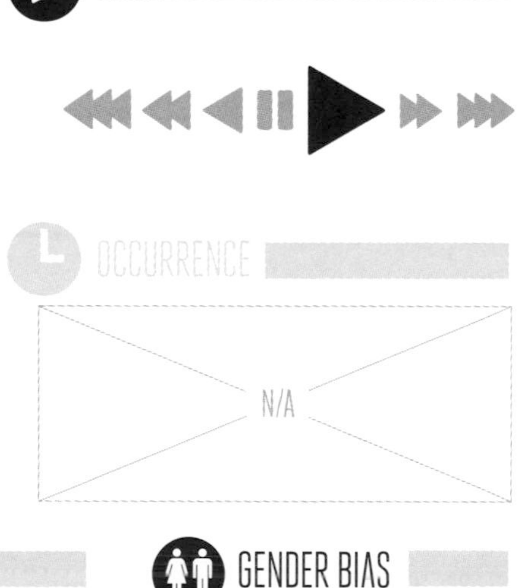

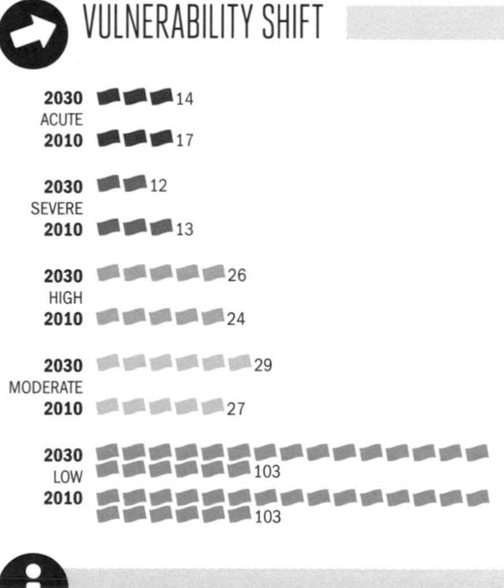

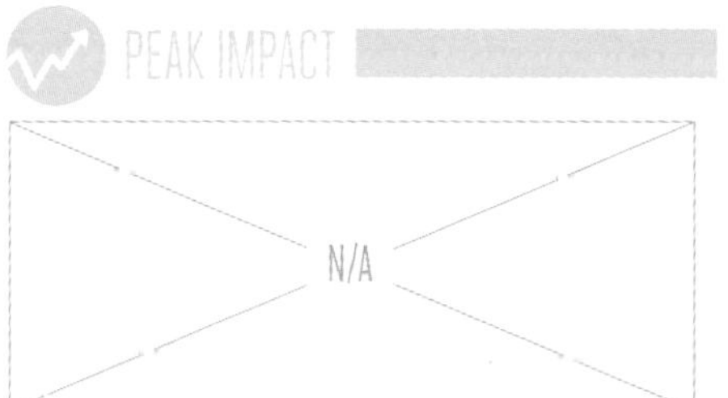

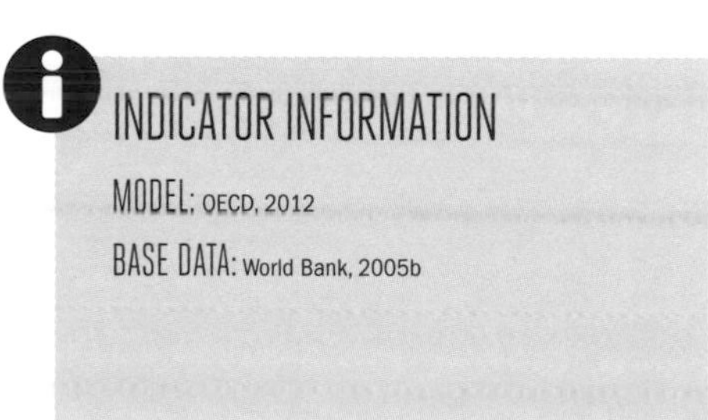

= 5 countries (rounded)

Acute Severe High Moderate Low

THE INDICATOR

The indicator measures the cost of the corrosive effect of acid rain on materials and infrastructure. Emissions of sulphur dioxide (SO2) are used to determine the level of acid rain, and that level is translated into damages according to intensity on the basis of a World Bank study in China and the assumed relation of infrastructure density to population density (EDGAR, 2012; World Bank, 2005; Hoekstra et al., 2010). Emissions were projected to 2030 on the basis of regional changes estimated by the Organization for Economic Co-operation and Development (OECD, 2012). The main weaknesses of the indicator relate to the extrapolation of the damage from a study in just one country and the simplified assumptions relating to infrastructure.

ESTIMATES COUNTRY-LEVEL IMPACT

COUNTRY	$ 2010	$ 2030
ACUTE		
Bangladesh	5	25
Bulgaria	5	10
China	400	2,250
Egypt	15	80
India	100	550
Israel	15	35
Japan	150	150
Jordan	1	10
Lebanon	10	40
Macedonia	1	1
Portugal	15	15
Russia	60	250
South Korea	80	450
Tunisia	1	10
SEVERE		
Albania	1	1
Belgium	15	15
Bosnia and Herzegovina	1	1
Hungary	5	15
Pakistan	10	40
Poland	20	50
Romania	5	15
South Africa	10	35
Syria	1	10
Thailand	10	45
Turkey	10	20
Ukraine	5	20
HIGH		
Algeria	1	5
Azerbaijan	1	1
Cameroon	1	1
Croatia	1	1
Czech Republic	5	10
Denmark	1	1
France	20	20
Germany	40	40
Indonesia	5	30
Iran	10	40
Iraq	1	5
Kazakhstan	1	5
Mexico	15	35
Morocco	1	5
Netherlands	5	5
Nigeria	1	5
North Korea		1
Oman		1
Slovakia	1	5
Slovenia	1	1
Tajikistan		
United Kingdom	40	45
United States	200	200
Venezuela	1	10
Vietnam	1	20
Zimbabwe		
MODERATE		
Argentina		1
Australia	1	1
Austria	1	1
Belarus	1	1
Brazil	5	15
Canada	5	5
Chile	1	1
Colombia	1	1
Estonia		
Finland		
Georgia		
Greece	1	1
Ireland		
Italy	10	10
Kyrgyzstan		
Latvia		
Libya		1
Malaysia	1	5
Peru		
Philippines	1	5
Saudi Arabia	1	10
Spain	5	5
Sweden	1	1
Switzerland		
Turkmenistan		
United Arab Emirates		1
Uzbekistan	1	1
Yemen		1
Zambia		
LOW		
Afghanistan		
Angola		
Antigua and Barbuda		
Armenia		
Bahamas		
Bahrain		
Barbados		
Belize		
Benin		
Bhutan		

$ Additional economic costs (million USD PPP) - yearly average

CARBON VULNERABILITY

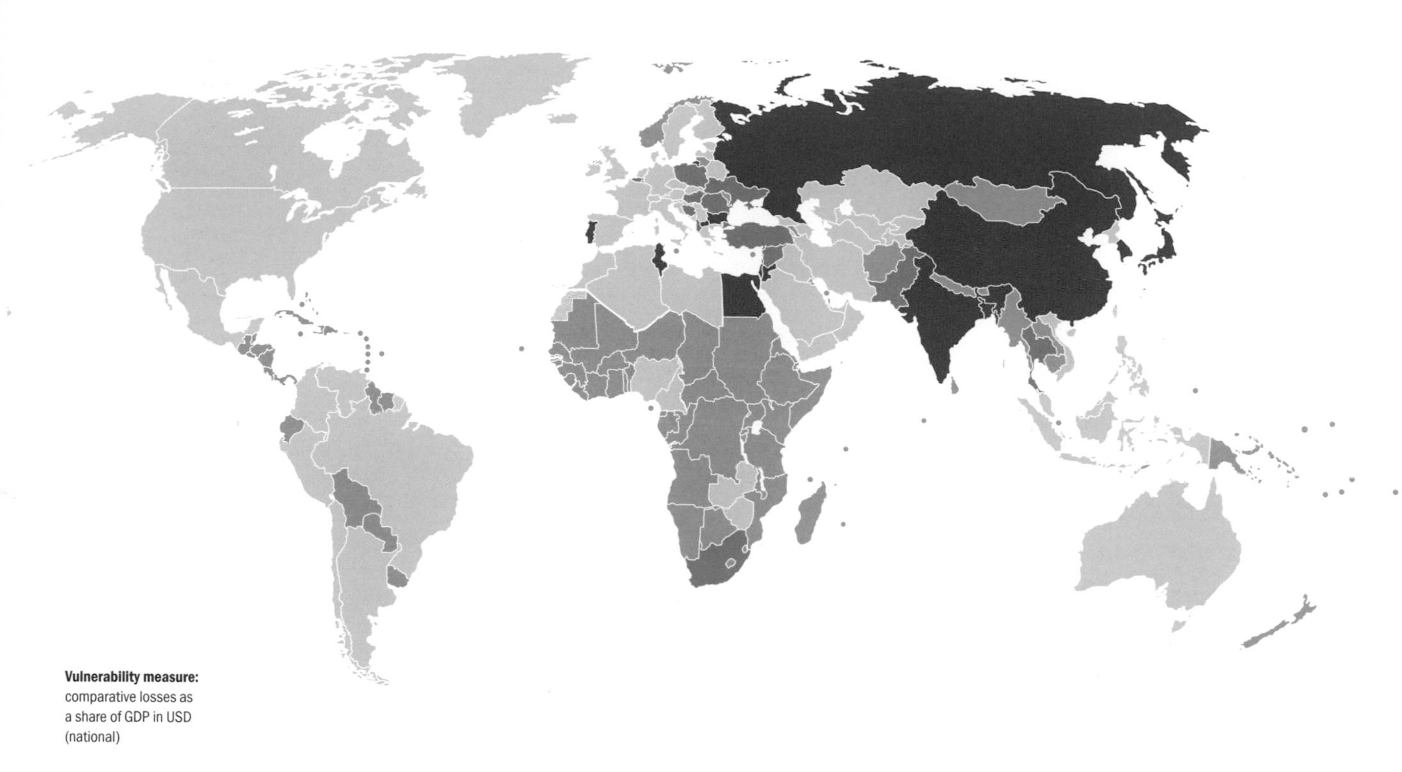

Vulnerability measure: comparative losses as a share of GDP in USD (national)

COUNTRY	2010	2030
Bolivia		
Botswana		
Brunei		
Burkina Faso		
Burundi		
Cambodia		
Cape Verde		
Central African Republic		
Chad		
Comoros		
Congo		
Costa Rica		
Cote d,Ivoire		
Cuba		
Cyprus		
Djibouti		
Dominica		
Dominican Republic		
DR Congo		
Ecuador		
El Salvador		
Equatorial Guinea		
Eritrea		
Ethiopia		
Fiji		
Gabon		
Gambia		
Ghana		
Grenada		
Guatemala		
Guinea		
Guinea-Bissau		

COUNTRY	2010	2030
Guyana		
Haiti		
Honduras		
Iceland		
Jamaica		
Kenya		
Kiribati		
Kuwait		
Laos		
Lesotho		
Liberia		
Lithuania		
Luxembourg		
Madagascar		
Malawi		
Maldives		
Mali		
Malta		
Marshall Islands		
Mauritania		
Mauritius		
Micronesia		
Moldova		
Mongolia		
Mozambique		
Myanmar		
Namibia		
Nepal		
New Zealand		
Nicaragua		
Niger		
Norway		

COUNTRY	2010	2030
Palau		
Panama		
Papua New Guinea		
Paraguay		
Qatar		
Rwanda		
Saint Lucia		
Saint Vincent		
Samoa		
Sao Tome and Principe		
Senegal		
Seychelles		
Sierra Leone		
Singapore		
Solomon Islands		
Somalia		
Sri Lanka		
Sudan/South Sudan		
Suriname		
Swaziland		
Tanzania		
Timor-Leste		
Togo		
Tonga		
Trinidad and Tobago		
Tuvalu		
Uganda		
Uruguay		
Vanuatu		

WATER

ESTIMATES GLOBAL CARBON IMPACT

2010 EFFECT TODAY

$ USD **LOSS** PER YEAR **5 BILLION**

2030 EFFECT TOMORROW

$ USD **LOSS** PER YEAR **10 BILLION**

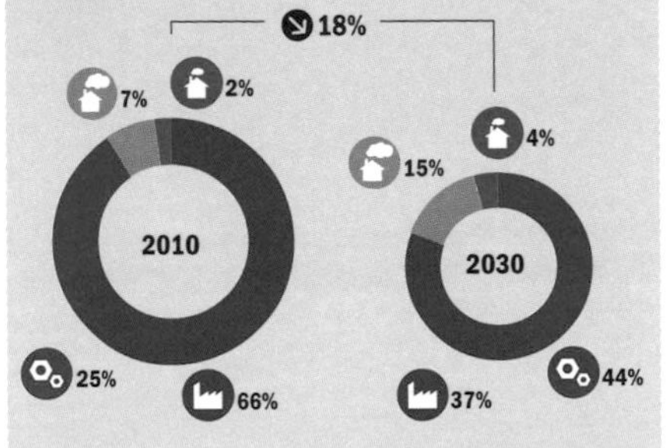

➔ Bodies of fresh water become acidic when continuously subjected to highly acidic rainfall as a result of air pollution from local or regional heavy industries

➔ Local vulnerabilities are higher where soils are more acidic and fail to reduce the acidity level of polluted rains

➔ Acidic water is toxic for fish, if used for irrigation it is toxic for crops, if drunk it is toxic for human health, and if used for industrial purposes, it can corrode and damage technical infrastructure

➔ If acidic water is not treated, the costs incurred further down the supply chain are likely to be greater and more harmful to populations and the economy

RELATIVE IMPACT

2010	474	11	
2030	571	8	

HOTSPOTS

2010		2030
1,500	USA	2,250
300	BELARUS	1,250
200	POLAND	650
100	UKRAINE	600
100	RUSSIA	500

GEOPOLITICAL VULNERABILITY

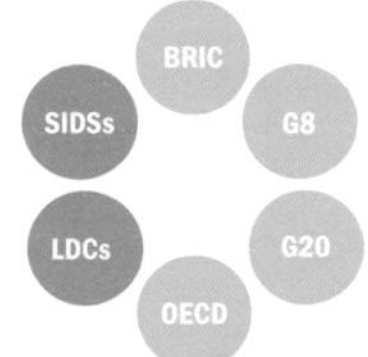

$ Economic Cost (2010 PPP non-discounted)
Developing Country Low Emitters | Developed
Developing Country High Emitters | Other Industrialized

 = Losses per million USD of GDP

Change in relation to overall global population and/or GDP

$ = Millions of USD (2010 PPP non-discounted)

Acid rain is a by-product of heavy industrial emissions, in particular nitrogen oxide (NOX) and sulphur dioxide (SO2). Acid rain has a variety of effects including the acidification of inland bodies of water, such as lakes and rivers. Problems resulting from acidic water include reductions in agricultural productivity, water biodiversity, human health and recreational options. (Driscoll et al., 2001; Vörösmarty et al., 2010). Water can, of course, be treated to reduce acidity, but at a cost. The level of heavy industrial emissions does not directly correspond to the highest levels of vulnerability because of the complex role that soil chemistry plays in attenuating or exacerbating the impact of acid rain. Soils that have been subjected to heavy emissions for long periods of time have their capacity to buffer acid rain depleted and allow more acidity to accumulate in bodies of water (Jeziorskietal et al., 2008). This explains why industrialized nations from Russia through western Europe to North America are particularly vulnerable to acid rain, while for the time being China, whose concentrations of acid rain are the world's highest, is still relatively resilient to its impact (OECD, 2012). China's buffering capacity has also been enhanced in the north of the country by natural alkaline dust blown in from the deserts (Larssen et al., 2006). Other recently industrialized countries like Thailand have been less fortunate and suffer more severe effects. The impact of air-borne pollution on water resources is widespread and understood to inflict significant damage for a wide-ranging group of economies across Africa, Asia and Europe in particular.

HAZARD MECHANISM

Practically everywhere where dense heavy industry is found today there are significant local sources of highly acidic aerosols, such as sulphur and nitrogen dioxide. A share of these aerosols finds its way to ground level within a certain proximity to the source of emissions (Mehta, 2010). Acidic emission debris is distributed either through acid rain or as dry deposits, where, if the supply is continuous, it accumulates and can render entire bodies of water highly acidic: in some northern and eastern areas of the US, the EPA gauged through a survey in the 1980s that 4.2% of all lakes and 2.7% of streams were acidic (Stoddard et al., 2003). Acidic water has measurable impacts on organisms, and at a certain level becomes lethal to most fish species (Ikuta et al., 2008). Acidic water is also toxic for human consumption in many cases, because it increases the rate at which heavy metals dissolve, among other concerns (Kumar, 2012). Plants, and hence agricultural production, also suffer losses as a result of sustained exposure to high levels of acidity (World Bank, 2005). Therefore, acidic water must be treated, or else risk incurring higher costs than that of treatment. Vulnerability to acid contamination of water varies considerably worldwide in accordance with the natural ability of land to neutralize acidity.

The chemical composition and absorptive potential of the soil in particular determines the rate at which acidity shocks can be diffused (Stoddard et al., 2003). Industrialized countries are seriously exposed since buffering capacity has been depleted by more than a century of harmful emissions: China, India and South Africa generally have a high soil neutralizing capacity, whereas the eastern US, western Europe and Russia all have high vulnerability to acid contamination (Vörösmarty et al., 2010).

IMPACTS

The global impact of acid rain due to industrial processes on water resources is estimated at a modest five billion dollars in 2010. It is assumed these effects will double by 2030 but remain stable as a share of GDP with losses of ten billion dollars a year.

Around 20 countries are considered acutely vulnerable to the impact of acid rain on water resources, in particular in Africa, Eastern Europe and South-East Asia. The largest share of the impact is estimated to concern Eastern European countries like Belarus and Poland, each of which experienced upwards of 200 million dollars of losses in 2010. The greatest total losses concern the US, with over 1.5 billion dollars of losses per year in 2010. Given the lower levels of emissions among lower-income and least developed countries, many of these are not affected to the same degree as industrialized and major emerging economies, so the effect is not considered a major impediment to poverty reduction efforts.

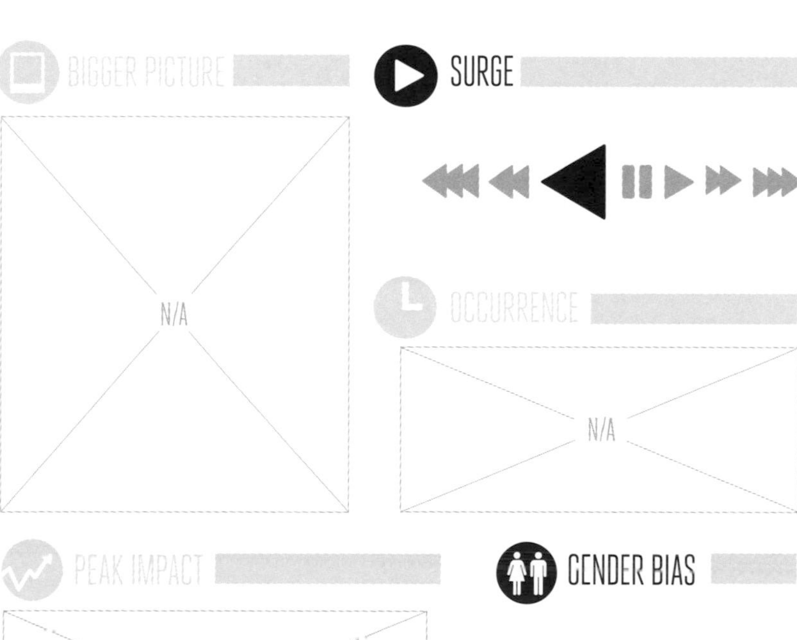

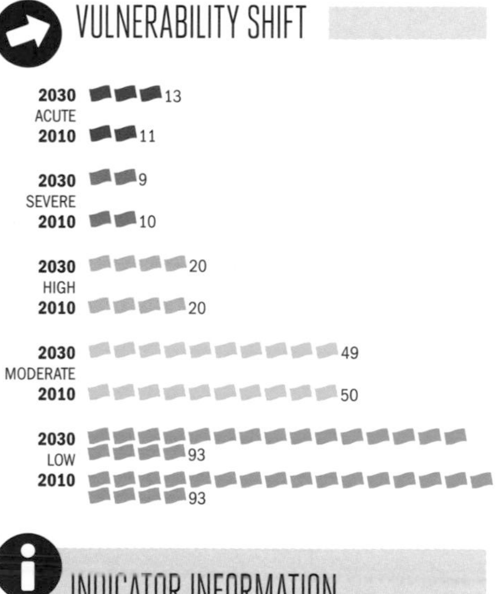

PEAK IMPACT

N/A

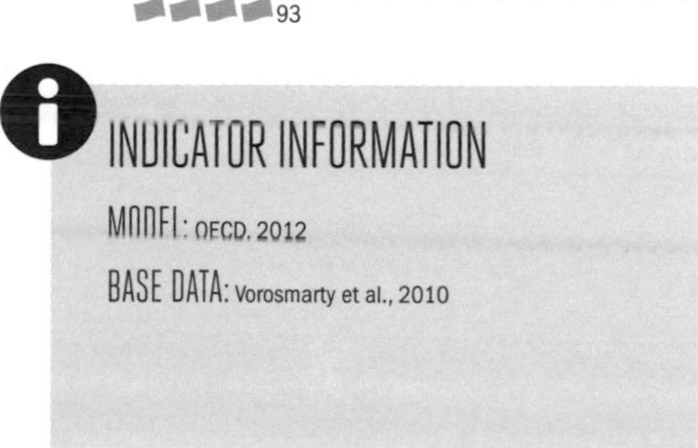

= 5 countries (rounded)

Acute Severe High Moderate Low

THE INDICATOR

The indicator measures the impact of acid rain on water. It assesses the extent to which emissions linked to acid rain would be likely to affect ground-level acidity of water bodies, and then calculates the cost of treating the acidified water for the anticipated demand of communities affected (OECD, 2012; Vörösmarty et al., 2010). The indicator assumes a minimal cost basis since untreated water in populated and/or agriculturally productive areas mapped for the purpose would be likely to have greater negative effects than the cost of water treatment (Hoekstra et al., 2010; Portmann et al., 2010). A weakness of the indicator is not factoring in possible changes in soil acid buffering capacity of such rapidly emerging economies like China, which may result in underestimation of 2030 impacts.

ESTIMATES COUNTRY-LEVEL IMPACT

	$			
COUNTRY	2010	2030	2010	2030
ACUTE				
Belarus	300	1,250	7,500	10,000
Bhutan	1	5	45	60
Bosnia and Herzegovina	5	25	300	400
Czech Republic	90	250	2,250	2,000
Finland	50	65	1,750	1,500
Latvia	25	100	1,000	1,500
Lithuania	65	300	2,250	3,000
Macedonia	10	45	350	500
Moldova	10	40	1,250	1,750
Paraguay	5	30	500	700
Poland	200	650	6,500	5,750
Romania	75	350	3,500	5,000
Ukraine	100	600	7,250	10,000
SEVERE				
Albania	1	15	150	250
Croatia	10	60	450	650
Estonia	5	15	200	200
Hungary	35	100	1,250	1,000
Laos	1	15	250	350
Portugal	50	65	1750	1,500
Slovenia	10	25	250	200
Sweden	60	80	1,750	1,500
Thailand	85	450	4,750	6,750
HIGH				
Brazil	90	400	6,750	7,750
Bulgaria	5	20	150	200
Burundi		1	200	250
Cambodia	1	10	250	350
Canada	150	200	4,250	3,500
Central African Republic		1	150	200
Cote d'Ivoire	1	10	600	800
Denmark	30	35	1,000	900
France	150	200	4,750	4,250
Germany	350	450	10,000	8,750
Ireland	15	20	400	350
Luxembourg	5	5	65	55
Netherlands	40	50	950	850
Norway	15	20	450	400
Russia	100	500	4,500	5,250
Rwanda	1	1	200	250
Spain	90	100	2,750	2,500
Uganda	1	10	750	1,000
United States	1,500	2,250	30,000	25,000
Vietnam	20	150	2000	3000
MODERATE				
Angola	1	5	150	200
Argentina				1
Australia	10	10	250	200
Austria	15	15	300	250
Bangladesh	1	10	400	550
Belgium	10	10	250	200
Bolivia	1	5	55	75
Burkina Faso			5	10
Cameroon	1	5	200	300
Chad		1	30	40
Chile				
China	45	300	3,250	3,750
Colombia	1	5	70	100
Congo	1	1	80	100
DR Congo	1	5	1,000	1,500
Ecuador		1	10	15
Eritrea			10	15
Ethiopia		1	30	40
Gabon				1
Ghana	1	5	250	350
Greece	10	15	350	300
Guinea			25	35
India	30	150	3,250	3,750
Indonesia	1	5	250	250
Italy	1	1	80	70
Japan	10	10	300	250
Kazakhstan	1	5	55	75
Kenya			5	5
Malawi		1	80	100
Malaysia	1	15	95	150
Mali			5	5
Mongolia				
Mozambique			15	20
Myanmar	1	5	200	300
Nepal			10	15
Nigeria	1	1	90	100
North Korea		1	20	30
Pakistan	1	15	350	500
Peru	1	10	80	100
Slovakia	5	15	150	100
South Korea	30	150	650	850
Sudan/South Sudan	1	1	100	150
Switzerland	1	1	30	25
Tanzania	1	5	350	450
Turkey	5	5	150	250
United Kingdom	95	100	2,500	2,000
Venezuela	5	35	400	550
Zambia			20	30
Zimbabwe			10	10

$ Additional economic costs (million USD PPP) - yearly average

CARBON VULNERABILITY

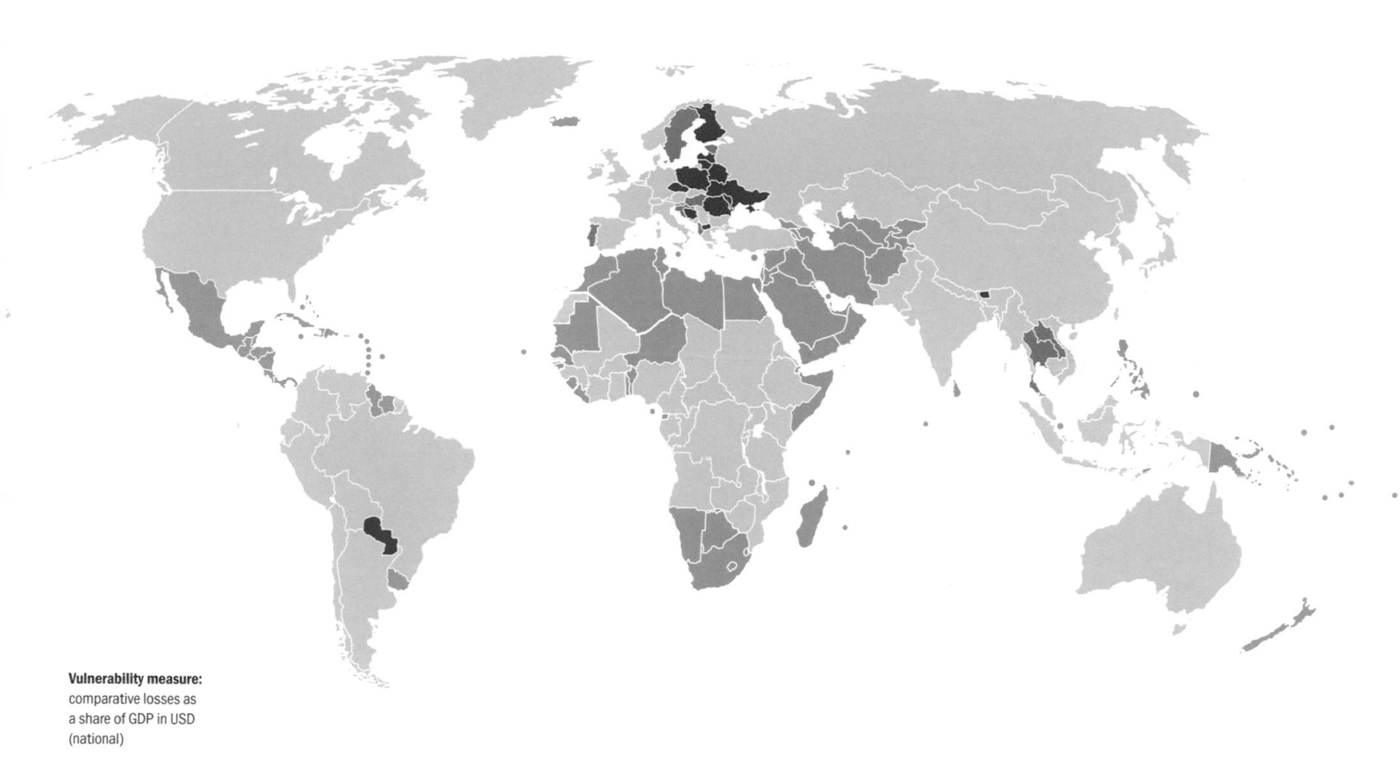

Vulnerability measure: comparative losses as a share of GDP in USD (national)

COUNTRY	2010	2030	2010	2030
LOW				
Afghanistan				
Algeria				
Antigua and Barbuda				
Armenia				
Azerbaijan				
Bahamas				
Bahrain				
Barbados				
Belize				
Benin				
Botswana				
Brunei				
Cape Verde				
Comoros				
Costa Rica				
Cuba				
Cyprus				
Djibouti				
Dominica				
Dominican Republic				
Egypt				
El Salvador				
Equatorial Guinea				
Fiji				
Gambia				
Georgia				
Grenada				
Guatemala				
Guinea-Bissau				
Guyana				
Haiti				
Honduras				
Iceland				
Iran				
Iraq				
Israel				
Jamaica				
Jordan				
Kiribati				
Kuwait				
Kyrgyzstan				
Lebanon				
Lesotho				
Liberia				
Libya				
Madagascar				
Maldives				
Malta				
Marshall Islands				
Mauritania				
Mauritius				
Mexico				
Micronesia				
Morocco				
Namibia				
New Zealand				
Nicaragua				
Niger				
Oman				
Palau				
Panama				
Papua New Guinea				
Philippines				
Qatar				
Saint Lucia				
Saint Vincent				
Samoa				
Sao Tome and Principe				
Saudi Arabia				
Senegal				
Seychelles				
Sierra Leone				
Singapore				
Solomon Islands				
Somalia				
South Africa				
Sri Lanka				
Suriname				
Swaziland				
Syria				
Tajikistan				
Timor-Leste				
Togo				
Tonga				
Trinidad and Tobago				
Tunisia				
Turkmenistan				
Tuvalu				
United Arab Emirates				
Uruguay				
Uzbekistan				
Vanuatu				
Yemen				

Volume of water to treat (millions m^3) - yearly average

COSTS

2010
172 BILLION

2030
630 BILLION

HEALTH IMPACT

AIR POLLUTION

INDOOR SMOKE

OCCUPATIONAL HAZARDS

SKIN CANCER

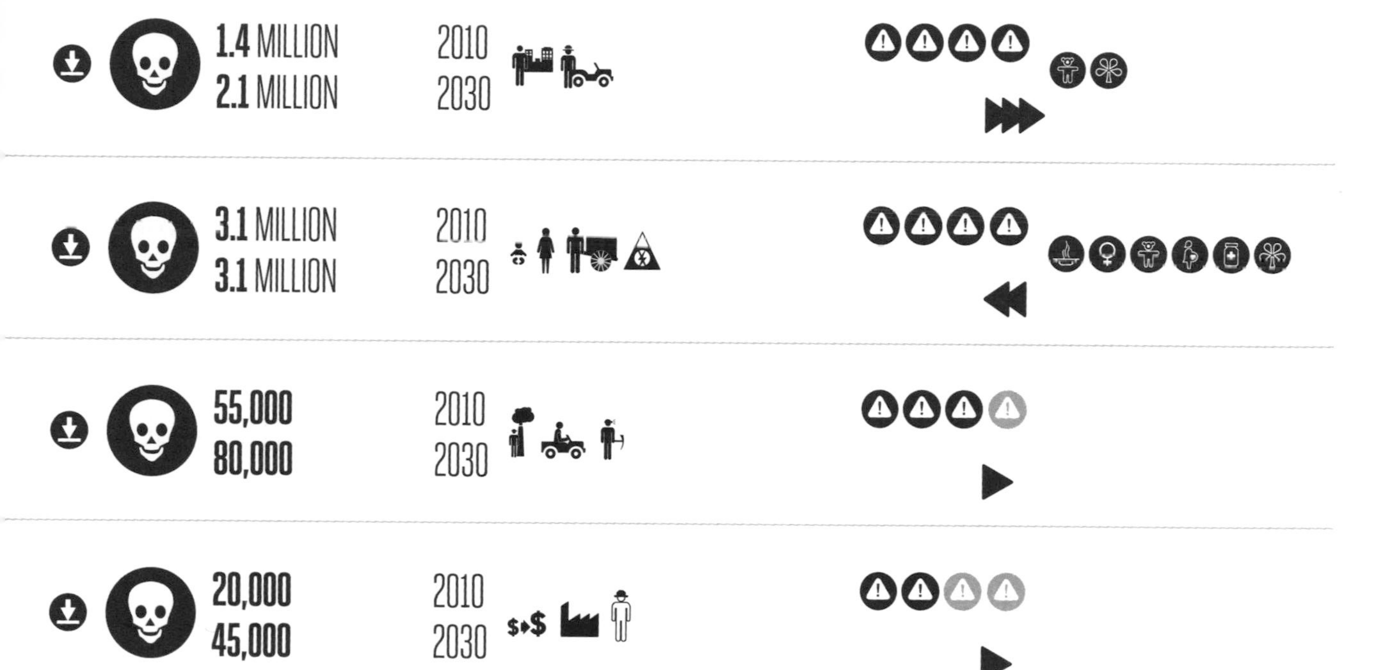
1.4 MILLION
2.1 MILLION
2010
2030
3.1 MILLION
3.1 MILLION
2010
2030
55,000
80,000
2010
2030
20,000
45,000
2010
2030

AIR POLLUTION

ESTIMATES GLOBAL CARBON IMPACT

2010 EFFECT TODAY

DEATHS PER YEAR **1.4 MILLION**

2030 EFFECT TOMORROW

DEATHS PER YEAR **2.1 MILLION**

MORTALITY IMPACT

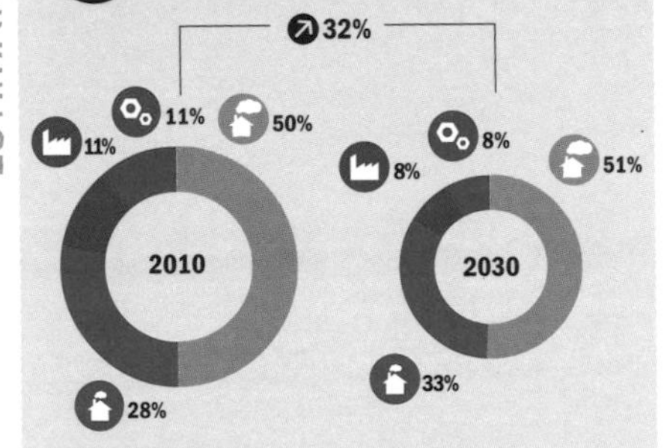

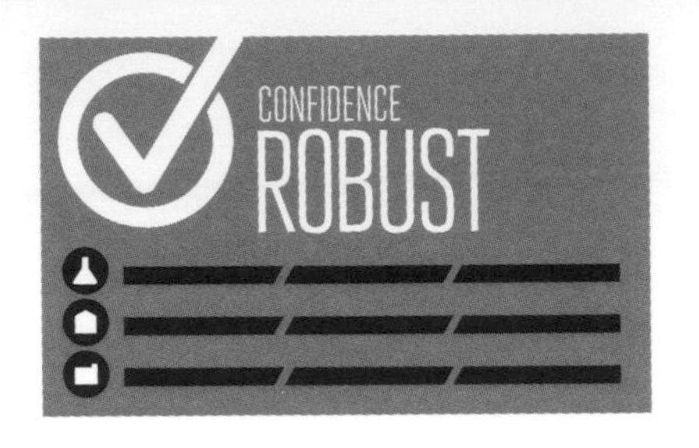

- Cities are home to over half the world's population and growing, all concentrated on only 2% of its surface area, producing 80% of all GHG emissions
- Where there are no strict emission controls, air contaminants from industry and transportation may become toxic and lethal
- Air pollution is a leading cause of death globally, triggering cancer, heart disease, and acute respiratory illnesses, and common asthma
- Technology and government regulation play a major role in making the air safer
- However, access to technology and capacity to implement regulation are lowest in parts of the developing world where air pollution is highest

RELATIVE IMPACT

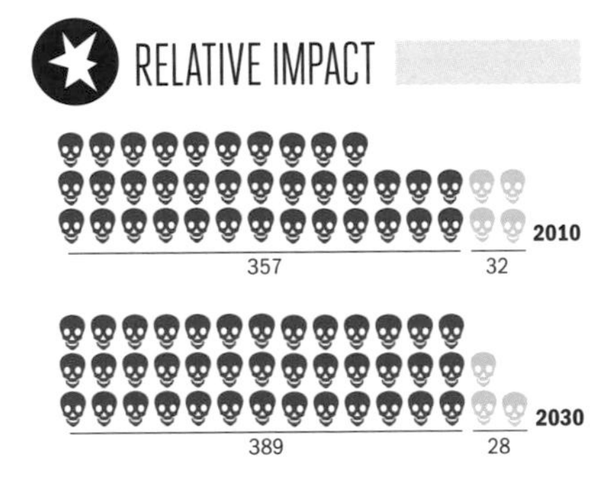

HOTSPOTS

2010		2030
500	CHINA	800
200	INDIA	350
45	PAKISTAN	100
55	UNITED STATES	75
65	RUSSIA	70

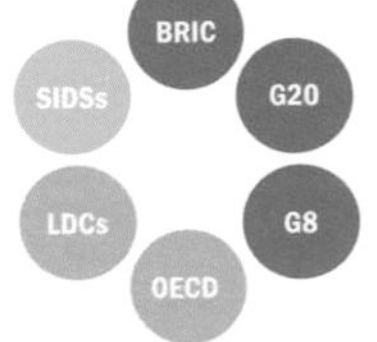

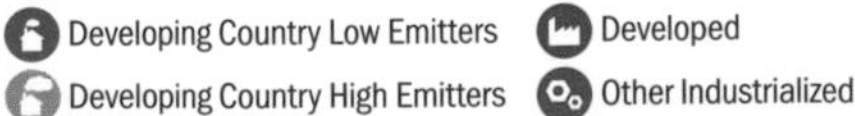

 = Deaths per million

Billion of USD (2010 PPP non-discounted)

Change in relation to overall global population and/or GDP

Preventing or reducing air contamination relies on a community's or region's determination to ensure safety and health. Technology, such as particle filters for vehicles, high quality refined fuels, and regulations on clean air are the main tools for limiting toxic emissions. Air pollution and its negative effects for health can and have been brought under control through these means in major economies of the world (Khan and Swartz, 2007). Although many developing countries have struggled to implement emission standards, they remain locked out of technological solutions for access, capacity, and financial reasons. However, some evidence for alternative regulation policies through incentives rather than penalties has demonstrated a potentially separate route (Blackman et al., 2010). Furthermore, low-tech responses, such as increasing urban tree cover, have also been proven to yield dividends for clean air (Nowak et al., 2006).

HAZARD MECHANISM

Air pollution is caused when fossil or biomass fuels are burnt, often incompletely, by vehicles, in industrial settings, or through residential heating and cooking (Barman et al., 2010). These emissions contaminate the local environment at ground level, resulting in illness, which is dependent on the length of exposure to pollutants and the dose received (Hewitt and Jackson eds., 2009). Fine particles suspended in the air through these processes are small enough to be inhaled and represent a primary hazard. Research consistently shows a high rate of disease resulting from prolonged exposure to elevated levels of ambient air pollution, in particular due to heart disease, lung cancer, and respiratory illnesses, but also asthma and other illnesses such as allergies (World Health Organization (WHO), 2004; Cohen et al., 2005; Chen et al., 2008; Brook et al., 2010; Bell et al., 2007; Sheffield et al., 2011; D'Amato, 2011). Reducing particulate concentrations in areas of high pollution by around half can cut mortality by 15% (WHO, 2006). Experts have calculated that half a year of life is added for every 10 micrograms (µg) fewer fine particulates (PM2.5) per cubic meter of ambient air, or a 1-2% increase in mortality rates for several major diseases per 10µg/m3 more particulates (Pope et al., 2009; Zanobetti and Schwartz, 2009). Currently, the global average of fine particle pollution is 20µg/m3 (PM2.5). China's major industrial zones have the world's highest concentrations, at over 100µg (PM2.5). More than half the population of East Asia currently exceeds the World Health Organization's 35µg (PM2.5) uppermost safety limit (WHO, 2006). By comparison, recommended levels are below 10µg, a full order of magnitude under China's lethal concentrations (Donkelaar et al., 2010). Urban residents of industrial centres in developing economies face the highest and fastest growing risks (Campbell-Lendrum and Corvalán, 2007).

IMPACTS

Air pollution is estimated to kill 1.4 million people a year today in industrial and fast-emerging economies. That impact is expected to exceed 2.1 million deaths per year in 2030. Even as global population increases steadily over the next 20 years, deaths caused by air pollution are expected to grow as a share of population since the carbon intensive growth and urbanization, particularly of developing countries, exposes wider populations to toxic air environments (Hewitt and Jackson eds., 2009). The most severe impacts are seen in former Soviet Union countries, such as Russia and the Ukraine, where heavy industrial emissions from the early 1990s, 1980s and earlier still contribute to high incidences of cancer, cardiopulmonary and respiratory illnesses. However, major emerging economies, especially China, Iran, and Pakistan have very similar and acute levels of vulnerability. Certain developed countries, such as Singapore and Greece, are highly vulnerable because they have important contemporary concentrations of small air particulates. Other advanced economies that have drastically cut pollutant levels, such as the UK or Latvia, also still experience an elevated disease burden from earlier periods of intense pollution.
In terms of total impacts, China is estimated to account for nearly 800,000 deaths due to air pollution by 2030, with India half that level at around 350,000 deaths. Pakistan, the US and Russia would each suffer 70-100,000 deaths by 2030.Children are particularly vulnerable in particular to mortality resulting from acute respiratory illnesses worsened by high levels of particulate exposure, as well as other sicknesses (WHO, 2004; Nordling et al., 2008; Charpin et al., 2009).

BIGGER PICTURE

SURGE

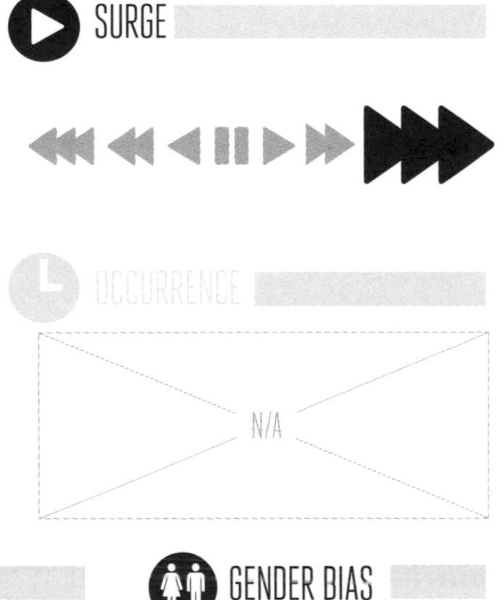

VULNERABILITY SHIFT

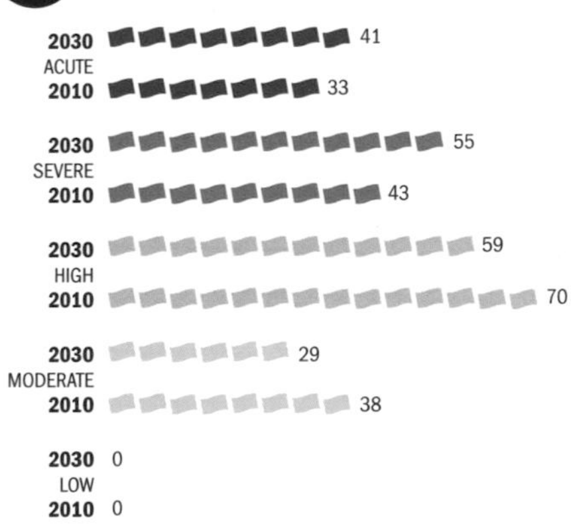

PEAK IMPACT

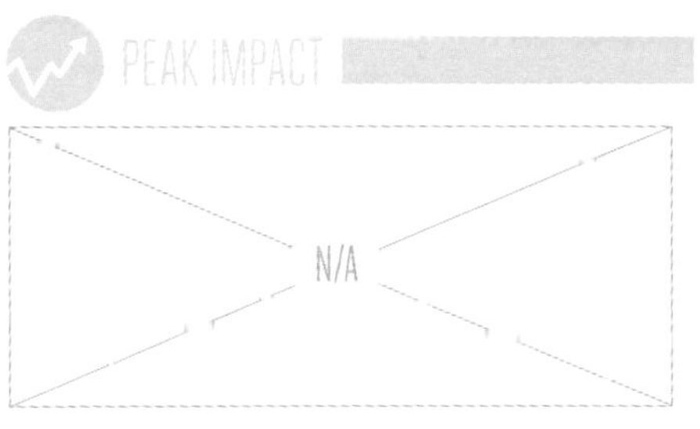

GENDER BIAS

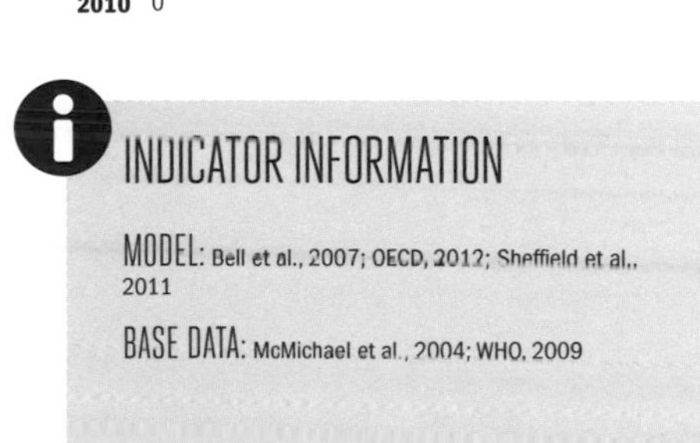

INDICATOR INFORMATION
MODEL: Bell et al., 2007; OECD, 2012; Sheffield et al., 2011
BASE DATA: McMichael et al., 2004; WHO, 2009

= 5 countries (rounded)

Acute Severe High Moderate Low

Effects are widely felt, with over one hundred countries experiencing heightened impacts. But a large number of countries are also relatively unaffected, paradoxically as a result of either very low or very high development, which either rules out industrialization or facilitates tight constraints on emissions, respectively. Given the short time frame of the Monitor's analysis (to 2030) and the way in which the assessment is calculated, it is possible that impacts are underestimated for such newly industrializing countries as Bangladesh or Thailand, where mortality may not show up in national health data for five to ten years, or later, after the explosion of pollution effects.

THE INDICATOR

The impact of air pollution is measured for four different diseases: acute respiratory illnesses, cardiopulmonary disease, lung cancer, and asthma. Regionally differentiated attributable risk factors from the WHO are relied upon for the first three diseases and an independent study for the asthma-related impact (WHO, 2004 and 2009; Bell et al., 2007). The Organization for Economic Co-operation and Development was referred to for projections of emissions and evolving impact, with mortality data from the WHO adjusted for 2030 in relation to expected economic development (OECD, 2012; Mathers and Loncar, 2005). The indicator is considered robust, due to the high quality of global analysis provided by the World Health Organization covering much of the impact estimated. The scientific basis for the cause-and-effect relationships involved have been rigorously studied for decades and are particularly well understood (Chen et al., 2008).

ESTIMATES COUNTRY-LEVEL IMPACT

COUNTRY	2010 (mortality)	2030 (mortality)	2010	2030
ACUTE				
Argentina	9,500	10,000	100,000	150,000
Armenia	2,000	2,000	20,000	30,000
Belarus	3,500	3,500	60,000	100,000
Bosnia and Herzegovina	2,000	2,000	20,000	30,000
Bulgaria	4,000	4,000	35,000	35,000
Chile	3,500	4,500	35,000	55,000
China	500,000	800,000	4,500,000	8,000,000
Congo	1,000	2,000	15,000	40,000
Cote d'Ivoire	3,500	5,500	60,000	150,000
Croatia	1,000	1,500	15,000	15,000
Cuba	3,000	3,500	30,000	45,000
Cyprus	300	350	5,000	8,500
Djibouti	300	400	3,000	5,500
Gabon	350	600	6,500	15,000
Georgia	2,000	2,000	25,000	35,000
Greece	3,500	4,000	40,000	45,000
Hungary	2,000	2,500	25,000	30,000
India	200,000	350,000	2,000,000	6,000,000
Iran	20,000	40,000	250,000	800,000
Iraq	7,500	10,000	70,000	150,000
Israel	2,000	3,000	25,000	45,000
Jordan	1,500	2,000	15,000	30,000
Kazakhstan	6,500	8,000	85,000	150,000
Latvia	1,000	1,000	10,000	15,000
Lebanon	1,000	1,500	15,000	20,000
Libya	2,500	3,500	25,000	45,000
Lithuania	700	750	8,000	10,000
Macedonia	600	700	7,500	10,000
Moldova	1,500	1,500	10,000	15,000
Mongolia	600	750	4,500	6,000
Morocco	6,500	9,000	65,000	100,000
North Korea	6,000	7,000	85,000	150,000
Pakistan	45,000	100,000	400,000	1,000,000
Portugal	3,000	3,000	40,000	50,000
Romania	7,500	8,000	70,000	80,000
Russia	65,000	70,000	900,000	1,000,000
Singapore	1,500	2,500	20,000	45,000
South Korea	10,000	15,000	300,000	600,000
Turkey	25,000	35,000	300,000	450,000
Ukraine	30,000	30,000	300,000	350,000
United Kingdom	15,000	15,000	200,000	350,000
SEVERE				
Afghanistan	4,000	10,000	55,000	200,000
Angola	2,000	4,000	50,000	150,000
Austria	1,000	1,500	20,000	35,000
Azerbaijan	1,500	2,000	20,000	35,000
Belgium	1,500	2,000	25,000	45,000
Benin	1,000	2,000	15,000	45,000
Brazil	25,000	30,000	300,000	450,000
Cameroon	3,500	5,500	50,000	150,000
Central African Republic	600	1,000	15,000	45,000
Chad	1,000	2,500	20,000	60,000
Czech Republic	1,500	1,500	15,000	20,000
Denmark	900	1,000	15,000	25,000
Dominican Republic	1,500	2,000	30,000	55,000
DR Congo	8,000	15,000	100,000	300,000
Egypt	15,000	20,000	150,000	300,000
Equatorial Guinea	100	200	3,000	8,500
Fiji	100	100	5,000	10,000
France	7,500	9,500	150,000	250,000
Germany	10,000	10,000	250,000	400,000
Guinea	1,500	2,500	25,000	70,000
Guinea-Bissau	200	400	5,000	15,000
Iceland	45	60	650	950
Indonesia	30,000	55,000	600,000	2,000,000
Italy	10,000	10,000	150,000	200,000
Japan	20,000	25,000	400,000	600,000
Kuwait	350	500	6,000	15,000
Kyrgyzstan	650	950	6,000	10,000
Maldives	25	70	400	1,500
Mauritania	500	900	8,000	25,000
Mexico	15,000	20,000	200,000	300,000
Mozambique	3,500	5,500	55,000	150,000
Myanmar	5,500	10,000	100,000	300,000
Netherlands	2,500	3,000	35,000	45,000
New Zealand	600	800	10,000	20,000
Nigeria	25,000	45,000	350,000	850,000
Oman	400	750	4,500	10,000
Peru	4,000	5,000	40,000	70,000
Philippines	10,000	25,000	350,000	1,500,000
Poland	6,500	7,500	75,000	100,000
Saudi Arabia	4,500	8,500	75,000	200,000
Senegal	1,500	2,500	20,000	45,000
Somalia	1,500	2,500	10,000	30,000
South Africa	7,500	9,000	150,000	400,000
Spain	8,000	8,500	150,000	200,000
Sudan/South Sudan	5,000	8,500	50,000	100,000
Suriname	95	100	1,000	1,500
Sweden	1,000	1,500	20,000	35,000
Syria	3,000	4,500	40,000	85,000
Tunisia	1,500	2,000	15,000	20,000
Turkmenistan	650	1,000	15,000	35,000
United States	55,000	75,000	850,000	1,500,000
Uruguay	650	800	9,000	15,000
Uzbekistan	3,500	5,000	35,000	75,000

Additional mortality - yearly average

CARBON VULNERABILITY

Acute · Severe · High · Moderate · Low

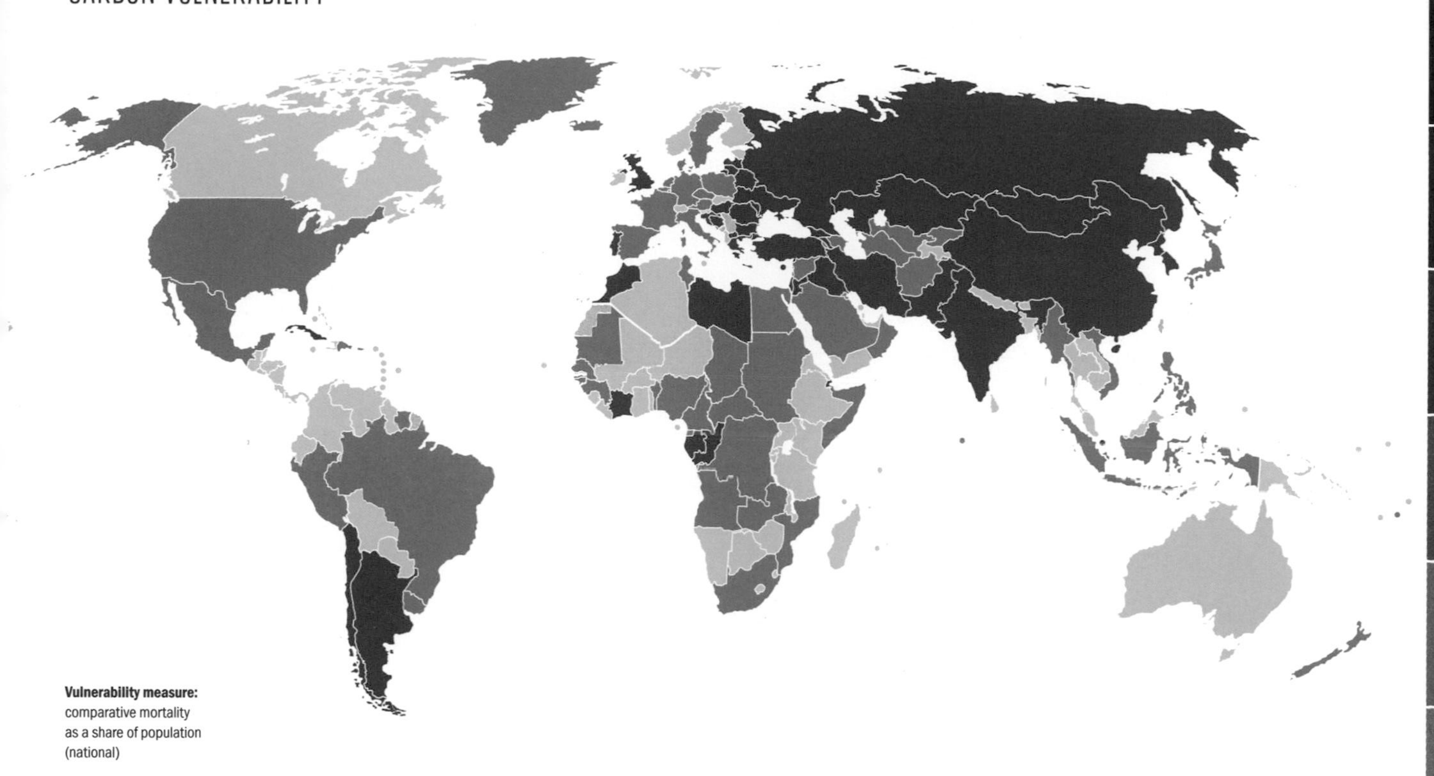

Vulnerability measure: comparative mortality as a share of population (national)

COUNTRY	2010	2030	2010	2030
Vietnam	10,000	20,000	200,000	550,000
Zambia	2,000	3,500	40,000	150,000
HIGH				
Albania	250	350	9,500	20,000
Algeria	2,000	3,000	65,000	200,000
Australia	1,500	2,000	45,000	95,000
Bahrain	75	100	1,500	3,000
Bangladesh	9,500	20,000	200,000	700,000
Belize	15	15	200	400
Botswana	150	250	5,000	15,000
Brunei	15	35	500	1,500
Burkina Faso	1,000	2,000	20,000	60,000
Burundi	350	700	15,000	60,000
Cambodia	650	1,500	25,000	100,000
Canada	2,500	3,000	45,000	80,000
Colombia	5,000	7,000	55,000	90,000
Costa Rica	250	300	3,000	5,000
Dominica	5	10	150	350
Ecuador	850	1,000	9,500	15,000
El Salvador	450	600	8,500	20,000
Eritrea	250	500	7,000	25,000
Ethiopia	3,500	6,500	100,000	400,000
Finland	600	700	15,000	20,000
Gambia	150	250	3,500	10,000
Ghana	2,000	3,500	40,000	100,000
Guatemala	600	900	10,000	25,000
Guyana	85	80	1,500	2,000
Haiti	900	1,000	10,000	25,000
Honduras	600	900	15,000	30,000
Ireland	200	250	5,500	10,000
Jamaica	300	400	4,000	7,500
Kenya	2,000	3,000	40,000	100,000
Lesotho	150	200	5,500	20,000
Liberia	350	750	8,000	25,000
Madagascar	1,000	2,000	20,000	65,000
Malawi	1,000	2,000	20,000	60,000
Malaysia	2,000	4,500	35,000	100,000
Mali	800	1,500	15,000	45,000
Namibia	150	250	5,500	20,000
Nicaragua	300	450	4,000	10,000
Niger	650	1,500	10,000	35,000
Norway	500	600	15,000	25,000
Panama	200	250	3,000	5,000
Paraguay	300	500	4,500	9,000
Qatar	100	150	1,500	2,000
Saint Vincent	10	10	100	200
Sao Tome and Principe	15	30	350	1,000
Sierra Leone	550	950	8,500	25,000
Slovakia	500	550	6,000	7,500
Slovenia	200	250	3,000	4,000
Sri Lanka	900	2,000	65,000	250,000
Swaziland	50	80	5,000	20,000
Switzerland	850	950	15,000	25,000
Tajikistan	300	450	4,000	10,000
Tanzania	3,500	6,000	60,000	150,000
Thailand	4,500	8,000	75,000	250,000
Togo	450	800	15,000	45,000
United Arab Emirates	600	800	8,000	10,000
Vanuatu	10	15	250	700
Venezuela	3,000	4,500	35,000	55,000
Yemen	1,500	4,000	20,000	50,000
Zimbabwe	1,500	2,000	15,000	45,000
MODERATE				
Antigua and Barbuda	1	1	55	100
Bahamas	10	15	550	1,500
Barbados		1	150	350
Bhutan	1	5	450	2,000
Bolivia	5	15	5,000	15,000
Cape Verde	10	20	1,000	4,500
Comoros	25	45	1,500	5,000
Estonia	1	1	800	1,500
Grenada			25	65
Kiribati	1	1	400	1,000
Laos	150	300	4,000	15,000
Luxembourg	15	25	550	1,500
Malta		1	450	1,000
Marshall Islands		1	150	500
Mauritius	5	15	2,500	10,000
Micronesia			100	350
Nepal	650	1,500	30,000	100,000
Palau			15	40
Papua New Guinea	150	250	7,000	20,000
Rwanda	350	550	9,500	30,000
Saint Lucia		1	100	300
Samoa		1	150	450
Seychelles		1	150	650
Solomon Islands		1	150	550
Timor-Leste	1	5	600	2,500
Tonga			100	300
Trinidad and Tobago	1	5	950	2,000
Tuvalu			15	50
Uganda	700	1,500	35,000	100,000

Additional persons affected - yearly average

INDOOR SMOKE

ESTIMATES GLOBAL CARBON IMPACT

2010 EFFECT TODAY

DEATHS PER YEAR **3.1 MILLION**

2030 EFFECT TOMORROW

DEATHS PER YEAR **3.1 MILLION**

MORTALITY IMPACT

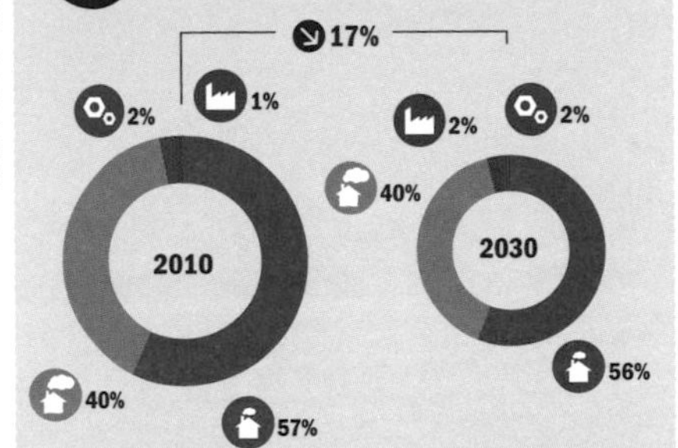

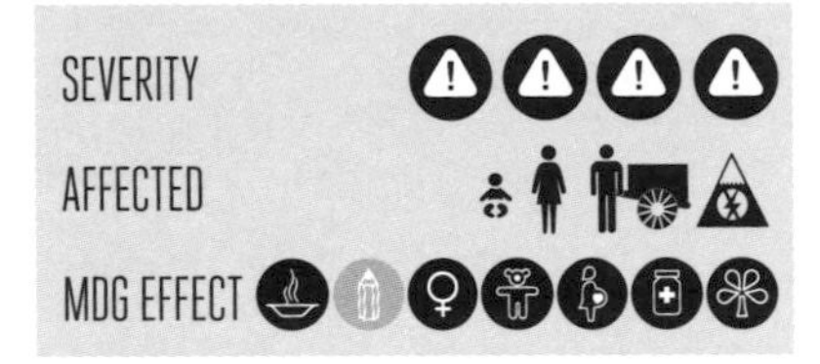

- The world is familiar with the fact that passive indoor tobacco smoke is a risk factor for lung cancer
- Indoor smoke from burning wood and coal for cooking and heating causes mortality on a much larger scale in developing countries
- Uneven sustainable development has locked out more than 1.3 billion people from access to electricity, so a large part of the world's population still cooks with indoor fires
- The practice means long-term exposure to toxic fumes, which can result in sickness ranging from chronic respiratory disease to lung cancer, tuberculosis and cardiovascular disease; it is a serious threat to human development

RELATIVE IMPACT

2010	125	8	
2030	128	8	

HOTSPOTS

2010		2030
850,000	CHINA	850,000
750,000	INDIA	700,000
95,000	INDONESIA	150,000
100,000	PAKISTAN	150,000
150,000	NIGERIA	100,000

GEOPOLITICAL VULNERABILITY

Deaths
Developing Country Low Emitters
Developing Country High Emitters
Developed
Other Industrialized

= Deaths per 100,000

Change in relation to overall global population and/or GDP

Passive cigarette smoke indoors is well understood to be a risk factor for lung cancer among non-smokers, and governments around the world have taken significant regulatory action to combat indoor tobacco smoking for just this reason (Taylor et al., 2007; McNabola and Gill, 2009). Indoor smoke has long been identified as one of the most serious risk factors for mortality worldwide, especially among lower-income developing countries (WHO, 1997). But millions of people still die every year as a result of burning fuels like coal, wood and other biomass (crop waste, dung) in their homes for basic cooking and heating purposes (WHO, 2009). Lack of access to electricity or other forms of modern clean-burning fuels, such as kerosene or gas, force a reliance on locally available fuels like wood, which can also aggravate local deforestation (IEA, 2011; UNEP, 2005). Continued reliance on traditional burning stoves, however, is estimated to close the poverty trap tighter on more than 100 million of the world's poorest due to the comprehensive health effects. The impact is particularly severe on women, who are more likely to be cooking on a regular basis, and for infants, who are more likely to be confined indoors when smoke exposure is highest (Amoli, 1997; Smith et al., 2000; Mishra et al., 2005).

HAZARD MECHANISM

When wood, coal or other forms of solid fuels are burned, almost all stoves commonly used in developing countries do not burn the fuel completely. This means fine particles are released into the enclosed air space and are inhaled, with damaging consequences for human lungs (Kleeman et al., 1999; Pope et al., 2002). Many houses lack ventilation or have poor ventilation, and the typical smoke released when stoves are used contains a potent and hazardous cocktail of toxins, including carbon monoxide, nitrogen and sulphur oxides, benzene, formaldehyde, butadiene and benzo(a)pyrene. Inhaling this smoke repeatedly over a number of years seriously predisposes those affected to illness and death tied to a wide range of health concerns, in particular chronic respiratory diseases (e.g. chronic obstructive pulmonary disease), lower respiratory illnesses, lung cancer and cardiovascular disease (WHO, 2004; Fullerton et al., 2008). Smoke inhalation is thought to impede the body's ability to resist tuberculosis, since exposure to indoor smoke has additionally been shown to substantially increase the risk of contracting that disease (Mishra et al., 1999a). Indoor smoke exposure can also lead to partial or complete visual impairment (acquired blindness), while people suffering from complete visual impairment are more than seven times more likely to die as a result of an unintentional injury than those with non-impaired vision (Mishra et al., 1999b; Lee et al., 2003). Other health concerns have been identified but are not covered here, such as the much higher risks of sudden antenatal death (stillbirth) shown to occur when mothers are exposed to indoor smoke (Mishra et al., 2005).

IMPACTS

The annual global impact of indoor smoke was estimated to be 3.1 million deaths for the year 2010. That figure of 3.1 million annual deaths is expected to remain stable but decline as a share of overall global population through 2030. Over 150 million people are estimated to be affected by illnesses stemming from indoor smoke every single year. The impact presents a comprehensive challenge to human development, with low-income developing countries in particular from Africa and Asia severely affected. Most sub-Saharan African countries are assessed as acutely or severely affected. China and India have by far the largest share of mortality, with an estimated 800,000 deaths each for the year 2010 and more than 30 million people affected by illness as a result of indoor smoke in each country. Other countries with large-scale impacts include Nigeria, Ethiopia, Pakistan, Indonesia, Bangladesh, Afghanistan and DR Congo.

While the majority of developing countries are experiencing serious effects, not a single developed country has vulnerability above Moderate, with only fractional numbers of annual deaths attributed to indoor smoke.

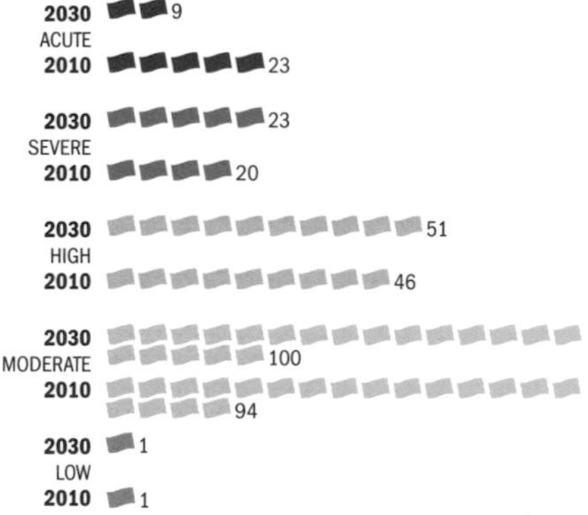

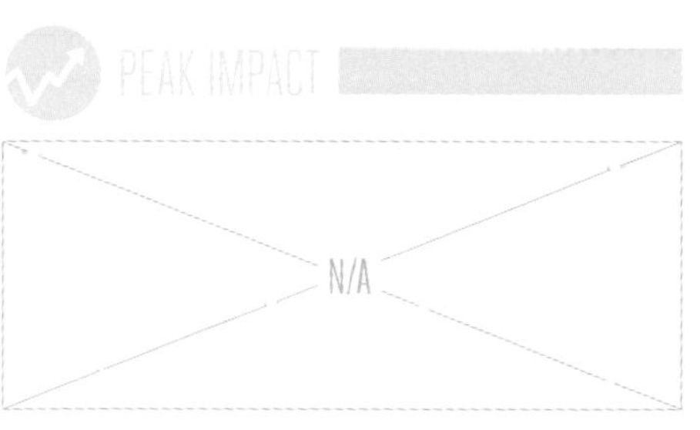

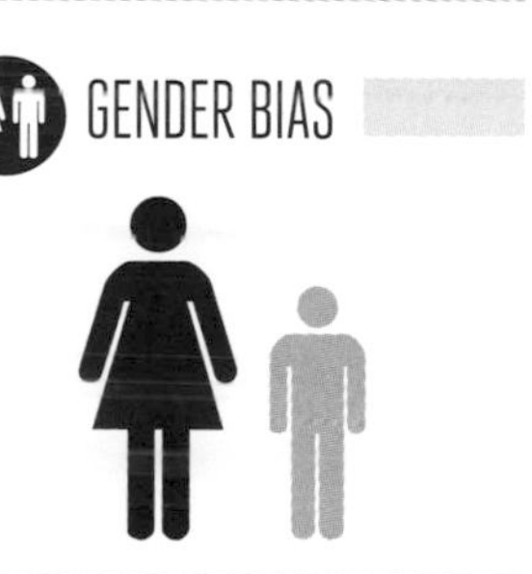

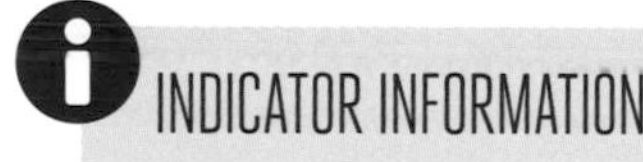

MODEL: OECD, 2012

BASE DATA: Fullerton et al., 2008; Mishra 1999; McMichael et al., 2004; WHO, 2009

= 5 countries (rounded)

THE INDICATOR

The indicator measures the human health impact of smoke inhalation from the incomplete combustion of wood, coal and other biomass fuels burned for cooking or heating within buildings, above all in developing countries. The indicator estimates the direct effect this practice has on chronic respiratory disease (chronic obstructive pulmonary disease), lower respiratory illnesses, lung cancer, cardiovascular disease and tuberculosis (WHO, 2004; Fullerton et al., 2008; Mishra et al., 1999a). It also measures the indirect effect of increased mortality due to injuries from partial or complete visual impairment (blindness) resulting from extended smoke exposure (Mishra et al., 1999b; Lee et al., 2003). The indicator relies on the World Health Organization's latest update of the global disease burden database (WHO BDD, 2011) and relies on the Organization for Economic Co-operation and Development's analysis to estimate how indoor smoking mortality is likely to evolve through to 2030 (OECD, 2012).

COUNTRY	2010	2030	2010	2030
ACUTE				
Afghanistan	80,000	100,000	4,500,000	6,000,000
Angola	35,000	35,000	3,000,000	3,000,000
Burundi	15,000	10,000	700,000	550,000
Cambodia	15,000	15,000	450,000	500,000
Mali	25,000	20,000	1,000,000	1,000,000
Niger	30,000	30,000	2,000,000	2,000,000
Rwanda	15,000	15,000	850,000	700,000
Sierra Leone	15,000	15,000	750,000	650,000
Somalia	15,000	15,000	750,000	750,000
SEVERE				
Bangladesh	90,000	95,000	3,000,000	3,500,000
Burkina Faso	20,000	20,000	1,000,000	1,000,000
Central African Republic	4,000	3,000	200,000	150,000
Chad	15,000	15,000	650,000	600,000
China	850,000	850,000	50,000,000	50,000,000
Cote d,Ivoire	20,000	15,000	750,000	550,000
DR Congo	75,000	75,000	5,000,000	4,500,000
Ethiopia	100,000	85,000	5,000,000	4,000,000
Guinea	8,750	7,250	350,000	300,000
Guinea-Bissau	1,750	1,500	100,000	85,000
Haiti	6,000	6,250	250,000	250,000
India	750,000	700,000	35,000,000	35,000,000
Kyrgyzstan	3,250	3,750	150,000	150,000
Laos	3,750	4,000	150,000	200,000
Liberia	5,250	5,250	300,000	300,000
Madagascar	20,000	15,000	900,000	750,000
Malawi	15,000	10,000	850,000	700,000
Myanmar	35,000	35,000	1,000,000	1,000,000
Nigeria	150,000	100,000	6,500,000	5,000,000
Pakistan	100,000	150,000	4,000,000	5,000,000
Senegal	10,000	8,750	400,000	350,000
Tajikistan	5,500	6,250	250,000	250,000
Togo	6,250	5,250	200,000	150,000
HIGH				
Armenia	1,000	950	40,000	35,000
Azerbaijan	2,750	2,750	100,000	100,000
Benin	6,750	5,750	350,000	300,000
Bhutan	300	400	15,000	20,000
Bolivia	2,000	2,500	100,000	150,000
Bosnia and Herzegovina	750	650	6,250	5,250
Botswana	800	500	50,000	30,000
Bulgaria	2,250	1,750	15,000	10,000
Cameroon	15,000	10,000	750,000	550,000
Congo	1,750	1,500	75,000	70,000
Eritrea	2,500	2,000	150,000	100,000
Estonia	200	200	2,500	2,750
Fiji	150	150	4,250	3,750
Gambia	1,000	800	45,000	30,000
Georgia	1,250	950	20,000	15,000
Ghana	10,000	8,250	450,000	350,000
Indonesia	95,000	150,000	5,000,000	6,500,000
Jamaica	750	750	50,000	50,000
Kenya	20,000	15,000	950,000	650,000
Macedonia	400	350	3,250	3,000
Marshall Islands	25	30	750	900
Mauritania	2,500	2,250	85,000	75,000
Micronesia	30	30	1,250	1,500
Moldova	800	700	20,000	15,000
Mongolia	650	650	20,000	20,000
Mozambique	15,000	10,000	750,000	550,000
Nepal	15,000	15,000	650,000	750,000
Papua New Guinea	2,750	3,250	100,000	150,000
Philippines	20,000	20,000	700,000	750,000
Poland	5,500	7,250	35,000	45,000
Romania	5,000	4,000	55,000	45,000
Samoa	60	60	3,000	3,250
Sao Tome and Principe	85	75	4,250	3,750
Slovakia	850	1,000	5,500	7,000
Solomon Islands	150	200	6,250	8,750
Sri Lanka	7,250	6,500	400,000	350,000
Sudan/South Sudan	20,000	15,000	900,000	750,000
Swaziland	400	250	25,000	15,000
Tanzania	20,000	20,000	1,500,000	1,000,000
Thailand	20,000	20,000	1,000,000	950,000
Tonga	30	35	1,500	1,750
Turkey	9,500	15,000	400,000	650,000
Tuvalu	5	5	150	150
Uganda	25,000	25,000	1,500,000	1,500,000
Ukraine	10,000	8,000	80,000	60,000
Uzbekistan	10,000	10,000	450,000	500,000
Vanuatu	55	65	2,500	3,000
Vietnam	45,000	40,000	1,500,000	1,500,000
Yemen	10,000	20,000	500,000	900,000
Zambia	10,000	9,000	550,000	500,000
Zimbabwe	5,500	4,000	250,000	150,000
MODERATE				
Albania	550	550	7,500	7,500
Algeria	1,250	1,500	35,000	40,000
Antigua and Barbuda	10	10	200	200
Argentina	3,250	3,250	20,000	20,000
Australia	1,500	2,250	15,000	25,000
Austria	300	400	3,500	4,500
Bahamas	20	20	200	200
Bahrain	20	25	250	250
Barbados	20	15	100	100

Additional mortality - yearly average

CARBON VULNERABILITY

Acute Severe High Moderate Low

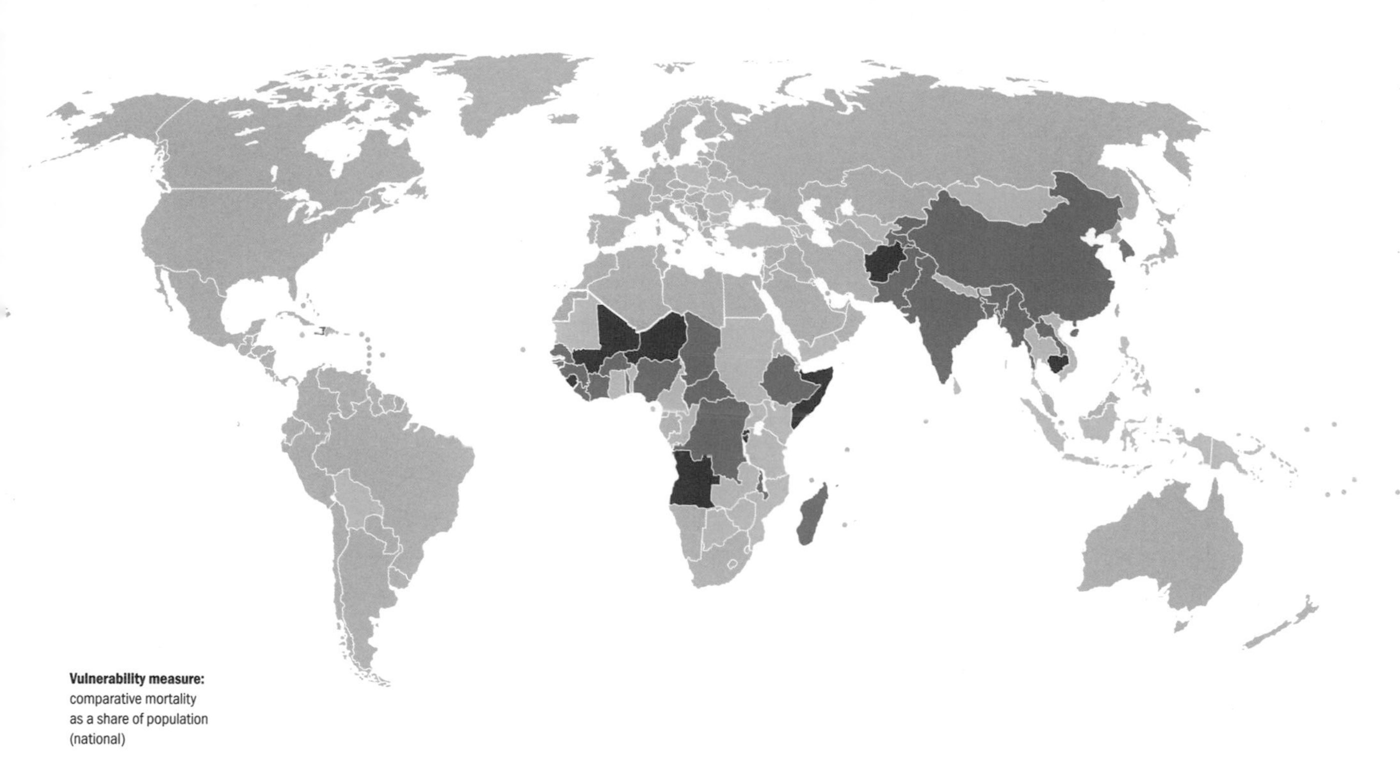

Vulnerability measure: comparative mortality as a share of population (national)

COUNTRY	2010	2030	2010	2030
Belarus	1,750	1,500	15,000	15,000
Belgium	350	450	3,750	5,000
Belize	30	30	1,750	1,750
Brazil	25,000	30,000	1,000,000	1,500,000
Brunei	15	15	150	150
Canada	1,500	2,250	15,000	25,000
Cape Verde	60	45	3,250	2,250
Chile	850	1,250	5,500	8,000
Colombia	4,500	4,750	250,000	250,000
Comoros	200	150	9,250	7,750
Costa Rica	400	450	20,000	25,000
Croatia	300	250	5,750	4,750
Cuba	1,250	1,000	50,000	45,000
Cyprus	75	70	850	800
Czech Republic	500	650	3,250	4,250
Denmark	150	250	2,000	2,500
Djibouti	150	100	4,750	3,000
Dominica	5	5	95	90
Dominican Republic	1,000	1,000	30,000	30,000
Ecuador	600	650	15,000	15,000
Egypt	8,000	8,750	100,000	100,000
El Salvador	700	700	35,000	35,000
Equatorial Guinea	40	35	250	200
Finland	200	250	2,250	2,750
France	1,500	2,000	15,000	25,000
Gabon	250	200	10,000	9,500
Germany	3,750	4,750	40,000	50,000
Greece	450	600	5,250	6,500
Grenada	10	10	250	200
Guatemala	2,000	2,500	150,000	200,000
Guyana	100	90	4,250	3,000
Honduras	1,500	1,500	80,000	90,000

COUNTRY	2010	2030	2010	2030
Hungary	1,250	1,500	8,000	9,750
Iceland	5	10	80	100
Iran	6,000	6,750	25,000	30,000
Iraq	2,750	3,500	65,000	80,000
Ireland	100	150	1,000	1,750
Israel	100	150	1,250	1,750
Italy	2,250	2,750	25,000	30,000
Japan	10,000	15,000	150,000	150,000
Jordan	350	450	1,500	1,750
Kazakhstan	2,000	2,000	20,000	20,000
Kiribati	15	15	60	70
Kuwait	70	85	800	950
Latvia	350	300	2,250	2,000
Lebanon	350	350	2,250	2,250
Lesotho	300	150	15,000	7,250
Libya	450	500	8,250	9,250
Lithuania	450	400	3,000	2,500
Luxembourg	15	25	150	250
Malaysia	3,250	3,500	20,000	20,000
Maldives	35	45	2,250	3,000
Malta	15	10	150	150
Mauritius	70	45	450	300
Mexico	9,500	15,000	500,000	750,000
Morocco	3,500	3,750	65,000	70,000
Namibia	200	150	10,000	8,500
Netherlands	400	550	4,500	6,000
New Zealand	300	450	3,500	5,000
Nicaragua	950	1,000	50,000	55,000
North Korea	650	600	2,750	2,250
Norway	150	200	1,750	2,250
Oman	150	200	850	1,250
Palau	1	5	15	20

COUNTRY	2010	2030	2010	2030
Panama	350	350	20,000	20,000
Paraguay	600	700	30,000	35,000
Peru	2,000	2,000	100,000	100,000
Portugal	350	450	4,250	5,250
Qatar	15	15	150	150
Russia	30,000	2,750	200,000	15,000
Saint Lucia	20	20	1,000	950
Saint Vincent	10	10	150	150
Saudi Arabia	1,250	1,750	15,000	20,000
Seychelles	5	5	30	25
Singapore	250	250	2,750	2,750
Slovenia	70	90	800	1,000
South Africa	5,500	4,000	300,000	250,000
Spain	1,750	2,250	40,000	45,000
Suriname	40	30	150	150
Sweden	400	500	4,250	5,500
Switzerland	250	300	2,750	3,250
Syria	1,750	2,250	75,000	90,000
Timor-Leste	200	200	850	900
Trinidad and Tobago	100	100	1,750	1,750
Tunisia	700	750	10,000	10,000
Turkmenistan	900	1,000	4,250	4,750
United Arab Emirates	80	80	900	900
United Kingdom	2,000	2,750	20,000	30,000
United States	15,000	25,000	200,000	300,000
Uruguay	350	350	2,250	2,250
Venezuela	1,500	1,500	35,000	35,000
LOW				
South Korea				

Additional persons affected - yearly average

OCCUPATIONAL HAZARDS

ESTIMATES GLOBAL CARBON IMPACT

2010 EFFECT TODAY

DEATHS PER YEAR **55,000**

2030 EFFECT TOMORROW

DEATHS PER YEAR **80,000**

MORTALITY IMPACT

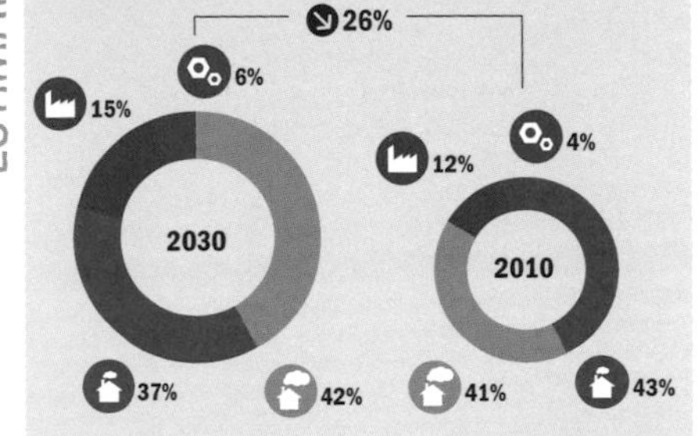

- A world economy relying on carbon-intensive forms of energy for 90% of its needs puts the health of millions of exposed workers at risk
- Hazardous professions range from coal miners facing elevated risks of stomach cancer to thermal power plant workers or truck drivers disproportionately exposed to chronic lung diseases
- Population level vulnerabilities are as high for developed countries as for the lowest-income developing countries
- Renewable and low-carbon forms of energy, such as windmills or solar panels, are significantly safer for the health and safety of industry workers and consumers alike

RELATIVE IMPACT

HOTSPOTS

2010		2030
15,000	INDIA	25,000
15,000	CHINA	25,000
3,250	UNITED STATES	4,000
1,750	INDONESIA	3,250
1,000	BANGLADESH	2,000

GEOPOLITICAL VULNERABILITY

Deaths
Developing Country Low Emitters
Developing Country High Emitters
Developed
Other Industrialized

= Deaths per 10 million

Change in relation to overall global population and/or GDP

Mining accidents that kill hundreds of workers, such as the 2005 Sunjiawan mine disaster in Fuxin, China, are vivid reminders of the risks faced as the world strives to feed a growing carbon economy. Coal is set to nearly double its contribution to global energy needs over the next 20 years (US EIA, 2011). Most occupational health risks linked to the carbon economy are less attention grabbing than mining explosions but cause a much more significant human toll. While miners face the highest dangers, elevated occupational risks also apply to power generation workers in thermal plants burning coal and gas, for example, and to commercially active drivers, especially in urban settings (Burke et al., 2011).

In situations where workers do not have access to adequate social protection, the risk to livelihoods and families is significant (Marriot, 2008). Carbon-intensive forms of energy exploitation are much more hazardous for human health than low-carbon or renewable alternatives (IPCC, 2012b). A carbon-neutral world economy would see virtually all of these health risks eliminated. In a transition phase, numerous measures and policy solutions exist to reduce the hazards workers face (Driscoll et al., 2004). Companies are, however, largely not implementing the necessary measures or covering the health costs resulting from a lack of safety measures. The soundest measures would considerably increase the costs of exploiting fossil fuels, so regulations to protect workers often result in an increase in outsourcing to companies not subjected to the same requirements as firms seek to regain profitability (Giuffrida et al., 2002; Johnstone et al., 2005).

HAZARD MECHANISM

Exposure to toxic fumes, carcinogenic airborne compounds and fine particles from exhaust emissions, silica and mining dust in addition to other carbon-intensive industrial hazards causes asthma, chronic respiratory diseases and, in the case of coal miners, coal worker's pneumoconiosis (Driscoll et al., 2004; Aydin, 2010). Coal miners additionally face greatly elevated risks of lung cancer as well as stomach cancer, since toxic particles inhaled are also understood to reach the stomach (Swean et al., 1995). Men are disproportionately affected by the sweeping health implications of these hazards since they make up the largest share of the workforce in these risk sectors (ILO, 2005).

IMPACTS

The annual global impact of carbon-intensive industries on the occupational health and safety of workers was estimated at 50,000 deaths for the year 2010, with the health of 5 million people affected. By 2030, the death toll is expected to increase to 80,000 deaths per year, with the health of 7 million people affected.

Effects are widespread globally in line with the comprehensive breadth of a carbon-intensive economy in all but the lowest-income low-emissions developing countries. Industrialized countries figure among those worst affected.

China and India are estimated to have the largest total impact, each with occupational mortality in excess of 10,000 deaths per year. The health of an estimated half million people in China and nearly one million in India is negatively affected. Other countries experiencing large-scale losses include the US, Indonesia, Russia and Bangladesh.

BIGGER PICTURE

SURGE

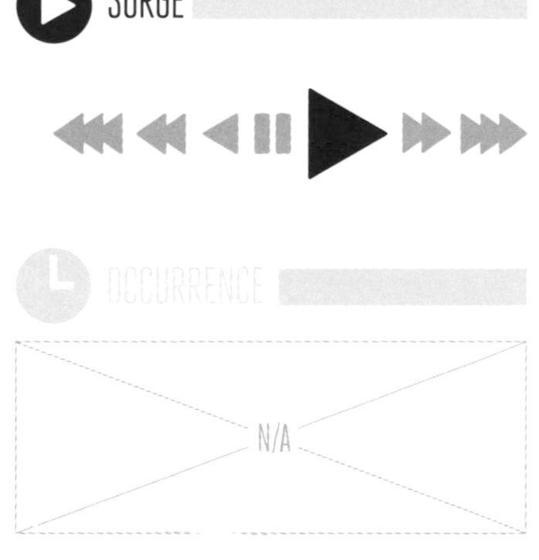

VULNERABILITY SHIFT

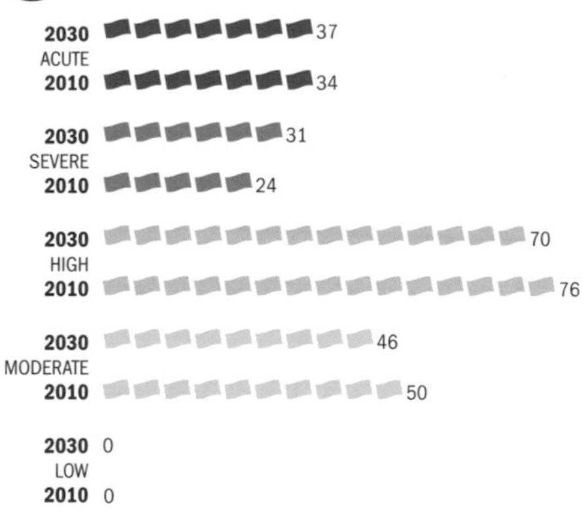

PEAK IMPACT

N/A

GENDER BIAS

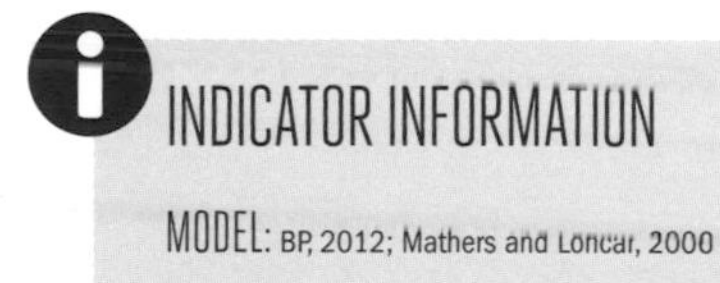

INDICATOR INFORMATION

MODEL: BP, 2012; Mathers and Loncar, 2000

BASE DATA: Aydin, 2010; CDCP, 2012; Driscoll et al., 2004; Swaen et al., 1995; World Energy Council, 2010; WHO, 2009

= 5 countries (rounded)

THE INDICATOR

The indicator measures the impact of the carbon economy on the health and well-being of people in professions that expose them to heightened safety risks, such as in GHG emissions-intensive industries and/or sectors comprising a core link in the supply chain that fuels the carbon economy. The indicator has two main components. The first concerns occupational risks related to asthma and chronic obstructive pulmonary disease among workers in the electricity generation, transportation and mining sectors based on ILO data, with corrections to achieve broad sector accuracy (Driscoll et al., 2004; ILO LABORSTA, 2012). The second concerns occupational risks specific only to coal-mining industry workers, including coal worker's pneumoconiosis (CWP), stomach cancer and unintentional accidents (Aydin, 2010; Swaen et al., 1995; IMFR, 2012). The indicator's main limitations relate to corrections for occupational employment data from the ILO that was not designed to identify GHG-intensive industries.

ESTIMATES COUNTRY-LEVEL IMPACT

COUNTRY	2010	2030	2010	2030
ACUTE				
Armenia	30	30	4,750	4,750
Australia	350	550	45,000	65,000
Austria	60	65	9,750	10,000
Bangladesh	1,000	2,000	150,000	200,000
Belarus	65	70	30,000	30,000
Belgium	150	150	20,000	20,000
Bulgaria	90	85	3,250	3,000
Canada	300	400	35,000	40,000
China	15,000	25,000	500,000	650,000
Colombia	300	450	20,000	20,000
Croatia	40	40	2,500	2,750
Cuba	85	100	7,750	8,750
Czech Republic	100	100	6,250	6,250
Denmark	75	75	7,750	8,000
Germany	700	750	100,000	100,000
Greece	90	90	5,750	5,750
Hungary	80	85	6,000	6,250
India	15,000	25,000	900,000	1,500,000
Indonesia	1,750	3,250	300,000	400,000
Italy	500	550	55,000	55,000
Kazakhstan	300	350	45,000	45,000
Macedonia	25	25	3,000	3,000
Malta	5	5	650	650
Mongolia	20	25	600	750
Netherlands	150	150	15,000	15,000
New Zealand	40	55	4,750	6,750
North Korea	200	300	30,000	40,000
Norway	55	55	8,500	8,500
Romania	150	150	8,250	8,250
Russia	1,500	1,500	350,000	350,000
South Africa	800	1,250	150,000	200,000
Spain	350	350	55,000	55,000
Sri Lanka	150	250	45,000	55,000
Sweden	65	70	10,000	10,000
Ukraine	350	350	45,000	45,000
United Kingdom	850	900	100,000	100,000
United States	3,250	4,000	300,000	400,000
SEVERE				
Bhutan	1	5	200	300
Bosnia and Herzegovina	25	25	3,750	3,750
Botswana	5	10	1,750	2,750
Dominica		1	100	100
Estonia	5	5	1,000	1,000
Finland	30	30	6,750	6,750
Iceland	1	1	200	250
Iran	300	450	150,000	200,000
Ireland	30	30	4,250	4,250
Jamaica	20	25	1,750	1,750
Japan	450	650	150,000	200,000
Kyrgyzstan	35	35	1,750	1,750
Laos	30	45	2,000	2,750
Luxembourg	5	5	500	550
Marshall Islands		1	80	100
Mauritius	5	5	2,500	3,750
Moldova	20	25	1,000	1,000
Myanmar	200	400	35,000	45,000
Pakistan	900	1,250	75,000	100,000
Philippines	450	650	250,000	300,000
Poland	200	200	20,000	20,000
Portugal	50	55	7,000	7,000
Singapore	15	25	4,000	5,250
Slovenia	10	15	1,250	1,250
South Korea	200	250	150,000	250,000
Swaziland	5	5	2,250	3,500
Switzerland	40	40	6,000	6,000
Thailand	250	450	20,000	25,000
Turkey	350	400	40,000	40,000
Tuvalu			10	10
Vietnam	400	550	50,000	65,000
HIGH				
Afghanistan	80	100	20,000	30,000
Algeria	100	150	35,000	55,000
Argentina	80	100	10,000	10,000
Barbados	1	1	150	150
Brazil	500	600	55,000	65,000
Brunei	1	1	200	250
Burundi	15	25	5,250	8,500
Cameroon	35	55	8,250	15,000
Cape Verde	1	1	300	450
Central African Republic	10	15	3,250	5,250
Chad	15	25	3,750	6,250
Chile	55	70	5,750	6,750
Comoros	1	1	450	750
Congo	10	15	2,250	3,500
Costa Rica	15	15	1,000	1,250
Cote d,Ivoire	40	60	8,750	15,000
Cyprus	1	5	1,500	1,500
Dominican Republic	30	35	15,000	15,000
Egypt	150	200	40,000	55,000
Equatorial Guinea	1	1	600	950
Fiji	1	5	2,000	2,500
France	250	250	60,000	60,000
Gabon	1	5	1,000	1,500
Gambia	1	5	650	1,000
Ghana	30	50	6,750	10,000

Additional mortality - yearly average

CARBON VULNERABILITY

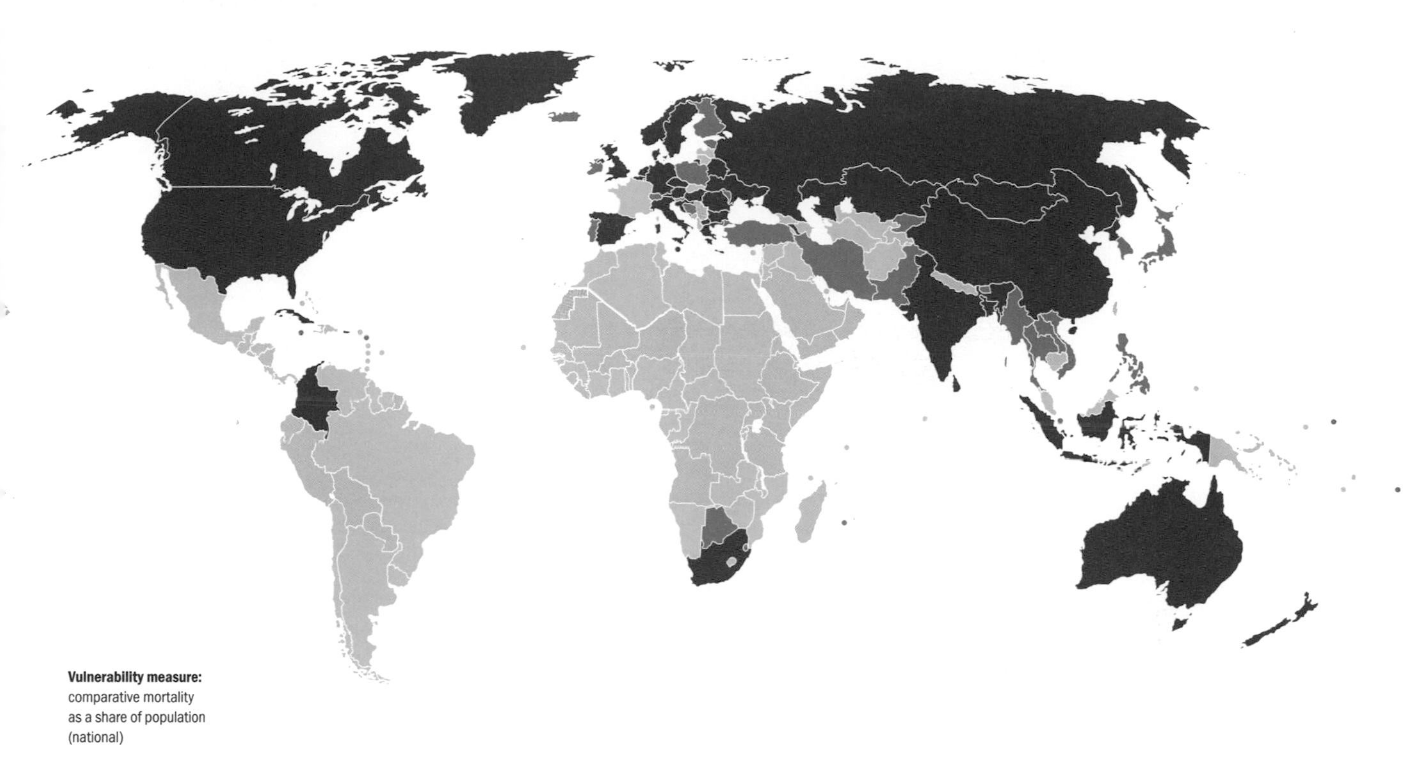

Vulnerability measure:
comparative mortality
as a share of population
(national)

COUNTRY	2010	2030	2010	2030
Guinea	15	25	3,500	5,750
Guinea-Bissau	5	5	1,000	1,500
Guyana	1	1	650	750
Honduras	15	20	5,750	6,500
Iraq	70	100	10,000	15,000
Israel	25	30	5,750	5,750
Jordan	10	15	2,000	3,000
Kiribati			150	250
Latvia	5	5	1,250	1,250
Lebanon	10	15	950	1,500
Lesotho	5	5	1,000	1,500
Libya	10	15	2,250	3,500
Lithuania	15	15	1,250	1,250
Malawi	20	35	5,000	7,750
Malaysia	50	75	15,000	15,000
Maldives	1	1	200	250
Mexico	250	350	25,000	30,000
Micronesia		1	55	70
Morocco	50	70	6,750	10,000
Mozambique	45	70	10,000	20,000
Namibia	5	5	2,250	3,500
Nigeria	300	500	65,000	100,000
Palau			10	10
Panama	10	10	1,250	1,500
Saint Lucia	1	1	95	100
Saint Vincent			45	50
Samoa	1	1	85	100
Sao Tome and Principe		1	75	100
Seychelles			60	95
Slovakia	15	15	1,250	1,250
Sudan/South Sudan	100	200	15,000	20,000
Suriname	1	1	150	150
Syria	40	60	15,000	20,000
Timor-Leste	1	5	350	450
Togo	10	15	2,500	4,250
Tonga	1	1	65	85
Trinidad and Tobago	1	5	900	1,000
Tunisia	15	25	1,250	2,000
Turkmenistan	10	10	6,250	6,000
Uruguay	10	10	1,500	1,750
Uzbekistan	55	60	9,500	9,500
Vanuatu	1	1	90	100
Venezuela	55	75	5,500	6,500
Zambia	35	50	10,000	15,000
Zimbabwe	20	35	3,250	5,500
MODERATE				
Albania	5	5	1,750	1,750
Angola	25	40	10,000	15,000
Antigua and Barbuda			35	40
Azerbaijan	5	5	3,250	3,250
Bahamas		1	450	500
Bahrain	1	1	450	650
Belize	1	1	85	95
Benin	10	15	2,250	3,750
Bolivia	10	15	3,750	4,250
Burkina Faso	15	20	3,250	5,250
Cambodia	1	1	200	300
Djibouti	1	1	250	350
DR Congo	85	150	20,000	30,000
Ecuador	20	25	2,500	2,750
El Salvador	10	10	2,750	3,000
Eritrea	5	10	2,000	3,250
Ethiopia	25	40	5,750	9,250
Georgia	5	5	3,750	3,750
Grenada			25	30
Guatemala	10	10	2,000	2,250
Haiti	10	10	4,250	4,500
Kenya	45	70	9,000	15,000
Kuwait	1	1	1,000	1,500
Liberia	5	10	1,500	2,250
Madagascar	25	40	5,250	8,500
Mali	10	20	2,500	4,250
Mauritania	5	5	1,250	2,000
Nepal	25	40	4,250	5,500
Nicaragua	10	10	1,250	1,500
Niger	10	15	2,000	3,250
Oman	1	5	650	1,000
Papua New Guinea	5	5	850	1,000
Paraguay	5	5	850	950
Peru	35	40	10,000	10,000
Qatar			65	100
Rwanda	10	20	2,750	4,250
Saudi Arabia	20	25	15,000	20,000
Senegal	10	15	2,000	3,250
Sierra Leone	1	5	500	800
Solomon Islands	1	1	90	100
Somalia	10	15	1,500	2,000
Tajikistan	5	5	800	800
Tanzania	30	50	6,500	10,000
Uganda	30	50	7,000	10,000
United Arab Emirates	1	1	1,250	1,750
Yemen	20	30	3,500	5,000

Additional persons affected - yearly average

SKIN CANCER

ESTIMATES GLOBAL CARBON IMPACT

2010 EFFECT TODAY

DEATHS PER YEAR **20,000**

2030 EFFECT TOMORROW

DEATHS PER YEAR **45,000**

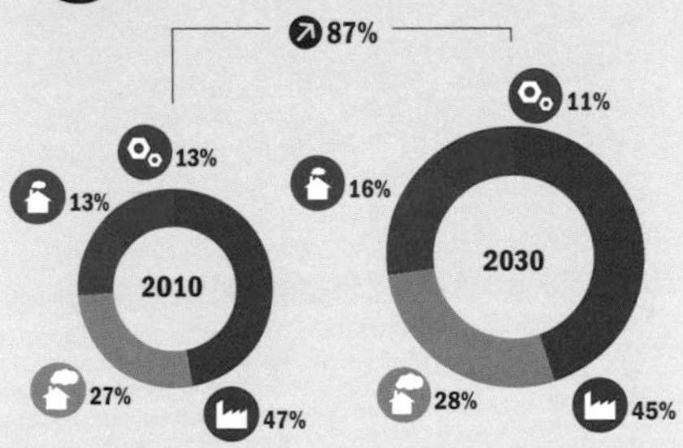

- Exposure to UV rays from the sun is the principal cause of skin cancers such as melanoma
- Greenhouse gases that warm the planet are also largely responsible for depleting the Earth's upper atmosphere, allowing more UV radiation to reach ground levels
- The highly successful Montreal Protocol has phased out most ozone-depleting substances, however, so the root cause of the problem is already being addressed, with ozone depletion now set to recover
- Skin cancer rates have and will continue to increase, though, because of the lapse of time between accumulated UV exposure and the development of skin cancer

RELATIVE IMPACT

122 | 10 **2010**

209 | 9 **2030**

HOTSPOTS

2010 **2030**

3,500 **USA** 8,000

2,000 **CHINA** 4,250

850 **GERMANY** 1,750

800 **UNITED KINGDOM** 1,750

850 **RUSSIA** 1,500

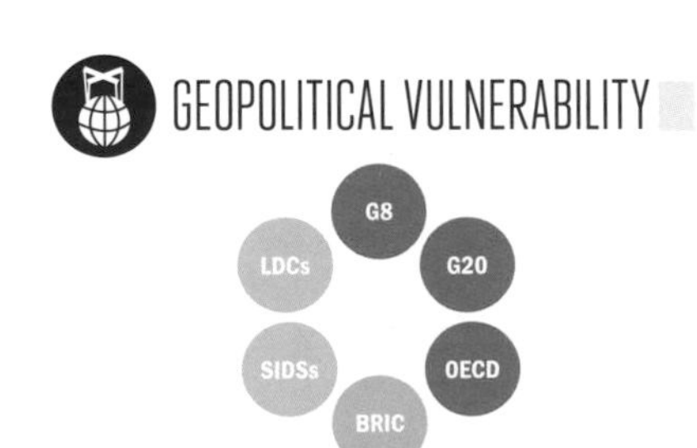

Deaths

Developing Country Low Emitters

Developing Country High Emitters

Developed

Other Industrialized

= Deaths per 10 million

Change in relation to overall global population and/or GDP

Tackling the hole in the ozone layer has been one of the most successful examples of international cooperation and environmental protection to date. The Montreal Protocol to the Vienna Convention for the Protection of the Ozone Layer has been effectively phasing out highly potent GHGs and ozone-depleting substances like chlorofluorocarbons (CFCs) and halocarbons (HCFCs). As a result, experts have suggested amending the Protocol, first signed in 1987, to tackle additional GHGs in order to support other global efforts on climate change (Molina et al., 2009).

The ozone layer was at its maximum level of depletion during the late 1990s and through the last decade but is expected to recover rapidly in the years ahead (Dameris, 2010). Much of the damage to human health, however, has already been done. The slow recognition of the risks involved and delayed action will ultimately result in hundreds of thousands of deaths due to skin cancer, mainly in developed countries, that would not have occurred had the ozone layer remained stable (Martens, 1998; UNEP, 2002b).

HAZARD MECHANISM

Excessive ultraviolet (UV) radiation from accumulated sun exposure is now well recognized as the main cause of skin cancer (Armstrong and Kricker, 2001; Saraiya et al., 2004; Ramos et al., 2004). Depletion of the ozone layer exposes populations to more UV radiation, increasing skin cancer rates (UNEP, 2002b; Lucas et al., 2006). Aside from the ozone layer itself, radiation levels vary due to a number of other factors, including: 1) sun elevation – when the sun is higher in the sky, more UV radiation reaches ground level, 2) latitude – radiation being higher closer to the equator, 3) altitude – with every 1,000 metres gained in altitude, UV radiation increases 10% and 4) ground reflection, in that snow will reflect up to 80% of all UV rays and sand only 15% (WHO, 2002a). People's behavioural patterns, such as an increasing trend in "sun-worshipping" or carelessness about sunscreen and other protection measures, also play an important role in incidence of skin cancer at the population level (Martens, 1998; Coups et al., 2008). Skin cancer is also a major occupational hazard for outdoor workers (Vecchia et al. (eds.), 2007). Fair-skinned people are more susceptible to cancer, and childhood exposure to UV increases risks, although the onset of melanoma and other skin cancers generally occurs later in life (Armstrong and Kricker, 2001).

IMPACTS

The annual global impact of the carbon economy on skin cancer is estimated to have been 20,000 deaths for the year 2010, with that figure rising to 45,000 deaths per year in 2030 in a doubling of impact as a share of global population. It is estimated that 65,000 people were affected by skin cancer in 2010 as aggravated by the carbon economy, a figure that is expected to increase to almost 150,000 people by 2030. Developed and industrialized or transition economies in Australasia, Europe and North America are most severely affected due to significant proportions of populations with high-risk skin types in these countries. Australia and New Zealand have the highest rates of carbon-economy-aggravated skin cancer mortality as a share of population. The largest total impacts are felt in the US, China, Germany, Russia, the UK, France and Italy. Estimated annual mortality for the US and China is at 3,500 and 2,000 respectively, rising to 8,000 and 4,500 by 2030.

THE INDICATOR

The indicator measures the impact on skin cancer rates due to UV radiation amplified by ozone depletion in the upper atmosphere (Martens, 1998). It relies on World Health Organization (WHO) data for skin cancer incidence (WHO BDD, 2012). The indicator is also adjusted to account for a number of closely related but independent factors, including the role of climate change in slowing or speeding the recovery of ozone in the upper atmosphere for different regions, the aging population, and the aggravating effect of increased artificial UV exposure (Bharath and Turner, 2009; Waugh et al., 2009). A key limitation is that the UV radiation impact was only available for Australia, which has had to serve as a global proxy, although the WHO base data already controls for prevalence of the disease internationally

BIGGER PICTURE

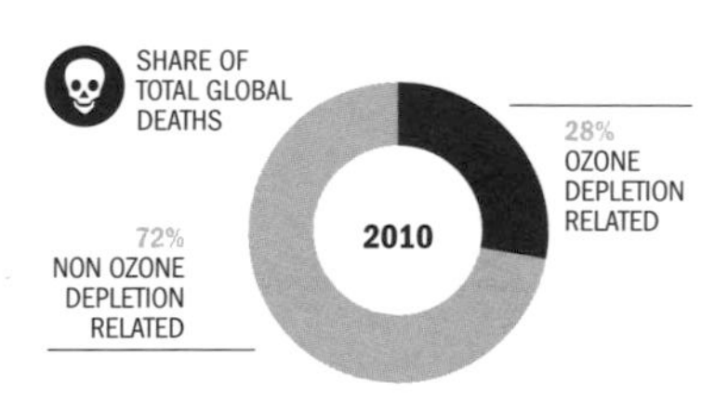

SURGE

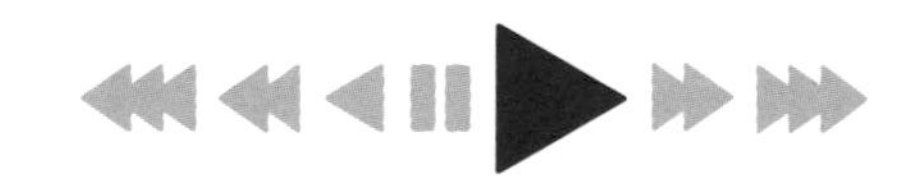

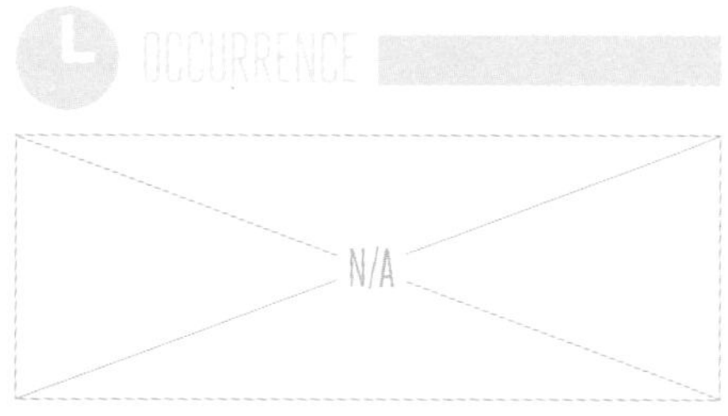

VULNERABILITY SHIFT

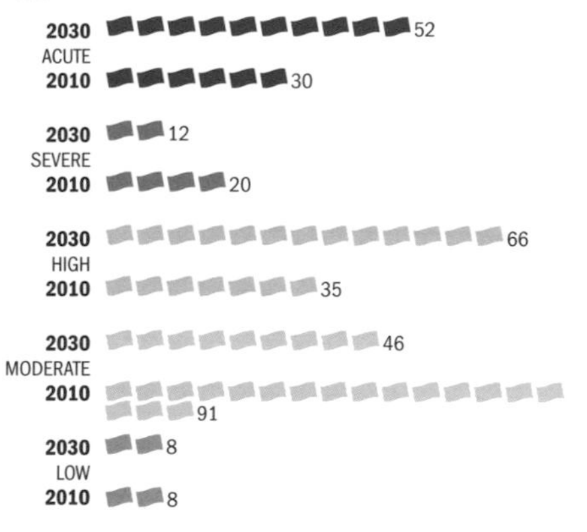

PEAK IMPACT

N/A

GENDER BIAS

INDICATOR INFORMATION

MODEL: Martens, 1998; WHO IARC, 2005

BASE DATA: WHO, 2009

 = 5 countries (rounded)

THE INDICATOR

The indicator measures the impact on skin cancer rates due to UV radiation amplified by ozone depletion in the upper atmosphere (Martens, 1998). It relies on World Health Organization (WHO) data for skin cancer incidence (WHO BDD, 2012). The indicator is also adjusted to account for a number of closely-related but independent factors, including the role of climate change in slowing or speeding the recovery of ozone in the upper atmosphere for different regions, the aging population, and the aggravating effect of increased artificial UV exposure (Bharath and Turner, 2009; Waugh et al., 2009). A key limitation is that the UV radiation impact was only available for Australia, which has had to serve as a global proxy, although the WHO base data already controls for prevalence of the disease internationally.

COUNTRY	2010 (mortality)	2030 (mortality)	2010 (cases)	2030 (cases)
ACUTE				
Argentina	250	600	450	1,000
Australia	500	1,250	2,500	6,000
Austria	100	250	550	1,000
Belarus	70	150	100	250
Belgium	100	200	500	1,000
Bhutan	5	20	10	30
Bosnia and Herzegovina	30	60	50	100
Bulgaria	95	150	150	300
Canada	300	700	1,500	3,500
Chile	95	200	150	400
Croatia	70	150	150	250
Cuba	100	200	200	350
Czech Republic	150	250	250	500
Denmark	80	150	400	800
El Salvador	40	100	70	200
Estonia	20	35	35	60
Fiji	5	15	10	25
Finland	60	150	300	600
France	750	1,500	3,500	7,500
Georgia	30	50	50	90
Germany	850	1,750	4,250	8,250
Greece	100	200	500	1,000
Hungary	150	250	250	500
Iceland	5	10	15	40
Ireland	55	150	250	650
Israel	85	200	400	1,000
Italy	650	1,250	3,000	5,750
Latvia	35	65	60	100
Lebanon	50	100	90	200
Lithuania	30	65	60	100
Luxembourg	5	10	20	50
Macedonia	35	70	60	100
Malta	1	5	15	25
Moldova	35	70	55	100
Netherlands	250	500	1,000	2,250
New Zealand	100	250	550	1,250
Norway	100	200	450	1,000
Papua New Guinea	75	200	100	350
Poland	500	1,000	900	1,750
Portugal	100	250	550	1,000
Romania	200	400	350	700
Russia	850	1,500	1,500	3,000
Slovakia	55	100	100	200
Slovenia	35	70	150	350
South Africa	350	650	650	1,250
Spain	400	750	2,000	3,750
Sweden	150	350	800	1,500
Switzerland	100	200	550	1,000
Ukraine	300	600	550	1,000
United Kingdom	800	1,750	3,750	8,000
United States	3,500	8,000	15,000	40,000
Uruguay	25	60	50	100
SEVERE				
Albania	10	25	20	40
Costa Rica	20	50	35	95
Djibouti	5	10	5	15
Ethiopia	300	850	450	1,250
Honduras	25	70	45	100
Kazakhstan	50	100	85	200
Mexico	400	950	750	1,750
Saint Vincent	1	1		1
Somalia	40	150	65	200
Tonga		1		1
Tuvalu				
Venezuela	100	250	200	500
HIGH				
Afghanistan	50	150	80	250
Angola	30	95	50	150
Antigua and Barbuda				1
Azerbaijan	10	30	20	50
Bahamas	1	1	5	10
Barbados	1	1		1
Belize	1	1	1	5
Bolivia	25	70	50	150
Brazil	600	1,500	1,000	2,500
Burundi	10	25	15	40
Cambodia	30	80	50	150
Cameroon	30	75	45	100
Central African Republic	5	15	10	25
China	2,000	4,250	3,750	7,750
Colombia	100	250	200	450
Congo	5	15	10	25
Cyprus	5	5	15	35
Dominica				
DR Congo	100	350	150	550
Ecuador	40	100	75	200
Eritrea	10	30	15	45
Gabon	1	5	5	15
Guatemala	40	100	70	200
Guinea-Bissau	1	5	1	5
Guyana	1	1	1	5
Indonesia	400	900	700	1,500
Iran	150	350	250	650
Jamaica	5	10	5	15
Japan	400	750	1,750	3,500

Additional mortality - yearly average

CARBON VULNERABILITY

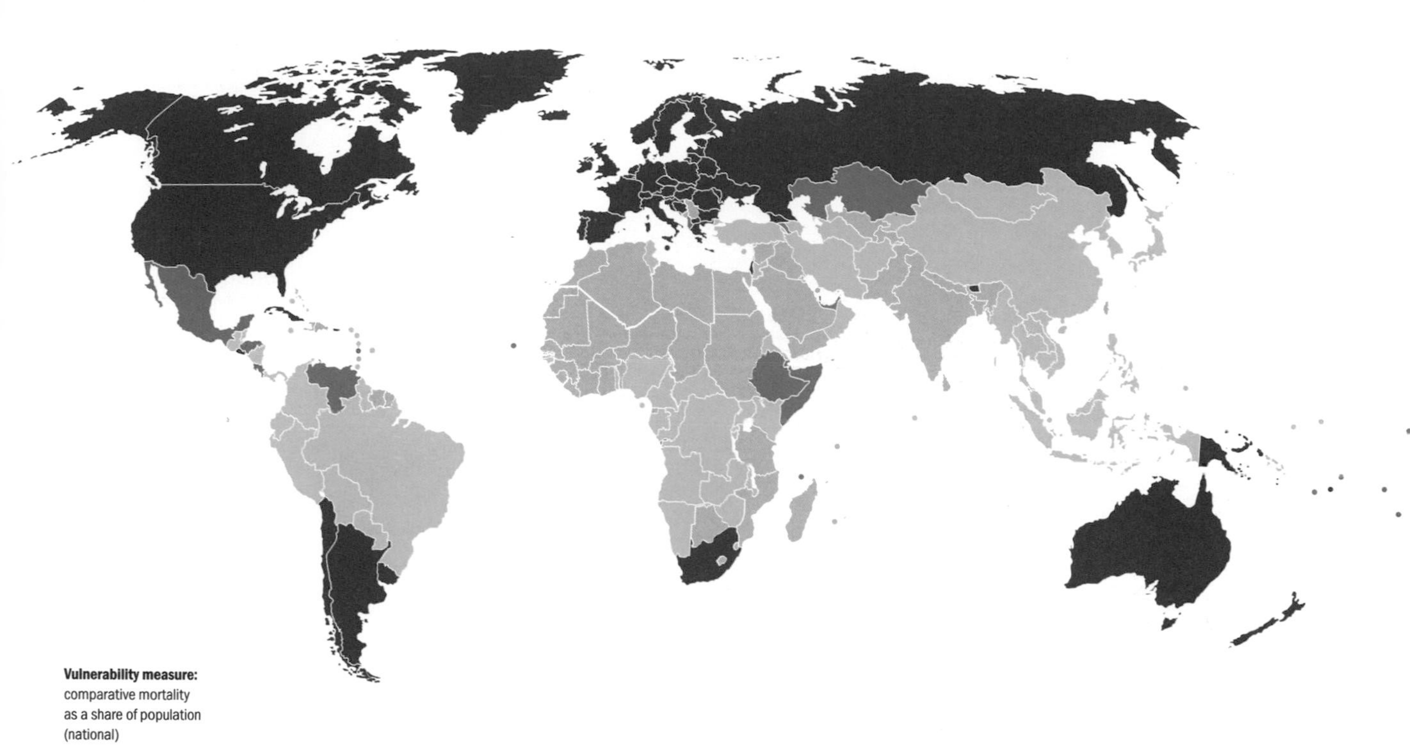

Vulnerability measure: comparative mortality as a share of population (national)

COUNTRY	2010	2030	2010	2030
Jordan	10	30	15	50
Kenya	50	150	85	200
Kyrgyzstan	5	15	10	25
Laos	15	35	20	60
Malawi	20	55	30	90
Malaysia	40	95	70	150
Maldives	1	1	1	5
Marshall Islands		1		
Micronesia		1		1
Mongolia	5	10	5	20
Myanmar	75	150	100	250
Namibia	5	10	5	20
Nicaragua	10	20	10	35
Nigeria	200	550	300	900
North Korea	45	90	70	150
Oman	5	15	5	25
Palau				
Panama	5	10	10	20
Paraguay	15	45	30	85
Peru	75	200	150	350
Philippines	200	450	350	800
Rwanda	15	45	25	70
Saint Lucia		1		
Sao Tome and Principe	1	1		1
Singapore	10	25	55	100
Solomon Islands	1	5	1	5
South Korea	100	250	550	1,250
Thailand	150	350	250	600
Togo	10	25	15	40
Trinidad and Tobago	1	5	1	5
Tunisia	15	35	25	65
Turkey	100	250	200	450
Turkmenistan	5	15	10	30
Uganda	45	150	70	250
Vietnam	250	600	400	950
Zambia	20	55	30	85
Zimbabwe	20	55	35	90
MODERATE				
Algeria	20	50	35	85
Bahrain		1	1	1
Bangladesh	85	200	150	350
Benin	10	25	15	40
Botswana	1	5	5	10
Brunei		1		1
Burkina Faso	10	35	15	55
Chad	10	35	15	55
Cote d,Ivoire	20	45	30	75
Dominican Republic	5	15	10	25
Egypt	45	100	80	200
Equatorial Guinea	1	1	1	5
Gambia	1	1	1	1
Ghana	25	60	40	100
Grenada				
Guinea	5	20	10	30
Haiti	1	1		1
India	400	900	800	1,500
Iraq	20	60	35	100
Kuwait	1	1	1	5
Lesotho	1	1	1	5
Liberia	1	10	5	15
Libya	1	10	5	15
Madagascar	10	35	20	60
Mali	5	20	10	35
Mauritania	5	10	5	15
Mauritius	1	1	1	5
Morocco	15	40	30	70
Mozambique	25	60	35	95
Nepal	15	35	20	55
Niger	10	40	15	60
Pakistan	90	250	150	400
Saudi Arabia	15	45	60	200
Senegal	5	20	10	30
Seychelles				
Sierra Leone	5	10	5	15
Sri Lanka	20	45	35	80
Sudan/South Sudan	45	100	70	200
Suriname		1		1
Swaziland	1	1	1	5
Syria	15	40	25	75
Tajikistan	5	10	5	20
Tanzania	15	40	25	65
Timor-Leste	1	1	1	5
Uzbekistan	25	65	40	100
Yemen	15	55	20	90
LOW				
Armenia				
Cape Verde				
Comoros				
Kiribati				
Qatar				
Samoa				
United Arab Emirates				
Vanuatu				

Additional persons affected - yearly average

INDUSTRY STRESS

AGRICULTURE

FISHERIES

FORESTRY

15 BILLION LOSS 2010
150 BILLION GAIN 2030
10 BILLION LOSS 2010
75 BILLION LOSS 2030
30 BILLION LOSS 2010
85 BILLION LOSS 2030

AGRICULTURE

ESTIMATES GLOBAL CARBON IMPACT

2010 EFFECT TODAY

USD **LOSS** PER YEAR **15 BILLION**

2030 EFFECT TOMORROW

USD **GAIN** PER YEAR **150 BILLION**

ECONOMIC IMPACT

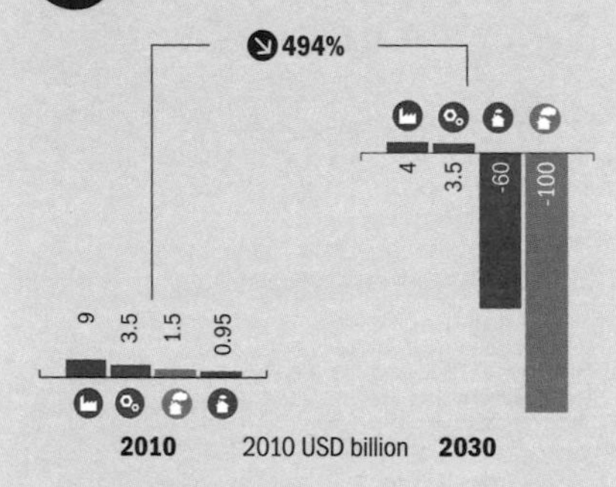

- Air pollution harms people and has damaging and toxic effects for plants, impairing agricultural productivity
- Not all emissions are toxic: CO2 is a natural ingredient in photosynthesis, necessary for enhanced plant growth in optimal conditions
- The positive effects of "carbon fertilization" are often cancelled out by negative effects of localized/regional air pollution
- Net losses are substantial; but as CO2 levels climb, so do positive effects on plant growth, and by 2030 will far outweigh harmful concerns linked to localized pollution, making the effect for agriculture the largest positive contribution of the carbon economy

RELATIVE IMPACT

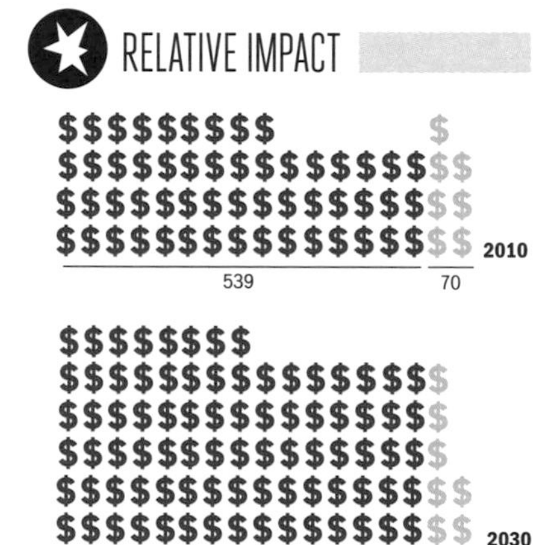

HOTSPOTS

2010		2030
6,750	USA	8,000
1,500	RUSSIA	4,750
350	SYRIA	2,500
200	IRAN	1,250
650	CANADA	1,250

GEOPOLITICAL VULNERABILITY

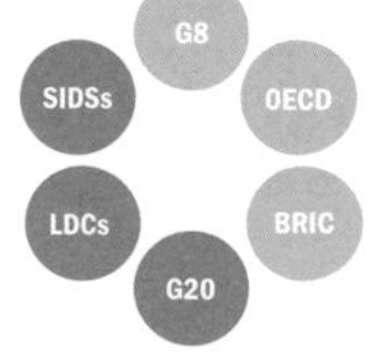

Economic Cost (2010 PPP non-discounted)
Developing Country Low Emitters · Developed
Developing Country High Emitters · Other Industrialized

$ = Losses per million USD of GDP

Change in relation to overall global population and/or GDP

$ = Millions of USD (2010 PPP non-discounted)

It has long been recognized that crop growth can be positively stimulated when the air contains more CO2 (Idso, 1989). It has also been assumed that this positive effect—thought to entail a 30% boost to agriculture in the medium term—offsets completely or partially all other negative effects of climate change, at least initially (Mendelsohn in Griffin (ed.), 2003). However, GHG emissions and their by-products or co-pollutants also have a wide range of negative effects on crops and their yields; these concerns have increased significantly, with the evidence of gigantic transcontinental atmospheric brown clouds, which shut out sunlight and choke plant life (Auffhammer et al., 2006; Ramanathan and Fen, 2009). Bangladesh has actually seen its sunlight hours shrink by one-quarter over the past approximately 30 years, as a result of the growing dimming effect of pollution, and its negative implications for agricultural productivity (Ashan et al., 2011; Ramanathan et al., 2008). Toxic pollutants, such as acid rain and ozone that are trapped at ground-levels further inhibit plant growth (World Bank, 2005: Leisner and Ainsworth, 2011). By 2030, ground ozone alone in the South Asian region is expected to surpass the level at which crop losses would attain 25% (Ramanathan et al., 2008). Extensive field-testing of crop responses to ambient CO2 has also slashed earlier estimates of potential benefits by half or more (Ainsworth et al., 2008; Leaky et al., 2009). Regional studies that attempt to "disentangle" all the different contributing factors have shown that the negative effects of the carbon economy and climate change outweigh any positive benefits, and worsen with further warming (Welch et al., 2010). From the perspective of the carbon economy alone, initial negative impacts should progressively be cancelled out as CO2 increases its concentration in the Earth's atmosphere. Today's losses are not significant or geographically pertinent enough to directly affect food security. The large-scale gains expected in 2030 are still only half the scale of the losses simultaneously estimated to be incurred as a result of climate change.

HAZARD MECHANISM

Common air pollutants from industrial and transportation sources affect agriculture in four key ways. First, ozone is a by-product of many carbon-intensive activities, and, while acting beneficially in the upper atmosphere, it is toxic for humans and plant life at ground level and limits agricultural productivity and growth potential in a variety of ways (OECD, 2012). Affected zones are shown to experience reductions in the productivity of a range of staple crops from 5 to 20% (Feng and Kobayashi, 2009; Leisner and Ainsworth, 2011; Wilkinson et al., 2012). Second, instance, acid rain, formed in particular from sulphur and nitrogen emissions, increases the acidity of soils with limited natural capacity to neutralize acidity loads; it is also toxic for plants, impairing productivity (World Bank, 2005; Wang et al., 2009; Ping et al., 2011). Third, in some areas a lowering of the plant photosynthesis potential for many crops is an impact of so-termed "global dimming," or a persistent reduction in solar energy due to widespread atmospheric pollution clouds which absorb and alter the transmission qualities of solar radiation (Stanhill and Cohen, 2000; Kumari et al., 2007; Wang et al., 2009; Ramanathan et al., 2008). However, some experts have argued that certain staple crops, such as shade-casting canopy-type plants, may benefit from more diffuse light refracted through immense atmospheric brown clouds (Zheng et al 2011; Roesch et al., 2012). All these effects are geographically restricted and mainly confined to regions peripheral or adjacent to the world's major industrial centres. The fourth effect, referred to as "carbon fertilization," is the only one considered to be positive and differs from the other concerns in that it can be felt globally, since CO2 is evenly dispersed in the earth's atmosphere. As a result, its benefits are more widespread and significant than the counteracting effects of ozone, acid rain, and dimming, but may only be gained up to a certain point (not surpassed by 2030); plants only receive the full benefits under optimal conditions, since accelerated growth requires more moisture and nutrients to sustain (Van Veen et al., 1991; Long et al., 2005 and 2006; IPCC, 2007).

IMPACTS

The global impact of carbon-related emissions on agriculture is today estimated at around 15 billion dollars a year in losses. By 2030 however, an incremental increase in losses tied to anticipated emissions growth is estimated to be largely offset through CO2-derived stimulus of the world's

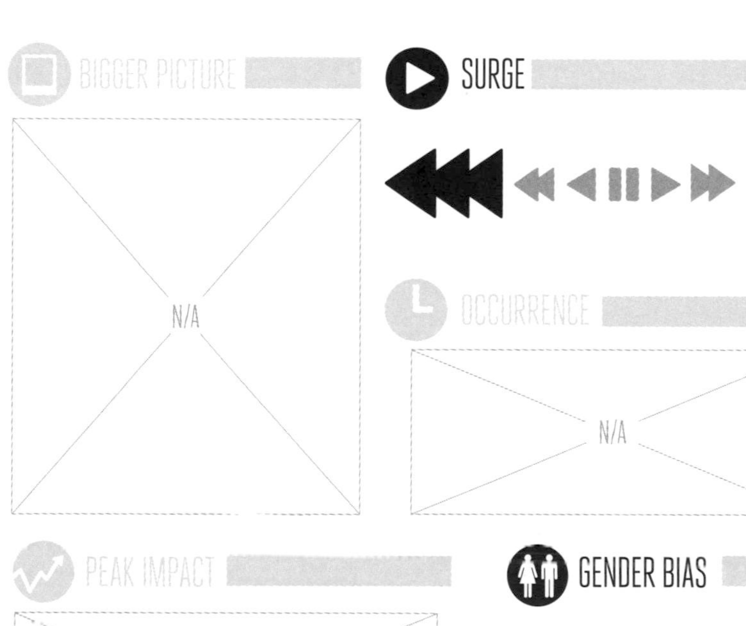

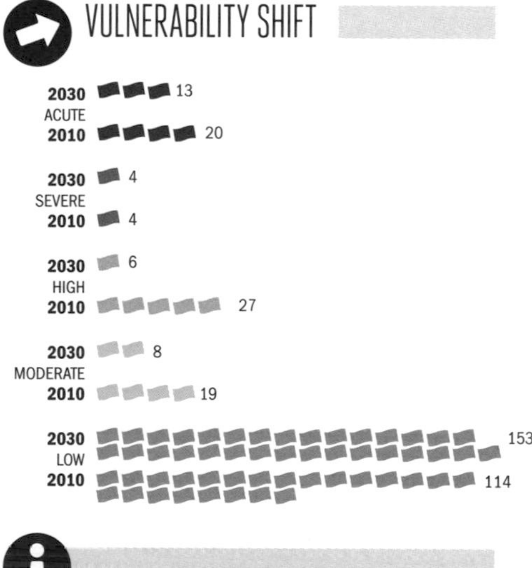

GENDER BIAS

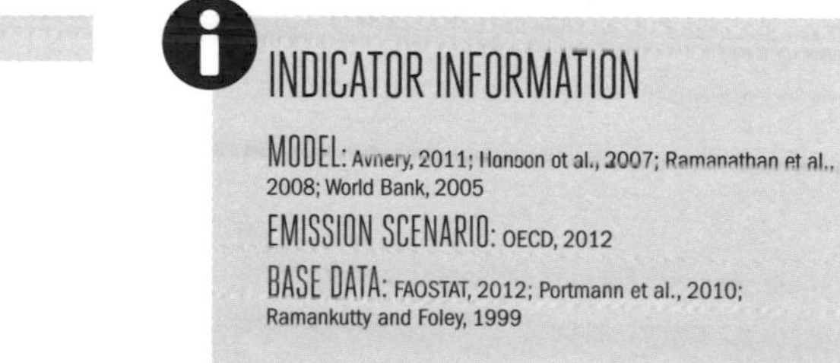

= 5 countries (rounded)

Acute Severe High Moderate Low

staple crops. Potential net gains could reach a substantial 170 billion dollars a year.

The most negative effects are quite restricted and concern a heterogeneous group, dominated by industrialized or newly industrialized economies, including numerous former Soviet Union countries. The US, China, Russia, and India experience the largest total losses, with the US incurring 7 billion dollars a year in costs in 2010 and the others between 1 and 2 billion dollars in losses.

Initially the positive end of the spectrum is dominated by low-income, low-emitting African and Pacific island nations, who, far from the toxic emissions of the fastest-growing emerging economies, enjoy less contaminated air but are predisposed to the benefits of carbon fertilization, as it is uniformly diffuse in the atmosphere. By 2030, the picture of countries benefitting is considerably altered through the possibility of widespread gains resulting from carbon fertilization. With its 80 billion dollars in benefits, China far exceeds the more modest gains experienced by a handful of large developing countries still expected to have agricultural sectors of significant size.

THE INDICATOR

The indicator combines the separate information of acid rain effects (sulfur dioxide and nitrogen dioxide) with ground-level ozone toxicity, and crop responses to solar radiation variation resulting from atmospheric pollutant clouds (World Bank, 2005; Avnery et al., 2011; OECD, 2012; Ramanathan et al., 2008; Hansen et al., 2007). Global crop and irrigation maps and agricultural production are based on independent models and UN Food and Agriculture Organization (FAO) data (Portmann et al., 2010; Ramankutty and Foley, 1999; FAOSTAT, 2012). Carbon fertilization effects have been attributed according to the mid-point of estimates aggregated by the IPCC (IPCC, 2007). Countries are deemed to benefit completely, partially, or not at all from the stimulation, depending on the severity of combined climate change and carbon effects as assessed in the Monitor at country level. Recent research is less optimistic regarding the potential benefits of CO² fertilization than presented here (Ainsworth et al., 2008; Leaky et al., 2009).

ESTIMATES COUNTRY-LEVEL IMPACT

COUNTRY	$ 2010	$ 2030
ACUTE		
Belarus	200	750
Botswana	15	90
Canada	650	1,000
Denmark	150	250
Estonia	40	250
Hungary	300	1,000
Iran	200	1,500
Lithuania	15	100
Mongolia	5	60
Qatar	40	300
Russia	1,500	5,000
Slovakia	95	400
Syria	350	2,500
SEVERE		
Finland	45	80
Kazakhstan	150	300
Pakistan	250	700
United States	6,500	8,000
HIGH		
Austria	75	100
Bulgaria	150	90
Ireland	25	30
Panama	10	20
Sudan/South Sudan	5	40
United Kingdom	450	850
MODERATE		
Australia	80	85
Belgium	100	40
Congo	1	1
Croatia	40	1
Czech Republic	100	65

COUNTRY	$ 2010	$ 2030
Latvia	10	5
Namibia	1	
Sweden	35	30
LOW		
Afghanistan	-10	-350
Albania	15	-100
Algeria	-1	-750
Angola	-25	-750
Antigua and Barbuda	-1	-20
Argentina	-25	-4,500
Armenia	-1	-90
Azerbaijan	20	-90
Bahamas	-1	-85
Bahrain	-1	-75
Bangladesh	-85	-3,500
Barbados		
Belize		-15
Benin	-10	-250
Bhutan	-1	-55
Bolivia	1	-150
Bosnia and Herzegovina	10	-95
Brazil	250	-3,000
Brunei	-5	-250
Burkina Faso	-10	-250
Burundi	-5	-100
Cambodia	-10	-700
Cameroon	-40	-1,000
Cape Verde	-1	-15
Central African Republic	-1	-35
Chad	-5	-200
Chile	10	-400
China	1,500	-80,000

COUNTRY	$ 2010	$ 2030
Colombia	-1	-700
Comoros		-1
Costa Rica	-10	-400
Cote d'Ivoire	-35	-800
Cuba	-10	-650
Cyprus		
Djibouti	-1	-55
Dominica		-10
Dominican Republic	-5	-250
DR Congo	-20	-450
Ecuador	-10	-550
Egypt	150	-2,000
El Salvador	-5	-200
Equatorial Guinea		-5
Eritrea	-1	-20
Ethiopia	-40	-1,500
Fiji	-1	
France	250	-950
Gabon	-5	-250
Gambia	-1	-40
Georgia	1	-75
Germany	250	-100
Ghana	-65	-1,500
Greece	-55	-400
Grenada	-1	-10
Guatemala	-10	-350
Guinea	-10	-250
Guinea-Bissau	-1	-50
Guyana	1	-10
Haiti	-1	-80
Honduras	-5	-300
Iceland		-1

$ Additional economic costs (million USD PPP) - yearly average

CARBON VULNERABILITY

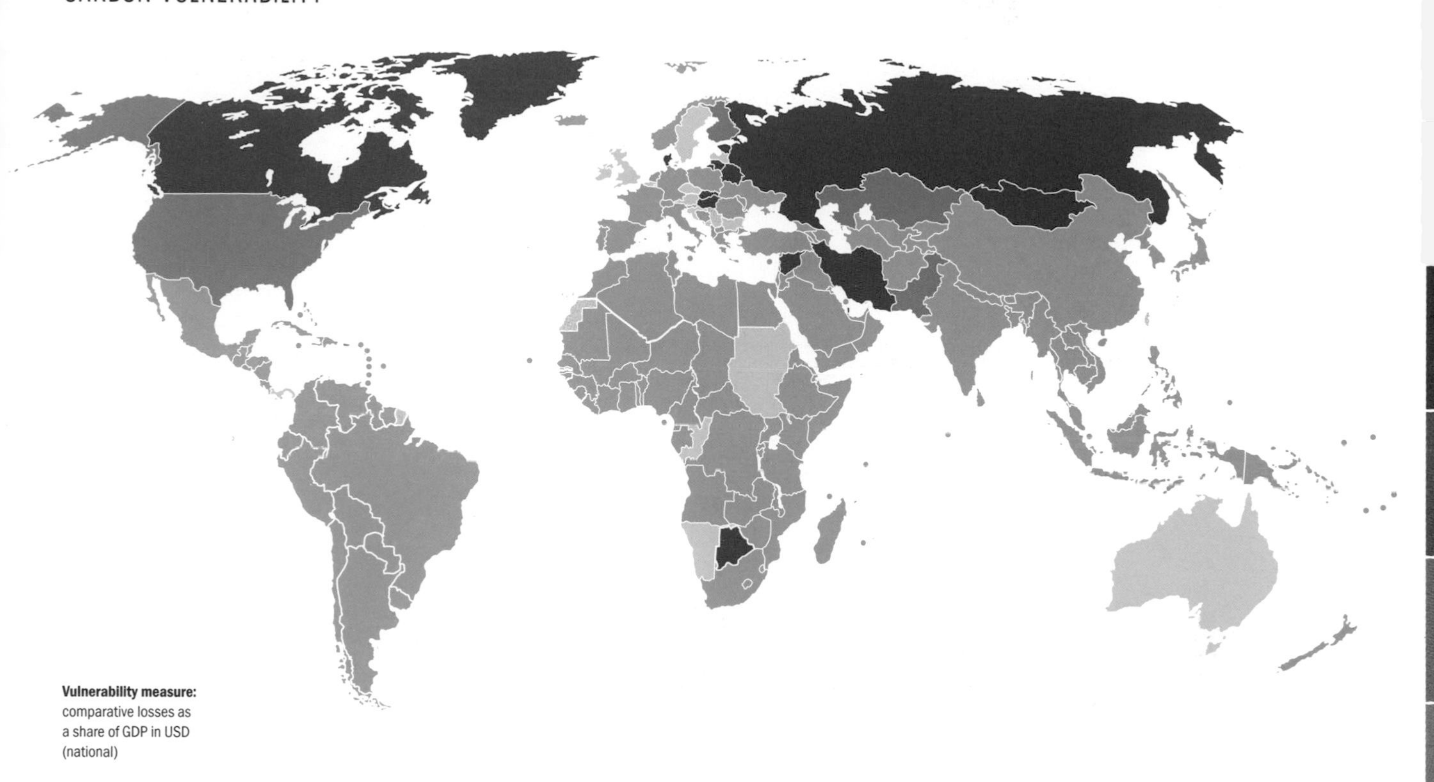

Vulnerability measure: comparative losses as a share of GDP in USD (national)

COUNTRY	2010	2030
India	1,500	-20,000
Indonesia	-200	-7,000
Iraq		-150
Israel	40	-150
Italy	150	-900
Jamaica	-10	-200
Japan	-200	-3,000
Jordan		-55
Kenya	-45	-1,000
Kiribati		-10
Kuwait	-10	-300
Kyrgyzstan	-5	-250
Laos	-10	-550
Lebanon	10	-40
Lesotho		-15
Liberia	-1	-40
Libya	-5	-500
Luxembourg		-1
Macedonia	30	-55
Madagascar	-15	-400
Malawi	-20	-450
Malaysia	-35	-2,000
Maldives	1	-10
Mali	-15	-400
Malta	-1	-5
Marshall Islands		-5
Mauritania	-5	-100
Mauritius	-5	-50
Mexico	75	-2,000
Micronesia		-15
Moldova	-5	-150
Morocco	-15	-900
Mozambique	-15	-450
Myanmar	-10	-550
Nepal	-30	-900
Netherlands	65	-60
New Zealand	-5	-85
Nicaragua	-1	-100
Niger	-5	-150
Nigeria	-400	-10,000
North Korea	5	-55
Norway	1	-20
Oman	-5	-200
Palau		-5
Papua New Guinea	-5	-200
Paraguay	5	-200
Peru		-500
Philippines	-30	-2,000
Poland	400	-150
Portugal	55	-50
Romania	50	-1,000
Rwanda	-10	-250
Saint Lucia	-1	-15
Saint Vincent		-10
Samoa	-1	-15
Sao Tome and Principe		-5
Saudi Arabia	-10	-450
Senegal	-10	-400
Seychelles	-1	-5
Sierra Leone	-5	-80
Singapore	-20	-550
Slovenia	5	-15
Solomon Islands	-1	-30
Somalia	-5	-200
South Africa	40	-300
South Korea	-95	-5,000
Spain	250	-1,000
Sri Lanka	-15	-550
Suriname		-15
Swaziland		-20
Switzerland	10	-50
Tajikistan	-1	-250
Tanzania	-40	-1,500
Thailand	-15	-4,500
Timor-Leste		-35
Togo	-5	-150
Tonga	-1	-10
Trinidad and Tobago	-5	-200
Tunisia	25	-250
Turkey	550	-1,000
Turkmenistan	-45	-1,000
Tuvalu		-1
Uganda	-25	-850
Ukraine	250	-1,500
United Arab Emirates	-15	-600
Uruguay	10	-20
Uzbekistan	-45	-1,500
Vanuatu	-1	-25
Venezuela	-10	-600
Vietnam	-100	-5,000
Yemen	-10	-350
Zambia	-5	-200
Zimbabwe	1	-25

FISHERIES

ESTIMATES GLOBAL CARBON IMPACT

2010 EFFECT TODAY

USD **LOSS** PER YEAR **10** BILLION

2030 EFFECT TOMORROW

USD **LOSS** PER YEAR **75** BILLION

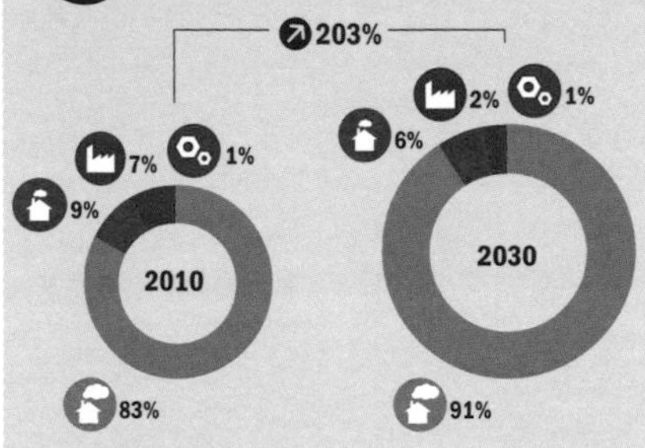

- One third of all the carbon dioxide burned by the world's economies is being absorbed by the oceans
- This uptake of CO_2 is fundamentally changing the acidity of the planet's oceans, making them less hospitable to aquatic life, especially coral, shellfish and krill
- Acid rain from heavy industrial sources also changes the pH of inland bodies of water, making them more acidic with a wide range of lethal and harmful effects for aquatic life
- These effects all have significant impacts on world fisheries
- They also risk destroying coral reefs, one of the world's most remarkable natural wonders, in a short-term timeframe

$$$$$$$ $ 2010 — 63 / 1

$$$$$$$$$$$ $ 2030 — 106 / 2

2010		2030
6,500	**CHINA**	65,000
500	**VIETNAM**	3,250
250	**SOUTH KOREA**	2,000
200	**THAILAND**	1,000
200	**INDONESIA**	800

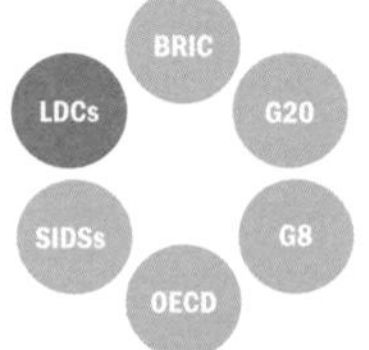

Economic Cost (2010 PPP non-discounted)
Developing Country Low Emitters | Developed
Developing Country High Emitters | Other Industrialized

$ = Losses per 100,000 USD of GDP

Change in relation to overall global population and/or GDP

$ = Millions of USD (2010 PPP non-discounted)

The increase in the acidity of the seas is unprecedented in the Earth's history: a single year's increase in ocean acidity today would have previously taken 100-200 years (Veron, 2008; Hoegh-Guldberg, 2011). When the oceans absorb CO2, corals, shellfish and other marine organisms are stressed and go into decline since acidic seas inhibit the availability of minerals they depend on (Burke et al., 2011). Signs of decline are already visible: when CO2 levels reached a level far below what they are today coral bleaching events became more common; the collapse of Galapagos Islands reefs in 1983 is an example (Baker et al., 2008; Hoegh-Guldberg, 2011). Bleaching is now evident in major reef systems, like the Great Barrier in Australia, that already show signs of serious degradation: a 15% decline in coral growth over several hundreds of monitored reef colonies since 1990 (De'ath et al., 2009). Most of the world's reefs are now in irreversible decline (Veron et al., 2009). Reefs are remarkably productive and act as anchors of the tropical sea ecosystem. Their disappearance would have catastrophic implications for the delicate balance of marine fisheries throughout the world. These negative effects are already beginning to be felt (Crossland et al., 1991; Silverman et al., 2009; Narita et al., 2011). Air pollution generated by the carbon economy has more acute effects still in inland waterways, where CO2 uptake is facilitated by acid rain in areas of heavy industrialization, which has further negative impacts for inland fisheries of all kinds (Ikuta et al., 2008). Research undertaken in Vietnam as a part of the Monitor's country study confirmed the direct relationship between water acidity (pH) and, for instance, disease control and the success of shrimp farming operations.

HAZARD MECHANISM

Two mechanisms are at work: 1) oceans are becoming more acidic as they absorb growing amounts - roughly a third - of the atmosphere's CO2 and other fossil fuel emissions produced through human activities (IPCC, 2007; Sabine and Feely, 2007); 2) acid rain derived from the mainly sulphur and nitrogen emissions released when fossil fuels are burned are increasing the acidity of fresh and brackish bodies of inland water near the source of pollution (Ikuta et al., 2008). Small but consistent increases in ocean acidity negatively affect the production of shellfish and coral since more acidic aquatic environments inhibit formation of mollusc shells, which are made of calcium carbonate (Narita et al., 2011). In krill, higher levels of acidity trigger or extinguish fertility (Kawaguchi et al., 2011). Closed bodies of inland water suffer more severe acidity surges. There is a clear progression of negative impacts from non-lethal to lethal depending on the pH level of the water (Ikuta et al., 2008). The fishing industry is negatively affected as a result.

IMPACTS

The global impact of GHG emissions on fishery production due to acidification processes is currently estimated at a relatively negligible ten billion dollars a year. However the impact triples as a share of GDP to 2030, by which time losses are estimated at around 45 billion dollars a year, an indicator of the devastating effects that could occur beyond this date if strong action on climate change is not forthcoming. Emissions will compound the potentially devastating effects of climate change and other unsustainable stresses on the world's waters and aquatic life. Harmfully, ocean acidification stress is most severe outside and at the frontiers of the tropics, perfectly complementing the damaging effects of climate change that are most significant inside the tropics (Burke et al., 2011).

Effects are widespread: approximately 40 countries are acutely vulnerable to the impact of GHG emissions on fisheries. Particularly affected are developing countries with proportionally large fisheries sectors.

Remarkably, nearly 90% of all losses are estimated to occur in China, mainly as a result of acid rain losses for inland fisheries and aquaculture, over and above ocean acidification effects. Other countries already suffering significant total losses (over 200 million dollars a year) include Vietnam, South Korea and the US.

BIGGER PICTURE

SURGE

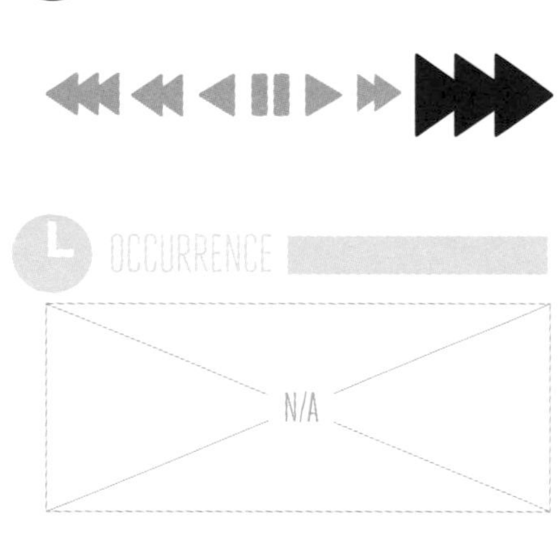

VULNERABILITY SHIFT

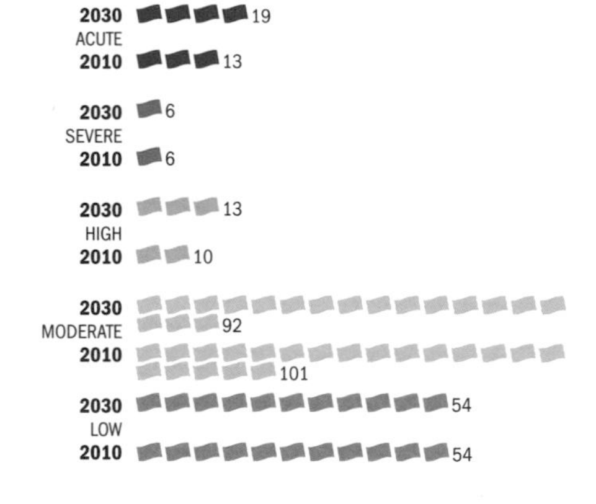

PEAK IMPACT

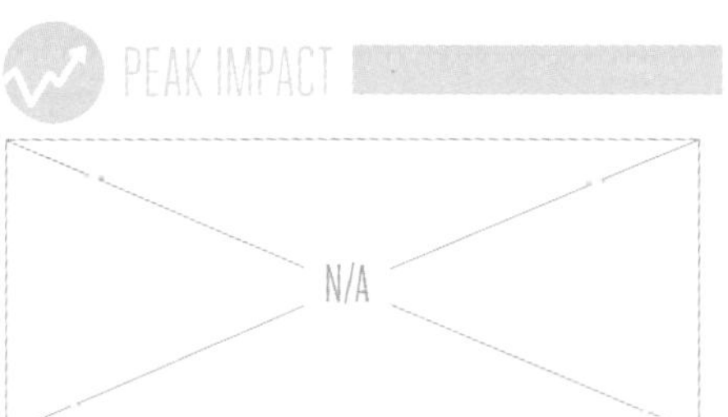

GENDER BIAS

INDICATOR INFORMATION

MODEL: IGBP-DIS SoilData(V.0), 2008, OECD,2012

BASE DATA: FAO FISHSTAT (2012); FAOSTAT (2012); Rubin et al., 1992

= 5 countries (rounded)

Acute Severe High Moderate Low

THE INDICATOR

The indicator relies on two separate studies assessing the effects for aquatic life of both acid rain on inland fisheries and ocean acidification (Ikuta et al., 2008; Narita et al., 2011). The indicator draws on the FAO's fisheries database (FAO FISHSTAT, 2012). The main limitations are that the detailed analysis of inland fisheries was only undertaken in one country and applied to other countries on the basis of emissions and fishery production. Clearly, further research is urgently required. The ocean acidification study enabled regional estimates of losses that were attributed to different countries on the basis of their fishery production. Regional aggregation compromised, to some degree, the accuracy of the results as not all countries in a region will react identically.

ESTIMATES COUNTRY-LEVEL IMPACT

COUNTRY	$ 2010	$ 2030
ACUTE		
Bangladesh	65	300
Belize		1
Cambodia	10	50
Chile	80	600
China	6,500	65,000
Ecuador	45	350
Estonia	35	250
Guyana	5	45
Iceland	1	10
Latvia	5	35
Lithuania	10	75
Malaysia	80	500
Mauritania	1	15
New Zealand	20	60
North Korea	10	100
South Korea	250	2,000
Suriname	1	15
Thailand	200	1,000
Vietnam	500	3,250
SEVERE		
Argentina	60	450
Bahamas	1	5
Canada	150	400
Indonesia	200	800
Peru	20	150
Venezuela	25	200
HIGH		
Bahrain	1	10
Cameroon	1	10
Denmark	10	25
Gabon	1	5
Gambia		1
Ireland	10	30
Mexico	45	350
Myanmar	1	15
Norway	15	40
Palau		
Philippines	40	150
Seychelles		1
Spain	35	100
MODERATE		
Algeria		1
Angola	1	1
Antigua and Barbuda		
Armenia		
Australia	10	30
Austria		
Azerbaijan		
Belarus		
Belgium		1
Benin		1
Bhutan		
Bosnia and Herzegovina		
Brazil	5	30
Brunei		1
Bulgaria	1	10
Cape Verde		
Colombia		1
Comoros		
Congo		1
Croatia	1	5
Cuba	1	5
Cyprus		
Czech Republic		
Dominican Republic		1
Egypt	1	5
Fiji		
Finland		
France	35	100
Georgia		
Germany	5	15
Ghana		1
Greece	5	15
Grenada		
Guinea-Bissau		
Haiti		
Hungary	1	1
India	150	550
Iran	5	15
Iraq		
Israel		1
Italy	20	60
Jamaica		
Japan	65	200
Kazakhstan		
Kuwait	1	5
Lebanon		
Liberia		
Macedonia		
Maldives		
Malta		
Mauritius		
Micronesia		
Moldova		
Morocco	1	5

$ Additional economic costs (million USD PPP) - yearly average

CARBON VULNERABILITY

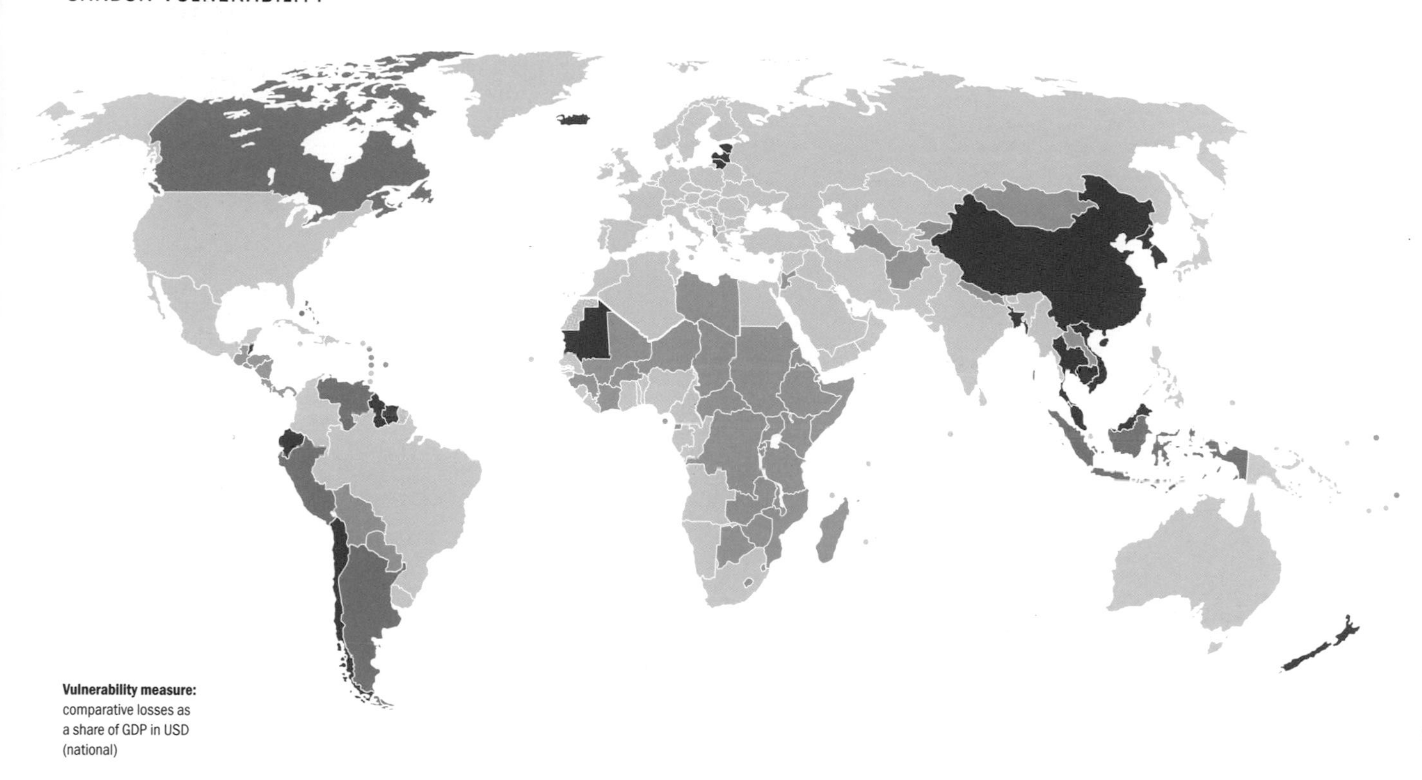

Vulnerability measure: comparative losses as a share of GDP in USD (national)

COUNTRY	2010	2030
Namibia		1
Netherlands	10	35
Nigeria	5	20
Oman		1
Pakistan	1	1
Papua New Guinea		
Poland	1	10
Portugal	1	5
Qatar		1
Romania		
Russia		
Saudi Arabia	5	45
Senegal		1
Sierra Leone		1
Singapore	1	10
Slovakia		
Slovenia		1
Solomon Islands		
South Africa		1
Sri Lanka	1	10
Sweden	1	1
Switzerland		
Syria	1	5
Tajikistan		
Timor-Leste		
Togo		
Tonga		
Trinidad and Tobago		1
Tunisia	1	5
Turkey	5	15
Ukraine	1	10
United Arab Emirates		1

COUNTRY	2010	2030
United Kingdom	25	75
United States	250	700
Uruguay	1	10
Uzbekistan		
Vanuatu		
Yemen		
LOW		
Afghanistan		
Albania		
Barbados		
Bolivia		
Botswana		
Burkina Faso		
Burundi		
Central African Republic		
Chad		
Costa Rica		
Cote d,Ivoire		
Djibouti		
Dominica		
DR Congo		
El Salvador		
Equatorial Guinea		
Eritrea		
Ethiopia		
Guatemala		
Guinea		
Honduras		
Jordan		
Kenya		
Kiribati		
Kyrgyzstan		

COUNTRY	2010	2030
Laos		
Lesotho		
Libya		
Luxembourg		
Madagascar		
Malawi		
Mali		
Marshall Islands		
Mongolia		
Mozambique		
Nepal		
Nicaragua		
Niger		
Panama		
Paraguay		
Rwanda		
Saint Lucia		
Saint Vincent		
Samoa		
Sao Tome and Principe		
Somalia		
Sudan/South Sudan		
Swaziland		
Tanzania		
Turkmenistan		
Tuvalu		
Uganda		
Zambia		
Zimbabwe		

FORESTRY

ESTIMATES GLOBAL CARBON IMPACT

2010 EFFECT TODAY

USD **LOSS** PER YEAR **30 BILLION**

2030 EFFECT TOMORROW

USD **LOSS** PER YEAR **85 BILLION**

- Commercial forestry in countries and regions with high levels of toxic emissions is experiencing productivity losses
- Ozone and acid rain impacts primary productivity and the growth rates of commercial forestry, generating losses in output
- Heavily forested nations especially in Africa and Southeast Asia suffer these effects disproportionately because of the relative significance of their forestry industries

ECONOMIC IMPACT

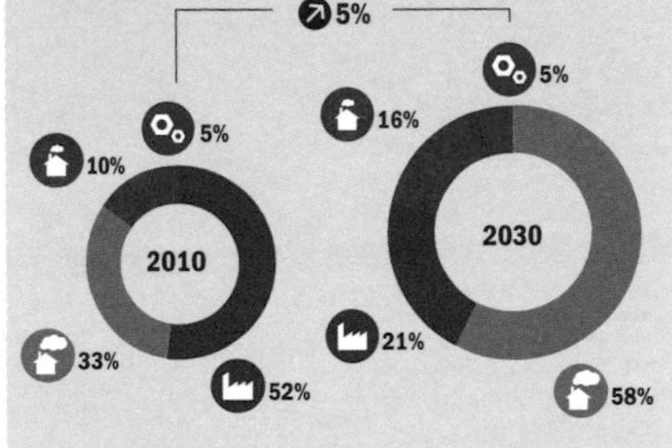

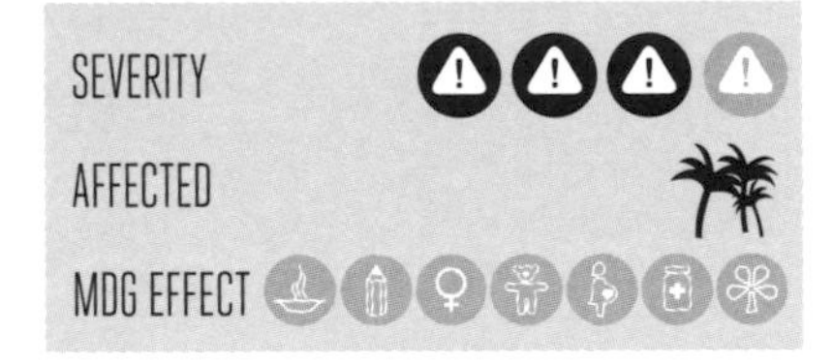

RELATIVE IMPACT

$$$$$$$$$$$$$ $ 2010
127 6

$$$$$$$
$$$$$$$$$$$$$ $ 2030
193 6

HOTSPOTS

2010 $ 2030

2010	Country	2030
3,500	**CHINA**	20,000
10,000	**USA**	15,000
900	**MALAYSIA**	5,000
1,500	**MEXICO**	4,750
1,000	**INDIA**	4,500

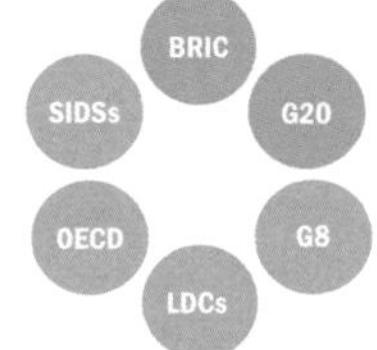

Economic Cost (2010 PPP non-discounted)
Developing Country Low Emitters
Developed
Developing Country High Emitters
Other Industrialized

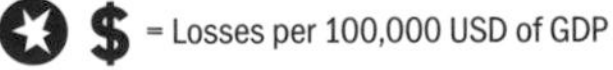

Change in relation to overall global population and/or GDP

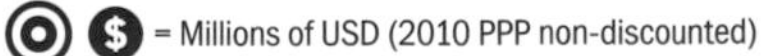

The earth's plant life is susceptible to environmental pollutants released into the air as a by-product of economic activities. Trees are by no means spared these effects, with losses already observable due to problems such as toxic ozone emissions at ground levels (Reilly et al., 2007).
Studies have shown how ambient levels of ozone (O3) in the atmosphere have already reduced tree productivity and will continue to do so rapidly as O3 continues to rise. Critically, this would reduce a major global carbon sink (Wittig et al., 2009). Likewise, acid rain also affects tree productivity, especially where soil acid buffering is low (Likens et al., 1996). In order to significantly reduce the losses these effects produce, particularly for the forestry sector, major economies would need to make synchronized efforts to curtail the heaviest forms of industrial pollution, such as sulphur and nitrogen dioxide emissions generated by coal power and other substances that lead to the production of O3. Trees are more resilient to heightened levels of ground-level O3 and other pollutants than most staple crops, if anticipated losses in other segments of the agricultural sector are taken as reference (Holm Olsen and Fenhann (eds.), 2008).

HAZARD MECHANISM

Emissions like sulphur and nitrogen dioxide and other ozone precursors lead to acid rain and high concentrations of O_3 at ground-level, which have long been shown to be toxic for the growth of plants, including trees (Wentzel, 1982; Mustafa, 1990). These effects directly impact plant and tree productivity, harming the growth of trees and forestry sector outputs (Reilly et al., 2007; Likens et al., 1996). In optimal conditions, higher levels of CO_2 in the atmosphere might also favour growth and expanded output (IPCC, 2007).

IMPACTS

The global impact of the carbon economy on forestry, independent of climate change, is estimated to currently cost 30 billion dollars a year. The level of impact is expected to grow modestly as a share of global GDP over the next 20 years, with losses of 80 billion dollars a year in 2030. Some 25 mainly forest countries in the tropics are acutely vulnerable to these effects and will see the most significant impact. Africa and Southeast Asia are generally worst off, with important concerns for poverty reduction efforts that might be compromised through declining agro-forestry productivity.
The US, China, Mexico, India and Japan are estimated to incur the largest total losses all at or in excess of one billion dollars per year in 2010, and growing rapidly by 2030.

BIGGER PICTURE

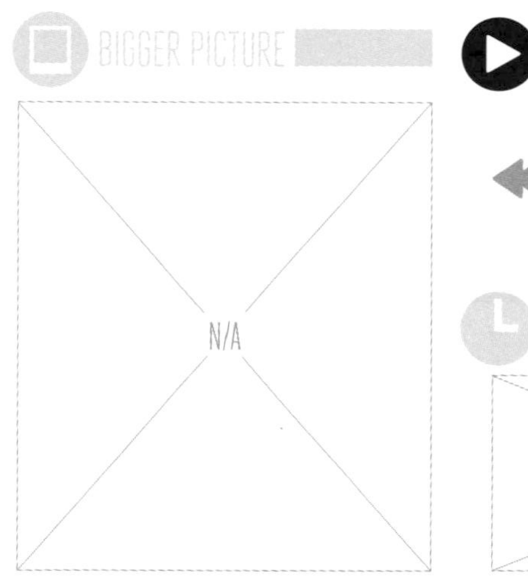

SURGE

OCCURRENCE

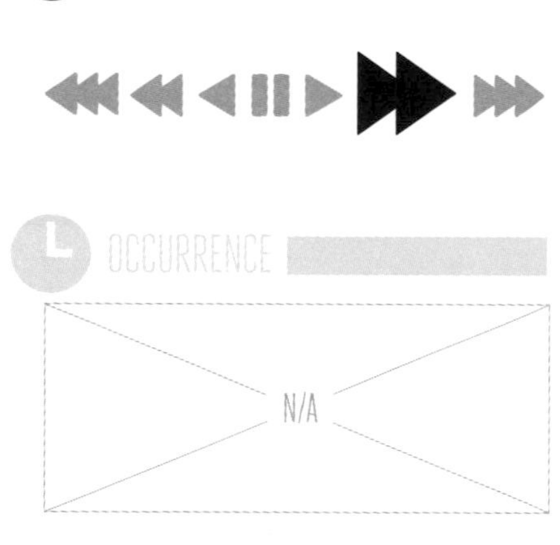

VULNERABILITY SHIFT

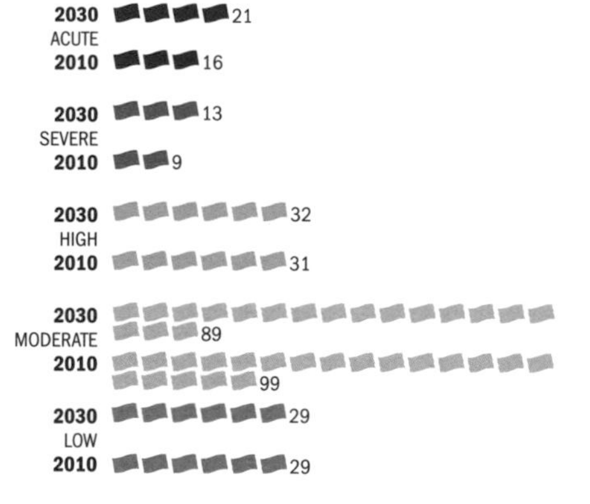

PEAK IMPACT

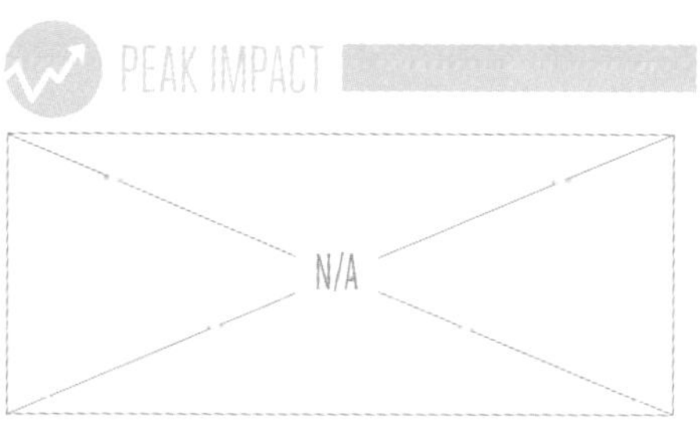

GENDER BIAS

INDICATOR INFORMATION

MODEL: Costanza et al., 1997; OECD, 2012; Reilly, 2008; Wentzel, 1982

BASE DATA: FAOSTAT (2012); Reilly, 2008

= 5 countries (rounded)

● Acute ● Severe ● High ● Moderate ● Low

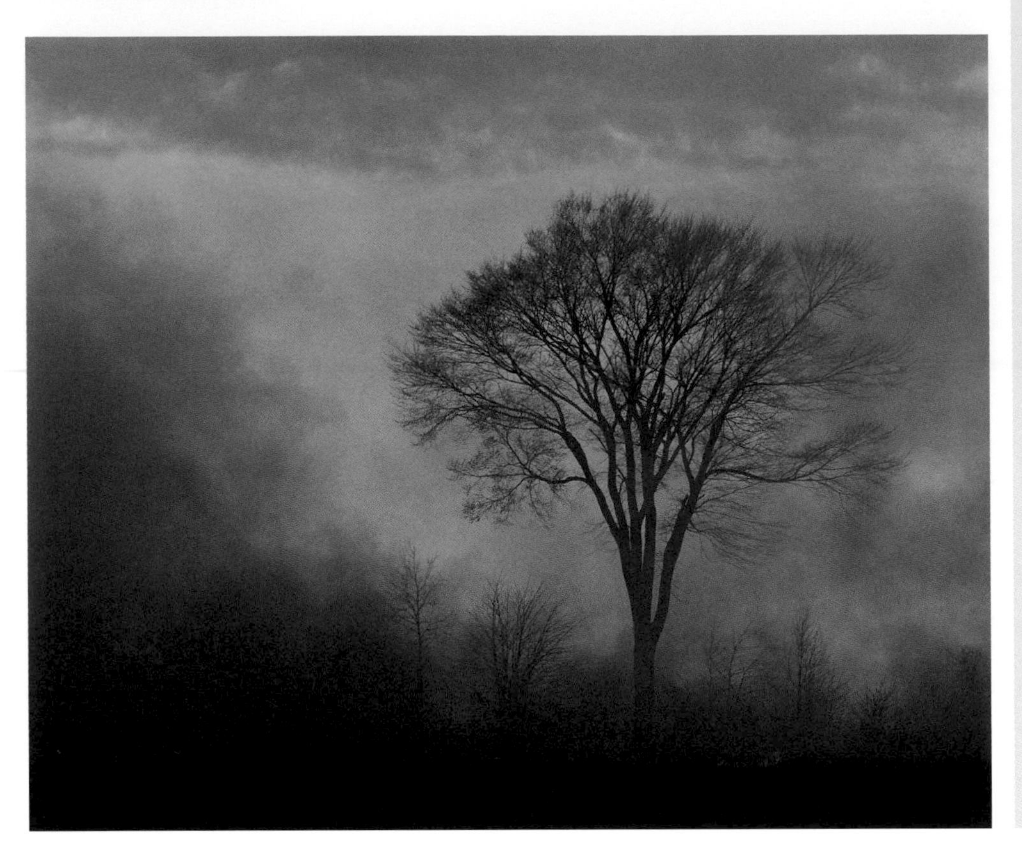

THE INDICATOR

The indicator measures the impact of air pollution on the forestry sector focusing in particular on the extent to which ground-level ozone (O3) and acid rain affect forest productivity. It relies on an ecosystem valuation approach to translate losses into GDP (Reilly et al., 2007; Wentzel, 1982; Costanza et al., 1997). Limitations relate to uncertainties over emissions leading to O3 and acid rain and the regional aggregation of O3 concentrations used (OECD, 2012). Also, research on the effects of acid rain on forests is very out of date. Further investigation is needed since coal energy, heavy in sulphur and nitrogen emissions, is poised to continue to be the world's leading global fuel for power generation well into the 2030s (US EIA, 2011).

ESTIMATES COUNTRY-LEVEL IMPACT

COUNTRY	$ 2010	$ 2030
ACUTE		
Bosnia and Herzegovina	45	100
Botswana	90	400
Bulgaria	150	450
Cameroon	50	250
Central African Republic	1	10
Colombia	450	2,500
Congo	70	300
Dominican Republic	150	750
Gabon	30	200
Georgia	45	100
Guyana	5	35
Laos	10	100
Lebanon	70	350
Lesotho	5	20
Malaysia	900	5,000
Panama	200	1,000
Peru	250	1,250
South Africa	500	2,000
Suriname	5	25
Zambia	50	250
Zimbabwe	10	45
SEVERE		
Australia	750	800
Belize	1	5
Bolivia	15	100
DR Congo	5	40
Ecuador	55	300
Indonesia	550	2,750
Mexico	1,500	4,750
Nigeria	150	750
Thailand	350	2,000
Timor-Leste	1	10
Turkey	500	1,000
United States	10,000	15,000
Venezuela	200	1,000
HIGH		
Angola	25	150
Argentina	250	1,250
Austria	150	200
Brazil	650	3,250
Brunei	5	25
Cambodia	5	70
Canada	350	500
Chad	1	15
China	3,500	20,000
Croatia	35	95
Equatorial Guinea	5	35
Finland	35	70
Guinea	1	5
Guinea-Bissau		1
India	1,000	4,500
Iran	200	1,000
Israel	70	200
Japan	950	1,000
Liberia		1
Mali	1	10
Morocco	30	150
Mozambique	5	35
Myanmar	10	75
Paraguay	5	25
Philippines	65	350
Romania	60	150
Russia	450	1,750
Slovakia	45	100
Somalia	1	5
South Korea	200	1,000
Tanzania	10	50
Yemen	10	50
MODERATE		
Afghanistan		
Albania		1
Algeria	20	100
Antigua and Barbuda		
Bahamas	1	5
Bahrain		
Bangladesh	10	55
Barbados		
Belgium		1
Benin	1	5
Bhutan		1
Burkina Faso	1	5
Burundi		
Cape Verde		
Chile	5	40
Comoros		
Costa Rica	1	10
Cote d,Ivoire	1	10
Cuba	1	10
Cyprus		
Denmark		1
Djibouti		
Dominica		1
Egypt		
El Salvador		1
France	250	300

$ Additional economic costs (million USD PPP) - yearly average

CARBON VULNERABILITY

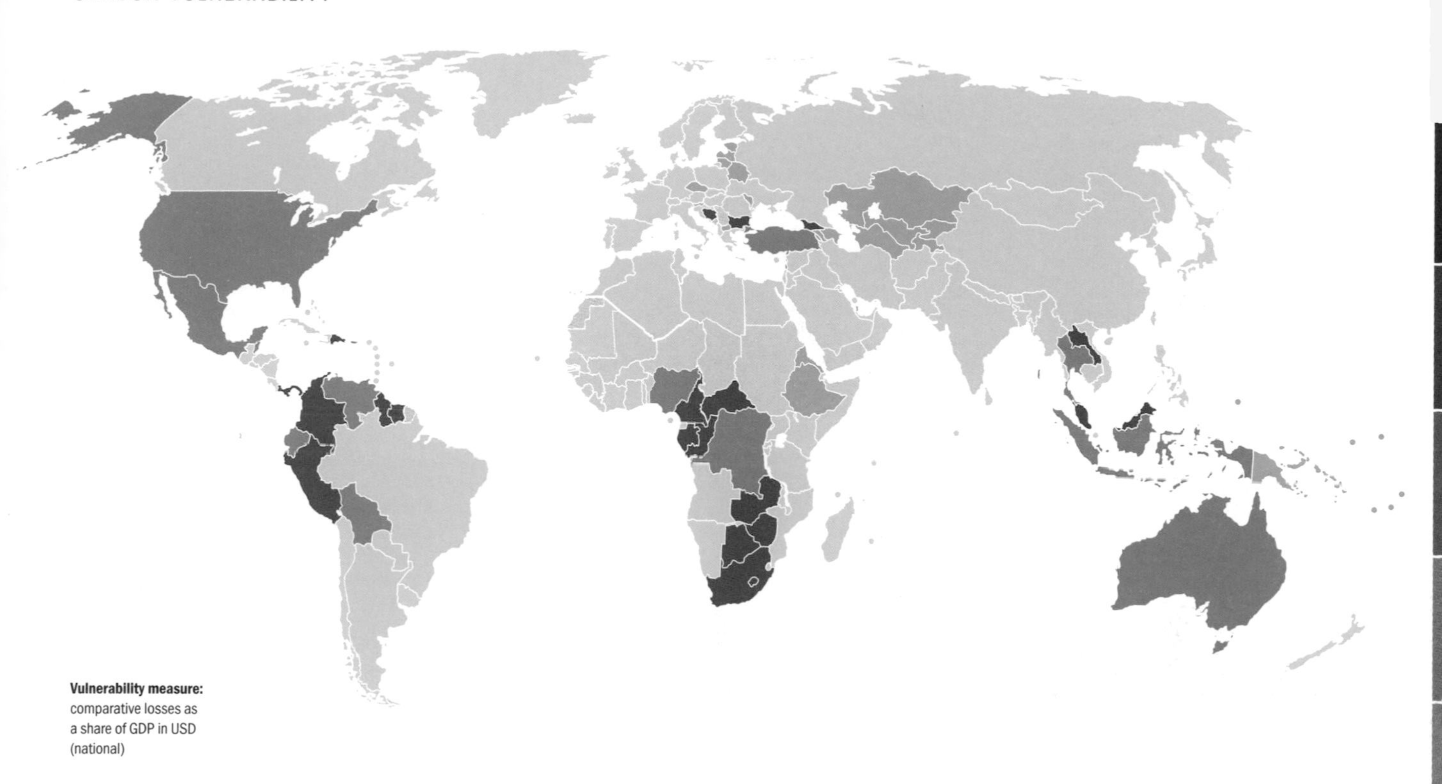

Vulnerability measure: comparative losses as a share of GDP in USD (national)

COUNTRY	2010	2030
Gambia		1
Germany	550	650
Ghana	1	15
Greece	35	40
Grenada		
Guatemala	1	10
Haiti		
Honduras	1	20
Hungary	1	5
Iceland		
Iraq	10	40
Ireland		1
Italy	200	250
Jamaica		1
Jordan		
Kenya	1	5
Kuwait		
Libya		
Luxembourg		1
Madagascar	1	10
Malawi	1	1
Maldives		
Malta		
Mauritania		1
Mauritius		
Mongolia	1	5
Namibia		1
Nepal		1
Netherlands	60	70
New Zealand	1	5
Nicaragua	1	10
Niger		1

COUNTRY	2010	2030
North Korea		1
Norway	10	25
Oman		
Pakistan	10	65
Poland	150	350
Portugal	1	5
Rwanda		
Saint Lucia		
Saint Vincent		
Sao Tome and Principe		
Saudi Arabia		1
Senegal	1	10
Seychelles		1
Sierra Leone		1
Singapore		
Spain	250	300
Sri Lanka		1
Sudan/South Sudan	1	10
Swaziland		
Sweden	40	90
Switzerland	40	50
Syria		
Togo		1
Trinidad and Tobago		1
Tunisia		1
Uganda	1	5
Ukraine	45	100
United Arab Emirates		
United Kingdom	1	5
Uruguay		1
Vietnam	25	200

COUNTRY	2010	2030
LOW		
Armenia		
Azerbaijan		
Belarus		
Czech Republic		
Eritrea		
Estonia		
Ethiopia		
Fiji		
Kazakhstan		
Kiribati		
Kyrgyzstan		
Latvia		
Lithuania		
Macedonia		
Marshall Islands		
Micronesia		
Moldova		
Palau		
Papua New Guinea		
Qatar		
Samoa		
Slovenia		
Solomon Islands		
Tajikistan		
Tonga		
Turkmenistan		
Tuvalu		
Uzbekistan		
Vanuatu		

METHODOLOGY

ARCHITECTURE

Foundations
In all, the Monitor comprises 34 indicators of the economic, human and ecological effects of climate change and the carbon economy. Indexes form the backbone of each indicator and are responsible for generating the relative level of vulnerability registered for each country.

Each index is determined exclusively on the basis of mortality and/or GDP per capita data, capturing only the climate change or carbon economy effect in isolation from other factors. In order to support fair socio-economic comparisons between countries, all estimates are made either in monetary terms (GDP losses) or in terms of mortality. Indicators in the Climate Environmental Disasters impact area are the only ones to combine both mortality and GDP per capita in order to determine the Monitor vulnerability level, where both variables are given full weighting. Combining the variables in this instance ensures a holistic interpretation of the full socio-economic spectrum of disaster vulnerability and does not seek to imply any value judgement on human life versus inanimate assets. Mortality, in many cases, might be fewer than 10 deaths per 10 million, so the smallest countries may not register vulnerability to extreme weather if economic losses are not accounted for. Additional variables of interest are provided for different indicators as appropriate in order to provide a fuller understanding of the impacts estimated to be taking place, such as populations at risk from desertification or illness rates for health indicators.

Breadth and Aggregation
The Monitor uses an enumerative methodology to estimate a wide range of distinct effects resulting from climate change and the carbon economy that can be summed to gauge overall country and global impacts in socio-economic terms. Each indicator represents a separate grouped set of effects that rely on independent research and data sets. All effects are unified by means of a common mathematical framework and assimilated into indexes that facilitate comparison and analysis between the 184 countries.

Impact Estimations
Each of the Monitor's 34 indicators provides cost or gain estimates for 2010 and 2030 that relate solely to climate change or the carbon economy. They are the results of this project's particular methodology and the underlying research and data sets chosen. Other choices, other methodologies and other projects will almost certainly yield different results. Ideally, comparable efforts by other research groups would help identify more readily the main areas of confluence and incongruence between the different findings and approaches that now exist.

Vulnerability Levels
The Monitor's vulnerability assessment system enables a comparison of impacts on a per capita basis across countries. The level of impact indicates the level of climate-related vulnerability. The five vulnerability levels used throughout the Monitor are statistically determined via (mean absolute) standard deviation, with the level "Low" representing near-zero or positive effects and the level "Acute" denoting impacts several degrees or intervals removed from (or above) Low. The upper three levels of vulnerability (Acute, Severe, High) also have two further sub-categories that are sometimes shown to illustrate where (at the top or low end) in these higher vulnerability categories the assessment places countries or groups. Vulnerability levels are determined for each indicator in relation to how all countries are collectively experiencing that particular effect. This is done at the effect level – Sea-Level Rise, for instance. So in some cases, effects for which a country has Acute vulnerability may be smaller in scale than concerns assessed at High vulnerability. Vulnerability levels indicate a country's deviation from the norm of impacts experienced for a given effect and do not necessarily indicate which effects present the highest risk to a country.
Aggregated indexes for the Climate and Carbon sections are determined by averaging or adding up the results of the lower tier assessments. Multi-dimensional vulnerability to Climate or Carbon is an average across all indexes and is only representative

of the degree to which countries are vulnerable to a wide range of effects, without considering the relative importance of different effects. The overall human (or mortality) impact or the overall economic impact data (indexes) on the other hand, represent the sum of all effects measured in the lower tiers and illustrate how these totals compare with other countries. The vulnerability levels are static so that progression of effects over time highlights the degree to which countries are estimated to be gaining or shedding vulnerability between 2010 and 2030. The whole statistical framework is an attempt to conserve the implications of the underlying scientific/research estimations, which are cited, together with key data, in the chapters for each indicator.

Calculating Climate and Carbon Effects
To calculate the impact of individual effects, the Monitor combines estimations from expert and scientific literature or models with bodies of ecological, economic or societal data. It is assumed that the impacts of climate change and the carbon economy are already at play in the world's economic, environmental and social systems. Therefore, to estimate the impact of either process, "climate" or "carbon", on current levels of welfare, it is necessary to keep a counterfactual in mind. The counterfactual is the situation that would have prevailed in the absence of climate change and/or carbon intensive practices. Incremental economic, environmental or social outcomes assessed here are therefore estimated deviations from a level of welfare that would otherwise have been higher or lower. Any opportunity costs only make sense if an alternative to the carbon economy is available. Therefore, costs and benefits must be contextualized against the costs of transitioning towards a low-carbon economy - for which analysis is provided at the front of this report.

Contextual Bases
The Monitor's system of analysis relies on reference projections in order to generate the most plausible understanding of how the world is likely to evolve between now and 2030. GHG emissions and temperature increases vary across indicators depending on the base research, with the most common scenario being the medium-high A1B marker scenario of the IPCC (IPCC, 2000). Climate change is understood as the change in weather versus, in most cases, a base year of 1975 (as the mid-point of the 1961 to 1990 climate). Projections for population and economic growth are drawn from Columbia University's Centre for International Earth Science Information Network based on the IPCC A1B scenario (CIESIN, 2002). Reference GDP and population data is drawn respectively from the International Monetary Fund and the UN population division (IMF WEO, 2012; UN pop div., 2012). For certain indicators other dynamic adjustments are made to key parameters, such as an anticipated income-driven decline in the prevalence of some communicable diseases, or structural evolutions to developing economies (Mathers and Loncar, 2005; OCED, 2012). Current responses to climate change, such as adaptation or mitigation, are assumed to be held at today's relative levels so that estimates for 2030 represent business as usual. The Monitor doesn't adjust for any future policy initiatives that could increase or stimulate adaptation to or mitigation of climate change.

THE APPROACH

Dealing with Climate Uncertainties
The Monitor is a pragmatic study. Exercises like the Monitor are by definition imperfect (Smith et al. in IPCC, 2001), above all because a variety of uncertainties exist in almost every tier of the analysis. There are six main sets of uncertainties involved in the Monitor's assessment:

- *Climate-related:* uncertainty about the levels of GHG emissions (present and future), temperature changes for different emission levels, effects for other weather variables such as wind and rainfall as a result of temperature changes, limitations of global or regional research (i.e. climate models) accurately describing effects at country or sub-national levels
- *Social and environmental:* uncertainty related to the varying quality or comprehensiveness of the base data, such as the accuracy of databases on current rates of illness, of reported disaster damage

MISSING THE FULL METHODOLOGICAL DOCUMENTATION?
The complete in-depth methodological documentation for the Monitor with technical descriptions for each of its indicators is available online at:
www.dararint.org/cvm2/method

or of biodiversity concentrations and projections of population growth
- *Economic/technological:* uncertainty related to future economic growth and advances in technology
- *Scientific/empirical:* uncertainty in estimating the effects of climate change in social, economic or ecological terms
- *Extrapolation:* in many cases, effects are estimated in just a few representative countries and are then extrapolated to provide a global picture, introducing possibilities for error
- *Aggregation/assimilation:* when compiling diverse data sets, models and pieces of information, judgements of different kinds sometimes must be made, which could introduce further margins of error.

Many of the above factors are closely interrelated, such as population, economic growth and emissions of GHGs.
Uncertainty is, therefore, very real to the study of climate change and must be taken seriously. However, the world cannot simply wait, inactive, until all uncertainties have been mathematically weighed even as climate changes are clearly observable as recorded in successive IPCC reports (IPCC, 1990, 1995, 2001 and 2007). The uncertainty of this study is also relatively contained for the field of climate change, given the short timeframe of much of the analysis compared to the near centennial or longer focus of most climate research. Neither is uncertainty restricted to the field of climate change. Major macroeconomic and corporate decisions are made every day, shaping global and local economies around the world that involve the highest degrees of uncertainty (Oxelheim and Wihlborg, 2008).
Studies like this one make best attempts to soundly balance all of the competing considerations. Deliberate steps are also taken to minimize uncertainties. For instance, the database of economic damage caused by extreme storms and floods that the Monitor uses is a hybrid of the main international provider in the public sector and one of the main global reinsurers (CRED/EM-DAT, 2012; Munich Re NatCat, 2012). Relying on just one of these reduces considerably the losses for several countries, decreasing the robustness of any conclusions.
On the other hand, the homogeneity of more than 15 models in predicting large increases in heavy rainfall as the planet warms is quite striking, considering many of them were developed separately by experts living in different countries over varying periods of time (Kharin et al., 2007; IPCC, 2012a).
That so much research in this field reaches similar conclusions is remarkable precisely because of the implausibly large uncertainties that apply. The “unequivocal” language of the IPCC regarding the existence and primary causes of recent global warming is a good example (IPCC, 2007). It results from an overwhelming burden of proof with no alternative explanations (Royal Society, 2005). And it explains why the leading scientific bodies of more than 50 countries, including those of major economies like the US and China, regularly communicate concern on climate change issues (IAP, 2009).
While there’s now clear consensus on the basics of climate change, the similar findings that result from similar assumptions from study to study do leave the door open to systemic risk. This could prevent anticipation of catastrophic outcomes. The economics field met with such a crisis following the collapse of the global financial system in 2008 (Krugman, 2009). Unlike business-cycle decisions, decisions on the climate do not leave as much scope for error and recuperation if full heed is paid to the conclusions of mainstream science and GHG emission modelling (IPCC, 2007; UNEP, 2011).
Experts say that, when making decisions in highly dynamic and uncertain conditions, those decisions should be robust to a wide range of possible outcomes, should involve learning for improved reactions to emerging risks and opportunities, and should be grounded in a wide range of analytical inputs so as not to exclude potentially important options or concerns (Lempert and Schlesinger, 2000; Vecchiato, 2012; Baddeley, 2010). This study offers just one further input to that process.

Precautionary Measures
The 1992 UN climate change convention (UNFCCC), the key international treaty on climate change, does stipulate precaution and binds its 195 parties to take cost-effective measures to prevent or minimize harm

COMMENTS AND SUGGESTIONS

Readers, specialists and users of the report are highly encouraged to forward any suggestions for improvements to the structure, focus and/or methodology of the Monitor to DARA. The research team is most grateful for every input received. Please contact DARA via: **cvm@daraint.org**

when threats of serious or irreversible damage are evident - even in the absence of full scientific certainty (UNFCCC, 1992).

The conclusions offered by this report point to serious harm. The findings are, however, based on estimates that could, in reality, be either substantially lower or substantially higher - as uncertainty is symmetrical. Caution, though, is particularly flagged because the Monitor's approach is less precautionary than it is conservative in several respects.

Limitations of Analysis

To begin with, the emission scenario chosen for most indicators is not the highest available. While the second edition of the Monitor is significantly more comprehensive than the first, numerous impacts are simply beyond the analysis here for lack of adequate reference studies or due to methodological difficulties. This particularly applies to so-called "socially contingent" impacts, such as the effects on social and political stability, conflict, crime, or cultural assets, such as World Heritage sites - for which plausible relationships have been mapped or argued (Stern, 2006; Ahmed et al., 2009; Burke et al., 2009 and 2010; CNA, 2007; Scheffran et al., 2012; Agnew, 2012; UNESCO, 2010). Neither does the mainly near-term Monitor factor in the potential costs of future large-scale abrupt impacts, although a number of prominent economists whose timeframes of analysis are more extended advise otherwise (Nordaus and Boyer, 2000; Hope, 2006). Still, it is equally possible that some of the impacts not considered here include positive outcomes for society (Tol, 2010).

Other more straightforward costs that are known lacunas for the field are also not adequately covered here. Agriculture is just one example. Costs associated with additional irrigation by farmers in a much warmer world are essentially unaccounted for in most agricultural models, even when high temperatures are expected to more than offset any additional rainfall (Cline, 2007). Furthermore, a broad range of staple crops are now understood to react more rapidly and negatively after exceeding a particular high temperature threshold than was previously understood to be the case (Schlenker and Roberts, 2009; Ackerman and Stanton, 2011).

Finally, this study uses the equivalent of a direct-cost approach for estimations, exploring impacts as losses or gains to independent sectors or as discrete gains/losses for those directly affected. This does not take into consideration the passing on of gains or losses elsewhere. It is, however, generally understood that markets can and do spread these effects further. Businesses for instance, pass on their prosperity or difficulties to their clients, competitors and suppliers, as well as to investors and financial markets (Kuik et al., 2008). That fact has led some experts to conclude that direct costs are, by definition, an underestimation (Bosello et al., 2005). One expert has estimated that direct damage costs could be multiplied by a factor of 20 in certain instances (Hallegatte, 2005).

Balancing Comprehensiveness and Accuracy

The Monitor attempts to contribute breadth and descriptiveness to the understanding of global climate-related issues without venturing too far into conjecture and methodological unknowns. Although the spectrum of over 30 indicators reviewed does range from the clearly speculative through to the more robust. The larger-scale impacts assessed in the Monitor are nevertheless evaluated as being more robust in general than the impacts of lesser macroeconomic significance also included here. Even when knowledge barriers allow for little more than speculation on the full nature of an effect, it was judged that not including these effects, such as tropical storms or impacts on the tourism industry - indicators endowed respectively with high uncertainty and low scientific foundations - would penalize the assessment more through a lack of comprehensiveness than might be gained through any enhanced certitude.

Uncertainties, once more, are fundamental to any understanding and response to climate change. As global warming accelerates, everyone from policy makers through to the general public will likely be required to engage and act more on the basis of uncertain and speculative information. Given the stage of development of climate policy, deliberately highlighting limitations within studies like this through inclusion of potentially vital information (while clearly signalling its shortcomings) can serve to shed light on how and where limitations lie, aid in pinpointing research priorities and provide greater clarity in separating out the less robust information from the more robust. This report aims to advance understanding in all such respects.

ASSESSMENT CATEGORIZATION/DISTINCTIONS

Overlap and Separating Effects

A very deliberate effort has been made to ensure that all indicators in the Monitor represent no - or at worst only marginal or statistically insignificant - overlap. The Climate Environmental Disasters indicator on drought is a case in point. Unlike the other disaster indicators, it does not account for any mortality impact. This is because the Hunger indicator under Health Impact is accounting for the ramifications of worsening food availability as a result of climate change, including drought. Another example relates to the Sea-Level Rise and Water indicators under Climate Habitat Change. The Water indicator measures the impact of a net change in water availability resulting from rainfall pattern alterations and heat. It does not, however, account for the saline contamination of water reservoirs in coastal areas caused by erosion due to rising sea levels, an effect captured under the Sea-Level Rise indicator.

Furthermore, two indicators, Heating and Cooling and Labour Productivity, both categorized under Climate Habitat Change, are near mirrors to one another and required adjustment to avoid overlap. Heating and Cooling estimates the rising or falling energy costs linked to the climate conditioning of indoor space to maintain unaltered levels of comfort as the planet warms. Labour Productivity measures the losses (or gains) to productivity incurred to the outdoor and indoor workforce exposed to increasing heat. The costs estimated in Heating and Cooling were removed from the Labour Productivity indicator to ensure no overlap.

The Carbon section is generally more clear-cut than the Climate section, which assesses almost double the number of effects. The greatest propensity for overlap concerns the Climate indicators for Agriculture, Desertification, Drought and Water, although the extent of this is still considered limited. This is because the Agriculture indicator is mainly measuring a departure from optimal growing conditions or how land value and production capacity evolve in relation to changing climate conditions, whereas Drought is estimating the implications - mainly for the agricultural sector - of the increasing occurrence of these major hydrological events, which are highly randomized and have severe repercussions that are not fully accounted for in climate productivity models of agricultural yield change. Desertification very specifically measures the highly accelerated degradation of arid lands due to heat and water stress and the associated depreciation of land investments and yield capacity. There is, however, some possibility of overlap due to the manner in which the land-value base estimates for agricultural losses are calculated as a component of the Monitor's Climate Agriculture indicator (see: Cline, 2007). As Desertification itself represents just 1% of estimated global losses due to climate change in 2010, any overlap would still be quite marginal to this study.

Rainfall and evaporation are other parameters built into the Agriculture indicator. Less favourable rainfall patterns or high levels of evaporation not compensated for by additional rain will invariably entail losses, especially for rain-fed only agriculture, some of which are certainly accounted for under the Agriculture indicator. The Drought indicator also measures farm losses due to extreme water scarcity. Independent from this, the Water indicator measures national variation in the water resource balance sheet and assumes that deficits due to climate change are made up at the lowest market price for water.

Where agriculture is rain-fed only, there is no overlap, since such farmers are not purchasing water on the market and are therefore not accounted for in water demand estimations. Where farmers rely on supplied irrigation, deviations from optimal conditions likely cause demand for water to increase as the farmer pays for the additional requirement (and incurs a cost). Alternatively, more water may not be purchased and yield losses could result (also incurring costs). But what the Water indicator measures is the overall change in supply to the market that the farmer purchases water from. It assumes that in order to maintain the same supply of water that existed prior to the onset of unfavourable conditions, costs will be incurred at the market rate for supplying more water.

That means it is accounting for the cost of retaining equilibrium market conditions to offset any scarcity at the time when the farmer is purchasing additional water. Of course, if the entire agricultural sector is purchasing more water, demand will also increase and so will the market price and the losses for the sector. Such intricacies can rarely be accounted for in agriculture models such as those the Monitor draws on for that indicator (Cline, 2007). Therefore, any overlap is largely contained.

Carbon: Conceptual Framework

The new Monitor now supplements analysis with a detailed assessment of the economic, health and environmental impacts of the carbon economy. This assessment forms the second part of the Monitor, labelled "Carbon". Of special interest in the Carbon part of the Monitor is the acquisition and consumption of fuels and the release of various types of greenhouse pollutants via combustion. The Monitor examines the costs and benefits of all these processes - extraction, production, consumption - independently of the wide-ranging costs and benefits resulting from climate change, which, of course, is caused by these processes.

It is important to qualify three points related to the Carbon section. First, highly hazardous sulphur dioxide emissions are included in the analysis, although strictly speaking, sulphur is not a GHG and is even widely understood to have cooling, rather than warming, properties (Kaufmann et al., 2011; Smith et al., 2011). Other research, however, has asserted that sulphur is a principal initiator of global warming since it decreases the atmosphere's capacity to oxidize and deplete GHGs (Ward, 2009). Either way, sulphur dioxide is typically emitted together with other GHGs in transportation and energy production - coal power, in particular, which is also responsible for 40% of CO_2 emissions - and various mitigation policies targeting these gases would in most instances implicate sulphur dioxide as well (Olivier et al., 2012). Hence sulphur emissions go hand in hand with a carbon economy and are largely incompatible with a low-carbon economy.

Second, when the Monitor discusses urban air pollution and indoor smoke concerns for human health, it includes the burning of biomass (e.g. wood, crop waste), especially in open or indoor fires, which may not necessarily contribute to global warming if the source of fuel is self-replenishing (such as crop waste). With nearly 3 billion people relying on traditional stoves for household needs worldwide, however, particulate-generating cooking stoves are still considered a major source of GHGs and, especially in arid countries with low biomass availability, can drive deforestation (Foell et al., 2011; Bensch and Peters, 2011). The burning of biomass, including in indoor settings, is in any case understood as a principal driver of current warming due to concentrated emissions of soot in highly populated tropical regions (Ramanathan and Carmichael, 2008). Measures to furnish clean burning stoves to households would also enhance GHG sinks. The Monitor did not, therefore, exclude this issue from the analysis.

The third issue relates to carbon fertilization, which is a phenomenon measured in the Carbon section (see: Carbon/Agriculture). However, the Hunger indicator in the Climate section (see: Climate/Hunger) nevertheless accounts for the positive role that carbon fertilization can play in reducing the degree of agricultural losses on the basis of a World Health Organization model (WHO, 2004).

DATA
TABLES

ACUTE

Country	Mortality TOTAL 2010	Mortality TOTAL 2030	Persons affected 1,000s 2010	Persons affected 1,000s 2030	Economic costs % GDP PPP 2010	Economic costs % GDP PPP 2030	Economic costs % GDP PPP 2010
Afghanistan	90,000	150,000	10,000	20,000	2.8%	4.9%	5.5%
Angola	45,000	45,000	10,000	15,000	4.1%	7.9%	9.2%
Armenia	3,000	3,000	95	95	0.6%	1.2%	0.5%
Bahamas	30	35	95	100	5.8%	15.8%	
Belize	45	55	30	40	7.7%	14.2%	5.3%
Benin	9,000	9,500	1,250	1,750	5.0%	10.2%	2.7%
Bolivia	3,000	3,500	1,000	1,500	3.3%	7.5%	8.8%
Bulgaria	7,000	6,000	85	80	0.7%	1.5%	0.7%
Burkina Faso	25,000	30,000	3,250	3,750	4.5%	8.6%	3.0%
Burundi	15,000	15,000	1,500	2,000	3.9%	8.7%	3.5%
Cambodia	15,000	20,000	1,750	2,000	4.9%	10.3%	2.7%
Cameroon	20,000	20,000	4,000	5,000	4.4%	9.0%	4.3%
Central African Republic	5,500	5,500	650	900	5.6%	11.9%	13.5%
Chad	20,000	20,000	2,500	3,000	5.0%	9.5%	3.1%
China	1,500,000	1,500,000	100,000	100,000	0.7%	1.3%	0.7%
Congo	3,500	4,500	450	650	3.4%	6.5%	8.0%
Cote d'Ivoire	25,000	25,000	2,250	3,250	4.6%	8.9%	3.7%
Dominica	15	15	60	80	5.9%	11.7%	0.1%
DR Congo	100,000	100,000	15,000	20,000	3.9%	8.5%	7.1%
Equatorial Guinea	250	350	250	350	3.1%	5.8%	5.0%
Fiji	300	300	95	95	6.2%	11.1%	0.2%
Gabon	700	950	250	350	5.8%	11.1%	23.1%
Gambia	1,500	1,000	250	300	9.0%	18.2%	1.7%
Guinea	10,000	10,000	1,250	1,500	8.0%	16.3%	4.3%
Guinea-Bissau	2,500	2,500	450	600	27.4%	47.2%	5.9%
Guyana	250	200	150	200	7.4%	12.6%	40.5%
Honduras	2,500	3,000	350	650	4.6%	9.0%	1.5%
India	1,000,000	1,500,000	250,000	450,000	2.2%	4.3%	1.0%
Kiribati	15	20	85	95	17.4%	28.1%	0.1%
Laos	4,000	4,500	650	800	3.5%	7.1%	3.0%
Liberia	6,000	7,000	600	700	9.9%	17.5%	6.1%
Madagascar	20,000	20,000	2,250	2,750	6.8%	11.8%	3.1%
Malaysia	5,500	8,000	2,750	3,250	3.6%	7.3%	2.2%
Maldives	70	150	250	350	9.2%	15.9%	0.2%
Mali	25,000	25,000	3,000	3,500	5.7%	11.9%	3.3%
Marshall Islands	30	35	55	60	31.3%	49.6%	0.4%
Mauritania	3,500	3,500	350	400	9.0%	16.6%	1.4%
Micronesia	30	35	20	25	10.3%	20.7%	0.3%
Mongolia	1,500	1,500	600	1,250	6.5%	8.4%	1.9%
Mozambique	25,000	25,000	6,000	8,500	7.7%	14.2%	3.6%
Myanmar	45,000	55,000	10,000	15,000	6.6%	12.9%	0.8%
Namibia	450	550	150	250	1.4%	13.5%	1.2%
Nicaragua	1,500	2,000	200	400	6.3%	11.8%	2.4%
Niger	35,000	40,000	4,000	4,500	5.3%	10.0%	4.9%
Pakistan	150,000	250,000	20,000	45,000	2.3%	4.4%	1.0%
Palau	5	5	5	5	8.6%	15.2%	0.1%

Additional mortality – yearly average; Additional economic costs in 2010 USD (negative numbers show gains) – yearly average; Additional persons affected – yearly average

2030

CLIMATE: Envi. Disasters · Habitat Change · Health Impact · Industry Stress

CARBON: Envi. Disas. · Habitat Change · Health Impact · Industry Stress

Afghanistan
Angola
Armenia
Bahamas
Belize
Benin
Bolivia
Bulgaria
Burkina Faso
Burundi
Cambodia
Cameroon
Central African Republic
Chad
China
Congo
Cote d'Ivoire
Dominica
DR Congo
Equatorial Guinea
Fiji
Gabon
Gambia
Guinea
Guinea-Bissau
Guyana
Honduras
India
Kiribati
Laos
Liberia
Madagascar
Malaysia
Maldives
Mali
Marshall Islands
Mauritania
Micronesia
Mongolia
Mozambique
Myanmar
Namibia
Nicaragua
Niger
Pakistan
Palau

Acute · Severe · High · Moderate · Low

		TOTAL		1,000s		% GDP PPP		% GDP PPP
		2010	2030	2010	2030	2010	2030	2010
ACUTE	Panama	550	650	250	400	4.2%	8.4%	2.1%
	Papua New Guinea	3,500	5,000	850	1,500	6.6%	12.1%	11.6%
	Paraguay	1,000	1,500	150	250	1.3%	3.0%	4.7%
	Rwanda	20,000	15,000	1,500	2,000	2.4%	4.5%	3.6%
	Sao Tome and Principe	100	100	20	35	9.1%	15.8%	1.3%
	Senegal	15,000	15,000	1,500	2,000	6.2%	12.3%	1.9%
	Seychelles	10	10	20	30	8.1%	19.1%	
	Sierra Leone	15,000	15,000	1,500	1,750	10.4%	20.5%	7.4%
	Solomon Islands	200	250	100	150	21.1%	34.1%	0.4%
	Somalia	20,000	20,000	3,000	4,000	16.7%	25.9%	3.4%
	Suriname	150	150	90	100	4.0%	7.2%	25.1%
	Timor-Leste	250	250	150	200	8.7%	16.0%	5.8%
	Togo	7,500	7,000	700	1,000	5.1%	10.2%	2.5%
	Tuvalu	5	5	10	10	11.0%	23.1%	0.4%
	Ukraine	45,000	40,000	3,250	4,000	0.8%	1.4%	0.4%
	Vanuatu	75	100	35	50	21.1%	44.8%	0.2%
	Vietnam	55,000	65,000	20,000	25,000	5.2%	10.7%	0.8%
	Zambia	15,000	15,000	1,750	2,250	3.1%	7.1%	5.2%
SEVERE	Antigua and Barbuda	10	10	60	75	5.1%	10.6%	0.1%
	Bangladesh	100,000	150,000	55,000	70,000	2.8%	6.8%	0.9%
	Belarus	5,500	5,500	100	150	0.7%	1.2%	0.7%
	Bosnia and Herzegovina	3,000	3,000	150	300	0.5%	1.0%	0.5%
	Botswana	1,000	850	200	250	0.9%	1.5%	3.3%
	Brunei	35	55	100	150	0.5%	0.7%	3.5%
	Cape Verde	90	85	85	150	5.8%	10.6%	0.2%
	Colombia	10,000	15,000	1,250	2,000	2.6%	5.2%	1.5%
	Comoros	300	300	90	95	4.5%	7.5%	0.9%
	Costa Rica	700	850	100	200	3.1%	6.3%	0.6%
	Djibouti	550	600	200	300	3.6%	6.6%	0.4%
	El Salvador	1,500	1,500	300	500	3.6%	7.2%	0.5%
	Eritrea	3,000	3,000	300	450	5.2%	8.6%	1.3%
	Ethiopia	100,000	100,000	10,000	15,000	2.0%	3.7%	2.7%
	Georgia	3,500	3,500	150	150	1.5%	2.9%	0.7%
	Ghana	15,000	15,000	2,250	2,750	4.4%	8.9%	1.7%
	Grenada	10	10	25	30	5.2%	10.3%	0.1%
	Guatemala	3,500	5,000	1,750	2,500	2.9%	5.8%	0.8%
	Haiti	8,000	9,000	1,500	1,750	3.7%	7.1%	1.2%
	Indonesia	150,000	200,000	30,000	40,000	3.5%	7.0%	1.8%
	Jamaica	1,000	1,500	200	300	3.9%	8.1%	0.2%
	Kazakhstan	9,000	10,000	250	350	0.3%	0.4%	0.4%
	Kyrgyzstan	4,000	4,500	600	1,000	4.2%	6.0%	0.7%
	Latvia	1,500	1,500	75	75	0.1%		0.3%
	Macedonia	1,000	1,000	20	20	0.9%	1.8%	0.5%
	Malawi	20,000	20,000	2,000	2,500	3.2%	7.4%	2.6%
	Mexico	25,000	40,000	5,000	8,250	3.1%	6.1%	0.7%
	Moldova	2,500	2,500	40	40	0.2%	0.4%	0.3%

Additional mortality – yearly average | Additional economic costs in 2010 USD (negative numbers show gains) – yearly average | Additional persons affected – yearly average

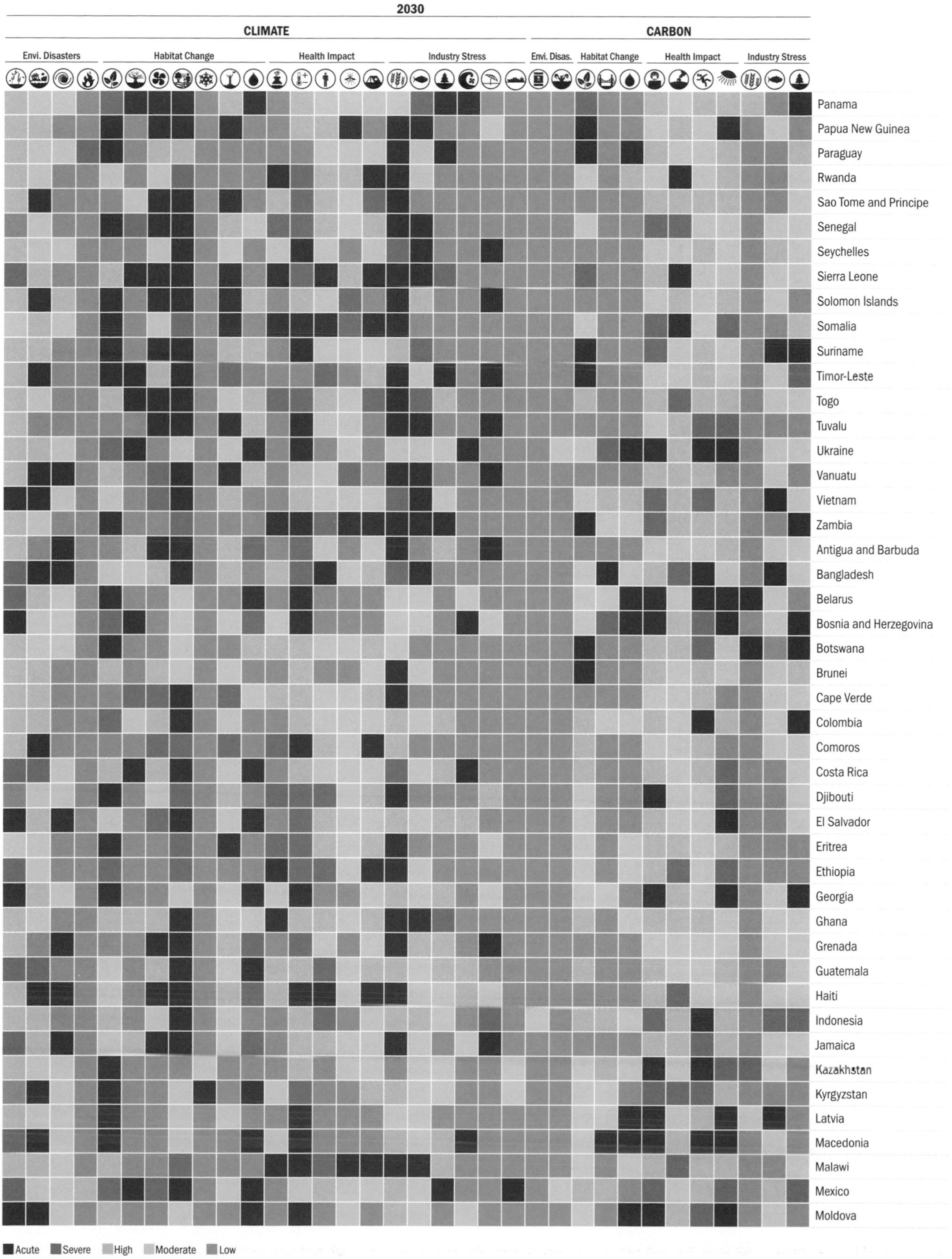

2030

CLIMATE				CARBON			
Envi. Disasters	Habitat Change	Health Impact	Industry Stress	Envi. Disas.	Habitat Change	Health Impact	Industry Stress

Panama
Papua New Guinea
Paraguay
Rwanda
Sao Tome and Principe
Senegal
Seychelles
Sierra Leone
Solomon Islands
Somalia
Suriname
Timor-Leste
Togo
Tuvalu
Ukraine
Vanuatu
Vietnam
Zambia
Antigua and Barbuda
Bangladesh
Belarus
Bosnia and Herzegovina
Botswana
Brunei
Cape Verde
Colombia
Comoros
Costa Rica
Djibouti
El Salvador
Eritrea
Ethiopia
Georgia
Ghana
Grenada
Guatemala
Haiti
Indonesia
Jamaica
Kazakhstan
Kyrgyzstan
Latvia
Macedonia
Malawi
Mexico
Moldova

Acute | Severe | High | Moderate | Low

Group	Country	TOTAL 2010	TOTAL 2030	1,000s 2010	1,000s 2030	% GDP PPP 2010	% GDP PPP 2030	% GDP PPP 2010
SEVERE	Nigeria	200,000	200,000	20,000	25,000	4.0%	7.6%	2.3%
SEVERE	North Korea	9,500	10,000	3,500	4,500	7.0%	10.9%	0.2%
SEVERE	Peru	7,000	9,000	1,750	2,500	1.3%	3.0%	2.8%
SEVERE	Philippines	35,000	50,000	9,000	10,000	3.5%	7.1%	0.9%
SEVERE	Romania	15,000	15,000	300	300	0.6%	1.1%	0.4%
SEVERE	Russia	100,000	80,000	8,000	15,000	0.7%	0.8%	1.0%
SEVERE	Samoa	65	70	25	35	5.2%	9.9%	0.3%
SEVERE	Sri Lanka	8,500	9,000	1,500	2,250	3.6%	7.4%	0.6%
SEVERE	Tajikistan	6,000	7,000	450	600	1.5%	2.6%	1.0%
SEVERE	Thailand	25,000	30,000	7,500	9,000	3.6%	7.2%	0.6%
SEVERE	Tonga	35	40	75	100	5.3%	9.6%	0.2%
SEVERE	Turkey	35,000	50,000	2,500	4,000	0.6%	1.2%	0.5%
SEVERE	Uganda	30,000	35,000	4,000	5,750	2.3%	5.4%	2.4%
SEVERE	Venezuela	5,000	6,500	1,500	1,750	3.1%	6.2%	1.3%
HIGH	Albania	850	950	100	150	0.6%	1.2%	0.3%
HIGH	Argentina	15,000	15,000	1,500	2,000	1.0%	1.5%	1.6%
HIGH	Australia	4,000	6,500	2,500	2,750	0.5%	0.8%	1.1%
HIGH	Austria	1,500	2,000	45	65	0.6%	1.2%	0.2%
HIGH	Azerbaijan	4,500	4,500	250	200	0.4%	0.7%	0.4%
HIGH	Barbados	25	25	35	45	2.5%	5.2%	0.1%
HIGH	Belgium	2,000	2,500	2,250	2,500	0.1%		0.1%
HIGH	Bhutan	400	600	150	250	2.0%	3.0%	1.9%
HIGH	Brazil	55,000	70,000	10,000	15,000	0.7%	1.4%	1.9%
HIGH	Canada	4,500	6,500	1,250	2,000	0.2%	0.1%	1.4%
HIGH	Chile	4,500	6,000	650	900	1.0%	1.9%	0.8%
HIGH	Croatia	1,500	2,000	200	350	1.4%	2.8%	0.3%
HIGH	Cuba	4,500	5,000	500	600	2.7%	5.4%	0.4%
HIGH	Cyprus	350	450	40	55	0.3%	0.6%	0.1%
HIGH	Czech Republic	2,500	3,000	25	30	0.4%	0.8%	0.2%
HIGH	Denmark	1,000	1,500	1,250	1,250	-0.1%	-0.3%	0.2%
HIGH	Dominican Republic	3,000	3,500	550	950	2.4%	4.8%	0.3%
HIGH	Ecuador	2,000	2,500	850	1,250	0.5%	1.3%	1.3%
HIGH	Egypt	25,000	30,000	4,000	6,000	0.5%	1.0%	0.2%
HIGH	Estonia	250	300	15	20	0.8%	0.7%	0.6%
HIGH	Finland	900	1,000	300	300	-0.8%	-1.6%	0.6%
HIGH	France	10,000	15,000	3,500	4,500	0.5%	0.9%	0.1%
HIGH	Germany	15,000	20,000	3,250	3,750			0.1%
HIGH	Greece	4,500	5,000	500	650	0.6%	1.1%	0.2%
HIGH	Hungary	3,500	4,500	45	50	0.2%	0.4%	0.3%
HIGH	Iceland	60	80	35	35	-0.3%	-2.6%	0.1%
HIGH	Iran	25,000	50,000	2,000	3,000	0.7%	1.5%	0.3%
HIGH	Iraq	10,000	20,000	3,000	7,250	0.6%	1.3%	0.5%
HIGH	Israel	2,000	3,500	50	75	0.1%	0.1%	0.1%
HIGH	Italy	15,000	15,000	3,000	4,250	0.1%	0.3%	0.1%
HIGH	Japan	35,000	40,000	6,750	7,500	0.1%	0.1%	0.2%
HIGH	Jordan	2,000	3,000	150	200	0.1%	0.3%	0.1%

Additional mortality – yearly average · Additional economic costs in 2010 USD (negative numbers show gains) – yearly average · Additional persons affected – yearly average

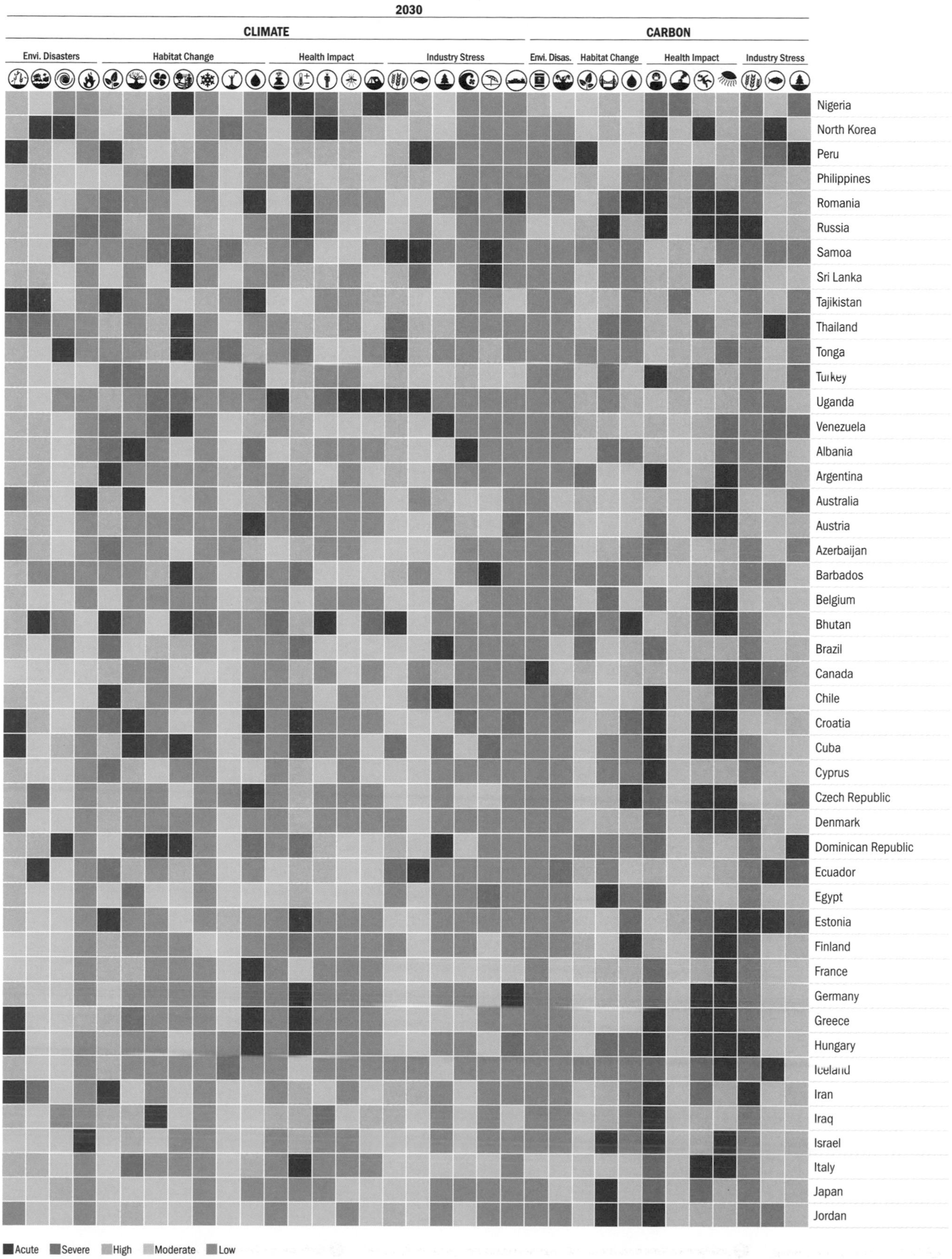

2030

CLIMATE: Envi. Disasters | Habitat Change | Health Impact | Industry Stress

CARBON: Envi. Disas. | Habitat Change | Health Impact | Industry Stress

Nigeria
North Korea
Peru
Philippines
Romania
Russia
Samoa
Sri Lanka
Tajikistan
Thailand
Tonga
Turkey
Uganda
Venezuela
Albania
Argentina
Australia
Austria
Azerbaijan
Barbados
Belgium
Bhutan
Brazil
Canada
Chile
Croatia
Cuba
Cyprus
Czech Republic
Denmark
Dominican Republic
Ecuador
Egypt
Estonia
Finland
France
Germany
Greece
Hungary
Iceland
Iran
Iraq
Israel
Italy
Japan
Jordan

Acute | Severe | High | Moderate | Low

	Country	TOTAL 2010	TOTAL 2030	1,000s 2010	1,000s 2030	% GDP PPP 2010	% GDP PPP 2030	% GDP PPP 2010
HIGH	Kenya	25,000	20,000	2,750	3,750	1.8%	3.7%	1.4%
	Kuwait	400	600	150	200	0.2%	0.5%	2.5%
	Lebanon	1,500	2,000	200	300	0.2%	0.5%	0.5%
	Lesotho	550	500	75	100	0.9%	1.9%	0.4%
	Libya	3,000	4,000	200	250	0.5%	1.0%	0.2%
	Lithuania	1,000	1,500	45	50	-0.1%	-0.1%	0.4%
	Mauritius	90	85	-40	-100	3.3%	6.7%	0.1%
	Morocco	10,000	15,000	2,750	4,250	1.1%	2.5%	0.1%
	Nepal	15,000	20,000	3,250	4,750	2.2%	4.1%	1.0%
	Netherlands	3,500	4,500	15,000	15,000	0.1%	-0.1%	0.1%
	New Zealand	1,000	1,500	650	800	0.4%	0.6%	1.0%
	Norway	800	1,000	300	350	-0.8%	-1.7%	0.2%
	Oman	550	1,000	55	80	0.9%	2.1%	0.1%
	Poland	15,000	15,000	350	350	0.1%	0.2%	0.3%
	Portugal	3,500	4,000	500	600	0.2%	0.4%	0.2%
	Saint Lucia	25	25	20	25	3.2%	6.6%	0.1%
	Saint Vincent	20	20	25	30	3.3%	6.3%	0.1%
	Saudi Arabia	6,000	10,000	700	900	0.2%	0.5%	0.4%
	Singapore	2,000	3,000	650	750			0.2%
	Slovakia	1,500	2,000	15	15	0.5%	1.1%	0.3%
	Slovenia	350	400	20	35	0.7%	1.5%	0.2%
	South Africa	15,000	20,000	10,000	20,000	0.9%	1.9%	0.7%
	South Korea	10,000	15,000	2,250	1,750	0.3%	0.4%	0.1%
	Spain	10,000	10,000	1,500	2,000	0.5%	1.0%	0.2%
	Sudan/South Sudan	30,000	30,000	5,250	6,750	2.6%	5.0%	0.9%
	Swaziland	550	450	150	200	0.8%	1.6%	1.0%
	Sweden	2,000	2,500	600	700	-0.7%	-1.4%	0.4%
	Switzerland	1,500	1,500	30	40	0.2%	0.3%	0.1%
	Syria	5,000	7,000	450	700	0.3%	0.7%	0.5%
	Tanzania	30,000	30,000	5,500	7,500	2.5%	4.8%	2.1%
	Trinidad and Tobago	150	150	85	100	2.2%	4.4%	
	Tunisia	2,500	3,000	950	1,250	0.9%	1.7%	0.1%
	Turkmenistan	1,500	2,000	200	200	1.1%	1.9%	0.2%
	United Kingdom	15,000	20,000	5,250	5,750	-0.1%	-0.3%	0.1%
	United States	80,000	100,000	10,000	15,000	0.3%	0.5%	0.8%
	Uruguay	1,000	1,000	250	300	1.6%	2.7%	0.7%
	Uzbekistan	15,000	20,000	650	750	0.4%	0.9%	0.7%
	Yemen	15,000	25,000	2,250	3,500	1.4%	2.8%	0.8%
	Zimbabwe	8,000	7,000	650	850	1.6%	3.3%	1.3%
MODERATE	Algeria	5,000	6,500	3,000	4,250	0.2%	0.5%	0.1%
	Bahrain	100	150	200	250	0.4%	0.8%	
	Ireland	350	550	300	300		-0.2%	0.1%
	Luxembourg	40	60	1	5	0.1%	0.2%	
	Malta	20	20	50	80	0.5%	0.9%	
	Qatar	100	150	60	90	0.1%	0.3%	0.1%
	United Arab Emirates	700	900	55	85	0.3%	0.7%	0.1%

Additional mortality – yearly average

Additional economic costs in 2010 USD (negative numbers show gains) – yearly average

Additional persons affected – yearly average

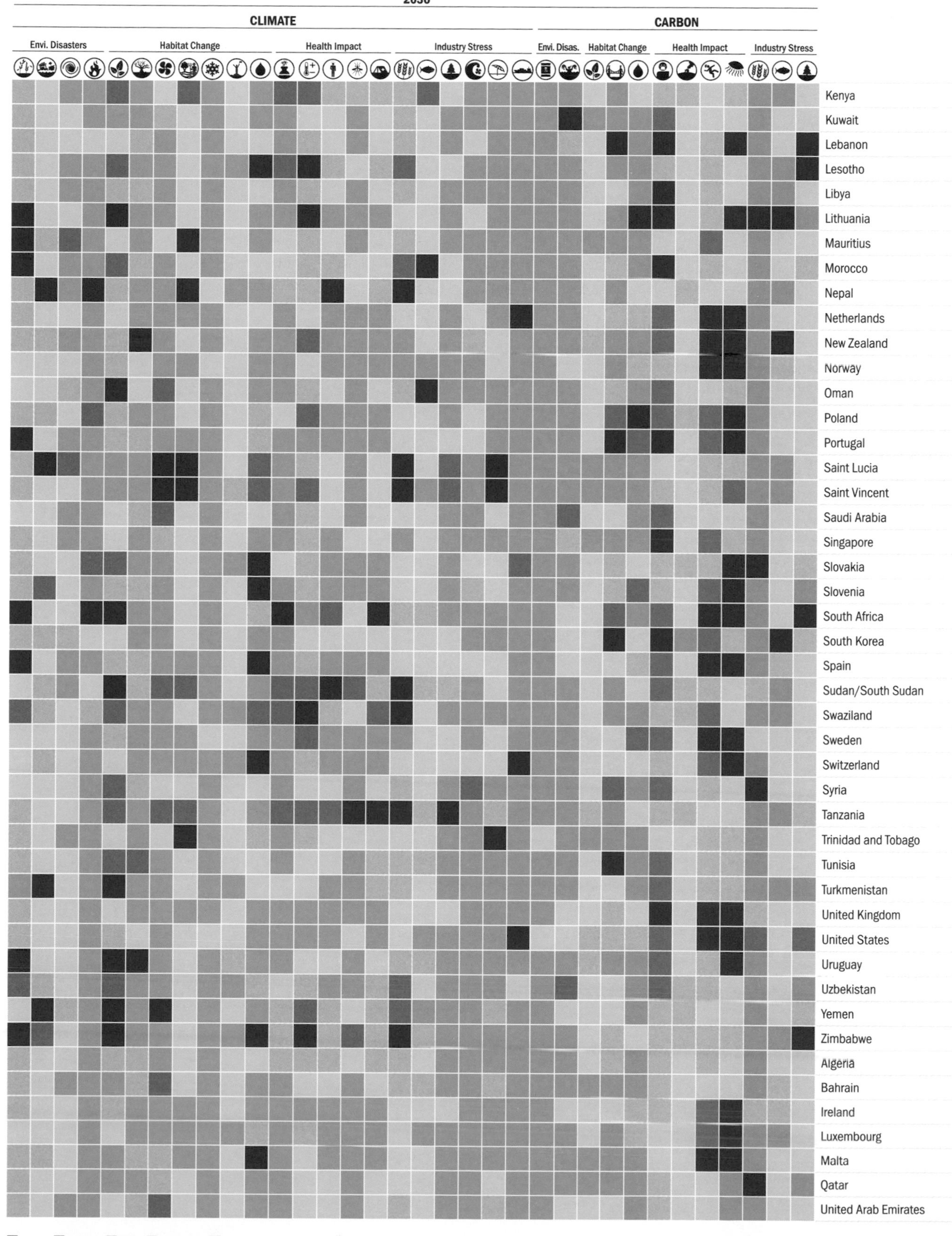
2030
CLIMATE
CARBON
Envi. Disasters
Habitat Change
Health Impact
Industry Stress
Envi. Disas.
Habitat Change
Health Impact
Industry Stress
Kenya
Kuwait
Lebanon
Lesotho
Libya
Lithuania
Mauritius
Morocco
Nepal
Netherlands
New Zealand
Norway
Oman
Poland
Portugal
Saint Lucia
Saint Vincent
Saudi Arabia
Singapore
Slovakia
Slovenia
South Africa
South Korea
Spain
Sudan/South Sudan
Swaziland
Sweden
Switzerland
Syria
Tanzania
Trinidad and Tobago
Tunisia
Turkmenistan
United Kingdom
United States
Uruguay
Uzbekistan
Yemen
Zimbabwe
Algeria
Bahrain
Ireland
Luxembourg
Malta
Qatar
United Arab Emirates
Acute
Severe
High
Moderate
Low

PARTNERS

ABOUT THE CLIMATE VULNERABLE FORUM

Founded in 2009, the Climate Vulnerable Forum is a semi-formal group of developing countries facing high degrees of insecurity due to climate change and actively seeking a concerted response to the climate crisis. Advocating ambitious directions for international climate change policy, the Forum proposed setting the temperature increase goal at 1.5° Celsius (2.7° Fahrenheit). This target was subsequently taken up by other groups of countries and played an important boundary definition role in the UN climate negotiations at Copenhagen in 2009 (COPP15). The Forum has insisted that decisions agreed at international talks on climate change and sustainable development be subject to accountability. Its members have committed themselves to low-carbon (Or even carbon neutral) national development pathways. The Forum currently has 20 members and meets periodically at head of government, ministerial and delegate levels. The Monitor is an analytical input and communication tool for Forum members. The two country studies included in this report (Ghana and Vietnam) were undertaken in member countries.

ABOUT DARA

Founded in 2003, DARA is an international organization headquartered in Madrid, Spain, committed to improving the effectiveness of aid for vulnerable populations suffering from conflict, disasters and climate change. It is an impartial, non-partisan and independent non-profit entity. DARA is actively engaged in field research and evaluation of aid programmes and operations in developing countries. Its specialized publications present data and analysis on aid accountability and effectiveness and emerging strategic concerns for the development, humanitarian and disaster reduction communities. DARA's Climate Vulnerability Initiative is mandated to develop the Monitor as an independent and politically impartial report. DARA convenes the external advisory bodies that provide third-party guidance and review inputs to this process. DARA alone is solely responsible for the final content of the report.

OTHER KEY PARTNERS AND SUPPORTERS

DARA is grateful to the number of partners with whom it has worked collaboratively in the development of this report.

Technical, quantitative and theoretical assistance has been provided by Commons Consultants, an advisory group based in Copenhagen, Denmark.

The Monitor's research contributes to Facilitating Enhanced Organizational Responsiveness West African Risk Reduction (FOREWARN), an initiative of the Humanitarian Futures Programme based at King's College, London. FOREWARN is supported by the Australian Agency for International Development (AusAID). FOREWARN is a collaborative project supporting the Economic Community of West African States (ECOWAS) to improve regional risk reduction capacity. It brings together DARA, the UN International Strategy for Disaster Reduction (UNISDR) and King's College programmes, including its African Leadership Centre. Research in Ghana which contributed to the Monitor was undertaken as a component of the FOREWARN initiative. Country research in Ghana was organized in close collaboration and with the support of the country's Environmental Protection Agency (EPA-Ghana) and its partners, the Ministry of Environment, Science and Technology and the National Disaster Management Organization (NADMO).

The Spanish International Development Cooperation Agency (AECID) funded the Monitor's country activities in Vietnam and supported the Monitor's development more generally. Research in Vietnam was organized by Live & Learn Vietnam with the participation of the Ministry of Natural Resources and Environment.

The Monitor's development additionally benefitted from the financial support of Fundación Biodiversidad, a public foundation of the Spanish government.

Additionally, UNDP country offices in Ghana and Vietnam facilitated and participated in country research activities.

ABBREVIATIONS

AECID: Agencia Española de Cooperación Internacional para el Desarollo

AusAID: Australian Agency for International Development

BRIC: Brazil, Russia, India, and China

C: Celsius/Centigrade

CAPP: Canadian Association of Petroleum Production

CAR: Central African Republic

CCS: Carbon capture and storage

CDC: Centers for Disease Control and Prevention

CDM: Clean Development Mechanism

CE: Climate Effect

CER: Certified Emission Reductions

CFCs: Chlorofluorocarbons

CIESIN: Columbia University's Center for International Earth Science Information Network

CIF: Climate Impact Factor/Carbon Impact Factor

CO_2: Carbon Dioxide

COP15: UN climate negotiations at Copenhagen in 2009

CRED: Centre for Research on the Epidemiology of Disasters

CRED/EM-DAT: CRED/Emergency Events Database

CReSIS: Center for Remote Sensing of Ice Sheets

CTI: The Carbon Tracker Initiative

CVI: Climate Vulnerability Initiative

CVF: Climate Vulnerable Forum

CWP: Coal Worker's Pneumoconiosis

DALY: Disability-adjusted life year

DCPP: Disease Control Priorities Project

DIVA: Dynamic Interactive Vulnerability Assessment

DR Congo: Democratic Republic of the Congo

EAC: Economics of Climate Adaptation Working Group

ECLAC: Economic Commission for Latin America and the Caribbean

ECOWAS: Economic Community of West African States

EDGAR: Emission Database for Global Atmospheric Research

EPA: Environmental Protection Agency

ERC: Environmental Research Consulting

EU: European Union

F: Fahrenheit

FAO: United Nations Food and Agriculture Organization

FOREWARN: Facilitating Enhanced Organizational Responsiveness West African Risk Reduction

G20: Group of Twenty Finance Ministers and Central Bank Governors

GDP: Gross Domestic Product

GEF: Global Environment Facility

GHF: Global Humanitarian Forum

GHG: Greenhouse gases

GIM: Generation Investment Management LLP

GNP: Gross National Product

GTZ: Deutsche Gesellschaft für Technische Zusammenarbeit

GWh: Gigawatt hour

HCFCs: Halocarbons

IAP: Interacademy Panel on International Issues

IEA: International Energy Agency

IFRC: The International Federation of Red Cross and Red Crescent Societies

ILO: International Labour Organization

IMF: International Monetary Fund

IPCC: Intergovernmental Panel on Climate Change

IPCC SRES: IPCC Special Report on Emissions Scenarios

ISO: International Organization for Standardization

IT: Information Technology

Kt CO_2: Kilotonne CO_2

LDCs: Least Developed Countries

LLDCs: Landlocked Developing Countries

MAD: Mean absolute deviation

MDGs: Millennium Development Goals

Munich Re: Münchener Rückversicherungs-Gesellschaft (Munich Reinsurance Company

NADMO: National Disaster Management Organization

NAPA: National Adaptation Programme for Action

NATO: North Atlantic Treaty Organization

NASA: National Aeronautics and Space Administration

NASA GISS: NASA Goddard Institute for Space Studies

NESDIS: National Environmental Satellite, Data, and Information Service

NOAA: National Oceanic and Atmospheric Administration

O_2: Ozone

ODA: Official Development Assistance

OECD: Organisation for Economic Co-Operation and Development

OPEC: Organization of the Petroleum Exporting Countries

OSDG: Oil Sands Developers Group

ORS: Oral rehydration solution

ORT: Oral rehydration therapy

pH: Water Acidity

PPM: Parts Per Million

PPP: Purchasing power parity adjusted/international dollar

RIO+20: United Nations Conference on Sustainable Development, "Earth Summit 2012", Rio de Janeiro, 13th-22nd June, 2012

RSNZ: The Royal Society of New Zealand

SIDSs: Small Island Developing States

SO_2: Sulphur Dioxide

UNCCD: United Nations Convention to Combat Desertification

UNDP: United Nations Development Programme

UNECE: United Nations Economic Commission for Europe

UNEP: United Nations Environment Programme

UNESCO: United Nations Educational, Scientific and Cultural Organization

UNFCCC: United Nations Framework Convention on Climate Change

UNHRC: United Nations High Commissioner for Refugees

UNISDR: UN International Strategy for Disaster Reduction

UNICEF: United Nations Children's Fund

US EIA: United States Energy Information Administration

US EPA: United States Environmental Protection Agency

USDAAF: United States Department of the Army and Air Force

USEIA: U.S. Energy Information Administration

UNISDR: United Nations International Strategy for Disaster Reduction

UNSD: United Nations Statistics Division

WBGT: Wet Bulb Globe Temperature

WHO: World Health Organization

WRI: World Resources Institute

GLOSSARY

ADAPTATION

An action or response that helps communities or their ecosystems cope with a changing climate. In particular, steps that reduce any losses or harm inflicted - the possible levels of which the Climate section of the Monitor attempts to estimate.

ADAPTIVE CAPACITY

The ability of a system to adjust to climate change, variability and extreme to moderate potential damages, to take advantage of opportunities, or to cope with the consequences.

Affected Communities

Communities that have seen their livelihoods compromised temporarily or permanently by climate change.

ANTHROPOGENIC

Produced as a result of human activity.

BLACK CARBON

An aerosol rich in carbon that absorbs sunlight and gives soot its black color. It is produced both naturally and by human as a result of the incomplete combustion of fossil fuels, biofuels, and biomass.

BIODIVERSITY

The international definition of biodiversity is "variability among living organisms" (CBD, 1992).

CARBON

The term "Carbon" is used as the moniker for the second part of the Monitor's assessment, which broadly speaking deals with socio-economic effects of the carbon economy. Carbon dioxide (CO⊠) is a principal greenhouse gas along with numerous other "heat-trapping" pollutants, such as methane, black carbon or nitrous oxide. Like these other pollutants, CO_2 is typically generated as a by-product of combustion when fuels of many different kinds are burned.

CARBON DIOXIDE (CO_2)

A naturally occurring gas and a by-product of burning fossil fuels, land use changes, and other industrial processes and is the main greenhouse gas that causes atmospheric temperature changes.

CLIMATE

Climate is taken to mean the average weather. The classical time period used by the World Meteorological Organization to determine the climate is 30 years. So the climate is the average weather over a given period of 30 years. Parameters such as temperature, rainfall and wind can be examined to determine key characteristics of the state of the climate at different periods in time, and to identify variation across time periods.

CLIMATE CHANGE

Climate change is a change in average weather. For the purpose of this study, it is assumed that human activities are the principal and overwhelming - if not exclusive- cause of the contemporary warming of the climate, in accordance with the broad consensus and more recent evidence on this subject (IPCC, 2007). According to the UN Framework Convention on Climate Change, climate change is also in addition to natural climate variability (UNFCCC, 1992).

CLIMATE DISPLACED PEOPLE

Persons displaced temporarily or permanently due to climate change and its impacts or shocks, notably land desertification, sea-level rise and weather-related disasters. It is almost never possible to identify an individual as exclusively a climate displaced person due to the range of factors that are likely involved in forced or voluntary movement of people.

CLIMATE EFFECT

Indicates the relative effects of climate change on social and economic variables at the country level. It is calculated based on observed values of social and economic variables and the effects of climate change.

Climate Impact Factor

The relative contribution of climate change to the development of a given variable.

CLIMATE MODEL

Numerical representations of the climate system based on the physical, chemical and biological properties of its components, their interactions and feedback processes. They account for all or some of its known properties.

CLIMATE SCENARIO

Probable representations of the future which are consistent with assumptions about future GHG emissions and other pollutants based on existing understanding of the effect of increased atmospheric concentrations GHGs on the global climate.

CLIMATE VULNERABILITY

The degree to which a community experiences harm (or not) as a result of a change in climate. Vulnerability encapsulates socio-economic concerns, such as income levels, access to information, education, social safety nets and other meaningful determinants of the resilience of a given community. It also encapsulates environmental or so-called "bio-physical" factors, such as geographic location, topography, natural resource supplies, vegetation and otherwise.

CLIMATE VULNERABILITY LEVEL

Aggregate vulnerability levels indicates the extent to which countries are affected in comparison with effects experienced by all other countries. Vulnerability levels are determined statistically, using mean absolute standard deviations.

CLIMATE VULNERABILITY MONITOR

The Climate Vulnerability Monitor provides a global overview of vulnerability to climate change and the carbon economy. It provides fair estimates of the types of impacts already faced by society. It also shows where the impacts are taking place and captures the evolving global vulnerability to climate change/carbon economy.

CONFIDENCE

Degree of accuracy and repeatability of a statistical test.

Cost-effectiveness Refers to the relationship between the economic input/cost of a given adaptation measure and the degree of beneficial output.

DESERTIFICATION

Land degradation in arid, semi-arid and sub-humid areas resulting from various factors including climatic variations and human activities (UNCCD, 2010).

DEVELOPMENT AID

Aid to support the economic, social, and political development of developing countries. The aim is to alleviate poverty in the long run. It is often termed Official Development Assistance (ODA).

DISABILITY-ADJUSTED LIFE YEAR (DALY)

This time-based measure combines years of life lost due to premature death and years of life lost due to time lived in states of less than full health. The DALY metric was developed in the original Global Burden of Disease 1990 study to assess the burden of disease consistently across diseases, risk factors, and regions.

DISASTER RISK REDUCTION

A framework for assessing measures for minimizing vulnerabilities and disaster risks throughout a society, to prevent or limit the adverse impacts of hazards.

DROUGHT

In general terms, drought is a recurring extreme climate event that, over a period of months or years, has precipitation levels that are below-normal (Dai, 2010).

EMISSION SCENARIO

Emissions scenarios describe future releases into the atmosphere of greenhouse gases, aerosols, and other pollutants and, along with information on land use and land cover, provide inputs to climate models. They are based on assumptions about driving forces such as patterns of economic and population growth, technology development, and other factors. Levels of future emissions are highly uncertain, so scenarios provide alternative images of how the future might unfold (WMO, 2012).

ENVIRONMENTAL DISASTERS

Disasters that are generated in whole or in part through human activities. This report measures the role of climate change or the carbon economy in extreme weather events or geographically restricted pollution disasters. Extreme weather events affected by climate change are natural phenomena, but their aggravation through climate change constitutes a human-induced contribution and influence on the final scale of disaster – disasters are also widely understood as socially constructed regardless of the natural phenomenon involved.

EXPOSURE TO CLIMATE CHANGE

Exposure to physical manifestations of alterations in weather conditions and the environment as a result of climate change. See also "Vulnerability - Physical vulnerability to climate change".

EXTREME WEATHER EVENT

Infrequent meteorological events having a significant impact on the society or ecosystem in a specific location.

FOOD SECURITY

Refers to the availability of food and people's access to it. A household is food secure when its occupants do not live in hunger or fear of starvation.

FOSSIL FUEL EMISSIONS

Emissions of greenhouse gases resulting from the combustion of fuels from fossil carbon deposits such as oil, gas and coal.

GLOBAL DIMMING

Reductions in solar radiation that reaches the Earth's surface during the last 50 years (Stanhill and Cohen, 2005).

GREENHOUSE EFFECT

Greenhouse gasses effectively absorb thermal infrared radiation, emitted by the Earth's surface, by the atmosphere itself due to the same gases, and by clouds. Atmospheric radiation is emitted to all sides, including downward to the Earth's surface. Thus, greenhouse gases trap heat within the surface-troposphere system (IPCC, 2007).

GREENHOUSE GASES (GHG)

Greenhouse gases are those gaseous constituents of the atmosphere, both natural and anthropogenic, that absorb and emit radiation at specific wavelengths within the spectrum of thermal infrared radiation emitted by the Earth's surface, the atmosphere itself, and by clouds. This property causes the greenhouse effect.

HABITAT CHANGE

Refers to shifts, changes or loss of human and ecological habitats due to climate change impacts.

HEALTH IMPACT

The impacts of climate change that have an effect (positive or negative) on human health.

HYDRO ENERGY

A "green energy" source in which running water is used to turn turbines, which in turn generates electrical energy (Eon Energy Lab, 2012).

HUMANITARIAN AID

Activties involving protection of civilians and those no longer taking part in hostilities, and provision of material or logistical assistance for people affected by humanitarian crises and to facilitate their return to normal lives and livelihoods.

INDUSTRY STRESS

The effect of climate change on specific industry sectors captured in this report is based on e.g. fisheries, forestry, and agricultural losses or gains.

LANDSLIDES

Landslides occur when masses of rock, earth or debris move down a slope and are caused by disturbances in the slope's natural stability. They often accompany heavy rains, droughts, earthquakes, or volcanic eruptions. This report only considers weather-related landslides.

MITIGATION

Mitigation is broadly understood as human actions and interve3ntions that stem global warming, i.e. that mitigate the warming effect.

OCEAN ACIDIFICATION

The ocean absorbs approximately one third of the carbon dioxide emitted to the atmosphere from the burning of fossil fuels. As carbon dioxide dissolves in seawater, the pH of the water decreases, which is called "acidification"(Ocean Acidification Network).

OIL SANDS

Oil sands are a major source of unconventional oil for fuel/energy. They comprise a mixture of sand, water, clay and bitumen. Bitumen is oil that needs to be diluted or heated in order to be pumped due to its heaviness or thickness (CAPP, 2012).

PERMAFROST

Ground (soil or rock and included ice and organic material) that remains at or below 0°C for at least two consecutive years (IPA, 2012).

PROJECTION

A future value calculated according to predetermined changes in the assumptions of the environment (IPCC, 2007).

RESILIENCE

The ability of a community or ecosystem to recover from, return to equilibrium, or bounce back following a shock.

SCENARIO

Model-generated set of market projections based on assumptions other than those used in the baseline. They are used to provide quantitative information on the impact of changes in assumptions on the outlook.

SEA-LEVEL RISE

The rising of sea-levels due mostly to thermal expansion and the melting of land-based ice.

SINK

Any process, activity or mechanism that removes a greenhouse gas, an aerosol, or a precursor of either from the atmosphere.

SOCIO-ECONOMIC IMPACT

Refers to climate change impacts of both social and economic character, comprising for instance mortality, illness (social) or monetary losses (economic).

SRES SCENARIOS

Emission scenarios developed the IPCC.

VULNERABILITY

The conditions determined by physical, social, economic, and environmental factors or

processes, which increase the susceptibility of a community to the impact of hazards.

VULNERABILITY - PHYSICAL VULNERABILITY TO CLIMATE CHANGE

Refers to people who live in regions that are prone to more than one type of physical manifestation of climate change: floods, storms, droughts, sea-level rise, etc (similar to "exposure").

VULNERABILITY - SOCIO-ECONOMIC VULNERABILITY TO CLIMATE CHANGE

Refers to the capacity of individuals, communities, ecosystems, economies, and societies to adapt to climate change impacts and avoid suffering from long-term, potentially irreversible, losses in well-being and stability. Also referred to as "underlying vulnerabilities".

WEATHER-RELATED DISASTERS

Natural disasters that are related to weather patterns, such as floods, droughts, and heat waves. Geophysical disasters such as earthquakes are not considered by this report.

WET BULB GLOBE TEMPERATURE (WBGT)

Composite temperature for estimating temperature, humidity, wind chill and solar radiation effect on humans.

BIBLIOGRAPHY

Ackerman et al. (2009)
F. Ackerman, S.J. DeCanio, R. B. Howarth, K. Sheeran (2009)
Limitations of integrated assessment models of climate change
Climatic Change, vol. 95:3-4, pp. 297-315

Ackerman and Stanton (2011)
Frank Ackerman and Elizabeth A. Stanton (2011)
Climate Economics: The State of the Art
Stockholm Environment Institute-U.S. Center

Adamo et al. (2011)
S. Adamo, S. Trzaska, G. Yetman, J. del Corral, M. Thomson, and C. Perez (2011)
Integration of Demographic, Climate, and Epidemiological Factors in the Modeling of Meningococcal Meningitis Epidemic Occurrence in Niger.
Poster presented at the 2011 Annual Meeting of the Population Association of America in Washington, D.C., March 30–April 1.
Retrieved:
http://www.ciesin.org/documents/adamo-model-meningoccal_paa_mar2011.pdf

Adeel et al. (2005)
Zafar Adeel, Uriel Safriel, David Niemeijer, and Robin White (2005)
Ecosystems and Human Well-being . Desertification Synthesis. A Report of the Millennium Ecosystem Assessment
Washington, DC, US: World Resources Institute,.

Adger et al. (2003)
W. N. Adger, S. Huq, K. Brown, D. Conway and M. Hulme (2003)
Adaptation to climate change in the developing world
Progress in Development Studies, vol. 3, no. 3, pp. 179-195

Aerts and Droogers (2009)
J. Aerts and P. Droogers (2009)
Climate Change in the Water Sector
In: P. Kabat, F. Ludwig, M. van der van der Valk and H. van van Schaik (eds): *Climate Change Adaptation in the Water Sector* (pp.87-107)
London, UK: Earthscan

Agnew (2012)
Robert Agnew (2012)
Dire forecast: A theoretical model of the impact of climate change on crime
Theoretical Criminology, vol. 16 no. 1, pp. 21-42

Agnew et al. (2009)
D. J. Agnew, J. Pearce, G. Pramod, T. Peatman, R. Watson, J. R. Beddington and T. J. Pitcher (2009)
Estimating the Worldwide Extent of Illegal Fishing
Plos one, vol.4, no.2

Agrawal et al. (2008)
M. Agrawal, M. Auffhammer, U.K. Chopra, L. Emberson, M. Iyngararasan, N. Kalra, M.V. Ramana, V. Ramanathan, A.K. Singh and J. Vincent (2008)
Impacts of Atmospheric Brown Clouds on Agriculture
Part II of Atmospheric Brown Clouds: Regional Assessment Report with Focus on Asia
Nairobi, Kenya: United Nations Environment Programme

Ahmed (2008)
E. W. Ahmed (2008)
Process water treatment in Canada's oil sands industry: I. Target pollutants and treatment objectives
Environmental Engineering Science, vol. 7, pp. 123-138

Ahmed et al. (2009)
S. A. Ahmed, N. S. Diffenbaugh and T. Whertel (2009)
Climate volatility deepens poverty vulnerability in developing countries
Environmental Research Lettters, vol. 4, no. 3 (8pp)

Ahrens and Rudolph (2006)
J. Ahrens and P.M. Rudolph (2006)
The Importance of Governance in Risk Reduction and Disaster Management
Journal of Contingencies and Crisis Management, vol. 14, Iss.4, pp. 207-220

Ainsworth et al. (2008)
FACE-ing the facts: inconsistencies and interdependence among field, chamber and modeling studies of elevated [CO2] impacts on crop yield and food supply
New Phytologist (2008), Letters

Akpinar-Ferrand and Singh (2010)
Ezgi Akpinar-Ferrand and Ashbindu Singh(2010)
Modeling increased demand of energy for air conditioners and consequent CO2 emissions to minimize health risks due to climate change in India
Environmental Science and Policy, vol. 13, Iss. 8, pp. 702-712

Akyeampong (2001)
Emmanuel Kwaku Akyeampong (2001)
Between the Sea & the Lagoon: An Eco-social History of the Anlo of Southeastern Ghana c. 1850 to recent times
Athens, Ohio, Ohio University Press

Allen et al. (2009)
C.D. Allen, A. Macalady, H. Chenchouni, D. Bachelet, N. McDowell, M. Vennetier, P. Gonzales, T. Hogg, A. Rigling, D.D. Breshears, R. Fensham, Z. Zhang, T. Kitzberger, J.-H. Lim, J. Castro, S. W. Running, G. Allard, A. Semerci, and N.Cobb (2009)
Climate-induced forest mortality: a global overview of emerging risks
Forest Ecology and Management, vol. 259, iss.4, pp. 660-684

Allen and Ingram (2002)
Myles R. Allen and William J. Ingram (2002)
Constraints on future changes in climate and the hydrologic cycle
Nature - insight review articles, vol. 419 , pp. 224-232

Allison et al. (2009)
E. H. Allison, A. L. Perry, M. Badjeck, W. N. Adger, K. Brown, D. Conway, A. S. Halls, G. M. Pilling, J. D. Reynolds, N. L. Andrew and N. K. Dulvy (2009)
Vulnerability of national economies to the impacts of climate change on fisheries
Fish and Fisheries, vol.10, iss.2, pp.173-196

Amelung et al. (2007)
Bas Amelung, Sarah Nicholls and David Viner (2007)
Implications of Global Climate Change for Tourism Flows and Seasonality
Journal of Travel Research, vol. 45, pp. 285-296

Amoli (1997)
K. Amoli (1997)
Bronchopulmonary disease in Iranian housewives chronically exposed to indoor smoke
European Respiratory Journal, vol.11, no:3, pp. 659-663

Anisimov (2009)
O. Anisimov (2009)
Probabilistic modeling of climate change impacts in permafrost regions
EGU General Assembly 2009, held 19-24 April, 2009 in Vienna, Austria, p.238
Retrieved: http://meetings.copernicus.org/egu2009

Appeaning Addo et al. (2011)
K. Appeaning Addo, P.N.Jayson-Quashigah and K. S. Kufogbe (2011)
Quantitative Analysis of Shoreline Change Using Medium Resolution Satellite Imagery in Keta, Ghana
Marine Science, vol.1, no.1, pp.1-9

Appeaning Addo and Larbi (2009)
K. Appeaning Addo and L. Larbi (2009)
Assessing the impact of sea level rise on vulnerable coastal communities in a remote sensing environment
Proceedings of AARSE Conference held in Addis Ababa
Retrieved: http://ugspace.ug.edu.gh:8080/xmlui/handle/123456789/1174

Archabald and Naughton-Treves (2001)
Karen Archabald and Lisa Naughton-Treves (2001)
Tourism revenue-sharing around national parks in Western Uganda: early efforts to identify and reward local communities
Environmental Conservation, vol. 28, iss. 02, pp 135-149

Ark et al. (2008)
Bart van Ark, Mary O'Mahony, and Marcel P. Timmer (2008)
The Productivity Gap between Europe and the United States: Trends and Causes
Journal of Economic Perspectives, vol. 22, no. 1, pp. 25–44

Armah (2005)
A.K. Armah (2005)
The Coastal Zone of Ghana: Vulnerability and Adaptation Assessment to Climate Change
Presentation from The Vulnerability and Adaptation Assessment Training Workshop, held in Maputo, Mozambique, from 18-22 April, 2005

Armstrong and Kricker (2001)
B. Armstrong and A. Kricker (2001)
The epidemiology of UV Induced Skin Cancer
Journal of Photochemistry and Photobiology B: Biology, vol. 63, Iss. 1–3, pp. 8-18

Arnell (2004)
Nigel W. Arnell (2004)
Climate change and global water resources: SRES emissions and socio-economic scenarios
Global Environmental Change, vol. 14, pp. 31–52

Arnell et al. (2011)
Nigel W. Arnell, Detlef P. van Vuuren, Morna Isaac (2011)
The implications of climate policy for the impacts of climate change on global water resources
Global Environmental Change, vol. 21, Iss. 2, pp. 592-603

Arora (2001)
S. Arora (2001)
Health, Human Productivity, and Long-Term Economic Growth
The Journal of Economic History, vol. 61, no. 3, pp. 699-749

Arrhenius (1896)
Svante Arrhenius (1896).
On the Influence of Carbonic Acid in the Air upon the Temnperature of the Ground.
The London, Edinburgh and Dublin Philosophical Magazine and Journal of Science. Fith Series. April 1896, vol XXI

Arrhenius (1908)
Svante Arrhenius (1908)
Worlds in the making. The evolution of the universe
New York, London, Harper and Brother Publishersn
Retrieved: http://openlibrary.org/books/OL7149587M/Worlds_in_the_making

Asano (2002)
Takashi Asano (2002)
Water from (Waste)Water -- The Dependable Water Resource
Paper written for the 2001 Stockholm Water Prize Laureate Lecture

Asante et al. (2010)
Felix Ankomah Asante, Ama Essel and Patrick Addai Aidoo (2010)
National Environmental, Economic And Development Study (NEEDS) for Climate Change: Ghana Country Report
Retrieved: http://unfccc.int/files/adaptation/application/pdf/ghananeeds.pdf

Asenso-Okyere et al. (2011)
K. Asenso-Okyere, C. Chiang, P. Thangata and K. Andam (2011)
Interactions between health and farmlabor Productivity
Food policy reports 23
International Food Policy Research Institute (IFPRI).

Ashan et al. (2011)
S. Ahsan, M. S. Ali, M. R. Hoque, M. S. Osman, M. Rahman, M. J. Babar, S. A. Begum, D. M. Rahman and K. R. Islam (2011)
Agricultural and Environmental Changes in Bangladesh in Response to Global Warming
In: R. Lal et al. (eds): *Climate Change And Food Security In South Asia* (Part 3, pp.119-134)
Springer Science and Bussiness Media

Ashbolt (2004)
Nicholas John Ashbolt (2004)
Microbial contamination of drinking water and disease outcomes in developing regions
Toxicology, vol. 198, pp. 229-238

Ashdown et al. (2011)
Lord Paddy Ashdown (2011)
Humanitarian Emergency Response Review
Department of International Development, UK

Auffhammer et al. (2006)
M.Auffhammer, V. Ramanathan, and J. R. Vincent (2006)
Integrated model shows that atmospheric brown clouds and greenhouse gases have reduced rice harvests in India
PNAS , vol. 103, no. 52, pp. 19668-19672

Avnery et al. (2011)
Avnery S., D.L. Mauzerall, J. Liu, L.W. Horowitz (2011)
Global Crop Yield Reductions due to Surface Ozone Exposure: 1. Year 2000 Crop Production Losses and Economic Damage
Atmospheric Environment, vol. 45, pp. 2284-2296.

Ayers (2010)
J. Ayers (2010)
Understanding the Adaptation Paradox: Can Global Climate Change Adaptation Policy be Locally Inclusive?
PhD thesis,The London School of Economics and Political Science.

Aydin (2010)
H. Aydin (2010)
Evaluation of the risk of coal workers pneumoconiosis (CWP): A case study for the Turkish hardcoal mining
Scientific Research and Essays, vol. 5, no. 21, pp. 3289-3297.

Baddeley (2010)
M. Baddeley (2010)
Herding, social influence and economic decision-making: socio-psychological and neuroscientific analyses
Philosopical Transactions of the Royal Society Biological Sciences, vol. 365, pp.281-290.

Baker et al. (2008)
A.C. Baker, P.W. Glynn, B. Riegl (2008)
Climate change and coral reef bleaching: An ecological assessment of long-term impacts, recovery trends and future outlook
Estuarine, Coastal and Shelf Science, vol. 80, iss. 4, pp. 435-471

Baltodano et al (eds.) (2008)
Javier Baltodano, Luisa Paz and Janice Wormworth (eds.) (2008)
Community-based forest governance: from resistance to proposals for sustainable use
Amsterdam, The Netherlands, Friends of the Earth International

Baran (2010)
Eric Baran (2010)
Strategic Environmental Assessment Of Hydropower On The Mekong Mainstream
Mekong Fisheries and Mainstream Dams
International Centre for Environmental Management

Barkin (2011)
J. Samuel Barkin (2011)
Degradation and Cooperation in the High Seas: The case of the International Fisheries Magament
In: S. Dinar (ed.): *Beyond Resource Wars: Scarcity, Environmental Degradation, and International Cooperation (Global Environmental Accord: Strategies for Sustainability and Institutional Innovation)* (pp. 141-164)
Cambridge, MA: Massachussetts Institute of Technology

Barman et al (2010)
S.C. Barman, N. Kumar, R. Singh, G.C. Kisku, A.H. Khan, M.M. Kidwai, R.C. Murthy, M.P.S. Negi, P. Pandey, A.K. Verma, G. Jain and S.K. Bhargava (2010)
Assessment of urban air pollution and it's probable health impact
Journal of Environmental Biology, vol. 2010, no. 31, Iss.(6), pp. 913-920

Barret and Wallace (2011)
Greg Barrett and Margaret Wallace (2011)
An Institutional Economics Perspective: The Impact of Water Provider Privatisation on Water Conservation in England and Australia
Water Resources Management, vol. 25, no. 5, pp. 1325-1340

Bates et al. (2008)
B.C.Bates, Z.W. Kundzewicz, S. Wu and J.P. Palutikof (Eds) (2008)
Climate Change and Water. Technical Paper of the Intergovernmental Panel on Climate Change
Geneva, IPCC Secretariat

Baumert and Selman (2003)
Baumert K. and Selman M (2003)
Data Note: Heating and Cooling Degree Days
World Resources Institute

Bayon and Jenkins(2010)
R. Bayon, M. Jenkins (2010)
The business of biodiversity
Nature, vol. 466, pp. 184-185

Beach et al. (2009)
W. W. Beach, D. W. Kreutzer, K. A. Campbell, and B. Lieberman (2009)
The Economic Impact of Waxman-Markey
WebMemo22, No. 2438
The Heritage Foundation (THF)

Becker et al (2010)
Gary S. Becker, Kevin M. Murphy and Robert H. Topel (2010, September, rev)
On the Economics of Climate Policy
Paper prepared for a conference on "Energy Policy and the Economy" jointly sponsored by the University of Chicago, Resources for the Future, and the University of Illinois.
Retrieved: http://www.econ.ucsb.edu/about_us/events/seminar_papers/topel.pdf

Bell et al. (2007)
Michelle L. Bell, Richard Goldberg, Christian Hogrefe, Patrick L. Kinney, Kim Knowlton, Barry Lynn, Joyce Rosenthal, Cynthia Rosenzweig, Jonathan A. Patz (2007)
Climate change, ambient ozone, and health in 50 US cities
Climatic Change, vol. 82, no. 1, pp. 61-76.

Bellard et al. (2012)
Bellard, C., Bertelsmeier, C., Leadley, P., Thuiller, W. and Courchamp, F. (2012),
Impacts of climate change on the future of biodiversity
Ecology Letters, vol. 15, iss. 4, pp. 365-377.

Bentham (1997)
C.G. Bentham (1997)
Health
In: J.P. Palutikof, S. Subak, and M.D. Agnew. (eds.): *Economic Impacts of the Hot Summer and Unusually Warm Year of 1995* (pp.87-95)
UK Department of the Environment

Bensch and Peters (2011)
G. Bensch and J. Peters (2011)
Combating Deforestation? Impacts of Improved Stove Dissemination on Charcoal Consumption in Urban Senegal
Ruhr Economic Papers ner. 306
Ruhr-Universität Bochum (RUB), Department of Economics.

Benton and Twitchett (2003)
Michael J. Benton and Richard J. Twitchett (2003)
How to kill (almost) all life: the end-Permian extinction event
TRENDS in Ecology and Evolution, vol.18, no.7

Bernardi et al. (2009)
E. Bernardi , C. Chiavari , B. Lenza , C. Martini , L. Morselli , F. Ospitali and L. Robbiola (2009)
The atmospheric corrosion of quaternary bronzes: The leaching action of acid rain
Corrosion Science, vol.51:1 , pp. 159-170

Berrittella et al. (2004)
M. Berrittella, A. Bigano, R. Roson, R. S.J. Tol (2004)
A General Equilibrium Analysis of Climate Change Impacts on Tourism
EEE Working Papers Series - N. 17

Betts et al. (2009)
R. A. Betts, M. Collins, D. L. Hemming, Ch. D. Jones, J. A. Lowe and M. Sanderson (2009)
When could global warming reach 4°C?
Phiosophical Transactios of the Royal Society, vol. 369, no.1934, pp. 67-84

Bharath and Turner (2009)
Bharath A.K. and Turner R.J. (2009)
Impact of climate change on skin cancer
Journal of the Royal Society of Medicine, vol. 102, no. 6, pp. 215-218.

Bilenko et al. (1999)

N. Bilenko, .D. Fraser and L. Naggan (1999)

Maternal knowledge and environmental factors associated with risk of diarrhea in Israeli Bedouin children

European Journal of Epidemiology, vol. 15, no. 10, pp. 907-912

Bindi and Olesen (2011)

Marco Bindi and Jørgen E. Olesen (2011)

The responses of agriculture in Europe to climate change

Regional Environmental Change, vol. 11, Suppl. 1, pp.S151-S158

Black et al. (2008)

R. E Black, L. H Allen, Z. A Bhutta, L. E Caulfield, M. de Onis, M. Ezzati, C. Mathers, J. Rivera (2008)

Maternal and child undernutrition: global and regional exposures and health consequences

The Lancet, Series, Maternal and Child Undernutrition 1

Blackman et al. (2010)

A.Blackman, B. Lahiri, W. ,M. Rivera Planter and C. Muñoz Piña (2010)

Voluntary environmental regulation in developing countries: Mexico's clean industry program

RFF Discussion Paper 07-36-REV

Resources For the Future

Retrieved: http://www.rff.org/RFF/Documents/RFF-DP-07-36-REV2.pdf

Blöschl and Montanari (2010)

G. Blöschl and A. Montanari (2010)

Climate change impacts- throwing the dice?

Hydrological Processes, vol. 24, pp. 374-381

Boateng (2009)

I.Boateng (2009)

Development of integrated shoreline management planning: a case study of Keta, Ghana

Proceedings of the Federation of International Surveyors Working Week 2009- Surveyors Key Role in Accelerated Development, Israel, 3-8 May

Retrieved: http://eprints.port.ac.uk

Bolte et al. (2009)

A. Bolte, C. Ammer, M.s Löf, G.J. Nabuurs, P. Schall and P. Spathelf (2009)

Adaptive Forest Management: A Prerequisite for Sustainable Forestry in the Face of Climate Change

Managing Forest Ecosystems, vol. 19, pp. 115-139

Bosello et al. (2005)

F. Bosello, R. Roson and R. S.J. Tol (2005)

Economy-Wide Estimates of the Implications of Climate Change: Human Health

Paper was presented at the Workshop on Infectious Diseases: Ecological and Economic Approaches held in Trieste on 13-15 April 2005.

Bouwer (2011)

L.M. Bouwer (2011)

Have Disaster Losses Increased due to Anthropogenic Climate Change?

Bulletin of the American Meteorological Society, vol. 92, pp. 39-46

Bouwer et al. (2010)

Laurens M. Bouwer, Philip Bubeck and Jeroen C.J.H. Aerts.

Changes in future flood risk due to climate and development in a Dutch polder area.

Global Environmental Change, vol. 20, Issue 3, pp. 463-471

Boyd and Banzhaf (2007)

James Boyd, Spencer Banzhaf (2007)

What are ecosystem services? The need for standardized environmental accounting units

Ecological Economics, vol. 63, pp. 616-626

BP (2012)

BP (2012)

BP Energy Outlook 2030

Brander (2007)

K. M. Brander (2007)

Global fish production and climate change

Proceedings of National Academy of Sciences, vol.104, no.50, pp. 19709-19714

Brashshaw et al. (2007)

Corey J. A. Bradshaw, Navjot S. Sodhi, Kelvin S.-H. Peh and Barry W. Brook

Global evidence that deforestation amplifies flood risk and severity in the developing world

Global Change Biology, vol. 13, pp. 2379-2395,

Breman (2001)

J.G. Breman (2001)

The Ears of the Hippopotamus: Manifestations, Determinants, and Estimates of the Malaria Burden

American Journal of Tropical Medical Hygiene, vol. 64, suppl. 1, 2, pp. 1-11

Bridge (2010)

J.R. Bridge (2010, August 31)

Mitigating Wildlife Disaster: Early Detection and Commitment

Disaster Recovery Journal

Retrieved: http://www.drj.com/2010-articles/online-exclusive/mitigating-wildfire-disaster-early-detection-and-commitment.html

Brinson and Malvárez (2002)

Mark M. Brinson and Ana Inés Malvárez (2002)

Temperate freshwater wetlands: types, status, and threats

Environmental Conservation, vol. 29 , iss. 2, pp. 115-133

Brook et al. (2008)

Barry W. Brook, Navjot S. Sodhi and Corey J.A. Bradshaw (2008)

Synergies among extinction drivers under global change

Trends in Ecology and Evolution, Vol.23, No.8

Brook et al. (2010)

Robert D. Brook, Sanjay Rajagopalan, C. Arden Pope III, Jeffrey R. Brook, Aruni Bhatnagar, Ana V. Diez-Roux, Fernando Holguin, Yuling Hong, Russell V. Luepker, Murray A. Mittleman, Annette Peters, David Siscovick, Sidney C. Smith Jr, Laurie Whitsel, Joel D. Kaufman (2010)

Particulate Matter Air Pollution and Cardiovascular Disease: An Update to the Scientific Statement From the American Heart Association (AHA)

Circulation, vol. 121, pp. 2331-2378

Brooks et al. (1999)

T.M. Brooks, S.L. Pimm and J. O. Oyugi (1999)

Time Lag between deforestation and Bird Extinction in Tropical Forest Fragments

Conservation Biology, vol. 13, no. 5, pp. 1140-1150

Brondizio and Moran (2008)

Eduardo S. Brondizio and Emilio F. Moran

Human dimensions of climate change: the vulnerability of small farmers in the Amazon

Philosophical Transaction of the Royal Society B, vol.363, pp.1803-1809

Brown and Funk (2009)

Molly E. Brown and Christopher C. Funk (2009)

Food Security Under Climate Change

Science , Vol. 319, no. 5863, pp. 580-581

Brown and Lall (2006)

C. Brown and U. Lall (2006)

Water and Economic Development: The Role of Variability and a Framework for Resilience

Natural Resources Forum, vol 30, pp. 306-317

Burke et al. (2009)

M. B. Burke, E. Miguel,S. Satyanath, J. A. Dykema, and D. B. Lobell (2010)

Warming increases the risk of civil war in Africa

Procedings of the National Academy of Sciences of the USA (PNAS), vol. 106 ,no. 49, pp. 20670-20674

Burke et al. (2011)

L. Burke, K. Reytar, M. Spalding and A. Perry (eds.) (2011)

Reefs at Risk Revisited

Washington, DC: World Resources Institute (WRI)

Burke et al (2010)

M. Burke, J. Dykema, D. Lobell, E. Miguel, S. Satyanath (2010)

Climate and civil war: is the relationship robust?

National Bureau Of Economic Research, Working Paper 16440.

Burke et al. (2011)

R. Burke, S. Clarke, C. Cooper (2011)

Occupational Health and Safety

Gower Publishing

Burns et al. (2011)

Douglas A. Burns (2011)

National Acid Precipitation Assessment, Program Report to Congress 2011: An Integrated Assessment

Washington, D.C.: Executive Office Of The President, National Science And Technology Council

Busch et al. (2011)

Jonah Busch, Fabiano Godoy, Will R. Turner and Celia A. Harvey (2011)

Biodiversity co-benefits of reducing emissions from deforestation under alternative reference levels and levels of finance

Conservation Letters, vol. 00, pp. 1-15

Buse et al. (2008)

Kent Buse, Eva Ludi and Marcella Vigneri (2008)

Sustaining and Scaling the Millennium Villages: Moving from rural investments to national development plans to reach the MDGs. Formative Review of MVP. Synthesis Report

London, UK, Overseas Development Institute

Butchart et al. (2010)

S. H. M. Butchart , M. Walpole, B. Collen, A. van Strien, J. P. W. Scharlemann, R. E. A. Almond, J. E. M. Baillie, B. Bomhard, C. Brown, J. Bruno, K. E. Carpenter, G. M. Carr , J. Chanson, A. M. Chenery, J. Csirke, N. C. Davidson, F. Dentener, M. Foster, A. Galli, J. N. Galloway, P. Genovesi, R. D. Gregory, M. Hockings, V. Kapos, J.-F. Lamarque, F. Leverington, J. Loh, M. A. McGeoch, L. McRae, A. Minasyan, M. Hernández Morcillo, T. E. E. Oldfield, D. Pauly, S. Quader, C. Revenga, J. R. Sauer, B. Skolnik, D. Spear, D. Stanwell-Smith, S. N. Stuart , A. Symes, M. Tierney, T. D. Tyrrell, J.-C. Vié and R. Watson (2010)

Global Biodiversity: Indicators of Recent Declines

Science, vol. 328, no: 5982, pp. 1164-1168

Byatt et al. (2006)

I. Byatt, R.M. Carter, C. R. de Freitas, I. M. Goklany, D.Holland, R. S. Lindzen, I.Castles, D. Henderson, N. Lawson, R. McKitrick, J. Morris, A. Peacock, C. Robinson and R. Skidelsky (2006)

The Stern Review: A Dual Critique

World Economics , vol. 7, No. 4, pp.

Callaghan and Power (2010)

J. Callaghan and S. B. Power (2010).

Variability and decline in the number of severe tropical cyclones making land-fall over eastern Australia since the late nineteenth century.

Climate Dynamics, vol. 37, Issue 3-4, pp. 647-662

Callendar (1938)

Callendar, G. S. (1938).

The artificial production of carbon dioxide and its influence on temperature.

Quarterly Journal of the Royal Meteorological Society, vol. 64, Issue 275, pp. 223-240

Campbell-Lendrum and Corvalán (2007)

Diarmid Campbell-Lendrum and Carlos Corvalán (2007)

Climate Change and Developing-Country Cities: Implications For Environmental Health and Equity

Journal of Urban Health, vol. 84, Suppl. 1, pp. 109-117.

Camuffo (1992)

Dario Camuffo (1992)

Acid rain and deterioration of monuments: How old is the phenomenon?

Atmospheric Environment. Part B. Urban Atmosphere, vol.26:2, pp. 241-247

Canada NEB (1996)

Canada National Energy Board (1996)
Canada's Oil Stands. Opportunities and Challenges to 2015: An update
Retrieved: http://www.neb-one.gc.ca/clf-nsi/rnrgynfmtn/nrgyrprt/lsnd/pprtntsndchllngs20152006/pprtntsndchllngs20152006-eng.pdf

Canada OPM (2006)

Canada Office of the Prime Minister (2006, July 14)
Address by the Prime Minister at the Canada-UK Chamber of Commerce
Notes for an Address by The Right Honourable Stephen Harper Prime Minister of Canada

CAPP (2011)

Canadian Association of Petroleum Production (2011)

Crude oil: Forecasts, Markets and Pipelines

CAPP

CAPP (2012)

Canadian Association of Petroleum Production (2012)

What Are Oil Sands?

Retrieved: http://www.capp.ca/CANADAINDUSTRY/OILSANDS/ENERGY-ECONOMY/Pages/what-are-oilsands.aspx

CARE (2012)

CARE (2012)

Update: Horn of Africa Food Security Emergency: July 2012

Retrieved:http://www.care.org/emergency/Horn-of-Africa-food-poverty-crisis-Dadaab-2011/pdf/Horn-of-Africa-emergency-one-year-report-July-2012.pdf

Castree et al. (eds.) (2009)

N.Castree, D. Demeritt, D. Liverman and B. Rhoads (eds) (2009)

A Companion to Environmental Geography

Blackwell Publishing Ltd

CBD (1992)

Convention on Biological Diversity (1992)

Convention on Biological Diversity

United Nations

CNA (2007)

The CNA Corporation (2007)

National Security and the Threat of Climate Change

CNA

Retrieved: http://www.cna.org

CDCP (2008)

Centers for Disease Control and Prevention (2008)

Heat-Related Deaths Among Crop Workers—United States, 1992-2006

Morbidity and Mortality Weekly Report , vol. 57 pp. 649-653

CDCP (2012)

Centers for Disease Control and Prevention

Various resources: Data & Statistics

http://www.cdc.gov/DataStatistics/

CEDRE (2012)

Centre of Documentation, Research and Experimentation on Accidental Water Pollution

Spills

Retrieved: http://www.cedre.fr/en/spill/alphabetical-classification.php

Center for Tankship Excellence (2012)

Center for Tankship Excellence (2012)

CTX version 4.6

Retrieved: http://www.c4tx.org/ctx/job/cdb/do_flex.html

Ceres (2010)

Ceres (2010)

Canada's Oil Sands Shrinking Window of Opportunity

Boston, MA, Ceres, Inc.

Retrieved: http://www.ceres.org/resources/reports/oil-sands-2010/view

Ceres (2011).

Ceres (2011)

Disclosing Climate Risks and Opportunities in SEC Filings: A Guide for Corporate executives, Attorneys and Directors.

Boston, MA, Ceres, Inc.

Retrieved: http://www.ceres.org/resources/reports/disclosing-climate-risks 2011/view

Ceron and Dubois (2004)

Jean-Paul Ceron and Ghislain Dubois (2004)

The potential Impacts of Climate Change on French Tourism

Current Issues in Tourism, vol. 8, no. 2. pp. 125-139

Chan et al. (2012)

Albert P.C. Chan, Michael C.H. Yam, Joanne W.Y. Chung and Wen Yi (2012)

Developing a heat stress model for construction workers

Journal of Facilities Management, vol. 10, iss. 1, pp.59 - 74

Charpin et al. (2009)

D. Charpin, C. Penard-Morand, C. Raherison, C. Kopferschmitt, F. Lavaud, D. Caillaud, I. Annesi-Maesano (2009)

Long-term exposure to urban air pollution measured through a dispersion model

and the risk of asthma and allergy in children.

Bulletin de l'Académie Nationale de Médecine, vol. 193, no. 6, pp. 1317-1329

Chaves et al. (2009)

M.M. Chaves, J. Flexas, and C. Pinheiro (2009)

Photosynthesis under Drought and Salt Stress: Regulation Mechanisms from Whole Plant to Cell

Annals of Botany, vol. 103, no. 4, pp. 551-560

Checkley et al. (2000)

W. Checkley, L. D Epstein, R. H Gilman, D. Figueroa, R. I Cama, J. A Patz, R. E Black (2000)

Effects of El Niño and ambient temperature on hospital admissions for diarrhoeal diseases in Peruvian children

The Lancet, vol. 355, Iss. 9202, pp. 442-450

Chen et al. (2008)

H. Chen, M.S. Goldberg and P.J. Villeneuve (2008)

A systematic review of the relation between long-term exposure to ambient air pollution and chronic diseases

Reviews on Environmental Health, vol. 23, no. 4, pp. 243-297

Cherwin (2009)

K.L. Cherwin (2009, August 3)

Effects of climate change on semi-arid grasslands: Does severe drought increase invasibility?

Presentation PS 3-38:

Paper presented in The 94th ESA (Ecological Society of America) Annual Meeting held in August 2-7, 2009

Cheung et al. (2009)

William W.L. Cheung, Vicky W.Y. Lam, Jorge L. Sarmiento, Kelly Kearney, Reg Watson and Daniel Pauly (2009)

Projecting global marine biodiversity impacts under climate change scenarios

Fish and Fisheries, vol.10:3, pp. 235-251

Cheung et al. (2010)

William W. L. Cheung, Vicky W. Y. Lam, Jorge L. Sarmiento, Kelly Kearney, Reg Watson, Dirk Zeller, and Daniel Pauly (2010)

Large-scale redistribution of maximum fisheries catch potential in the global ocean under climate change

Global Change Biology, vol. 16, no. 11, pp. 24-35.

Cheung et al. (2011)

William. L. Cheung, Vicky. W. Y. Lam, Jorge. L. Sarmiento, Kelly Kearney , Reg Watson and Daniel Pauly (2011)

The state of biodiversity and fisheries in regional seas

Fisheries Centre research reports, vol.19, no.3, pp:27-31

Chu et al. (2009)

J. T. Chu, J. Xia , C.-Y. Xu and V. P. Singh (2009)

Statistical downscaling of daily mean temperature, pan evaporation and precipitation for climate change scenarios in Haihe River, China

Theoretical and Applied Climatology, vol. 99, pp.149-161

Churchill and Matul (2012)

C. Churchill and M. Matul (eds.) (2012)

Protecting the poor: A microinsurance compendium . Volume II

Geneva, Switzerland, International Labour Office

Christian Aid (2007)

Christian Aid (2007)

Human tide: The forced migration crisis

UK, Christian Aid

Retrieved: http://www.christianaid.org.uk/images/human-tide.pdf

CIA (2012)

CIA (2012)

The World Factbook

Retrieved: https://www.cia.gov/library/publications/the-world-factbook/

CIESIN (2002)

Centre for International Earth Science Information Network (2002)

Country-level Population and Downscaled Projections based on the B2 Scenario, 1990-2100, [digital version]

Palisades, NY: CIESIN, Columbia University.

Retrieved: http://www.ciesin.columbia.edu/datasets/downscaled.

CIESIN Website (2012)

Center for International Earth Science Information Network (CIESIN)

Socioeconomic Data and Applications Center

http://sedac.ciesin.columbia.edu/

Cline (1992)
William R. Cline (1992)
The Economics of Global Warming
Washington, DC, Institute for International Economics

Cline (2007)
William R. Cline (2007)
Global Warming and Agriculture: Impact Estimates by Country
Washington, DC: Center for Global Development.

Climate Analytics (2012)
Climate Analytics (2012)
The Climate Analysis Indicators Tool (CAIT): CAIT International (database)
Retrieved: http://www.wri.org/project/cait/

Clune et al. (2012)
Stephen Clune, John Morrissey and Trivess Moore (2012)
Size matters: House size and thermal efficiency as policy strategies to reduce net emissions of new developments
Energy Policy, vol. 48, pp.657-667

Cohen (2011)
M.A. Cohen (2011)
Deepwater Drilling: Recommendations for a Safer Future
Resources , Winter/Spring 2011, no.177
Resources For the Future

Cohen et al. (2005)
A.J. Cohen, H. Ross Anderson, B. Ostro, K.D. Pandey, M. Krzyzanowski, N. Künzli, K. Gutschmidt, A. Pope, I. Romieu, J.M. Samet, K. Smith (2005)
The global burden of disease due to outdoor air pollution
Journal of Toxicology and Environmental Health, Part A., vol. pp. 1-7

Conway (2005)
Declan Conway (2005)
From headwater tributaries to international river: Observing and adapting to climate variability and change in the Nile basin
Global Environmental Change, vol. 15, pp. 99-114

Corcoran et al. (2007)
E.Corcoran, C. Ravilious and M. Skuja (2007)
Mangroves of Western and Central Africa
Cambridge, United Kingdom, UNEP World Conservation Monitoring Centre

Corti et al. (2009)
T. Corti, V. Muccione, P. Köllner-Heck, D. Bresch, and S. I. Seneviratne (2009)
Simulating past droughts and associated building damages in France
Hydrology and Earth System Sciences Discussions, vol. 6, no. 2, pp. 1463-1487.

Costanza et al. (1997)
Robert Costanza, Ralph d'Arge, Rudolf de Groot, Stephen Farber, Monica Grasso, Bruce Hannon, Karin Limburg, Shahid Naeem, Robert V. O'Neill, Jose Paruelo, Robert G. Raskin, Paul Sutton, & Marjan van den Belt (1997)
The value of the world's ecosystem services and natural capital
Nature, vol. 387.

Costanza et al. (2007)
R Costanza, B Fisher, K Mulder, S Liu, T Christopher (2007)
Biodiversity and ecosystem services: A multi-scale empirical study of the relationship between species richness and net primary production
Ecological Economics, vol. 61, no. 2-3, pp. 478-491.

Coups et al. (2008)
E. Coups, S. Manne, C. Heckman (2008)
Multiple Skin Cancer Risk Behaviors in the U.S. Population
American Journal of Preventive Medicine, vol. 34, Iss. 2, pp. 87-93

Cowling et al. (2008)
R. M. Cowling, B. Egoh, A. T. Knight, P. J. O'Farrell, B. Reyers, M.u Rouget, D. J. Roux, A. Welz and A. Wilhelm-Rechman (2008)
An operational model for mainstreaming ecosystem services for implementation
PNAS , vol. 105 , no. 28 , pp. 9483-9488

CRED/EM-DAT (2012)
Center for Research on the Epidemiology of Disasters (2012)
EM DAT - The International Disasters Database
Retrieved: http://www.emdat.be/advanced-search

CReSIS (2012)
Center for Remote Sensing of Ice Sheets (2012)
Sea Level Rise Maps
Haskell Indian Nations University.
Retrieved: https://www.cresis.ku.edu/data/sea-level-rise-maps

Crossland et al. (1991)
C.J. Crossland, B.G. Hatcher and S.V. Smith (1991)
Role of coral reefs in global ocean production
Coral Reefs, vol. 10, no. 2, pp. 55-64

Crowe et al. (2010)
J. Crowe, J. M. Moya-Bonilla, B. Román-Solano, and A. Robles-Ramírez (2010)
Heat exposure in sugarcane workers in Costa Rica during the non-harvest season
Global Health Action, Nov 2010, vol. 3.

Crutzen et al (2010)
Paul. J. Crutzen
Anthropocene man
Nature, vol. 467: 7317

Cruz and Alexander (2010)
M.G. Cruz and M.E. Alexander (2010)
Assessing crown fire potential in coniferous forests of western North America: a critique of current approaches and recent simulation studies.
International Journal of Wildland Fire, vol. 19, pp. 377-398

CTI (2011)
The Carbon Tracker Initiative (2011)
Unburnable Carbon - Are the world's financial markets carrying a carbon bubble?
Investor Watch
Retrieved: http://www.carbontracker.org/carbonbubble

Curriero al. (2002)
Frank C. Curriero, Karlyn S. Heiner, Jonathan M. Samet, Scott L. Zeger, Lisa Strug and Jonathan A. Patz (2002)
Temperature and Mortality in 11 Cities of the Eastern United States
American Journal of Epidemiology, Vol. 155, no. 1, pp. 80-87.

Curtis (2004)
Ian A. Curtis (2004)
Valuing ecosystem goods and services: a new approach using a surrogate market and the combination of a multiple criteria analysis and a Delphi panel to assign weights to the attributes
Ecological Economics, vol. 50, pp. 163- 194

Dai (2011)
A. Dai (2011)
Drought under Global Warming: A Review
Wiley Interdisciplinary Reviews: Climate Change, vol. 2, iss.1, pp. 45-65

D'Amato (2011)
Gennaro D'Amato (2011)
Effects of climatic changes and urban air pollution on the rising trends of respiratory allergy and asthma
Multidisciplinary Respiratory Medicine , vol. 6, no. 1, pp. 28-37

Dameris (2010)
M. Dameris (2010)
Depletion of the Ozone Layer in the 21st Century
Angewandte Chemie, vol. 49, pp. 489-491

Dawson et al. (2009)
J. Dawson, D. Scott and G. McBoyle (2009)
Climate change analogue analysis of ski tourism in the northeastern USA
Climate Research, vol. 39, pp. 1-9

DARA and CVF (2010)
DARA and the Climate Vulnerable Forum (2010)
Climate Vulnerability Monitor-"The State of the Climate Crisis"-2010 Report of the Climate Vulnerability Initiative.
Fundación DARA Internacional.

Dasgupta (2007)
Partha Dasgupta (2007)
Commentary: The Stern Review's Economics of Climate Change
National Institute Economic Review No. 199 , Iss. 4

Dasgupta et al. (2009)
S. Dasgupta, B. Laplante, C. Meisner, D. Wheeler and J. Yan (2009)
The impact of sea level rise on developing countries: a comparative analysis
Climatic Change, vol. 93, no. 3-4, pp.379-388

DCPP (2006)
World Bank (2006)
Disease Control Priorities in Developing Countries (2nd edition).
New York: Oxford University Press
Washington D.C., US: World Bank

De'ath et al. (2009)
G. De'ath, J.M. Lough, K. E. Fabricius (2009)
Declining Coral Calcification on the Great Barrier Reef
Science, vol. 323, pp. 116-119

De Cian and Tavoni (2010)
E. De Cian and M. Tavoni (2010)
The Role of International Carbon Offsets in a Second- best Climate Policy: A Numerical Evaluation.
Nota di Lavoro 33.2010
Fondazione Eni Enrico Mattei

de Dear and Brager (1998)
R. de Dear and G.S. Brager (1998)
Developing an adaptive model of thermal comfort and preference
ASHRAE Transactions , vol. 108, part. I

Dennehy (2000)
P. Dennehy (2000)
Transmission of rotavirus and other enteric pathogens in the home
Pediatric Infectious Disease Journal, vol. 19, iss. 10, pp. S103-S105

De Sherbinin et al. (2007)
Alex De Sherbinin, Andrew Schiller and Alex Pulsipher (2007)
The vulnerability of global cities to climate hazards
Environment and Urbanization, vol. 19, no.1, pp. 39-64.

Dessai et al (2009)

S. Dessai, M. Hulme, R. Lempert and R. Pielke Jr (2009)

Climate prediction: a limit to adaptation?, in W.N. Adger,I. Lorenzoni and K.L. O'Brien (eds) *Adapting to Climate Change: Thresholds, Values, Governance (pp. 64-78)*

Cambridge University Press

de Wit and Stankiewicz (2006)

Maarten de Wit and Jacek Stankiewicz (2006)

Changes in Surface Water Supply Across Africa with Predicted Climate Change

Science, vol. 311, pp. 1917-1921

Ding et al. (2011)

Y. Ding, M.J. Hayes, and M. Widhalm (2010)

Measuring Economic Impacts of Drought: A Review and Discussion

Disaster Prevention and Management, vol. 20, no. 4, pp. 434-446

DIVA (2003)

DINAS-COAST (2003)

Dynamic Interactive Vulnerability Assessment (DIVA)

Dixon et al. (2003)

Robert K. Dixon, Joel Smith and Sandra Guill (2003)

Life on the Edge: Vulnerability and Adaptation of African Ecosystems to Global Climate Change

Mitigation and Adaptation Strategies for Global Change, vol. 8, pp. 93–113

Dodman and Satterthwaite (2008)

David Dodman and David Satterthwaite (2008)

Institutional Capacity, Climate Change Adaptation and the Urban Poor

IDS Bulletin, vol. 39, no. 4

Institute of Development Studies (IDS)

Dolan and David (1992)

R. Dolan and R.E. Davis (1992)

An Intensity Scale for Atlantic Coast Northeast Storms.

Journal of Coastal Research, vol. 8, no.4, pp.840-843

Domingues et al. (2008)

Catia M. Domingues, John A. Church, Neil J. White, Peter J. Gleckler, Susan E. Wijffels, Paul M. Barker and Jeff R. Dunn (2008)

Improved estimates of upper-ocean warming and multi-decadal sea-level rise

Nature, vol. 453, pp. 1090-1093

Donat et al. (2011)

Donat M.G., G. C. Leckebusch, S. Wild, and U. Ulbrich (2011)

Future changes in European winter storm losses and extreme wind speeds inferred from GCM and RCM multi-model simulations

Natural Hazards and Earth System Sciences, vol. 11, no. 5, pp 1351-1370.

Donkelaar et al. (2010)

Aaron van Donkelaar, R. V. Martin, M. Brauer, R. Kahn, R. Levy, C. Verduzco, and P.J. Villeneuve (2010)

Global Estimates of Ambient Fine Particulate Matter Concentrations from Satellite-Based Aerosol Optical Depth: Development and Application

Environmental Health Perspectives, vol. 118, no. 6, pp. 847-855

Donner and Rodriguez (2008)

William Donner and Havidán Rodríguez (2008)

Population Composition, Migration and Inequality: The Influence of Demographic Changes on Disaster Risk and Vulnerability

Social Forces, vol. 87, no. 2, pp. 1089-1114

Donohoe (2003)

M. Donohoe (2003)

Causes and Health Consequences of Environmental Degradation and Social Injustice

Social Science & Medicine, vol. 56, pp. 573-587

Donovan and Butry (2009)

Geoffrey H. Donovan and David T. Butry (2009)

The value of shade: Estimating the effect of urban trees on summertime electricity use

Energy and Buildings, vol. 41, pp. 662–668

Dore (2005)

Mohammed H.I. Dore (2005)

Climate change and changes in global precipitation patterns: What do we know?

Environment International, vol. 31, pp.1167 - 1181

Douglas-Westwood (2010)

Douglas-Westwood/ New York (2010)

Global Deepwater Prospects-2010

Presentation for the Deep Offshore Technology International Conference held in Houston, Texas, 2 February 2010

Driscoll et al. (2001)

C.T. Driscoll, G.B. Lawrence, A.J. Bulger, T.J. Butler, C.S. Cronan, C. Eagar, K.F. Lambert, G.E. Likens, J.L. Stoddard, and K.C. Weathers (2001)

Acidic Deposition in the Northeastern United States: Sources and Inputs, Ecosystem Effects, and Management Strategies

BioScience, vol. 51, no. 3, pp. 180-198

Driscoll et al. (2004)

Tim Driscoll, Kyle Steenland, Deborah Imel Nelson, James Leigh (2004)

Occupational airborne particulates: Assessing the environmental burden of disease at national and local levels

Environmental Burden of Disease Series, no. 7.

Geneva, Switzerland: World Health Organization

Easterling (2011)

William E. Easterling (2011)

Guidelines for Adapting Agriculture to Climate Change

In: Hillel and Rosenzweig (eds.): Handbook of Climate Change and Agroecosystems: Impacts, Adaptation, and Mitigation

London, UK, Imperial College Press

EACC (2010)

Economics of Adaptation to Climate Change (2010)

Economics of Adaptation to Climate Change-Synthesis Report

The World Bank

ECLAC (2011)

Economic Commission for Latin America and the Caribbean (ECLAC) (2011)

An Assessment of the Economic Impact of Climate Change on the Tourism Sector in Barbados

United Nations ECLAC

Edenhofer et al. (2010)

O. Edenhofer, B. Knopf, T. Barker, L. Baumstark, E. Bellevrat, B. Chateau, P. Criqui, M. Isaac, A. Kitous, S. Kypreos, M. Leimbach, K. Lessmann, B. Magné, S. Scrieciu, H. Turton, D. P. van Vuuren (2010).

The Economics of Low Stabilization: Model Comparison of Mitigation Strategies and Costs

The Energy Journal, vol. 31 (Special Issue 1), pp.11-48

EDGAR (2012)

Emission Database for Global Atmospheric Research (EDGAR)

EDGAR 3.2 Fast Track 2000 dataset (32FT2000)

PBL Netherlands Environmental Assessment Agency

http://131.224.244.83/en/themasites/edgar/emission_data/edgar_32ft2000/index.html

Eisenack et al. (2012)

Klaus Eisenack, Rebecca Stecker, Diana Reckien and Esther Hoffmann (2012)

Adaptation to climate change in the transport sector: a review of actions and actors

Mitigation and Adaptation Strategies for Global Change, vol. 17, no. 5 , pp.451-469

Elliot et al. (2011)

M. Elliott, A. Armstrong, J. Lobuglio, J. Bartram (2011)

Technologies for climate change adaptation: the water sector

Roskilde, Denmark: UNEP Risø Centre on Energy, Climate and Sustainable Development

Elsasser and Bürki (2002)

Hans Elsasser and Rolf Bürki (2002)

Climate change as a threat to tourism in the Alps

Climate Research, vol. 20, pp. 253–257

EM-DAT CRED (2012) - See: CRED (above)

Energy Information Administration Website (2012)

Energy Information Administration Website

Various sources

Engelhard (2011)

G. H. Engelhard, J. R. Ellis, M. R. Payn, R. Hofstede, and J. K. Pinnegar (2011)

Ecotypes as a concept for exploring responses to climate change in fish assemblages

ICES Journal of Marine Science , vol. 68, iss.3, pp. 580-591

Enserink (2010)

M. Enserink 82010)

Yellow Fever Mosquito Shows Up in Northern Europe

Science, vol. 329, no. 5993, p. 736

Environmental Protection Agency (2010)

Environmental Protection Agency (2010)

Various resources

http://www.epa.gov/enviro/index.html

Eon Energy Lab(2012)

Eon Energy Lab(2012)

What is Hydro Energy?

Retrieved: http://www.eon-energylab.co.uk/what-is-hydro-energy/

EPA-Ghana (2011)

Environmental Protection Agency (EPA)- Ghana (2011)

Ghana's Second National Communication to The UNFCCC, 2011

GEF, EPA and UNDP

Epstein (2001)

P.R. Epstein (2001)

Climate Change and Emerging Infectious Disease

Microbes and Infection, vol. 3, iss. 9, pp. 747-754

Epule et al. (2012)

Epule Terence Epule, Changhui Peng , Laurent Lepage and Zhi Chen

Rainfall and Deforestation Dilemma for Cereal Production in the Sudano-Sahel of Cameroon

Journal of Agricultural Science, vol. 4, no. 2;

ERC (2009)

Environmental Research Consulting (2009)

Largest Oil Spills Worldwide

Environmental Research Consulting

Esikuri ed. (1999)

Enos E .Esikuri, Hassan M . Hassan and Gunter W. Riethmacher (eds.) (1999)

Drylands, Poverty and Development. Proceedings of the June15 and 16 ,1999 World Bank Round Table

The International Bank for Reconstruction and Development/ The World Bank

Etkin (2004)
Etkin, Dagmar Schmidt (2004)
Modeling Oil Spill Response and Damage Costs. In *Proceedings of the 5th Biennial Freshwater Spills Symposium*
Washington, DC: US Environmental Protection Agency

Euskirchen et al. (2006)
E.S. Euskirchen, A.D. McGuire, D.W. Kicklighter, Q. Zhuang, J.S. Clein, R.J. Dargaville, D.G. Dye, J.S. Kimball, K.C. McDonald, J.M. Melillo, V.E. Romanovsky, and N.V. Smith (2006)
Importance of recent shifts in soil thermal dynamics on growing season length, productivity, and carbon sequestration in terrestrial high-latitude ecosystems
Global Change Biology, vol. 12, no. 4, pp. 731-750

Evans and Geerken (2004)
Jason Evans and Roland Geerken (2004)
Discrimination between climate and human-induced dryland degradation
Journal of Arid Environments, vol. 57, pp. 535-554

Falkenmark and Molden (2008)
Malin Falkenmark and David Molden (2008)
Wake Up to Realities of River Basin Closure
International Journal of Water Resources Development, vol. 24, no.2, pp. 201-215

FAO (2007)
FAO (2007)
Adaptation to climate change in agriculture, forestry and fisheries: Perspective, framework and priorities
Rome, Food and Agriculture Organization of the United Nations

FAO (2011)
FAO (2011)
The State of Food Insecurity in the World. How does international price volatility affect domestic economies and food security?
Rome, Food and Agriculture Organization of the United Nations

FAO (2012)
FAO (2012)
The State of World Fisheries and Aquaculture 2012
Rome, Food and Agriculture Organization of the United Nations

FAO AQUASTAT (2012)
FAO AQUASTAT (2012)
AQUASTAT Database
http://www.fao.org/nr/water/aquastat/dbases/index.stm

FAO FISHSTAT (2012)
FAO FISHSTAT (2012)
FishStat Plus Database
http://www.fao.org/fishery/statistics/software/fishstat/en

FAOSTAT (2012)
FAOSTAT
Various Resources
http://faostat.fao.org/

Farber et al. (2002)
Stephen C. Farber, Robert Costanza, Matthew A. Wilson (2002)
Economic and ecological concepts for valuing ecosystem services
Ecological Economics, vol. 41, pp.375-392

Feng and Kobayashi (2009)
Zhaozhong Feng and Kazuhiko Kobayashi (2009)
Assessing the impacts of current and future concentrations of surface ozone on crop yield with meta-analysis
Atmospheric Environment, vol. 43, Iss. 8, pp 1510-1519

Feng and Liu (2012)
Xi Zhou Feng and Zheng Ping Liu (2012)
Discussion on Permafrost Hazards of Railway Engineering and Prevention Measures: A Case Study on Qinghai-Tibet Railway
Advanced Materials Research, vols. 550-553, pp. 2493-2497

Ficke et al. (2007)
Ashley. D. Ficke, Christopher. A. Myrick, Lara. J. Hansen (2007)
Potential impacts of global climate change on freshwater fisheries
Reviews in Fish Biology and Fisheries, vol. 17, no. 4, pp. 581-613

Fisk (2000)
William J. Fisk (2000)
Health and Productivity Gains from Better Indoor Environments and their Relationship with Building Energy Efficiency
Annu. Rev. Energy Environ. vol. 25, pp. 537-66

Foell et al (2011)
W. Foell, S. Pachauri, D. Spreng, H.Zerriffi (2011)
Household cooking fuels and technologies in developing economies
Energy Policy, vol. 39, Issue 12, pp.7487-7496

Fraser et al. (2011)
E. D. G. Fraser, , A. J. Dougill, K. Hubacek, C. H. Quinn, J. Sendzimir, and M. Termansen (2011)
Assessing vulnerability to climate change in dryland livelihood systems: conceptual challenges and interdisciplinary solutions
Ecology and Society, vol. 16, no. 3, iss. 3

Fredén (2011)
Fredrik Fredén (2011).
Impacts of dams on lowland agriculture in the Mekong River catchment
Seminar series nr 207
Bachelor's degree thesis in Physical Geography, Department of Earth and Ecosystem Sciences , Lund University, Sweden

Friedler (2001)
Eran Friedler (2001)
Water reuse - an integral part of water resources management: Israel as a case study
Water Policy, vol. 3, pp. 29-39

Friedlingstein et al (2010).
P. Friedlingstein, R. A. Houghton, G. Marland, J. Hackler, T. A. Boden, T. J. Conway, J. G. Canadell, M. R. Raupach, P. Ciais & C. Le Quéré (2010)
Update on CO emissions.
Nature Geoscience vol 3, pp. 811-812

Friedman (2009)
Thomas L. Friedman (2009)
Hot, Flat, and Crowded: Why The World Needs A Green Revolution – and How We Can Renew Our Global Future
Farrar, Straus & Giroux

Fullerton et al. (2008)
D. G. Fullerton, N. Bruce and S. B. Gordon (2008)
Indoor air pollution from biomass fuel smoke is a major health concern in the developing world
Transactions of the Royal Society of Tropical Medicine and Hygiene, vol. 102, no. 9, pp. 843-851.

Füssel (2009)
Hans-Martin Füssel (2009)
Review and quantitative analysis of indices of climate change exposure, adaptive capacity, sensitivity, and impacts. In: *World Development Report 2010* (Background note)
The World Bank.

Füssel (2010)
Hans-Martin Füssel (2010)
How inequitable is the global distribution of responsibility, capability, and vulnerability to climate change: A comprehensive indicator-based assessment
Global Environmental Change, vol. 20 , issue 4, pp. 597 - 611

Füssel (2012)
Hans-Martin Füssel (2012):
Vulnerability of Coastal Populations, in: O. Edenhofer, J. Wallacher, H. Lotze-Campen, M. Reder, B. Knopf and J. Müller (eds) : Climate Change, Justice and Sustainability Linking Climate and Development Policy (chapter 5, pp. 45-57)
Dordrecht, Netherlands: Springer Science+Business Media

Gallup and Sachs (2001)
J.L. Gallup and J.D. Sachs (2001)
The Economic Burden of Malaria
American Journal of Tropical Medical Hygiene, vol. 64, suppl. 1, pp. 85-96

Gardiner (2004)
Stephen M. Gardiner (2004)
Ethics and Global Climate Change
Ethics, vol. 114 , pp. 555-600

Garfunkel ed. (2010)
Adam Garfunkel (ed.) (2010)
Universal Ownership. Why environmental externalities matter to institutional investors ?
United Nations Environment Programme Finance Initiative (UNEP FI) and The Principles for Responsible Investment (PRI).

Garg et al. (2009)
A. Garg, R.C. Dhiman, S. Bhattacharya, and P.R. Shukla (2009)
Development, Malaria and Adaptation to Climate Change: A Case Study from India
Environmental Management, vol. 43, no. 5, pp. 779-789

Geist and Lambin (2004)
Helmut J. Geist and Eric F. Lambin (2004)
Dynamic Causal Patterns of Desertification
BioScience, vol. 54, no. 9, pp. 817-829

Geng et al. (2001)
S.Geng, Y. Zhou, M. Zhang and K. S. Smallwood (2011)
A Sustainable Agro-ecological Solution to Water Shortage in the North China Plain (Huabei Plain)
Journal of Environmental Planning and Management, vol. 44, Iss. 3, pp. 345-355

Geoworldmap (2012)
Geoworldmap
Geobytes' GeoWorldmap Database
Retrieved: http://www.geobytes.com/FreeServices.htm

GHF (2009)
Global Humanitarian Forum (2009)
Human Impact Report : Climate Change- The Anatomy of a Silent Crisis
Geneva, Switzerland: Global Humanitarian Forum.

Ghana SS (2010)
Ghana Statistical Service (2010)
Population and Housing Census (PHC)
Accra, Ghana Statistical Service (GSS)

Giesey et al. (2010)
J.P. Giesy, J.C. Anderson, and S.B. Wiseman (2010)
Alberta oil sands development
Proceedings of the National Academy of Sciences of the United States (PNAS), vol. 107, no.3, pp. 951-952

Gilad et al. (2003)
Oren Gilad, Susan Yun, Mark A. Adkison, Keith Way, Neil H. Willits, Herve Bercovier and Ronald P. Hedrick (2003)
Molecular comparison of isolates of an emerging fish pathogen, koi herpesvirus, and the effect of water temperature on mortality of experimentally infected koi
Journal of General Virology, vol.84, no:10, pp.2661-2667

Gilchrest et al. (1999)

B.A. Gilchrest, M.S. Eller, A.C. Geller, and M. Yaar (1999)

The Pathogenesis of Melanoma Induced by Ultraviolet Radiation

New England Journal of Medicine, vol. 340, pp. 1341-1348

GIM (2012)

Generation Investment Management LLP(2012)

Sustainable Capitalism

Retrieved: http://www.generationim.com/media/pdf-generation-sustainable-capitalism-v1.pdf

Gisladottir and Stocking (2005)

G. Gisladottir and M. Stocking (2005)

Land Degradation Control and its Global Environmental Benefits

Land degradation & Development, vol. 16, pp. 99-112

Giuffrida et al. (2002)

A. Guiffrida, R. Fiunes and W. Savedoff (2002)

Occupational Risks in Latin America and the Caribbean: Economic and Health Dimensions

Health Policy and Planning, vol. 17, no.3, pp. 235-246

Glanz (ed.) (1987)

Michael H. Glantz (ed.) (1987)

Drought and Hunger in Africa

Cambridge University Press

Glewwe and Jacoby (1993)

Paul Glewwe and Hanan Jacoby (1993)

Delayed Primary School Enrollment and Childhood Malnutrition in Ghana: An Economic Analysis

Living Standards Measurement Study Working paper, No. 98

Washington, DC, The International Bank for Reconstruction and Development/ The World Bank.

GoA (2012)

Government of Alberta (2012)

Alberta Energy: Facts and Statistics

Retrieved http://www.energy.gov.ab.ca/OilSands/791.asp Page

Gonzalez et al. (2010)

P. Gonzalez, R. P. Neilson, J. M. Lenihan and Raymond J. Drapek (2010)

Global patterns in the vulnerability of ecosystems to vegetation shifts due to climate change

Global Ecology and Biogeography, vol.19, iss. 6, pp.755-768

Gooroochurn and Sinclair (2005)

Nishaal Gooroochurn and M. Thea Sinclair (2005)

Economics of tourism taxation: Evidence from Mauritius

Annals of Tourism Research, vol. 32, iss. 2, pp.478-498

Gosling et al. (2009)

S.N. Gosling, J.A. Lowe, G.R. McGregor, M. Pelling, and B.D. Malamud (2009)

Associations Between Elevated Atmospheric Temperature and Human Mortality: A Critical Review of the Literature

Climatic Change, vol. 92, no. 3-4, pp. 299-341

Graff Zivin and Neidell (2010)

Joshua Graff Zivin Matthew J. Neidell (2010)

Temperature and the Allocation of Time: Implications for Climate Change

NBER Working Paper Series . Working Paper 15717

National Bureau of Economic Research

Retrieved: http://www.nber.org/papers/w15717

Graham and Reilly (2011)

B. Graham, W.K. Reilly (2011)

Deep Water: The Gulf Oil Disaster and the Future of Offshore Drilling

Report to the President National Commission on the BP Deepwater Horizon Oil Spill and Offshore Drilling

Grant (2010)

J.K. Grant (2010)

What Can We Learn From The 2010 BP Oil Spill?: Five Important Corporate Law and Life Lessons

McGeorge Law Review, Vol. 42, p. 809, 2011

Gray (1997)

Tim. S. Gray (1997)

Marine biodiversity: patterns, threats and conservation needs

Biodiversity and Conservation, vol.6, no.1, pp. 153-175

Greenpeace USA (2009)

Greenpeace USA (2009, May 22)

Broad Coalition Criticizes Climate Bill

Retrieved: http://www.greenpeace.org/usa/en/media-center/news-releases/broad-coalition-criticizes-cli/

Gregory et al. (2009)

P. J. Gregory, S. N. Johnson, A. C. Newton and J. S. I. Ingram (2009)

Integrating pests and pathogens into the climate change/ food security debate

Journal of Experimental Botany, vol. 60, no. 10, pp. 2827-2838

Grieve and Short (2007)

C Grieve and K Short (2007)

Implementation of Ecosystem-Based Management in Marine Capture Fisheries - case studies from WWF's marine ecorregions

World Wide Fund for Nature

Grinsted et al. (2009)

Aslak Grinsted, J. C. Moore and S. Jevrejeva (2009)

Reconstructing sea level from paleo and projected temperatures 200 to 2100AD

Climate Dynamics, vol. 34,no. 4, pp.461-472

GWI (2008)

Global Water Intelligence (2008)

World water prices rise by 6.7%

Global Water Intelligence - Archive: Global Water Intelligence, Vol 9, Iss. 9

Retrieved: http://www.globalwaterintel.com/archive/9/9/analysis/world-water-prices-rise-by-67.html

Hales et al. (2000)

S. Hales, S. Kovats, and A. Woodward (2000)

What El Niño can tell us about human health and global climate change

Global Change & Human Health, vol. 1, iss. 1, pp. 66-77

Hallegatte (2005)

Stéphane Hallegatte (2005)

Accounting for Extreme Events in the Economic Assessment of Climate Change

Nota Di Lavoro 1.2005. Fondazione Eni Enrico Mattei Note di Lavoro Series Index.

Halpern et al. (2008)

B. S. Halpern, S. Walbridge, K. A. Selkoe, C. V. Kappel, F. Micheli, C. D'Agrosa , J. F. Bruno, K. S. Casey, C. Ebert, H. E. Fox, R. Fujita, D. Heinemann, H. S. Lenihan, E. M. P. Madin, M. T. Perry, E. R. Selig, M. Spalding, R. Steneck and R. Watson (2008)

A Global Map of Human Impact on Marine Ecosystems

Science, vol. 319, no: 5865, pp.948-952

Hamududu and Killingtveit (2012)

Byman Hamududu and Aanund Killingtveit (2012)

Assessing Climate Change Impacts on Global Hydropower

Energies, vol. 5, pp. 305-322

Hamilton (2008)

L.S. Hamilton (2008)

Forests and Water. A thematic study prepared in the framework of the Global Forest Resources Assessment 2005

FAO Forestry Paper 155

Rome, Food and Agriculture Organization of the United Nations

Hamilton et al. (2005)

Jacqueline M. Hamilton, David J. Maddison, Richard S.J. Tol (2005)

Climate change and international tourism: A simulation study

Global Environmental Change, vol. 15, pp. 253-266

Hanna et al. (2011a)

E. G Hanna, T. Kjellstrom, Ch. Bennett and K. Dear (2011)

Climate Change and Rising Heat: Population Health Implications for Working People in Australia

Asia-Pacific Journal of Public Health, vol. 23, no. 2, suppl 14S-26S

Hancock et al. (2003)

P. A. Hancock and I. Vasmatzidis (2003)

Effects of heat stress on cognitive performance: the current state of knowledge

International Journal of Hyperthermia, vol. 19, no. 3, pp. 355-372

Hancock et al. (2007)

P.A. Hancock, J. M. Ross and J.L. Szalma (2007)

A meta-analysis of performance response under thermal stressors

Human Factors, vol. 49, iss. 5, pp. 851-877

Hansen (2006)

Jim Hansen (2006, 19 October)

The Planet in Peril- Part I: Global Warming, artic ice melt and rising oceans will shrink nations and change world maps

YaleGlobalOnline

Retrieved: http://yaleglobal.yale.edu/content/planet-peril-%E2%80%93-part-i

Hansen et al. (2005)

James Hansen, Larissa Nazarenko, Reto Ruedy, Makiko Sato, Josh Willis, Anthony Del Genio,Dorothy Koch, Andrew Lacis, Ken Lo, Surabi Menon, Tica Novakov, Judith Perlwitz, Gary Russell, Gavin A. Schmidt and Nicholas Tausnev (2005)

Earth's Energy Imbalance: Confirmation and Implications

Science , Vol. 308, no. 5727 pp. 1431-1435

Hansen et al. (2007)

J. Hansen, M. Sato, R. Ruedy, P. Kharecha, A. Lacis, R. Miller, L. Nazarenko, K. Lo, G. A. Schmidt, G. Russell, I. Aleinov, S. Bauer, E. Baum, B. Cairns, V. Canuto, M. Chandler, Y. Cheng, A. Cohen, A. Del Genio, G. Faluvegi, E. Fleming, A. Friend, T. Hall, C. Jackman, J. Jonas, M. Kelley, N. Y. Kiang, D. Koch, G. Labow, J. Lerner, S. Menon, T. Novakov, V. Oinas, Ja. Perlwitz, Ju. Perlwitz, D. Rind, A. Romanou, R. Schmunk, D. Shindell, P. Stone, S. Sun, D. Streets, N. Tausnev, D. Thresher, N. Unger, M. Yao, and S. Zhang (2007)

Dangerous human-made interference with climate: A GISS modelE study

Atmospheric Chemistry and Physics, vol. 7, pp. 2287-2312.

Hansen et al. (2008)

A. Hansen, P. Bi, M. Nitschke, P. Ryan, D. Pisaniello and C. Tucker (2008)

The Effect of Heat Waves on Mental Health in a Temperate Australian City

Environmental Health Perspectives , vol.116, no.10, pp. 1369-1375

Hansen et al. (2012)

J. Hansen, M. Sato, and R. Ruedy (2012)

Perception of climate change

PNAS PLUS (2012, August 6), doi:10.1073/ pnas.1205276109

Hare (1997)

Bill Hare (1997)

Fossil fuels and Climate Protection: The Carbon Logic

Greenpeace International

Hare in Mastny (2009)

W. L. Hare (2009)

A Safe Landing for the Climate

In: Mastny (Ed.): *State of the World 2009: into a Warming World* (chapter 2)

World Watch Institute

Harley et al. (2006)

Christopher D. G. Harley, A. Randall Hughes, Kristin M. Hultgren,

BenjaminG.Miner, Cascade J. B. Sorte, Carol S. Thornber, Laura F. Rodriguez,

Lars Tomanek and Susan L. Williams (2006)

The impacts of climate change in coastal marine systems

Ecology Letters, vol.9:2, pp. 228-241

Harris et al. (2007)

A. Harris, S.Rahman, F. Hossain, L. Yarborough , A. C. Bagtzoglou, G. Easson (2007)

Satellite-based Flood Modeling Using TRMM-based Rainfall Products

Sensors , vol. 7, pp. 3416-3427

Harrison et al. (1999)

S.J. Harrison, S.J. Winterbottom and C. Sheppard (1999)

The potential effects of climate change on the Scottish tourist industry

Tourism Management, vol. 20, Iss, 2, pp. 203-211

Hart (1996)

Stuart. L. Hart (1996)

Beyond Greening: Strategies for a sustainable world

Harvard Business Review

Haya (2007)

Barbara Haya (2007)

Failed Mechanism: How the CDM is Subsidizing Hydro Developers and Harming the Kyoto Protocol

Berkley, CA, International Rivers

Hella and Zavaleta (2009)

N. E. Heller, E. S. Zavaleta (2009)

Biodiversity management in the face of climate change: A review of 22 years of recommendations

Biological Conservation, vol. 142, pp. 14-32

Helm et al. (2010)

Helm, K. P., N. L. Bindoff, and J. A. Church (2010)

Changes in the global hydrological-cycle inferred from ocean salinity

Geophyical Research Letters, vol. 37, L18701

Hellmann et al. (2008)

J.J. Hellmann, J. E. Byers,.B. G. Bierwagen and J. S. Dukes (2008)

Five Potential Consequences of Climate Change for Invasive Species

Conservation Biology, vol. 22, No. 3, pp. 534-543

Hewitt and Jackson eds. (2009)

C. Nick Hewitt and Andrea V. Jackson (2009)

Atmospheric Science for Environmental Scientists

Wiley- Blackwell Publishing

Hidalgo et al. (2009)

H. G. Hidalgo , T. Das, M. D. Dettinger,D. R. Cayan, D. W. Pierce, T. P. Barnett, G. Bala, A. Mirin,A. W. Wood,C. Bonfils, B. D. Santer, and T. Nozawa (2009)

Detection and Attribution of Streamflow Timing Changes to Climate Change in the Western United States

Journal of Climate , vol. 22 pp. 3838-3855

Hiddink and Hofstede (2008)

J. G. Hiddink and R. Ter Hofstede (2008)

Climate induced increases in species richness of marine fishes

Global Change Biology, vol. 14:3, pp. 453-460

Hill et al. (2004)

David J. Hill, J. Mark Elwood, Dallas R. English (2004)

Prevention of Skin Cancer

Kluwer Academic Publishers: the Netherlands

Hoegh-Guldberg (2011)

O. Hoegh-Guldberg (2011)

The current and future impacts of climate change and ocean acidification on the Great Barrier Reef

Report prepared for an objections hearing in the Land Court of Queensland

regarding the proposed Wandoan Coal Mine

Hoegh-Guldberg et al. (2007)

O. Hoegh-Guldberg, P. J. Mumby, A. J. Hooten, R. S. Steneck, P. Greenfield, E. Gomez, C. D. Harvell, P. F. Sale, A. J. Edwards, K. Caldeira, N. Knowlton, C. M. Eakin, R. Iglesias-Prieto, N. Muthiga, R. H. Bradbury, A. Dubi, and M. E. Hatziolos (2007)

Coral Reefs Under Rapid Climate Change and Ocean Acidification

Science, vol. 318, pp. 1737-1742

Hoegh-Guldberg and Bruno (2010)

Ove Hoegh-Guldberg and John F. Bruno (2010)

The Impact of Climate Change on the World's Marine Ecosystems

Science, vol. 328, no.5985, pp. 1523-1528

Hoekstra et al. (2010)

Jonathan M. Hoekstra, Jennifer L. Molnar, Michael Jennings, Carmen Revenga, Mark D. Spalding, Timothy M. Boucher, James C. Robertson, Thomas J. Heibel, and Katherine Ellison (2010)

The Atlas of Global Conservation: Changes, Challenges, and Opportunities to Make a Difference

Berkeley: University of California Press

Retrieved: http://preview.grid.unep.ch/index.php?preview=home&lang=eng

Holm Olsen and Fenhann (2008)

K. Holm Olsen and J. Fenhann (2008)

A Reformed CDM – including new Mechanisms for Sustainable Development

Roskilde, Denmar , Capacity Development for CDM (CD4CDM) Project , UNEP Risø Centre

Holman et al. (2008)

Corey Holman, Bobbie Joyeux and Christopher Kask (2008)

Labor productivity trends since 2000, by sector and industry

Monthly Labor Review ,February 2008, pp. 64-82

Hooper et al. (2012)

David U. Hooper, E. Carol Adair, Bradley J. Cardinale, Jarrett E. K. Byrnes, Bruce A. Hungate, Kristin L. Matulich, Andrew Gonzalez, J. Emmett Duffy, Lars Gamfeldt, Mary I. O'Connor (2012)

A global synthesis reveals biodiversity loss as a major driver of ecosystem change

Nature

Hope (2006)

Chris Hope (2006)

The Marginal Impact of CO2 from PAGE2002: An Integrated Assessment Model Incorporating the IPCC's Five Reasons for Concern

The Integrated Assessment Journal , vol. 6, Iss. 1 , pp. 19-56

HPN (2012)

Humanitarian Practice Network (2012)

Special feature: The crisis in the Horn of Africa

Humanitarian Exchange, no. 53

Overseas Development Institute (ODI)

Hübler et al. (2007)

Michael Hübler, Gernot Klepper , Sonja Peterson (2007)

Costs of Climate Change: The Effects of Rising Temperatures on Health and Productivity in Germany

Kiel Working Paper No. 1321 .

Kiel, Germany, Kiel Institute for the World Economy

Hughes et al. (2003)

T. P. Hughes, A. H. Baird, D. R. Bellwood, M. Card, S. R. Connolly, C. Folke, R. Grosberg, O. Hoegh-Guldberg, J. B. C. Jackson, J. Kleypas, J. M. Lough, P. Marshall, M. Nystro¨m, S. R. Palumbi, J. M. Pandolfi, B. Rosen, J. Roughgarden (2003)

Climate Change, Human Impacts, and the Resilience of Coral Reefs

Science, vol. 301, pp.929-933

Hughes and Diaz (2008)

M.K. Hughes and H.F. Diaz (2008)

Climate variability and change in the drylands of Western North America

Global and Planetary Change, vol. 64, Iss. 3-4, pp. 111-118

Huifang Guo et al. (2012)

Huifang Guo, Zhigang Song, Shengyuan Yang (2012)

Corrosion of permeable concrete under simulated acid rain

Key Engineering Materials, vol: 517, pp. 352-356

Hunter (2003)

P.R. Hunter (2003)

Climate change and waterborne and vector-borne disease

Journal of Applied Microbiology, vol. 94, pp. 37S-46S

Huntington (2006)

Thomas G. Huntington (2006)

Evidence for intensification of the global water cycle: Review and synthesis

Journal of Hydrology, vol. 319, pp. 83-95

Hutchings et al. (2010)

Jeffery. A. Hutchings, Cóilín Minto, Daniel Ricard, Julia K. Baum, Olaf P. Jensen (2010)

Trends in the abundance of marine fishes

Canadian Journal of Fisheries and Aquatic Sciences, vol. 67:8, pp. 1205-1210

IAP (2009)

Interacademy Panel on International Issues (2009)

IAP Statement on Tropical Forests and Climate Change

Retrieved: http://www.interacademies.net/File.aspx?id=10070

IBRD WB (2010)

The International Bank for Reconstruction and Development/ The World Bank (2010)

Economics of Adaptation to Climate Change. Synthesis Report

Washington DC, The International Bank for Reconstruction and Development / The World Bank

ICI (2010)

Initiatives Conseil International (2010)

Etat des lieux autour du barrage de Bagré au Burkina Faso. Rapport Final

IUCN, The Global Water Initiative and International Institute for Environment and Development

Idso (1989)

S.B., Idso (1989)

Carbon dioxide and global change

Tempe, AZ (USA); Institute for Biospheric Research

IEA (2011)

International Energy Agency (2011)

World Energy Outlook 2011

Retrieved: http://www.worldenergyoutlook.org

IEA (2011a)

International Energy Agency (2011)

Energy for all. Financing access for poor. Special yearly excerpt of the world energy outlook 2011

OECD/IEA

IEA (2012a)

International Energy Agency (2012)

IEA Response System for Oil Supply Emergencies 2012

Paris, International Energy Agency

Retrieved:http://www.iea.org/media/delegates/seq/meetings/march12/IEA-SEQ(2012)9.pdf

IEA (2012b)

International Energy Agency (2012)

Energy Statistics and Balances of Non-OECD Countries, Energy Statistics of OECD Countries, and Energy Balances of OECD Countries

Retrieved 2010: http://www.iea.org/stats/index.asp

IFP (2011)

IFP Énergies Nouvelles,Economics and Information Watch and Management Division (2011)

Investment in exploration-production and refining 2011

IFP Énergies Nouvelles

Ikuta et al. (2000)

K. Ikuta, T. Yada, S. Kitamura, N. Branch, F. Ito, F., M. Yamagichi, M., T. Nishimura, T. Kaneko, M. Nagae, A. Ishimatsu, M. Iwata (2000)

Effects of Acidification on Fish Reproduction

UJNR Technical Report, No. 28.

Ikuta et al.(2008)

Kazumasa Ikuta, Takashi Yada, Shoji Kitamura, Toyoji Kaneko, Maki Nagae, Atsushi Ishimatsu and Munohiko Iwata (2008)

Effects of Acidification on Fish Reproduction

UJNR Technical Report No. 28

ILO (2005)

International Labor Office (2005)

Women´s Employment: Global Trends and ILO Responses

ILO Contribution 49th Session of the Commission on the Status of Women, United Nations, New York

ILO (2012)

ILO (2012)

Various resources: LABORSTA Database

http://laborsta.ilo.org/

ILO (2011)

ILO (2011)

Global Employment Trends 2011: The challenge of a jobs recovery

Geneva, Switzerland, International Labour Office

IMF (2011)

IMF (2011)

World Economic Outlook (2011 data and statistics)

International Monetary Fund

IMFR (2012)

International Mining Fatality Review (2012)

NSW Government

Retrieved: http://www.resources.nsw.gov.au/safety/publications/statistical-publications/international-mining-fatality-review

IMF WEO (2012)

IMF World Economic Outlook Database (2012)

Retrieved:http://www.imf.org/external/pubs/ft/weo/2012/01/weodata/index.aspx

Imhoff et al. (2004)

Imhoff Marc L., Lahouari Bounoua, Taylor Ricketts, Colby Loucks, Robert Harriss, and William T. Lawrence (2004)

Spatial Distribution of Net Primary Productivity (NPP)

Data distributed by the Socioeconomic Data and Applications Center (SEDAC)

http://sedac.ciesin.columbia.edu/es/hanpp.html

Immerzeel et al. (2012)

Walter W. Immerzeel, L. P. H. van Beek, M. Konz, A. B. Shrestha and M. F. P. Bierkens (2012)

Hydrological response to climate change in a glacierized catchment in the Himalayas

Climatic Change, vol. 110, pp. 721 736

Ingene et al. (2010)

Charles A. Ingene, Jianfeng Jiang and Rahul Govind (2010)

Labor Productivity in Retailing: A Modern Assessment

In: M. K. Brady and M. D. Hartline (Eds.): Marketing Theory and Applications. 2010 AMA Winter Educators' Conference (p.107)

Chicago, IL, U.S.A., American Marketing Association

IOM (2008)

IOM (2008)

Migration and Climate Change No. 31

IOM Migration Research Series

Geneva, Switzerland, International Organization for Migration

IPA (2012)

International Permafrost Association (2012)

What is Permafrost?

Retrieved: http://ipa.arcticportal.org/resources/what-is-permafrost

IPCC (1990)

Intergovernmental Panel on Climate Change (1990)

IPCC First Assessment Report (FAR). Overview Chapter.

Retrieved:http://www.ipcc.ch/ipccreports/1992%20IPCC%20Supplement/IPCC_1990_and_1992_Assessments/English/ipcc_90_92_assessments_far_overview.pdf

IPCC (1995)

Intergovernmental Panel on Climate Change (1995)

IPCC Second Assessment. Climate Change 1995

Retrieved: http://www.ipcc.ch/pdf/climate-changes-1995/ipcc-2nd-assessment/2nd-assessment-en.pdf

IPCC (2002)

IPCC (2002)

Climate Change and Biodiversity. IPCC Technical Paper V

Retrieved: http://www.ipcc.ch/pdf/technical-papers/climate-changes-biodiversity-en.pdf

IPCC (2000)

IPCC (2000)

IPCC Special Report Emissions Scenarios (SRES)

Retrieved: http://www.ipcc.ch/pdf/special-reports/spm/sres-en.pdf

IPCC (2001)

IPCC (2001)

Climate Change 2001: Synthesis Report. Summary for Policymakers

Retrieved: http://www.ipcc.ch/pdf/climate-changes-2001/synthesis-spm/synthesis-spm-en.pdf

IPCC (2007)

IPPC (2007)

Fourth Assessment Report : Climate Change 2007 (AR4)

Geneva, Switzerland: GRID Arendal & Intergovernmental Panel on Climate Change

IPCC (2007b)

IPCC (2007b)

Technical Summary. Climate Change 2007: Impacts, Adaptation and Vulnerability. Contribution of Working Group II to the Fourth Assessment Report of the Intergovernmental Panel on Climate Change,

Cambridge, UK: Cambridge University Press.

IPCC (2012a)

IPPC (2012a)

Managing the risks of extreme events and disasters to advance Climate Change adaptation

Special Report of Working Groups I and II of the Intergovernmental Panel on Climate Change [Field, C.B., V. Barros, T.F. Stocker, D. Qin, D.J. Dokken, K.L. Ebi, M.D. Mastrandrea, K.J. Mach, G.-K. Plattner, S.K. Allen, M. Tignor, and P.M. Midgley (eds.)].

Cambridge, UK, and New York, NY, USA, Cambridge University Press

IPCC (2012b)

IPCC (2012b)

Renewable Energy Sources and Climate Change Mitigation

Special Report of the Intergovernmental Panel on Climate Change

Cambridge University Press

http://srren.ipcc-wg3.de/report/IPCC_SRREN_Full_Report.pdf

IPCC Data (2012)

IPCC Data (2012)

IPCC Data Distribution Centre

Retrieved: http://www.ipcc-data.org/

Irish et al. (2008)

Jennifer L. Irish, Donald T. Resio, Jay J. Ratcliff (2008)

The Influence of Storm Size on Hurricane Surge

Journal of Physical Oceanography, vol. 38, no. 9, pp. 2003-2013

Isaac and van Vuuren (2009)

Morna Isaac and Detlef P. van Vuuren (2009)

Modeling global residential sector energy demand for heating and air conditioning in the context of climate change

Energy Policy, vol. 37, no. 2, pp. 507-521.

Isaac et al. (2008)

Morna Isaac, Detlef, P. van Vuuren (2008)

Modeling global residential sector energy demand for heating and air conditioning in the context of climate change

Energy Policy, vol.37, Iss. 2, pp. 507-521

Ismail and El Shamy (2009)

A.I.M. Ismail and A.M. El-Shamy (2009)

Engineering behaviour of soil materials on the corrosion of mild steel

Applied Clay Science, vol.42:3-4, pp. 356-362

ISO (1989)
ISO (1989)
ISO. Hot Environments—Estimation of the Heat Stress onWorkingMan, Based on the WBGT-Index (Wet Bulb Globe Temperature). ISO Standard 7243
Geneva, International Standards Organization; 1989

Jamison et al. (eds.) (2006)
D.T. Jamison, J. G. Breman, A. R. Measham, G. Alleyne, M. Claeson, D. B. Evans, P. Jha, A. Mills, P. Musgrove (2006)
Disease Control Priorities in Developing Countries
Oxford University Press and the World Bank

Jansson (2010)
Jansson, Tor (2010)
Success Factors in Microfinance Greenfielding.
Washington, DC, US, World Bank
Retrieved: https://openknowledge.worldbank.org/handle/10986/10488 License

Jetten and Focks (1997)
T.H. Jetten and D.A. Focks (1997)
Potential Changes in the Distribution of Dengue Transmission under Climate Warming
The American Journal of Tropical Medicine and Hygiene, vol. 57, no. 3, pp. 285-297

Jeziorski et al. (2008)
A. Jeziorski, N.D. Yan, A.M. Paterson, A.M. DeSellas, M.A. Turner, D.S. Jeffries, B. Keller, R.C. Weeber, D.K. McNicol, M.E. Palmer, K. McIver, K. Arseneau, B.K. Ginn, B.F. Cumming, and J.P. Smol (2008)
The Widespread Threat of Calcium Decline in Fresh Waters
Science, vol. 322, pp. 1374-1377

Jiangang (2011)
Niu Jiangang (2011)
Investigation on the properties of fly ash concrete attacked by acid rain
Electric Technology and Civil Engineering (ICETE), pp.2335-2339

Johns et al. (1997)
T.C. Johns, R.E. Carnell, J.F. Crossley, J.M. Gregory, J.F.B. Mitchell, C.A. Senior, S.F.B. Tett, and R.A. Wood, 1997
The second Hadley Centre coupled ocean-atmosphere GCM: Model description, spinup and validation.
Climate Dynamics, vol 13, p103-134.
Retrieved: http://www.metoffice.gov.uk/research/modelling-systems/unified-model/climate-models/hadcm2

Johnson et al (eds.) (2006)
Pierre-Marc Johnson, Karel Mayrand and Marc Paquin (eds.)(2006)
Governing Global Desertification: Linking Environmental Degradation, Poverty and Participation
Hampshire, UK: Ashgate Publishing

Johnstone et al. (2005)
R. Johnstone, C. Mayhew, M. Quinlan (2005)
Outsourcing Risk? The Regulation of Occupational Health and Safety Where Subcontractors Are Employed
Comparative Labor Law and Policy Journal, vol. 22, pp. 351-394

Jones and Phillips eds. (2011)
A L Jones and M Phillips eds. (2011)
Disappearing Destinations: Climate Change and Future Challenges for Coastal Tourism
CABI

Jonkeren et al. (2007)
O. Jonkeren , P. Rietveldt, J. van Ommeren (2007)
Climate Change and Inland Waterway Transport: Welfare Effects of Low Water Levels on the River Rhine
Journal of Transport Economics and Policy, vol. 41, iss. 3, pp. 387-411.

Jonkman et al. (2008)
S.N. Jonkman, M. Bočkarjova, M. Kok and P. Bernardini (2008)
Integrated hydrodynamic and economic modelling of flood damage in the Netherlands
Ecological Economics, vol. 66, no. 1, pp.77 - 90

Jorgenson and Vu (2011)
D. Jorgenson, and K. Vu (2011)
Technology and Labor Productivity
Development Outreach, vol. 13, Iss. 1

Jung et al. (2010)
M. Jung, M. Reichstein, P. Ciais, S. I. Seneviratne, J. Sheffield, M. L. Goulden, G. Bonan, A. Cescatti, J. Chen, R. de Jeu, A. J. Dolman, W. Eugster, D. Gerten, D. Gianelle, N. Gobron, J. Heinke, J. Kimball, B. E. Law, L. Montagnani, Q. Mu, B. Mueller, K. Oleson, D. Papale, A. D. Richardson, O. Roupsard, S. Running, E. Tomelleri, N. Viovy, U. Weber, C. Williams, E. Wood, S. Zaehle and K. Zhang (2010)
Recent decline in the global land evapotranspiration trend due to limited moisture supply
Nature (Letters), vol. 467, pp. 951-954

Kaczmarek et al. (eds.) (1996)
Z. Kaczmarek, K. M. Strzepek, L. Somlyódy, V. Priazhinskaya (1996)
Water Resources Management in the Face of Climatic/Hydrologic Uncertainties
Springer

Kang et al. (2004)
S. Kang, X. Su, L. Tong, P. Shi, X. Yang, Y. Abe, T. Du,Q. Shen And J. Zhang (2004)
The impacts of human activities on the water-land environment of the Shiyang River basin, an arid region in northwest China
Hydrological Sciences–Journal–des Sciences Hydrologiques, vol. 49, no.3, pp. 413-427

Kaplan (1952)
Lewis D. Kaplan (1952)
On the pressure dependence of radiative heat transfer in the atmosphere
Journal of Meteorology, vol. 9, no. 1.

Kaufmann et al. (2011)
R. K. Kaufmanna,1, H. Kauppib, M. L. Mann, and J. H. Stock (2011)
Reconciling anthropogenic climate change with observed temperature 1998–2008
Procedings of the National Academy of Sciences of the USA (PNAS), vol. 108, no. 29, pp.11790–11793

Kawaguchi et al. (2011)
S. Kawaguchi, H. Kurihara, R. King, L. Hale, T. Berli, J.P. Robinson, A. Ishida, M. Wakita, P. Virtue, S. Nicol and A. Ishimatsu (2011)
Will krill fare well under Southern Ocean acidification?
Biology Letters, vol.7, pp. 288-291

Kelly et al. (2010)
E.N. Kelly, D.W. Schindler, P.V. Hodson, J.W. Short, R. Radmanovicha, and C.C. Nielsen (2010)
Oil sands development contributes elements toxic at low concentrations to the Athabasca River and its tributaries
Proceedings of the National Academy of Sciences of the United States (PNAS), vol 107, no 37

Kelly and Goulden (2008)
Anne E. Kelly and Michael L. Goulden (2008)
Rapid shifts in plant distribution with recent climate change
Proceedings of the National Academy of Sciences (PNAS), vol. 105, no. 33, pp. 11823-11826

Kennedy and Munce (2003)
W.L. Kennedy and T.A. Munce (2003)
Invited Review: Aging and Human Temperature Regulation
Journal of Applied Physiology, vol. 95, pp. 2598-2603

Khan (2007)
M. S. A. Khan (2007)
Disaster preparedness for sustainable development in Bangladesh
Disaster Prevention and Management: An International Journal, vol. 17, no. 5, pp. 662-671

Khan and Swartz (2007)
M.E. Kahn and J. Schwartz (2007)
Urban Air Pollution Progress Despite Sprawl: The "Greening" of the Vehicle Fleet.
Journal of Urban Economics, vol. 63, no. 3, pp. 775-787,

Kharas (2010)
Homi Kharas (2010)
The Emerging Middle Class In Developing Countries
OECD Development Centre

Kharin et al. (2007)
Viatcheslav V. Kharin, Francis W. Zwiers, Xuebin Zhang, and Gabriele C. Hegerl (2007)
Changes in Temperature and Precipitation Extremes in the IPCC Ensemble of Global Coupled Model Simulations
Journal of Climate, vol. 20, pp. 1419-1444.

Kingombe (2011)
Christian Kingombe (2011)
Achieving pro-poor growth through investment in rural feeder roads: the role of impact evaluation
ODI Background Notes, August 2011
Overseas Development Institute

Kleeman et al. (1999)
M. J. Kleeman, J. J. Schauer and G. R. Cass (1999)
Size and Composition Distribution of Fine Particulate Matter Emitted from Wood Burning, Meat Charbroiling, and Cigarettes
Environmental Science and technology, vol. 33, iss.20, pp. 3516-3523

Klein et al. (2001)
R. J. T. Klein, R. J. Nicholls, S. Ragoonaden, M. Capobianco, J. Aston and E. N. Buckley (2001)
Technological Options for Adaptation to Climate Change in Coastal Zones
Journal of Coastal Research, vol. 17, no. 3, pp. 531-543

Kiparsky et al. (2012)
Michael Kiparsky, Anita Milman, and Sebastian Vicuña (2012)
Climate and Water: Knowledge of Impacts to Action on Adaptation
Annual Review of Environment and Resources, vol. 37

Kjellstrom et al. (2009 a)
Kjellstrom T., Kovats R.S., Lloyd S.J., Holt T., Tol R.S. (2009)
The Direct Impact of Climate Change on Regional Labor Productivity
Archives of Environmental & Occupational Health, vol. 64, no. 4.

Kjellstrom et al. (2009 b)
Tord Kjellstrom, Ingvar Holmer and Bruno Lemke (2009 b)
Workplace heat stress, health and productivity - an increasing challenge for low and middle-income countries during climate change
Global Health Action 2009

Kjellstrom et al (2009d)
T. Kjellstrom, I. Holmer, B. Lemke (2009 b)
Workplace heat stress, health and productivity - an increasing challenge for low and middle-income countries during climate change
Global Health Action, vol.2

Kjellstrom ed. (2009)
Tord Kjellstrom (2009)
Global Health Action Special Volume 2009. Climate change and global health: linking science with policy. Heat, work and health: implications of climate change
Sweden, Umeå University, Co-Action Publishing

Knutson et al (2010)
T. Knutson, C. Landsea and K. Emanuel (2010)
Tropical Cyclones and Climate Change
In: C. L. Chan and J. D. Kepert (eds.): *Global Perspectives on Tropical Cyclones: From Science to Mitigation*
World Scientific Publishing

Knutti et al. (2008)
R. Knutti, M. R. Allen, P. Friedlingstein, J. M. Gregory, G. C. Hegerl, G. A. Meehl, M. Meinshausen, J. M. Murphy, G.-K. Plattner, S. C. B. Raper, T. F. Stocker, P. A. Stott, H. Teng, and T. M. L. Wigley (2008)
A Review of Uncertainties in Global Temperature Projections over the Twenty-First Century
Journal of Climate, vol. 21, no. 11, pp. 2651–2663.

Koenigg and Abegg (1997)
Urs Koenig and Bruno Abegg (1997)
Impacts of Climate Change on Winter Tourism in the Swiss Alps
Journal of Sustainable Tourism, vol. 5, no. 1, pp.46-58

Koetse and Rietveld (2009)
Mark J. Koetse, Piet Rietveld (2009)
The impact of climate change and weather on transport: An overview of empirical findings
Transportation Research Part D, vol. 14 , pp. 205–221

Kolokotroni et al. (2010)
M. Kolokotroni, M. Davies, B. Croxford, S. Bhuiyan and A. Mavrogianni (2010)
A validated methodology for the prediction of heating and cooling energy demand for buildings within the Urban Heat Island: Case-study of London
Solar Energy, vol. 84, iss. 12, pp. 2246-2255,

KPMG (2008)
KPMG (2008)
Climate Changes your Business. KPMG´s review of the business risks and economic impacts as sector level
KPMG International

Kramer et al. (2000)
Koen Kramer, Stefan J. Vreugdenhil, D.C. van der Werf (2008)
Effects of flooding on the recruitment, damage and mortality of riparian tree species: A field and simulation study on the Rhine floodplain
Forest Ecology and Management, vol. 255, Iss. 11, pp.3893-3903

Krawchuk et al. (2009)
Meg A. Krawchuk, Max A. Moritz, Marc-André Parisien, Jeff Van Dorn, Katharine Hayhoe (2009)
Global Pyrogeography: the Current and Future Distribution of Wildfire
PLoS ONE, vol. 4, no. 4. , iss. 4, pp. e5102-e5102

Krugman (2009)
P. Krugman (2009, September 6))
How Did Economists Get It So Wrong?
The New York Times
Retrieved:http://www.nytimes.com/2009/09/06/magazine/06Economic-t.html?_r=1

Kshirsagar et al. (2007)
N. Kshirsagar, N. Mur, U. Thatte, N. Gogtay, S. Viviani, M. Préziosi, C. Elie, H. Findow, G. Carlone, R. Borrow, V. Parulekar, B. Plikaytis, P. Kulkarni, N. Imbault, and F.M. LaForce (2007)
Safety, Immunogenicity, and Antibody Persistence of a New Meningococcal Group A Conjugate Vaccine in Health Indian Adults
Vaccine, vol. 25, suppl. 1, pp. A101-A107

Kuik et al. (2008)
O. Kuik, B. Buchner, M. Catenacci, A. Goria, E. Karakaya and R. S. J. Tol (2008)
Methodological aspects of recent climate change damage cost studies
The Integrated Assessment Journal, vol. 8, Iss. 1 , pp. 19–40

Kumar (2012)
Harendra Kumar (2012)
Human Health Hazards in Relation to Environmental Damage: A Review
Advances in Asian Social Science, vol. 1, no. 1, PP. 135- 138

Kumari et al. (2007)
B. Padma Kumari, A. L. Londhe, S. Daniel and D. B. Jadhav (2007)
Observational evidence of solar dimming: Offsetting surface warming over India
Geophysical Research Letters, vol. 34, L21810

Kurukulasuriya et al. (2006)
P. Kurukulasuriya, R.Mendelsohn, R. Hassan, J. Benhin, T. Deressa, M. Diop, H.Mohamed Eid, K. Yerfi Fosu, G. Gbetibouo, S. Jain, A. Mahamadou, R. Mano, J.Kabubo-Mariara, S. El-Marsafawy, E. Molua, S. Ouda, M. Ouedraogo, I. Se´ne, D. Maddison, S. Niggol Seo, and Ariel Dinar (2006)
Will African Agriculture Survive Climate Change?
The World Bank Economic Review, vol. 20, no. 3

Kurz et al. (2008)
W. A. Kurz, C. C. Dymond, G. Stinson, G. J. Rampley, E. T. Neilson, A. L. Carroll, T. Ebata and L. Safranyik (2008)
Mountain pine beetle and forest carbon feedback to climate change
Nature (Letters), Vol. 452

Laan et al. (2011)
T. Laan, Ch. Beaton and B. Presta (2011)
Strategies for Reforming Fossil-Fuel Subsidies: Practical lessons from Ghana, France and Senegal
International Institute for Sustainable Development(IISD)

LaForce et al. (2007)
F.M. LaForce, K. Konde, S. Viviani, M. Préziosi (2007)
The Meningitis Vaccine Project
Vaccine, vol.25, suppl. 2, pp. A97-A100

LaForce and Okwo-Bele (2011)
F.M. LaForce and J. Okwo-Bele (2011)
Eliminating Epidemic Group A Meningococcal Meningitis in Africa through a New Vaccine
Health Affairs, vol. 30, no. 6, pp. 1049-1057

Laguna and Capelle-Blancard (2010)
M-A. Laguna, G. Capelle-Blancard (2010, may 5)
How does the stock market respond to petrochemical disasters?
Vox, Research-based policy analysis and commentary from leading economists
Retrieved: http://www.voxeu.org/article/how-does-stock-market-respond-petrochemical-disasters?quicktabs_tabbed_recent_articles_block=1

Larsen and Goldsmith (2007)
Peter Larsen and Scott Goldsmith (2007)
How much Might Climate Change Add to Future Costs for Public Infrastructure?
Understanding Alaska, Research Summary, no. 8.
Institute of Social and Economic Research, University of Alaska Anchorage

Larssen et al. (2006)
Thorjørn Larssen, Espen Lydersen, Dagang Tang, Yi He, Jixi Gao, Haiying Liu, Lei Duan, Hans M. Seip, Rolf D. Vogt, Jan Mulder, Min Shao,Yanhui Wang, He Shang, Xiaoshan Zhang, Svein Solberg, Wenche Aas, Tonje Økland, Odd Eilertsen, Valt er Angell, Quanru Liu, Dawei Zhao, Renjun Xiang, Jinshong Xiao and Jiahai Luo (2006)
Acid Rain in China
Environmental Science & Technology (January 15, 2006) pp.418- 425
American Chemical Society

Larson et al. (2001)
K.J Larson, H Ba⊠agaoglu, M.A Mariño (2001)
Prediction of optimal safe ground water yield and land subsidence in the Los Banos-Kettleman City area, California, using a calibrated numerical simulation model
Journal of Hydrology, vol. 242, Iss. 1–2, pp. 79-102

Last et al. (2010)
Peter. R. Last, William. T. White, Daniel. C. Gledhill, Alistair. J. Hobday, Rebecca Brown, Graham. J. Edgar and Gretta Pecl (2010)
Long-term shifts in abundance and distribution of a temperate fish fauna: a response to climate change and fishing practices
Global Ecology and Biogeography, vol. 20:1, pp. 58-72

Lavell (2008)
Allan Lavell (2008)
Relationships between Local and Community. Disaster Risk Management and Poverty Reduction: A Preliminary Exploration.
Background paper for: Global Assessment Report on Disaster Risk Reduction (2009)
Geneva, ISDR (International Strategy for Disaster Reduction) Secretariat. United Nations

Leaky et al. (2009)
Andrew D. B. Leakey, Elizabeth A. Ainsworth, Carl J. Bernacchi, Alistair Rogers, Stephen P. Long and Donald R. Or (2009)
Elevated CO2 effects on plant carbon, nitrogen, and water relations: six important lessons from FACE
Journal of Experimental Botany, vol. 60, no. 10, pp. 2859–2876

Leblanc et al. (2008)
M.J. Leblanc, P. Tregoning, G. Ramillien, S.O. Tweed, and A. Fakes (2008)
Basin-Scale, Integrated Observations of the Early 21st Century Mulityear Drought in Southeast Australia
Water Resources Research, vol. 45

Lee et al. (2003)
Lee David J·, Gómez-Marín Orlando, Lam Byron L, Zheng D Diane (2003)
Visual impairment and unintentional injury mortality: the National Health Interview Survey 1986-1994
American journal of ophthalmology, vol. 136, no. 6, pp. 1152-1154.

Lee et al. (2003b)
Yung-Ling Lee, Ying-Chu Lin, Tzuen-Ren Hsiue, Bing-Fang Hwang, Yueliang Leon Guo (2003)
Indoor and Outdoor Environmental Exposures, Parental Atopy, and Physician-Diagnosed Asthma in Taiwanese Schoolchildren
Pediatrics, vol. 112, no.5, pp. 389-395

Lee and Jetz (2008)
Tien Ming Lee and Walter Jetz (2008)
Future battlegrounds for conservation under global change
Proceedings of the Royal Society B, vol. 275, pp. 1261–1270

Lehner et al. (2001)

Bernhard Lehner, Gregor Czisch and Sara Vassolo (2001)

Europe's Hydropower Potential Today and in the Future

In: Lehner B. et al.: *EuroWasswer: Model-based assessment of European water resources and hydrology in the face of global change.* Kassel World Water Series 5, Ch. 8, pp. 8.1-8.22.

Kassel, Germany: Center for Environmental Systems Research, University of Kassel

Lehner et al. (2005)

Bernhard Lehner, Gregor Czisch and Sara Vassolo (2005)

The impact of global change on the hydropower potential of Europe: a model-based analysis

Energy Policy, vol. 33, iss.7, pp. 839-855,

Leisner and Ainsworth (2011)

Courtney P. Leisner and Elizabeth A. Ainsworth (2011)

Quantifying the effects of ozone on plant reproductive growth and development

Global Change Biology, vol. 18, Iss. 2, pp. 606–616

Le Manach et al. (2012)

Frede ric Le Manach, Charlotte Gough, Alasdair Harris, Frances Humber, Sarah Harper and Dirk Zeller (2012)

Unreported fishing, hungry people and political turmoil: the recipe for a food security crisis in Madagascar

Marine Policy, vol.36:1, pp. 218-225

Lempert and Schlesinger (2000)

R. J. Lempert and M.E. Schlesinger (2000)

Robust Strategies for Abating Climate Change

Climatic Change , vol. 45, no. 3-4 , pp. 387-401

Lesnoff et al. (2012)

M. Lesnoff, C. Corniaux, and P. Hiernaux (2012)

Sensitivity Analysis of the Recovery Dynamics of a Cattle Population Following Drought in the Sahel Region

Ecological Modelling, vol. 232, pp. 28-39

Lewis et al. (2011)

S. L. Lewis, P. M. Brando, O. L. Phillips, G. M. F. van der Heijden and D. Nepstad (2011)

The 2010 Amazon Drought

Science, Vol. 331, p.554

Likens et al. (1996)

G.E. Likens, C.T. Driscoll and D.C. Buso (1996)

Long-Term Effects of Acid Rain: Response and recovery of a Forest Ecosystem

Science, New Series, vol. 272, no. 5259, pp. 244-246

Lin et al. (2009)

S. Lin, M. Luo, R.J. Walker, X. Liu, S. Hwang, and R. Chinery (2009)

Extreme High Temperatures and Hospital Admissions for Respiratory and Cardiovascular Diseases

Epidemiology, vol. 20, iss. 5, pp. 738-746

Lin et al. (2011)

Z. Lin, F. Niu, H. Liu, J. Lu (2011)

Disturbance-related thawing of a ditch and its influence on roadbeds on permafrost

Cold Regions Science and Technology, vol. 66, iss. 2-3, pp. 105-114

Lin et al. (2011b)

Cui Lin, San-Juan Chen, Wen He, Li-Cai Zhao (2011b)

Effect of Acid Rain on Corrosion Behavior of Mild Steel

Journal of Iron and Steel Research, vol. 23:6, pp. 18-23

Linnerooth-Bayer and Melcher (2006)

J. Linnerooth-Bayer and R. Melcher (2006)

Insurance for Assisting Adaptation to Climate Change in Developing Countries: A Proposed Strategy

Climate Policy, vol.6, no. 6, pp. 621-636

Long et al. (2005)

Stephen P. Long, Elizabeth A. Ainsworth, Andrew D. B. Leakey and Patrick B. Morgan (2005)

Global food insecurity. Treatment of major food crops with elevated carbon dioxide or ozone under large-scale fully open-air conditions suggests recent models may have overestimated future yields

Phil. Trans. R. Soc. B, vol. 360, pp. 2011–2020

Lobell et al. (2008)

David B. Lobell, Marshall B. Burke, Claudia Tebaldi, Michael D. Mastrandrea, Walter P. Falcon and Rosamond L. Naylor.

Prioritizing Climate Change Adaptation Needs for Food Security in 2030

Science, vol. 319, pp.607-610

Long et al. (2006)

Stephen P. Long, Elizabeth A. Ainsworth, Andrew D. B. Leakey, Josef No¨sberger,Donald R. Ort (2006)

Food for Thought: Lower-Than- Expected Crop Yield Stimulation with Rising CO2 Concentrations

Science, vol. 312, pp. 1918- 1921

Lorius et al. (1985)

C. Lorius, C. Ritz, J. Jouzel, L. Merlivat and N. I. Barkov (1985)

A 150,000-year climatic record from Antarctic ice

Nature, vol. 316, pp. 591-596.

Lotze-Campen et al. (2012)

H. Lotze-Campen, C. Müller, A. Popp and H.-M. Füssel (2012)

Food Security in a Changing Climate

In: O. Edenhofer, J. Wallacher, H. Lotze-Campen, M. Reder, B. Knopf and J. Müller (eds.): *Climate Change, Justice and Sustainability* (pp. 33-43)

London and New York, Springer Dordrecht Heilderberg

Lovins (2010)

Amory B. Lovins (2010)

Profitable Solutions to Climate, Oil, and Proliferation

AMBIO: A Journal of the Human Environment, vol. 39, no. 3, pp.236-248

Ludi (2009)

Eva Ludi (2009)

Climate change, water and food security

ODI Background Notes, Background Note March 2009

Ly (1980)

Cheng K Ly (1980)

The role of the Akosombo Dam on the Volta river in causing coastal erosion in central and eastern Ghana (West Africa)

Marine Geology, vol. 37, Iss. 3–4, pp. 323-332,

Lucas et al. (2006)

R. Lucas, T. McMichael, W. Smith and B. Armstrong (2006)

Solar Ultraviolet Radiation: Global Burden of Disease from Solar Ultraviolet Radiation

Environmental Burden of Disease Series, no. 13

Geneva, Switzerland, WHO Public Health and the Environment

Luecke (2006)

Christina L. Luecke (2006)

Gender differences during heat strain at critical WBGT

Graduate School Theses and Dissertations. University of South Florida (USF). Paper 2609.

Retrieved: http://scholarcommons.usf.edu/etd/2609

Lütken (2012)

Soren E. Lütken (2012)

Penny Wise , Pound Foolish? Is the original intention of cost efficient reduction throught the CDM beig fulfilled?

UNEP Risoe Climate Working Paper Series No. 1

UNEP Risoe Centre

Macdonald et al. (2005)

R.W. Macdonald, T. Harner and J. Fyfe (2005)

Recent climate change in the Arctic and its impact on contaminant pathways and interpretation of temporal trend data

Science of the Total Environment, vol. 342, Iss. 1-3, pp.5-86,

Mace et al. (2005)

Georgina Mace, Hillary Masundire, Jonathan Baillie (2005).

Biodiversity

in: R. Hassan, R. Scholes and N. Ash (eds.): *Ecosystems and Human Well-being: Current State and Trends* (Chapter 4)

Millennium Ecosystem Assessment

Maldives MEEW (2007)

Maldives Ministry of Environment, Energy and Water (2007)

National Adaptation Programme of Action (NAPA)

Republic of Maldives, Ministry of Environment, Energy and Water

Malhi et al. (2008)

Y. Malhi, J. Timmons Roberts, R.A. Betts, T.J. Killeen, W. Li, C.A. Nobre (2008)

Climate Change, Deforestation, and the Fate of the Amazon

Science, vol. 319, no. 5860, pp. 169-172

Marengo et al. (2011)

Jose A. Marengo, Javier Tomasella, Lincoln M. Alves, Wagner R. Soares, and Daniel A. Rodriguez (2011)

The drought of 2010 in the context of historical droughts in the Amazon region

Geophysical Research Letters, vol. 38, L12703

Marriott (2008)

A. Marriott (2008)

Extending Health and Safety Protection to Informal Workers: an analysis of small scale mining in KwaZulu-Natal

Research Report No. 76

Durban: School of Development Studies, University of KwaZulu-Natal.

Martens (1998)

W.J.M. Martens (1998)

Health Impacts of Climate Change and Ozone Depletion: An Ecoepidemiologic Modeling Approach

Environmental Health Perspectives, vol. 106, Supp.1, pp. 241-251

Martens et al. (1999)

P. Martens, R.S. Kovats, S. Nijhof, P. de Vries, M.T.J. Livermore, D.J. Bradley, J. Cox, and A.J. McMichael (1999)

Climate Change and Future Populations at Risk of Malaria

Global Environment Change, vol. 9, suppl. 1, pp. S89-S107

Mathers and Loncar (2005)

Mathers CD, Loncar D. (2005)

Updated projections of global mortality and burden of disease, 2002-2030: data sources, methods and results

Working Paper, World Health Organization, Geneva

Mathers and Loncar (2006)

Mathers CD, Loncar D. (2006)

Projections of global mortality and burden of disease from 2002 to 2030

PLoS Medicine, vol. 3, no. 11

Maturu (1979)

N. Rao Maturu (1979)

Nutrition and Labour Productivity

International Labour Review, vol. 118, no. 1

Mayewski and White (2002)

Paul Andrew Mayewski and Frank White (2002)

The Ice Chronicles: the Quest to Understand Global Climate Change

Lebanon, New Hampshire, U.S.A., University Press of New England

Mc Adam (2011)

Jane Mc Adam (2011)

Climate Change Displacement and International Law: Complementary Protection

Standards. Legal and Protection Policy Research Series

Geneva, Switzerland, United Nations High Commissioner for Refugees (UNHCR)

McCay (2004)

D.F. McCay (2004)

Estimation of potential impacts and natural resource damages of oil

Journal of Hazardous Materials, vol. 107 , pp. 11-25

McCluney et al. (2012)

K. E. McCluney, J. Belnap, S.L. Collins, A. L., González, E.M. Hagen, J. Nathaniel Holland, B. P. Kotler, F.T. Maestre, S.D, Smith, and B. O. Wolf (2012)

Shifting species interactions in terrestrial dryland ecosystems under altered water availability and climate change

Biological Reviews, vol. 87, iss. 3, pp. 563-582

McGuire (2009)

D. McGuire (2009)

U.S. Global Climate Change Impacts Report, Alaska Region

American Geophysical Union, Fall Meeting 2009, abstract #GC23B-07

McKibben (2012)

Bill McKibben (2012, July 19)

Global Warming's Terrifying New Math

Rolling Stone Magazine

Retrieved: http://www.rollingstone.com/politics/news/global-warmings-terrifying-new-math-20120719

McKinnon and Utley (2005)

S. Helgerman McKinnon and R. Utley (2005)

Heat Stress: Understanding Factors and Measures Helps SH&E Professionals Take a Proactive Management Approach

Professional Safety , April 2005, pp. 41-47

McKinsey & Company (2009)

McKinsey & Company (2009)

Charting our Water Future: Economic Frameworks to Inform Decision Making

Munich: 2030 Water Resources Group

McMahon et al. (2010)

S. M. McMahon, G.G. Parker and D. R. Miller (2010)

Evidence for a recent increase in forest growth

Proceedings of the National Academy of Sciences (PNAS), vol. 10, no. 8, pp. 3611-3615

McMichael et al. (2006)

A.J. McMichael, R.E. Woodruff, and S. Hales (2006)

Climate change and human health: present and future risks

Lancet, vol. 367, pp. 859 - 69

McMillan and Rodrik (2012)

Margaret McMillan and Dani Rodrik (2012)

Globalization, Structural Change, and Productivity Growth

IFPRI Discussion Paper 01160

International Food and Policy Research Institute

McNabola and Gill (2009)

Aonghus McNabola and Laurence William Gill (2009)

The Control of Environmental Tobacco Smoke: A Policy Review

International Journal of Environmental Research and Public Health, vol. 6, Iss.2, pp. 741-758

McNeil and Letschert (2008)

McNeil Michael A. and Letschert Virginie E. (2008)

Future Air Conditioning Energy Consumption in Developing Countries and what can be done about it: The Potential of Efficiency in the Residential Sector.

Lawrence Berkeley National Laboratory

Mc Cright and Dunlap (2011)

Aaron M. McCright and Riley E. Dunlap (2011)

The Politicization of Climate Change and Polarization in the American Public's Views of Global Warming, 2001–2010

The Sociological Quarterly, vol. 52, pp. 155–194

McSweeney et al. (2012)

C. McSweeney, M. New and G. Lizcano (2012)

UNDP Climate Change Country Profiles: Ghana

Retrieved: http://country-profiles.geog.ox.ac.uk

Meinshausen et al (2009)

M.Meinshausen, N. Meinshausen, W. Hare, S.C.B. Raper, K. Frieler, R. Knutti, D. J. Frame and M. R. Allenm (2009)

Greenhouse-gas emission targets for limiting global warming to 2 6C

Nature (Letters), vol 458, pp. 1158-1163

Mellanby (ed.) (1988)

Kenneth Mellanby (ed.) (1988)

Air Pollution, Acid Rain and the Environment

New York, US: Elsevier Science Publishing Co.

Memon et al. (2011)

Rizwan Ahmed Memon, Dennis Y. C. Leung, Chun-Ho Liu and Michael K. H. Leung (2011)

Urban heat island and its effect on the cooling and heating demands in urban and suburban areas of Hong Kong

Theoretical and Applied Climatology, vol. 103, no. 3-4, pp. 441-450

Mendelsohn et al. (2011)

Mendelsohn R., Kerry E., and Chonabayashi S. (2011)

The Impact of Climate Change on Global Tropical Storms Damages

Policy Research Working Paper no. 5562

The World Bank

Mendelsohn et al (2012)

Robert Mendelsohn, Kerry Emanuel, Shun Chonabayashi and Laura Bakkensen (2012)

The impact of climate change on global tropical cyclone damage

Nature Climate Change, vol. 2, pp.205–209

Mendelsohn (2003)

Robert Mendelsohn (2003)

Assesing the market damages from Climate Change

in Griffin (ed): *Global Climate Change: The Science, Economics and Politics*

Northampton, MA, USA, Edgar Elwar Publishing Limited

Messner and Meyer (2005)

Frank Messner and Volker Meyer (2005)

Flood damage, vulnerability and risk perception – challenges for flood damage research

In: J. Schanze, E. Zeman and J.Marsalek (eds.): *Flood Risk Management: Hazards, Vulnerability and Mitigation Measures* (pp. 149-167)

Nato Science Series, Springer Publisher.

Mehta (2010)

P. Mehta (2010)

Science behind Acid Rain: Analysis of its Impacts and Advantages on Life and Heritage Structures

South Asian Journal of Tourism and Heritage, vol. 3, no. 2, pp. 123-132

Michelozzi et al. (2009)

P. Michelozzi, G. Accetta, M. De Sario, D. D'Ippoliti, C. Marino, M. Baccini, A. Biggeri, H.R. Anderson, K. Katsouyanni, F. Ballester, L. Bisanti, E. Cadum, B. Forsberg, F. Forastiere, P.G. Goodman, A. Hojs, U. Kirchmayer, S. Medina, A. Paldy, C. Schindler, J. Sunyer, C.A. Perucci, and on behalf of the PHEWE Collaborative Group (2009)

High Temperature and Hospitalizations for Cardiovascular and Respiratory Causes in 12 European Cities

American Journal of Respiratory and Critical Care Medicine, vol. 179, no. 5, pp. 383-389

Miles et al. (2004)

Lera Miles, Alan Grainger and Oliver Phillips (2004)

The impact of global climate change on tropical forest biodiversity in Amazonia

Global Ecology and Biogeography, vol. 13, pp. 553-565

Miller et al. (2008)

N.L. Miller, K. Hayhoe, J. Jin and M. Auffhammer (2008)

Climate, Extreme Heat, and Electricity Demand in California

Journal of Applied Meteorology and Climatology, vol. 47, pp.1834–1844

Millard-Ball and Schipper (2011)

Adam Millard-Ball and Lee Schipper (2011)

Are We Reaching Peak Travel? Trends In Passenger Transport In Eight Industrialized Countries

Transport Reviews, vol. 31, Iss. 3

Millennium Ecosystem Assessment (2005)

Millennium Ecosystem Assessment (2005)

Millennium Assessment Report: Ecosystems and Human Well-Being

Washington D.C., US: World Resources Institute

http://www.maweb.org/en/index.aspx

Mills (2005)

Evan Mills (2005)

Insurance in a Climate of Change

Science, vol. 309, pp. 1040-1044

Min (2007)

Hong-Ghi Min (2007)

Estimation of Labor Demand Elasticity for the RMSM-LP: Revised Minimum Standard Model for Labor and Poverty Module

International Business & Economics Research Journal, vol. 6, no. 7, pp. 29-34.

Mirza et al. (2003)

M. M. Q. Mirza, R. A. Warrick and N. J. Ericksen (2003)

The Implications of Climate Change on Floods of the Ganges, Brahmaputra and Meghna Rivers in Bangladesh

Climatic Change, vol. 57, Issue 3, pp. 287 - 318

Mishra et al. (1999a)

Mishra V.K., Retherford R.D., Smith K.R. (1999a)

Biomass Cooking Fuels and Prevalence of Blindness in India

Journal of Environmental Medicine, vol. 1, pp. 189-199.

Mishra et al. (1999b)

Mishra V.K., Retherford R.D., Smith K.R. (1999b)

Biomass Cooking Fuels and Prevalence of Tuberculosis in India

International Journal of Infectious Diseases, vol. 3, no. 3, pp. 119-129.

Mishra et al. (2005)

Vinod Mishra, Robert D. Retherford , Kirk R. Smith (2005)

Cooking smoke and tobacco smoke as risk factors for stillbirth

International Journal of Environmental Health Research, vol.5:16, pp. 397-410

Molesworth et al. (2003)

A.M. Molesworth, L.E. Cuevas, S.J. Connor, A.P. Morse, and M.C. Thomson (2003)

Environmental Risk and Meningitis Epidemics in Africa

Emerging Infectious Diseases, v. 9, no. 10, pp. 1287-1293

Molina et al., (2009)

M. Molina, D. Zaelke, K. Madhava Sarma, S. Andersen, V. Ramanathan and D. Kaniaru (2009)

Reducing Abrupt Climate Change Risk Using the Montreal Protocol and Other Regulatory Actions to Complement Cuts in CO2 Emissions

PNAS, vol. 106, no. 49, pp. 20626-20621

Morrison et al. (2009)

J. Morrison, M. Morikawa, M. Murphy and P. Schulte (2009)

Water Scarcity and Climate Change: Growing Risks for Businesses and Investors.

Boston, MA, Ceres.

Morse et al. (2009)

W. C. Morse, J. L. Schedlbauer, S. E. Sesnie, B. Finegan, C. A. Harvey,S. J. Hollenhorst, K. L. Kavanagh, D. Stoian, and J. D. Wulfhorst (2009)

Consequences of Environmental Service Payments for Forest Retention and Recruitment in a Costa Rican Biological Corridor

Ecology and Society, vol. 14, no.1, iss. 23

Mortimore (2003)

Michael Mortimore (2003)

Is There A New Paradigm of Dryland Development?

Annals of Arid Zone, vol. 42, Iss. 3&4, pp. 459-481

Morton (2007)

John F. Morton (2007)

The impact of climate change on smallholder and subsistence agriculture

PNAS, vol. 104 no. 50, pp. 19680-19685

Moser and Rose (2012)

Christoph Moser and Andrew K. Rose (2012)

Why Do Trade Negotiations Take So Long?

Paper presented for CEEI Conference (November 2011) "European Integration in a Global Economic Setting - CESEE, China and Russia

Motiram and Vakulabharanam (2007)

Sripad Motiram and Vamsi Vakulabharanam (2007)

Corporate and Cooperative Solutions for the Agrarian Crisis in Developing Countries

Review of Radical Political Economics, vol. 39, pp. 360-367

Muehlenbachs et al. (2011)

Lucija Muehlenbachs, Mark A. Cohen, and Todd Gerarden (2011)

Preliminary Empirical Assessment of Offshore Production Platforms in the Gulf of Mexico

Resources for the Future Discussion Paper 10-66

Resources for the Future

Mueller and Quisumbing (2011)

Valerie Mueller and Agnes Quisumbing (2011)

How Resilient are Labour Markets to Natural Disasters? The Case of the 1998 Bangladesh Flood

Journal of Development Studies, vol. 47, Iss. 12

Muller (2012)

R. A. Muller (2012, July 28)

The Conversion of a Climate-Change Skeptic

The New York Times

Retrieved: http://www.nytimes.com/2012/07/30/opinion/the-conversion-of-a-climate-change-skeptic.html?pagewanted=all

Müller et al. (2007)

B. Müller, N. Höhne and C. Ellermann (2007)

Differentiating (Historic) Responsibilities for Climate Change.Summary Report

Paper launched at a SBSTA.27 special side event on "Scientific and methodological aspects of the Proposal by Brazil" in Nusa Dua, Bali, 5 December 2007

Munasinghe (1993)

Mohan Munasinghe (1993)

Environmental Economics and Biodiversity Management in Developing Countries

Ambio, Vol. 22, No. 2/3, pp. 126-135

Munday et al. (2008)

Philip. L. Munday, Geoffrey. P. Jones, Morgan. S. Pratchett, Ashley. J. Williams (2008)

Climate change and the future for coral reef fishes

Fish and Fisheries, vol.9:3, pp. 261-285

Munich Re (2010)

NatCat SERVICE/Munich Re (2010)

TOPICS GEO. Natural catastrophes 2010: Analyses, assessments, positions

Retrieved: http://www.munichre.com/en/reinsurance/business/non-life/georisks/natcatservice/default.aspx

Munich Re (2012)

NatCat SERVICE/Munich Re (2012)

Statistics on natural catastrophes

Retrieved: http://www.munichre.com/en/reinsurance/business/non-life/georisks/natcatservice/default.aspx

Munton et al. in Young (ed.) 1999

D. Munton, M. Soroos, E. Nikitina and M. Levy (1999)

Acid Rain in Europe and North America

In: Oran R. Young (ed.): *The Effectiveness of International Environmental Regimes: Causal Connections Behavioral Mechanisms* (pp. 155-248)

Massachusetts Institute of Technology

Murray et al. (2012)

S.J. Murray, P.N. Foster and I.C. Prentice (2012)

Future global water resources with respect to climate change and water withdrawals as estimated by a dynamic global vegetation model

Journal of Hydrology, Vols. 448–449, pp. 14-29

Mustafa (1990)

Mohamad G. Mustafa (1990)

Biochemicalbasis of ozonetoxicity

Free Radical Biology and Medicine, vol. 9, Iss. 3, pp. 245–265

Narita et al. (2011)

D. Narita, K. Rehdanz, R. Tol (2011)

Economic Costs of Ocean Acidification: A Look into the Impacts on Shellfish Production

Working Paper no. WP391

Economic and Social Research Institute (ESRI)

NASA Climate (2012)

NASA Climate (2012)

Global Climate Change Portal at the Earth Science Communications Team at

National Aeronautics and Space Administration's (NASA) Jet Propulsion Laboratory/California Institute of Technology

Retrieved: http://climate.nasa.gov

NASA GISS (2012)

NASA Goddard Institute for Space Studies (2012)

Surface Temperature Dataset

Retrieved: http://www.giss.nasa.gov/

Nelleman et al. (2011)

Nellemann, C., Verma, R., and Hislop, L. (eds). 2011.

Women at the frontline of climate change: Gender risks and hopes. A Rapid Response Assessment.

United Nations Environment Programme, GRID-Arendal

Nelson et al. (2001)

Nelson, F. E., Anisimov O.A., and Shiklomanov N.I. (2001)

Model output from the 'frost index' permafrost model: variations in circumpolar frozen ground conditions and modeled future conditions

Boulder, CO: National Snow and Ice Data Center

Nelson et al. (2002)

F. E. Nelson, O. A. Anisimov And N. I. Shiklomanov (2002)

Climate Change and Hazard Zonation in the Circum-Arctic Permafrost Regions

Natural Hazards , vol. 26, pp. 203–225,

Nelson et al. (2009)

G.C. Nelson, M. W. Rosegrant, J. Koo, R. Robertson, T. Sulser, T. Zhu, C. Ringler, S. Msangi, A. Palazzo, M. Batka, M. Magalhaes, R. Valmonte-Santos, M. Ewing, and D. Lee (2009)

Climate Change: Impact on Agriculture and Costs of Adaptation

Washington, D.C.: International Food Policy Research Institute

Nicholls and Cazenave (2010)

Robert J. Nicholls and Anny Cazenave (2010)

Sea-Level Rise and Its Impact on Coastal Zones

Science, vol.328, pp. 1517-1520

Nicholson et al. (1998)

S.E. Nicholson, C.J. Tucker, and M.B. Ba (1998)

Desertification, Drought, and Surface Vegetation: An Example from the West African Sahel

Bulletin of the American Meteorological Society, vol. 79, iss. 5, pp. 815-829

Niehaus et al. (2002)

M. D. Niehaus, S. R. Moore, P. D. Patrick, L. L. Derr, B. Lorntz, A. A. Lima and R. L. Guerrant (2002)

Early Childhood Diarrhea is Associated with Diminished Cognitive Function 4 to 7 Years Later in Children in a Northeast Brazilian Shantytown

American Journal of Tropical Medicine and Hygiene, vol. 66, no. 5, pp. 590–593

Niemelä et al. (2002)

R. Niemelä, M. Hannula, S. Rautio, K. Reijula and J. Railio (2002)

The effect of air temperature on labour productivity in call centres - a case study.

Energy and Buildings, vol. 34, Iss. 8, pp. 759-764

NIOSH (1986)

National Institute for Occupational Safety and Health (1986)

Occupational Exposure to Hot Environments. Revised Criteria 1986

Publication No. 86-113

U.S. Department of Health and Human Services. Public Health Service. Centers for Disease Control. NIOSH

NOAA NESDIS (2012)

National Environmental Satellite, Data and Information Service (NESDIS) (2012)

National Climatic Data Center

Retrieved: http://www.nesdis.noaa.gov/ClimateResources.html

Nohara et al. (2006)

Daisuke Nohara, Akio Kitoh, Masahiro Hosaka, and Taikan Oki (2006)

Impact of Climate Change on River Discharge Projected by Multimodel Ensemble

J. Hydrometeor, vol. 7, no 5., pp. 1076-1089.

Nordhaus (2006)

William D. Nordhaus (2006)

Geography and macroeconomics: New data and new findings

Procedings of the National Academy of Sciences of the USA (PNAS), vol. 103, no. 10, pp.3510-3517

Nordhaus (2007)

William D. Nordhaus (2007)

A Review of the Stern Review on the Economics of Climate Change

Journal of Economic Literature, vol. XLV , pp. 686-702

Nordhaus (2008)

William D. Nordhaus (2008)

A Question of Balance. Weighing the Options on Global Warming Policies

New Haven & London,Yale University Press

Nordhaus (2010)

William D. Nordhaus (2010)

Economic aspects of global warming in a post-Copenhagen environment

Procedings of the National Academy of Sciences of the USA (PNAS),PNAS Early edition, June 14, 2010

Retrieved: http://www.pnas.org/content/early/2010/06/10/1005985107.full.pdf+html

Nordhaus (2011)

William D. Nordhaus (2011)

Integrated Economic and Climate Modeling

Cowles Foundation Discussion Paper No. 1839

New Haven, Connecticut, Cowles Foundation For Research In Economics,Yale University

Retrieved: http://cowles.econ.yale.edu/

Nordhaus (2012)

William D. Nordhaus (2012, April 26)

In the Climate Casino: An Exchange (response)

The New York Review of Books

Retrieved: http://www.nybooks.com/articles/archives/2012/apr/26/climate-casino-exchange/?pagination=false

Nordaus and Boyer (1999)

W. Nordhaus and J. Boyer (1999)

Roll the DICE Again: Economic Models of Global Warming ("manuscript edition")

Cambridge, Massachusetts. MIT Press

Nordhaus and Boyer (2000)

William D. Nordhaus and Joseph Boyer (2000)

Warming the World: Economic Models of Global Warming

Cambridge, Massachusetts, Massachussetts Institute of Technology

Nordling et al. (2008)

E. Nordling, N. Berglind, E. Melén, G. Emenius, J. Hallberg, F. Nyberg, G. Pershagen,M. Svartengren, M. Wickman, T. Bellander (2008)

Traffic-Related Air Pollution and Childhood Respiratory Symptoms, Function and Allergies

Epidemiology, vol. 19, Iss. 3, pp. 401-408

Nowak et al. (2006)

D. J. Nowak, D.E. Crane and J.C. Stevens (2006)

Air pollution removal by urban trees and shrubs in the United States

Urban Forestry and Urban Greening, vol. 4, pp.115-123

NSIDC (2008)

National Snow and Ice Data Center (NSIDC) (2008, June)

Glaciers

Retrieved: http://nsidc.org/sotc/glacier_balance.html

NSIDC (2012)

National Snow and Ice Data Center (NSIDC) (2012)

Artic Sea Ice Extent

Retrieved: http://nsidc.org/arcticseaicenews/files/2000/08/N_stddev_timeseries1.png

Nutbeam (2000)

D. Nutbeam (2000)

Health Literacy as a Public Health Goal: A Challenge for Contemporary Health Education and Communication Strategies into the 21st Century

Health Promotion International, vol. 15, no. 3, pp. 259-267

NWP (2012)

Netherlands Water Partnership (2012, January 24)

Dutch consortium granted contract to assist Vietnamese government in long term Mekong Delta plan

Dutch Water Sector

Retrieved:http://www.dutchwatersector.com/news/news/2012/01/dutch-consortium-granted-contract-to-assist-vietnamese-government-in-long-term-mekong-delta-plan/

ODI (2010)

Overseas Development Institute (2010)

Millennium Development Goals Report Card. Learning from Progress

London, UK, ODI

Retrieved: http://www.odi.org.uk/resources/details.asp?id=4908&title=mdgs-progress

OECD (2012)

OECD (2012)

OECD Environmental Outlook to 2050: The Consequences of Inaction

OECD CRS (2012)

OECD Creditor Reporting System (2012)

OECD Stats Extracts Data base

Retrieved: http://stats.oecd.org/Index.aspx?DatasetCode=CRSNEW

Okafor et al. (2009)

P. C. Okafor, U. J. Ekpe, U. J. Ibok, B. O. Ekpo, E. E. Ebenso And C. O. Obadimu (2009)

Atmospheric Corrosion of Mild Steel in The Niger Delta Region of Nigeria. Part 1: Characterization of The Calabar, Cross River State Environment

Global Journal of Environmental Sciences, vol. 8, no. 1, pp. 9 - 18

Olefs et al. (2009)

M. Olefs, M. Kuhn and A. Fischer (2009)

The effect of climate change on the runoff behaviour of glacierised Alpine catchments with regard to reservoir power stations

EGU General Assembly 2009, held 19-24 April, 2009 in Vienna, Austria

Retrieved: http://meetings.copernicus.org/egu2009

Olivier et al. (2012)

J.G.J. Olivier, G. Janssens-Maenhout, J. A.H.W. Peters (2012)

Trends in global CO2 emissions; 2012 Report

The Hague: PBL Netherlands Environmental Assessment Agency; Ispra: Joint Research Centre.

Olsen et al. (2011)

M. S. Olsen, T. V. Callaghan, J. D. Reist, L. O. Reiersen, D. Dahl-Jensen, M. A. Granskog, B. Goodison, G. K. Hovelsrud, M. Johansson, R. Kallenborn, J. Key, A. Klepikov, W. Meier, J. E. Overland, T. D. Prowse, M. Sharp, W. F. Vincent, J. Walsh (2011)

The Changing Arctic Cryosphere and Likely Consequences: An Overview

Ambio, vol. 40, pp. 111-118

Olson and Morton (2012)

K. R. Olson and L.Wright Morton (2012)

The impacts of 2011 induced levee breaches on agricultural lands of Mississippi River Valley

Journal of Soil and Water Conservation, vol. 67, no. 1, pp. 5A-10A

O'Neill et al. (2005)

Jim O'Neill, Dominic Wilson, Roopa Purushothaman and Anna Stupnytska (2005)

How Solid are the BRICs?

Global Economics Paper, Issue no. 134

Goldman Sachs Economic Research

Retrieved: https://portal.gs.com

O'Reilly et al. (2003)

O'Reilly C.M., Alin S.R., Plisnier P.D., Cohen A.S., McKee B.A. (2003)

Climate Change decreases aquatic ecosystem productivity of Lake Tangayik, Africa

Nature, vol. 424, no. 6950, pp. 766-768.

OSDG (2009)

The Oil Sand Development Group (2009)

Extracting Oil Sands - In-Situ and Mining Methods; Fact Sheet, Oct 2009

Retrieved: http://www.oilsandsdevelopers.ca/wp-content/uploads/2009/06/Extraction-Fact-Sheet-October-2009.pdf

Oteng-Abbabio et al. (2011)

Martin Oteng-Ababio, Kwadwo Owusu and Kwasi Appeaning Addo (2011)

The vulnerable state of the Ghana coast: The case of Faana-Bortianor

JAMBA: Journal of Disaster Risk Studies, vol. 3, no.2,, pp. 429-442

Oxelheim and Wihlborg (2008)

I. Oxelheim and C. Wihlborg (2008)

Corporate Decision-Making With Macroeconomic Uncertainty: Performance And Risk Management.

Oxford, UK, Oxford University Press

Oxfam (2012)

Oxfam (2012)

Food Crisis in Sahel

Retrieved September 2012: http://www.oxfam.org/en/sahel

Oygard et al. (1999)

Ragnar Øygard, Trond Vedeld and Jens Aune (1999)

Good Practices in Drylands Management

Washington, DC: The International Bank for Reconstruction and Development/ The World Bank

Pagiola (2006)

Stefano Pagiola (2006)

Payments for Environmental Services in Costa Rica

Munich Personal RePEc Archive (MPRA) Paper No. 2010

Palmer et al. (2008)

M. A Palmer, C. A Reidy Liermann, C. Nilsson, M. Flörke, J. Alcamo, P S. Lake, and N. Bond (2008)

Climate change and the world's river basins: anticipating management options. *Frontiers in Ecology and the Environment*, vol. 6, iss. 2, pp. 81-89.

Pandey et al. (eds.) (2007)

S. Pandey, H. Bhandari, and B. Hardy (2007)

Economic Cost of Drought and Farmers' Coping Mechanisms: A Study of Rainfed Rice Systems in Eastern India

Los Baños (Philippines): International Rice Research Institute

Pandey et al. (2010)

V. Pandey, M.S. Babel, S. Shrestha and F. Kazama (2010)

Vulnerability of freshwater resources in large and medium Nepalese river basins to environmental change

Water science and technology, vol. 61, no. 6, pp. 1525-1534

Parker et al. (2006)

T.J. Parker, K.M. Clancy, and R.L. Mathiasen (2006)

Interactions among fire, insects and pathogens in coniferous forests of the interior western United States and Canada

Agricultural and Forest Entomology, vol. 8, pp. 167-189

Parry et al. (2004)

M.L. Parry, C. Rosenzweig, A. Iglesias, M. Livermore, G. Fischer (2004)

Effects of climate change on global food production under SRES emissions and socio-economic scenarios

Global Environmental Change, vol. 14, pp. 53-67

Parry et al. (2009)

Martin Parry, Alex Evans, Mark W. Rosegrant and Tim Wheeler (2009)

Climate change and hunger: Responding to the challenge

Rome, Italy, World Food Programme

Parry et al (2009b)

M. Parry, N. Arnell, P. Berry, D. Dodman, S. Fankhauser, C. Hope, S. Kovats, R. Nicholls, D. Satterthwaite, R. Tiffin andTim Wheeler (2009b)

Assessing the Costs of Adaptation to Climate Change- A review of the UNFCCC and other recent estimates

International Institute for Environment and Development (IIED)

Patz et al. (1996)

J.A. Patz, P.R. Epstein, T.A. Burke, and J.M. Balbus (1996)

Global climate Change and Emerging Infectious Diseases

The Journal of the American Medical Association, vol. 275, no. 3, pp. 217-223

Patz et al. (2005)

J.A. Patz, D. Campbell-Lendrum, T. Holloway, and J.A. Foley (2005)

Impact of Regional Climate Change on Human Health

Nature, vol. 438, pp. 310-317

Pavlenko and Glukhareva (2010)

V. I. Pavlenko, E. K. Glukhareva (2010)

Development of Oil and Gas Production and Transportation Infrastructure of Russian West Arctic Offshore Regions

Proceedings of the Ninth ISOPE Pacific/Asia Offshore Mechanics Symposium held in Busan, Korea, November 14-17, 2010

Peduzzi et al. (2012)

P. Peduzzi, B. Chatenoux, H. Dao, A. De Bono, C. Herold, J. Kossin, F. Mouton, and O. Nordbeck (2012)

Global trends in tropical cyclone risk

Nature Climate Change, vol. 2, no. 6, pp. 89-294.

Pelling and Uitto (2001)

Mark Pelling and Juha I. Uitto (2001)

Small island developing states: natural disaster vulnerability and global change

Environmental Hazards, vol. 3, pp. 49-62

Pereira et al. (2002)

L. Santos Pereira, T. Oweis and A. Zairi (2002)

Irrigation management under water scarcity

Agricultural Water Management, vol. 57, Iss. 3, pp. 175-206

Pereira et al. (2010)

H. M. Pereira, P. W. Leadley, V. Proença, R. Alkemade, J. P. W. Scharlemann, J. F. Fernandez-Manjarrés, M. B. Araújo, P. Balvanera, R. Biggs, W. W. L. Cheung, L. Chini, H. D. Cooper, E. L. Gilman, S. Guénette, G. C. Hurtt, H. P. Huntington, G. M. Mace, T. Oberdorff, C. Revenga, P. Rodrigues, R.J. Scholes, U. Rashid Sumaila, Matt Walpole (2010)

Scenarios for Global Biodiversity in the 21st Century

Science, vol. 330, pp. 1496-1501

Pereira de Lucena et al. (2009)

A.F. Pereira de Lucena, A. Salem Szklo, R. Schaeffer, R. Rodrigues de Souza, B. Soares Moreira, C. Borba, I. Vaz Leal da Costa, A. O. Pereira Júnior, S. H. Ferreira da Cunha (2009)

The vulnerability of renewable energy to climate change in Brazil

Energy Policy, vol. 37, iss. 3, pp. 879-889

Pereira de Lucena et al. (2010)

A.F. Pereira de Lucena, R. Schaeffer and A. Salem Szklo (2010)

Least-cost adaptation options for global climate change impacts on the Brazilian electric power system

Global Environmental Change, vol. 20, no. 2, pp. 342-350

Perez-Lombard et al. (2008)

Perez-Lombard L., Ortiz J. and Pout C. (2008)

A Review on Buildings Energy Consumption Information

Energy and Buildings, vol. 40, no. 3, pp. 394-398.

Perry et al. (2005)

Allison. L. Perry, Paula. J. Low, Jim. R. Ellis, John D. Reynolds (2005)

Climate Change and Distribution Shifts in Marine Fishes

Science, vol. 308, no. 5730, pp. 1912-1915

Peters et al (2012).

Glen P. Peters, Gregg Marland, Corinne Le Quéré, Thomas Boden, Josep G. Canadell & Michael R. Raupach (2012).

Rapid growth in CO2 emissions after the 2008–2009 global financial crisis

Nature Climate Change, vol 2, pp. 2–4.

Petit et al. (1999)

J. R. Petit, J. Jouzel, D. Raynaud, N. I. Barkov, J.-M. Barnola, I. Basile,M. Bender, J. Chappellaz,M. Davisk, G. Delaygue, M. Delmotte, V. M. Kotlyakov, M. Legrand, V. Y. Lipenkov, C. Lorius, L. Pe´ pin, C. Ritz,E. Saltzmank and M. Stievenard (1999)

Climate and atmospheric history of the past 420,000 years from the Vostok ice core, Antarctica

Nature ,vol. 399 , pp. 429-436

Pfeffer et al.(2008)

W. T. Pfeffer, J. T. Harper and S. O'Neel (2008)

Kinematic Constraints on Glacier Contributions to 21st-Century Sea-Level Rise

Science, Vol. 321 no. 5894, pp. 1340-1343

Pielke et al. (2008)

R. A. Pielke Jr., J. Gratz, Ch. W. Landsea, D. Collins, M. A. Saunders and R. Musulin (2008)

Normalized Hurricane Damage in the United States: 1900–2005

Natural Hazards Review, February 2008, pp.29-42

Pilcher et al. (2002)

J.J. Pilcher, E. Nadler and C. Busch (2002)

Effects of hot and cold temperature exposure on performance: a meta-analytic review.

Ergonomics, vol. 45, no. 10 pp. 682-698.

Ping et al. (2011)

Liu Ping,Xia Fei,Pan Jiayong,Chen Yiping,Peng Huaming and Chen Shaohua (2011)

Discuss on Present Situation and Countermeasures for Acid Rain Prevention and Control in China

Environmental Science and Management, vol. 12

Plass (1956)

Gilbert N. Plass (1956)

The Carbon Dioxide Theory of Climatic Change

Tellus, vol. 8, Iss. 2, pp. 140–154

Pope et al. (2002)

C. Arden Pope III, Richard T. Burnett, Michael J. Thun, Eugenia E. Calle, Daniel Krewski, Kazuhiko Ito and George D. Thurston (2002)

Lung Cancer, Cardiopulmonary mortality, and long-term exposure to fine particulate air pollution

Journal of American Medical Association, vol.287, no.9, pp. 1132-1141

Pope et al. (2009)

C. Arden Pope III, M. Ezzati, and D. W. Dockery (2009)

Fine-Particulate Air Pollution and Life Expectancy in the United States

Th e New England Journal of Medicine, vol. 360, no. 4, pp. 376-386.

Pope et al. (eds.) (2010)

V. Pope, J. Lowe, L. Kendon, F. Carroll and S. Tempest (eds.)(2010)

Advance : Improved science for mitigation policy advice

Met office. Hadley Centre

Portmann et al. (2010)

Portmann, F.T., Siebert S., and Döll P. (2010)

Global Data Set of Monthly Irrigated and Rainfed Crop Areas Around the Year 2000 (MIRCA2000)

Frankfurt, Germany: The Institute of Physical Geography, University of Frankfurt

Retrieved: http://www.geo.uni-frankfurt.de/ipg/ag/dl/forschung/MIRCA/index.html

Postel and Thompson (2005)

Sandra L. Postel and Barton H. Thompson, Jr. (2005)

Watershed protection: Capturing the benefits of nature's water supply services

Natural Resources Forum, vol. 29, pp. 98–108

Priyadarshi (2009)

Shishir Priyadarshi (2009)

Reforming Global Trade in Agriculture: A Developing- Country Perspective

Carnegie Endowment for International Peace

Prospero and Lamb (2003)

J.M. Prospero and P.J. Lamb (2003)

African Droughts and Dust Transportation to the Caribbean: Climate Change Implications

Science, vol. 302, pp. 1024-1027

Prudhomme et al. (2002)

C. Prudhomme, N.Reynard and S. Crooks (2002)

Downscaling of global climate models for flood frequency analysis: where are we now?

Hydrological Proceses, vol. 16, pp.1137–1150

Puigdefábregas (1998)

J. Puigdefábregas (1998)

Ecological Impacts of Global Change on Drylands and Their Implications for Desertification

Land Degradation & Development, vol. 9, pp. 393-406

Quarantelli (2001)

E.L. Quarantelli (2001)

Statistical and Conceptual Problems in the Study of Disasters

Disaster Prevention and Management, vol. 10, no. 5, pp. 325-338

Quarantelli (2003)

E. L. Quarantelli (2003)

Urban Vulnerability to Disasters in Developing Countries: Managing Risks

In: A. Kreimer, M. Arnold, and A. Carlin (Eds.): *Building Safer Cities. The Future of Disaster Risk* (p.211-231)

Disaster Risk Management Series No. 3

Washington, D.C., The International Bank for Reconstruction and Development /The World Bank

Radić and Hock (2011)

Valentina Radic and Regine Hock (2011)

Regionally differentiated contribution of mountain glaciers and ice caps to future sea-level rise

Nature Geoscience (Letters), vol. 4, pp. 91-94

Rahmstorf (2009)

Stefan Rahmstorf (2009)

A Semi- Empirical Approach to Projecting Future Sea-Level Rise

Science, vol. 315, pp. 368-370

Raleigh (2010)

C. Raleigh (2010)

Political Marginalization, Climate Change, and Conflict in African Sahel States

International Studies Review, vol. 12, pp.69–86

Ramanathan and Carmichael (2008)

V. Ramanathan and G. Carmichael (2008)

Global and regional climate changes due to black carbon

Nature Geoscience, vol. 1 , pp. 221-227

Ramanathan and Fen (2009)

V. Ramanathan, Y. Feng (2009)

Air pollution, greenhouse gases and climate change: Global and regional perspectives

Atmospheric Environment, vol. 43 , pp. 37–50

Ramanathan et al. (2008)

V. Ramanathan, M. Agrawal, H. Akimoto, M. Aufhammer, S. Devotta, L. Emberson, S.I. Hasnain, M. Iyngararasan, A. Jayaraman, M. Lawrance, T. Nakajima, T. Oki, H. Rodhe, M. Ruchirawat, S.K. Tan, J. Vincent, J.Y. Wang, D. Yang, Y.H. Zhang, H. Autrup, L. Barregard, P. Bonasoni, M. Brauer, B. Brunekreef, G. Carmichael, C.E. Chung, J. Dahe, Y. Feng, S. Fuzzi, T. Gordon, A.K. Gosain, N. Htun, J. Kim, S. Mourato, L. Naeher, P. Navasumrit, B. Ostro, T. Panwar, M.R. Rahman, M.V. Ramana, M. Rupakheti, D. Settachan, A. K. Singh, G. St. Helen, P. V. Tan, P.H. Viet, J. Yinlong, S.C. Yoon, W.-C. Chang, X. Wang, J. Zelikoff and A. Zhu (2008)

Atmospheric Brown Clouds: Regional Assessment Report with Focus on Asia.

Nairobi, Kenya, United Nations Environment Programme (UNEP)

Ramankutty and Foley (1999)

N. Ramankutty and J. A. Foley (1999)

Estimating historical changes in global land cover: Croplands from 1700 to 1992

Global Biogeochemical Cycles, vol. 13, no. 4, pp. 997–1027

Ramos et al. (2004)

J. Ramos, J. Villa, A. Ruiz, R. Armstrong and J. Matta (2004)

Cancer Epidemiology, Biomarkers and Prevention: UV Dose Determines Key Characteristics of Nonmelanoma Skin Cancer

Cancer Epidemiology Biomarkers Prevention, vol. 13, no.12, pp. 2006-2011

Ramsey (1995)

J.D. Ramsey (1995)

Task performance in heat: a review.

Ergonomics, vol. 38, no. 1, pp. 154-65.

Ratter et al. (2012)

B. M.W. Ratter, K. H.I. Philipp and H. von Storch (2012)

Between hype and decline: recent trends in public perception of climate change

Environmental Science and Policy, Vol. 18, pp. 3-8

Ravallion et al. (2007)

Martin Ravallion, Shaohua Chen and Prem Sangraula (2007)

New Evidence on the Urbanization of Global Poverty

Development Research Group, World Bank.

Reeve and Toumi (1999)

N. Reeve and R. Toumi (1999)

Lightning activity as an indicator of climate change

Quarterly Journal of the Royal Meteorological Society, vol. 131, iss. 608, pp. 1539-1565

Reilly et al. (2007)

J. Reilly, S. Paltsev, B. Felzer, X. Wang, D. Kicklighter, J. Melillo, R. Prinn, M. Sarofim, A. Sokolov, C. Wang (2007)

Global economic effects of changes in crops, pasture, and forests due to changing climate, carbon dioxide, and ozone

Report No. 149

MIT Joint Program on the Science and Policy of Global Change

Reiter (2001)

P. Reiter (2001)

Climate Change and Mosquito-Borne Disease

Environmental Health Perpective, vol. 109, suppl. 1, pp. 141 161

Restuccia et al. (2004)

D. Restuccia, D. Tao Yang and X. Zhu (2004)

Agriculture and Aggregate Productivity: A Quantitative Cross-Country Analysis

Journal of Monetary Economics, vol. 55, no.2, pp. 234-250

Reynolds et al. (2011)

J. F. Reynolds, A. Grainger, D. M. Stafford Smith, G. Bastin, L. Garcia-Barrios,R. J. Fernandez, M. A. Janssen, N. Ju¨ Rgens, R. J. Scholes, A. Veldkamp, M. M. Verstraete, G. Von Maltitz And P. Zdruli (2011)

Scientific Concepts for an Integrated Analysis of Desertification

Land Degradation & Development, vol. 22, pp. 166–183

Riahi et al. (2007)

Keywan Riahi, Arnulf Grübler and Nebojsa Nakicenovic (2007)

Scenarios of long-term socio-economic and environmental development under climate stabilization

Technological Forecasting & Social Change, vol. 74, pp. 887–935

Rijnsdorp et al. (2009)

Adriaan. D. Rijnsdrop, Myron. A. Peck, Georg. H. Engelhard, Christian Mollmann, John. K. Pinnegar (2009)

Resolving the effect of climate change on fish populations

Ices Journal of Marine Science, vol. 66:7, pp. 1570-1583

RiskMetrics Group (2010)

Yulia Reuter, Doug Cogan, Dana Sasarean, Mario López Alcalá, and Dinah Koehler (2010)

Canada's Oil Sands Shrinking Window of Opportunity

Boston, MA: CERES

Robine et al. (2008)

JM. Robine, SLK. Cheung, S. Le Roy, H. Van Oyen, C. Griffiths, JP.Michel and FR. Herrmann (2008)

Death toll exceded 70000 in Europe in Europe during the summer of 2003

C R Biol, vol. 331, pp. 171-178

Rodríguez Díaz et al. (2007)

J. A. Rodríguez Díaz, E. K. Weatherhead, J. W. Knox and E. Camacho (2007)

Climate change impacts on irrigation water requirements in the Guadalquivir river basin in Spain

Regional Environmental Change, vol. 7, no. 3, pp. 149-159

Roe and Elliot (2004)

Dilys Roe and Joanna Elliott (2004)

Poverty reduction and biodiversity conservation: rebuilding the bridges

Oryx, Vol 38, No. 2 , pp. 137-139

Roesch et al. (2012)

Roesch, A.; Wild, M.; Ammann, C. (2012)

Global dimming and brightening - evidence and agricultural implications

EGU General Assembly 2012, held 22-27 April, 2012 in Vienna, Austria, p.14479

Rogers and Hall (2003)

P. Rogers and A. W. Hall (2003)

Effective Water Governance

Tec. Background Papers No. 7

Global Water Partnership

Rohde et al (2012)

Robert Rohde, Richard A. Muller, Robert Jacobsen,Elizabeth Muller, Saul Perlmutter, Arthur Rosenfeld, Jonathan Wurtele,Donald Groom and Charlotte Wickham (2012)

A New Estimate of the Average Earth Surface Land Temperature. Spanning 1753 to 2011

Submitted to the Third Santa Fe Conference on Global and Regional Climate Change Manuscript # 2012JD018202

Berkeley Earth

Retrieved: http://berkeleyearth.org/pdf/results-paper-july-8.pdf

Romanovsky et al. (2010)

V. E.Romanovsky, S.S. Marchenko, M. Brubaker (2010)

Current and Projected Changes in Permafrost and Societal Impacts of Permafrost Degradation (Invited)

American Geophysical Union, Fall Meeting 2010, abstract #GC54A-10

Rooney et al. (2012)

R.C. Rooney, S.E. Bayley, and D.W. Schindler (2012)

Oil sands mining and reclamation cause massive loss of peatland and stored carbon

Proceedings of the National Academy of Sciences of the United States, vol. 109, no. 13, pp. 4933-4937

Rosenberg and Beard (2011)

R. Rosenberg and C.B. Beard

Vector-borne Infections

Emerging Infectious Diseases, vol. 17, no.5, pp. 769-770

Rosengrant et al. (2002)

Mark W. Rosegrant, Ximing Cai and Sarah A. Cline (2002)

World water and Food to 2025 dealing with scarcity

International Food Policy Research Institute

Rothberg et al. (2008)

Michael B. Rothberg, Sarah D. Haessler, and Richard B. Brown (2008)

Complications of Viral Influenza

The American Journal of Medicine, no. 121, pp. 258-264.

RSNZ (2010)

The Royal Society of New Zealand (2010)

Sea Level Rise

Emerging Issues, September 2010

Retrieved: www.royalsociety.org.nz

Rubel and Kottek (2010)
Franz Rubel and Markus Kottek (2010)
Observed and projected climate shifts 1901-2100 depicted by world maps of the Köppen-Geiger climate classification
Meteorologische Zeitschrift, vol. 19, no. 2, pp. 135-141.

Rubin (2009)
Jeff Rubin (2009)
Why Your World is About to Get a Whole Lot Smaller: Oil and the End of Globalisation
London, Great Britain, Virgin Books- Random House

Rudeva and Gulev (2007)
Irina Rudeva And Sergey K. Gulev (2007)
Climatology of Cyclone Size Characteristics and Their Changes during the Cyclone Life Cycle
Monthly Weather Review, vol. 135, pp. 2568-2587

Ruesch and Gibbs (2008)
Ruesch Aaron and Holly K. Gibbs (2008)
New IPCC Tier-1 Global Biomass Carbon Map for the Year 2000
Carbon Dioxide Information Analysis Center
Oak Ridge, Tennessee: Oak Ridge National Laboratory
http://cdiac.ornl.gov

Sabater and Tockner (2010)
Sergi Sabater and Klement Tockner (2010)
Effects of Hydrologic Alterations on the Ecological Quality of River Ecosystems
The Handbook of Environmental Chemistry, vol. 8, pp. 15-39

Sabine and Feely (2007)
Christopher L. Sabine and Richard A. Feely (2007)
The Oceanic Sink for Carbon Dioxide
in D.S. Reay C. N.Hewitt, K.A. Smith and J. Grace (eds.): *Greenhouse Gas Sinks* (pp. 31-49)
CAB International

Sahin and Hall (1996)
Vildan Sahin and Michael J. Hall (1996)
The effects of afforestation and deforestation on water yields
Journal of Hydrology, vol. 178, pp. 293-309

Saleska et al. (2011)
S.R. Saleska, N. Restrepo-Coupe, K.T. Wiedemann, R. da Silva, D. Amaral, B.J. Christoffersen, J. Wu, L.F. Alves, P.B. Camargo, R.C. Oliveira, A.R. Huete, K. Didan and R. Solano (2011)
Amazon Forest Vegetation and Carbon Dynamics under Drought and Flood
American Geophysical Union, Fall Meeting 2011, abstract #B23E-01

Salick and Byg (2007)
Jan Salick and Anja Byg (2007)
Indigenous Peoples and Climate Change
Oxford, UK: Tyndall Centre for Climate Change Research,

Samuelson and Nordhaus (1948)
Paul Anthony Samuelson and William D. Nordhaus (1948)
Economics. 19th Edition, International Edition.
McGraw-Hill/Irwin 2010 – first published 1948

Saraiya et al. (2004)
M. Saraiya, K. Glanz, P. Briss, P. Nichols, C. White, D. Das, J. Smith, B. Tannor, A. Hutchinson, K. Wilson, N. Gandhi, N. Lee, B. Rimer, R. Coates, J. Kerner, R. Hiatt, P. Buffler and P. Rochester (2004)
Interventions to Prevent Skin Cancer by Reducing Exposure to Ultraviolet Radiation: A Systematic Review
American Journal of Preventative Medicine, vol. 27, no. 5, pp. 422-266

Sari and Soytas (2008)
Ramazan Sari and Ugur Soytas (2008)
Are global warming and economic growth compatible? Evidence from five OPEC countries?
Applied Energy, vol. 86, pp. 1887–1893

Scarborough (2011)
H. Scarborough (2011)
Intergenerational equity and the social discount rate
Australian Journal of Agricultural and Resource Economics, vol.55 pp., no.2, 145-158

SCBD (2010)
Secretariat of the Convention on Biological Diversity (2010)
Global Biodiversity Outlook 3
Montréal, Secretariat of the Convention on Biological Diversity

Schönning and Stenström (2004)
C. Schönning and T.A. Stenström (2004)
Guidelines for the Safe Use of Urine and Faeces in Ecological Sanitation Systems
Report 2004-1. Stockholm: Swedish Environmental Institute (SEI)

Severson-Baker and Reynolds (2005)
C.Severson-Baker and M. Raynolds (2005)
Oil Sands Fever; The environmental implications of Canada's Oil Sands Rush
The Pembina Institute
Retrieved: http://www.pembina.org/pub/203

Schipper and Pelling (2006)
L. Schipper and M. Pelling, M. (2006)
Disaster risk, climate change and international development: scope for, and challenges to integration
Disasters, vol. 30, iss. 1, pp. 19–38

Shah et al. (2000)
J.Shah, T. Nagpal, T. Johnson, M. Amann2, G. Carmichael, W. Foell, C. Green, J.-P. Hettelingh, L. Hordijk, J. Li, C. Peng, Y. Pu, R. Ramankutty and D. Streets (2000)
Integrated Analysis for Acid Rain in Asia: Policy Implications and Results of RAINS-ASIA Model
Annual Review of Energy and the Environment, vol. 25:1, pp. 339- 375

Shakhova et al. (2008)
N. Shakhova, I. Semiletov, A. Salyuk, D. Kosmach (2008)
Anomalies of methane in the atmosphere over the East Siberian shelf: Is there any sign of methane leakage from shallow shelf hydrates?
EGU General Assembly 2008, Geophysical Research Abstracts, vol. 10, EGU2008-A-01526

Shakhova et al. (2010)
N. Shakhova, I. Semiletov, A. Salyuk, D. Kosmach and O. Gustafsson (2010)
Extensive methane venting to the atmosphere from sediments of the East Siberian Arctic Shelf
Science, vol. 327, pp. 1246–1250

Sheffield et al. (2011)
Perry E. Sheffield, Kim Knowlton, Jessie L. Carr, and Patrick L. Kinney (2011)
Modeling of Regional Climate Change Effects on Ground-Level Ozone and Childhood Asthma
American Journal of Preventive Medicine, vol. 41, no. 3, pp. 251-257.

Sheffield and Wood (2008)
Justin Sheffield and Eric F. Wood (2008)
Projected changes in drought occurrence under future global warming from multi – model, multiscenario, IPCC AR4 simulations
Climate Dynamics, vol. 31, no.1, pp 79 – 105.

Sherwood and Huber (2010)
Steven C. Sherwood and Matthew Huber (2010)
An adaptability limit to climate change due to heat stress
Procedings of the National Academy of Sciences of the USA (PNAS), vol. 107, no.21, pp.9552-9555

Shvidenko et al. (2005)
Anatoly Shvidenko, Charles Victor Barber and Reidar Persson (2005)
Forest and Woodland Systems
In: R. Hassan, R. Scholes and N. Ash (eds.): *Ecosystems and Human Well-being: Current State and Trends* (Chapter 21)
Millennium Ecosystem Assessment

Silverman et al. (2009)
J. Silverman, B. Lazar, L. Cao, K. Caldeira and J. Erez (2009)
Coral reefs may start dissolving when atmospheric CO2 doubles
Geophysical Research Letters, vol. 36, L05606, pp. 1-5

Simons (2010)
Craig Simons (2010)
The Green Guru: Mohamed Nasheed
The Daily Beast, Newsweek .
Retrieved: http://www.thedailybeast.com/

SCBD (2009)
Secretariat of the Convention on Biological Diversity (2009)
Biodiversity, Development and Poverty Alleviation: Recognizing the Role of Biodiversity for Human Well-being.
Montreal, SCBD

Scheffran et al. (2012)
J. Scheffran, M. Brzoska, J. Kominek, P.M. Link, J. Schilling (2012)
Climate Change and Violent Conflict
Science, vol. 336, pp.869-871

Schlenker and Roberts (2009)
W. Schlenker and M. J. Roberts (2009)
Nonlinear temperature effects indicate severe damages to U.S. crop yields under climate change
Procedings of the National Academy of Sciences of the USA (PNAS), vol. 106, no. 37, pp.15594-15598

Scott (2003)
Daniel Scott (2003)
Climate Change and Tourism in the Mountain Regions of North America
Paper presented in the 1st International Conference on Climate Change and Tourism, Djerba, Tunisia, 9-11 April 2003

Scott (2011)
Daniel Scott (2011)
Why sustainable tourism must address climate change
Journal of Sustainable Tourism, vol. 19, Iss. 1, pp. 17-34

Scott et al. (2009)
Daniel Scott, Chris de Freitas and Andreas Matzarakis (2009)
Adaptation in the Tourism and Recreation Sector
Biometeorology, vol. 1, no. I, pp. 171-194

Scott et al. (2010)
Daniel Scott, Paul Peeters and Stefan Gössling (2010)
Can tourism deliver its "aspirational" greenhouse gas emission reduction targets?
Journal of Sustainable Tourism, vol. 18, iss. 3, pp. 393-408

Smith et al. (2000)
Kirk R Smith, Jonathan M Samet, Isabelle Romieu, Nigel Bruce (2000)
Indoor air pollution in developing countries and acute lower respiratory infections in children
Thorax, International Journal of Respiratory Medicine, vol. 55:6, pp. 518-532

Smith et al. (2001)

J. B. Smith, H.J. Schellnhuber and M. M. Qader Mirza (2001)

Vulnerability to Climate Change and Reasons for Concern: A Synthesis (chapter 19)

In: *IPCC Third Assessment Report: Climate Change 2001 (TAR). Working Group II: Impacts, Adaptation and Vulnerab*ility (pp. 915-159).

Retrieved: http://ipcc.ch/ipccreports/tar/wg2/pdf/wg2TARchap19.pdf

Smith et al (2011)

S. J. Smith, J. van Aardenne, Z. Klimont, R. J. Andres, A. Volke and S. Delgado Arias

Anthropogenic sulfur dioxide emissions: 1850–2005

Atmospheric Chemistry and Physics, vol. 11, pp. 1101-1116

Smit and Wandel (2006)

B. Smit and J. Wandel (2006)

Adaptation, adaptive capacity and vulnerability

Global Environmental Change, vol. 16, iss. 3, pp. 282-292,

Sokolov et al. (2009)

A. P. Sokolov, P. H. Stone, C. E. Forest, R. Prinn, M. C. Sarofim,M. Webster,S. Paltsev, and C. A. Schlosser (2009)

Probabilistic Forecast for Twenty-First-Century Climate Based on Uncertainties in Emissions (Without Policy) and Climate Parameters

Journal of Climate, vol. 22, pp. 5175-5204.

Solonin and Katsyuba (2003)

Y.G. Solonin and E.A. Katsyuba (2003)

Thermoregulation and Blood Circulation in Adults during Short-Term Exposure to Extreme Temperatures

Human Physiology, vol. 29, no. 2, pp. 188-194

Solow (1956)

Robert M. Solow (1956)

A Contribution to the Theory of Economic Growth

The Quarterly Journal of Economics, vol. 70, no. 1 , pp. 65-94

Srinivasan et al. (2010)

U. T.Srinivasan, W. L. Cheung, R. Watson and U. Rashid Sumaila (2010)

Food security implications of global marine catch losses due to overfishing

Journal of Bioeconomics, vol. 12, no.3, pp.183-200.

Stanhill and Cohen (2000)

Gerald Stanhill and Shabtai Cohen (2000)

Global dimming: a review of the evidence for a widespread and significant reduction in global radiation with discussion of its probable causes and possible agricultural consequences

Agricultural and Forest Meteorology, vol. 107, pp. 255–278

Steiger (2011)

Steiger Robert (2011)

The impact of snow scarcity on ski tourism: an analysis of the record warm season 2006/2007 in Tyrol (Austria)

Tourism Review, vol. 66, no. 3, pp. 4 - 13.

Stern (2006)

Nicholas Stern (2006)

The Stern Review on the Economic Effects of Climate Change
London, HM Treasury

Stidger (2001)

R W Stidger (2001)

Alaska Dot Deals With Permafrost Thaws

Better Roads, vol. 71, no. 6, pp, 30-31

Stifel et al. (2012)

David Stifel, Bart Minten, and Bethlehem Koro (2012)

Economic Benefits and Returns to Rural Feeder Roads: Evidence from a Quasi-Experimental Setting in Ethiopia

ESSP II Working Paper 40

International Food Policy Research Institute and Ethiopian Development Research Institute

Stoddard et al. (2003)

Stoddard, J. L., J. S. Kahl, F. A. Deviney, D. R. DeWalle, C. T. Driscoll, A. T. Herlihy, J. H. Kellogg, P. S. Murdoch, J. R. Webb, and K. E. Webster (2003)

Response of surface water chemistry to the Clean Air Act Amendments of 1990

EPA/620/R-03/001

Corvallis, Or: U.S. Environmental Protection Agency

Storm and Naastepad (2009)

S. Storm and C.W.M. Naastepad (2009)

Labor Market Regulation and Productivity Growth: Evidence for Twenty OECD Countries (1984–2004)

Industrial Relations: A Journal of Economy and Society, vol. 48, Iss. 4, pp. 629- 654

Stromberg et al. (2010)

J. C. Stromberg, S. J. Lite and M. D. Dixon (2010)

Effects of stream flow patterns on riparian vegetation of a semiarid river: Implications for a changing climate.

River Research and Applications, vol. 26, Iss. 6, pp. 712–729.

Stuart et al. (2004)

S. N. Stuart, J. S. Chanson, N. A. Cox, B. E. Young, A. S.L. Rodrigues, D. L. Fischman, R. W.Waller (2004)

Status and Trends of Amphibian Declines and Extinctions Worldwide

Sciencexpress, 14 October 2004

Su et al. (2009)

Zhao-gui Su, Zhong-an Jiang and Zhong-qiang Sun (2009)

Study on the heat hazard of deep exploitation in high-temperature mines and its evaluation index

Procedia Earth and Planetary Science, vol. 1, Iss. 1, pp. 414-419

Sullivan (2011)

Caroline A. Sullivan (2011)

Quantifying water vulnerability: a multi-dimensional approach

Stochastic Environmental Research and Risk Assessment, vol. 25, no. 4, pp. 627-640

Sultan et al. (2005)

B. Sultan, K. Labadi, J. Guégan, and S. Janicot (2005)

Climate Drives the Meningitis Epidemics Onset in West Africa

PLoS Medicine, vol.2, no.1

Sumaila and Cheung (2010)

Ussif Rashid Sumaila and William W. L. Cheung (2010)

Cost of Adapting Fisheries to Climate Change

Development and climate change discussion paper, no. 5.

Washington D.C., The Worldbank

Retrieved:http://documents.worldbank.org/curated/en/2010/08/12779737/cost-adapting-fisheries-climate-change

Sutton and Constanza (2002)

Paul C. Sutton and Robert Costanza (2002)

Global estimates of market and non-market values derived from nighttime satellite imagery, land cover, and ecosystem service valuation

Ecological Economics, vol. 41, pp. 509–527

Swaen et al. (1995)

Swaen, G.M., Meijers, J.M.M. and Slangen, J.J.M. (1995)

Risk of gastric cancer in pneumoconiotic coal miners and the effect of respiratory impairment

Occupational and Environmental Medicine, vol. 52, pp. 606-610.

Swinnen and Squicciarinim (2012)

Johan Swinnen and Pasquamaria Squicciarini (2012)

Mixed Messages on Prices and Food Security

Science, Vol. 335, no. 6067, pp. 405-406

Swiss Re (2010)

Swiss Re (2010)

Natural catastrophes and man-made disasters in 2009: catastrophes claim fewer victims, insured losses fall

Sigma, No. 1/2010

Zurich, Switzerland, Swiss Reinsurance Company Ltd.

Swiss Re (2011)

Swiss Re (2011)

Natural catastrophes and man-made disasters in 2010: a year of devastating and costly events

Sigma, No. 1/2011

Zurich, Switzerland, Swiss Reinsurance Company Ltd.

Swiss Re (2012)

Swiss Re (2012)

Natural catastrophes and man-made disasters in 2011: historic losses surface from record earthquakes and floods

Sigma, No. 2/2012

Zurich, Switzerland, Swiss Reinsurance Company Ltd.

Syed et al. (2010)

Tajdarul H. Syed, James S. Famiglietti, Don P. Chambers, Josh K. Willis, and Kyle Hilburn (2010)

Satellite-based global-ocean mass balance estimates of interannual variability and emerging trends in continental freshwater discharge

PNAS, vol. 107, no. 42, pp. 17916–17921

Tabarelli et al. (2010)

M. Tabarelli, A. Venceslau Aguiar, M.C. Ribeiro, J.P. Metzger,C.A. Peres (2010)

Prospects for biodiversity conservation in the Atlantic Forest: Lessons from aging human-modified landscapes

Biological Conservation, vol. 143, Iss. 10, pp. 2328-2340

Tachie-Obeng et al. (2012)

E. Tachie-Obeng, E. Edwin Gyasi, S. Adiku,B. Hewitson, M. Abekoe and G. Ziervogel (2011)

Farmer adaptation options to climate change: A case study of maize production in savanna and transitional zones of Ghana.

PhD Thesis University of Ghana and University of Cape Town

Tarnocai et al. (2009)

C. Tarnocai, J. G. Canadell, E. A. G. Schuur, P. Kuhry, G. Mazhitova and S. Zimov (2009)

Soil organic carbon pools in the northern circumpolar permafrost region

Global Biogeochemical Cycles, vol. 23, GB2023

Taylor et al. (2007)

Richard Taylor, Robert Gumming, Alistair Woodward, Megan Black (2007)

Passive smoking and lung cancer: a cumulative meta-analysis

Australian and New Zealand Journal of Public Health, vol. 25:3, pp. 203-211

TCT and McKinsey & Co (2008)
The Carbon Trust and McKinsey & Co (2008)
Climate change – a business revolution? How tackling climate change could create or destroy company value
The Carbon Trust
Retrieved: http://www.carbontrust.com/media/84956/ctc740-climate-change-a-business-revolution.pdf

Tebaldi et al. (2011)
C. Tebaldi, J. M. Arblaster, and R. Knutti (2011)
Mapping model agreement on future climate projections
Geophysical Research Letters, vol. 38, L23701, 5 pp

Teh et al. (2008)
Louise Teh, William W.L. Cheung, Andy Cornish, Clarus Chu and U. Rashid Sumaila, (2008)
A survey of alternative livelihood options for Hong Kong's fishers
International Journal of Social Economics, vol. 35, Iss. 5, pp.380 - 395

Tenenbaum (2009)
David J. Tenenbaum (2009)
Oil Sands Development: A Health Risk Worth Taking?
Environmental Health Perspectives, vol. 117, no. 4, pp. A150–A156

The Royal Society (2005)
The Royal Society (2005)
A guide to facts and fictions about climate change
Retrieved:http://royalsociety.org/uploadedFiles/Royal_Society_Content/News_and_Issues/Science_Issues/Climate_change/climate_facts_and_fictions.pdf

Thomas et al. (2004)
Chris D. Thomas, Alison Cameron, Rhys E. Green, Michel Bakkenes, Linda J. Beaumont, Yvonne C. Collingham, Barend F. N. Erasmus, Marinez Ferreira de Siqueira, Alan Grainger, Lee Hannah, Lesley Hughes, Brian Huntley, Albert S. van Jaarsveld, Guy F. Midgley, Lera Miles, Miguel A. Ortega-Huerta, A. Townsend Peterson, Oliver L. Phillips, and Stephen E. Williams (2004)
Extinction risk from climate change
Nature, vol. 427, no. 8, pp. 145-148

Thomson et al. (2009)
M.C. Thomson, I. Jeanne, and M. Djingarey (2009)
Dust and Epidemic Meningitis in the Sahel: A Public Health and Operational Research Perspective
IOP Conference Series: Earth and Environmental Science, vol. 7

Tilman et al. (2002)
D. Tilman, K. G. Cassman, P. A. Matson, R. Naylor and S. Polasky (2002)
Agricultural sustainability and intensive production practices
Nature (insight review articles), vol. 418 , pp. 671-677

Tol (2009)
Richard S. J. Tol (2009)
The Economic Effects of Climate Change
Journal of Economic Perspectives, vol. 23,no. 2, pp. 29–51

Tol (2010)
Richard S.J. Tol (2010)
The Costs And Benefits Of EU Climate Policy For 2020
Copenhagen Consensus Center

Tol (2011)
Richard S. J, Tol. (2011) :
The social cost of carbon.
ESRI working paper, No. 377
Dublin, Economic and Social Research Institute (ESRI)
Retrieved: http://hdl.handle.net/10419/50128

Tol and Yohe (2006)
G. Yohe, M. E. Schlesinger and N. G. Andronova (2006)
Reducing the risk of a collapse of the Atlantic thermohaline circulation
The Integrated Assessment Journal, vol. 6, Iss. 1 , Pp. 57–73

Tol and Yohe (2007)
Richard S. J. Tol and Gary W. Yohe (2007)
Climate Change. A Stern Reply to the Reply to the Review of the Stern Review
World Economics, vol. 8 , No. 2, pp.153-159

Törnqvist et al. (2008)
Torbjörn E. Törnqvist, Davin J. Wallace, Joep E. A. Storms, Jakob Wallinga,Remke L. Van Dam, Martijn Blaauw, Mayke S. Derksen, Cornelis J. W. Klerks, Camiel Meijneken and Els M. A. Snijders (2008)
Mississippi Delta subsidence primarily caused by compaction of Holocene strata
Nature Geoscience (Letters), vol. 1, pp.173-176

Toulemon and Barbieri (2006)
Toulemon Laurent and Magali Barbieri (2006)
The Mortality Impact of the August 2003 Heat Wave in France
Paper prepared for presentation at the 2006 Population of America Association Meeting, Los Angeles, March 30-April 1st.

Trenberth (2011)
K.E. Trenberth (2011)
Changes in Precipitation with Climate Change
Climate Research, 47, pp. 123-138

Trenberth (2012)
Kevin E. Trenberth (2012)
Framing the way to relate climate extremes to climate change
Climatic Change, 2012, pp. 1-8

Tryse (2010)
David Tryse (2010)
Oil Spill Database
http://earth.tryse.net/oilspill.html

Turner II et al. (2007)
B.L. Turner II, E.F. Lambin, and A. Reenberg (2007)
The Emergence of Land Change Science for Global Environmental Change and Sustainability
Proceedings of the National Academy of Sciences, vol. 104, no. 52, pp.20666-20671

Tyndall (1869)
John Tyndall (1969)
Heat considered as a mode of motion
New York, D. Appleton & Company (Google eBook)
Retrieved:http://books.google.ch/books?id=1Vs9AAAAYAAJ&hl=es&pg=PR1#v=onepage&q&f=false

UN (2011)
UN (2011)
Global Drylands: A UN system-wide response
United Nations Environment Management Group

UN (2012)
UN (2012)
The Millennium Development Goals Report 2012
New York, United Nations

UNCCD (2010)
UN Convention to Combat Desertification (2010)
Drylands Soil . Sustaining life on earth
United Nations Convention to Combat Desertification
Bonn :UN Convention to Combat Desertification (UNCCD) Secretariat
Retrieved:http://www.unccd.int/Lists/SiteDocumentLibrary/Publications/DrylandsSoilUNCCDBrochureFinal.pdf

UNCCD (2011)
UN Convention to Combat Desertification (2011)
Desertification: a visual synthesis
Bonn: UN Convention to Combat Desertification (UNCCD) Secretariat
Retrieved:http://www.unccd.int/Lists/SiteDocumentLibrary/Publications/Desertification-EN.pdf

UNDP (2007)
UNDP (2007)
Human Development Report 2007/2008. Fighting Climate Change: Human Solidarity in a Divided World
United Nations Development Programme (UNDP), United Nations

UNDP (2011)
UNDP (2011)
Human development report 2011
United Nations Development Programme (UNDP), United Nations

UNECE (2012)
UNECE (2012)
UNECE Statistical Database
Retrieved: http://w3.unece.org/pxweb/

UNECE (2012a)
UNECE (2012a)
Transport Division Database
Carriage of goods by Inland Waterways (million, tonne-km)
Retrieved: http://w3.unece.org/pxweb/dialog/varval.asp?ma=ZZZ_TRInlWaterTonKm_r&path=../database/STAT/40-TRTRANS/06-TRInlWater/&lang=1&ti=Carriage+of+goods+by+Inland+Waterways+%28million%2C+tonne-km%29

UNEP/GRID Website
UNEP/GRID Website
Global Risk Data Platform

UNEP (2002)
United Nations Environment Programme (2002)
Global Environment Outlook 3: Past, present and future perspectives
London, UK: UNEP -Earthscan Publications

UNEP (2002b)
United Nations Environment Programme (2002b)
Environmental Effects of Ozone Depletion and It´s Interactions with Climate Change: 2002 Assessment
Secretariat for The Vienna Convention for the Protection of the Ozone Layer, The Montreal Protocol on Substances that Deplete the Ozone Layer United Nations Environment Programme

UNEP (2005)
United Nations Environment Programme (2005)
Geo Year Book, An overview of our changing environment
Retrieved: http://www.unep.org/geo/yearbook

UNEP (2010)
UNEP Finance Initiative (2010)
Universal Ownership: Why environmental externalities matter to institutional investors
PRI Association and UNEP Finance Initiative

UNEP (2011)
UNEP (2011)
Bridging the Emissions Gap
United Nations Environment Programme (UNEP)

UNEP Risoe (2012)
UNEP Risoe (2012)
CDM/JI Pipeline Analysis and Database
Retrieved: http://www.cdmpipeline.org

UNESCO (2010)

UNESCO, World Commission on the Ethics of Scientific Knowledge and Technology (COMEST) (2010)

The Ethical Implications of Global Climate Change

Paris, France, United Nations Educational, Scientific and Cultural Organization

UNFCCC (1992)

UNFCCC (1992)

United Nations Framework Convention on Climate Change

Retrieved: http://unfccc.int/resource/docs/convkp/conveng.pdf

UNFCCC (2009)

UNFCCC (2009)

UN Climate Conference at Copenhagen (COP15)

Retrieved: http://unfccc.int/resource/docs/2009/cop15/eng/l07.pdf

UN-HABITAT (2012)

UN-HABITAT (2012)

Urban Indicators

UN-HABITAT Global Urban Indicators database

Retrieved: http://www.unhabitat.org/stats/Default.aspx

UNHRC (2008)

United Nations Human Rights Council (2008)

Resolution 7/23. Human rights and climate change

Retrieved: http://ap.ohchr.org/documents/E/HRC/resolutions/A_HRC_RES_7_23.pdf

UNHRC (2009)

United Nations Human Rights Council (2009)

Resolution 10/4. Human rights and climate change

Retrieved: http://ap.ohchr.org/documents/E/HRC/resolutions/A_HRC_RES_10_4.pdf

UNHRC (2011)

United Nations Human Rights Council (2011)

Resolution 18/22 Human rights and climate change

Retrieved: http://daccess-dds-ny.un.org/doc/RESOLUTION/GEN/G11/167/48/PDF/G1116748.pdf?OpenElement

UN CHS (2010)

United Nations Compendium of Housing Statistics

Compendium of Human Settlements Statistics

Retrieved: http://unstats.un.org/unsd/demographic/sconcerns/housing/housing2.htm

UNISDR (2009)

UNISDR (2009)

Global Assessment Report on Disaster Risk Reduction.

Geneva, Switzerland, United Nations

UNISDR (2011)

UNISDR (2011)

Global Assessment Report on Disaster Risk Reduction

Geneva, Switzerland, United Nations, International Strategy for Disaster Reduction

UNISDR (2012)

United Nations Office for Disaster Risk Reduction (2012)

Terminology On Disaster Risk Reduction

Retrieved: http://www.unisdr.org/eng/library/lib-terminology-eng%20home.htm

UN Pop Div. (2012)

UN Department of Economic and Social Affairs Population Division (2012)

World population Database

Retrieved: http://www.un.org/esa/population/unpop.htm

UNSD (2010)

United Nations Statistics Division (2010)

UNSD Statistical Databases

http://unstats.un.org/unsd/databases.htm

UNSD (2012)

United Nations Statistics Division (2012)

UNSD Statistical Databases

http://unstats.un.org/unsd/databases.htm

UNWTO (2012)

United Nations World Tourism Organization (2012)

Tourism Indicators

Retrieved: http://www.unwto.org/facts/eng/ITA&TR.htm

US CB Website (2000)

United States Census Bureau Website

Historical Census of Housing Tables. Home Values

Census of Housing

Retrieved: http://www.census.gov/hhes/www/housing/census/historic/values.html

UoC and Vietnam MPI (2010)

University of Copenhagen and Ministry of Planning and Investment of Vietnam(2010)

The Fisheries Sector in Vietnam: A Strategic Economic Analysis

Retrieved:http://www.ciem.org.vn/home/en/upload/info/attach/13018993735150_FishReportUoCCIEM.pdf

USDAAF (2003)

USDAAF (2003)

Heat Stress Control and Heat Casualty Management

Technical Bulletin Medical 507 /*Air Force Pamphlet* 48-152 (I)

Headquarters, Department of the Army and Air Force

US DoT (2010)

U.S. Department of Transportation (2010)

Freight Transportation: Global Highlights, 2010

Washington, DC, U.S. Department of Transportation

US EIA (2011)

U.S. Energy Information Administration (2011)

The International Energy Outlook 2011

Retrieved: http://www.eia.gov/ieo/pdf/0484(2011).pdf

US EPA (2007)

United States Environment Protection Agency (2007)

Measuring Acid Rain

Retrieved: http://www.epa.gov/acidrain/measure/index.html

US EPA (2010)

United States Environment Protection Agency (2010)

Effects of Acid Rain - Materials

Retrieved: http://www.epa.gov/acidrain/effects/materials.html

US Forest Service (2010)

US Forest Service (2010)

Potential vegetation distribution (average for 1961-1990) simulated using the MC1 model with CRU (TS 2.0) historical climate at a half degree spatial grain over the globe

Data Basin Dataset, PNW Research Station

Retrieved: http://www.arcgis.com/home/item.html?id=b2b92d2efcdc40738e9f1ce6ff49fde2

US State Dpt. (2012)

US State Department (2012, August 2)

Remarks at Dartmouth College by Todd Stern, Special Envoy for Climate Change in Hanover, NH

Under Secretary for Economic Growth, Energy, and the Environment. Bureau of Oceans and International Environmental and Scientific Affairs. US State Department

Retrieved: http://www.state.gov/e/oes/rls/remarks/2012/196004.htm

Uyarra et al. (2005)

M. C. Uyarra, I. M. Côte, J. A. Gill , R. R.T. Tinch ,D. Viner and A, R.Watkinson (2005)

Island-specific preferences of tourists for environmental features: implications of climate change for tourism-dependent states

Environmental Conservation, vol. 32, iss. 1, pp. 11-19

Van Noort et al. (2012)

Van Noort S.P., Águas R., Ballesteros S., and Gomes M.G. (2012)

The role of weather on the relation between influenza and influenza-like illness

Journal of Theoretical Biology, no. 298, pp. 131-137

Vanat (2011)

Vanat Laurent (2011)

2011 International report on mountain tourism - Overview of the key industry figures for ski resorts May 2011

France: Institut de la Montagne

Van den Bergh (2009)

Jeroen C. J. M. van den Bergh (2009)

Safe climate policy is affordable—12 reasons

Climatic Change, vol. 101, no. 3-4, pp. 339-385

Van Veen et al. (1991)

J. A. Van Veen, E. Liljeroth, L. J. A. Lekkerkerk and S. C. van de Geijn (1991)

Carbon Fluxes in Plant-Soil Systems at Elevated Atmospheric CO2 Levels

Ecological Applications, vol. 1, no. 2, pp. 175-181

Vecchia et al. (Eds.) (2007)

P. Vecchia, M. Hietanen, B. Stuck, E. Van Deventer, S. Niu (eds.) (2007)

Protecting Workers from Ultraviolet Radiation

International Commission on Non-Ionizing Radiation Protection (ICNIRP)

Vecchiato (2012)

R. Vecchiato (2012)

Environmental uncertainty, foresight and strategic decision making:An integrated study.

Technological Forecasting and Social Change, vol. 79, Issue 3, pp. 436-447

Veitch and Clout (eds.) (2004).

C. R. Veitch and M. N. Clout (eds.) (2004)

Turning the tide: the eradication of invasive species (proceedings of the international conference on eradication of island invasives)

Occasional Paper of the IUCN Species Survival Comission No.27

Verbruggen and Marchohi (2010)

A.Verbruggen and M.A Marchohi (2010)

Views on peak oil and its relation to climate change policy

Energy Policy, vol. 38, pp. 5572-5581

Verheyen (2005)

Roda Verheyen (2005)

Climate Change Damage and International Law: Prevention, Duties and State Responsibility (Developments in International Law)

Martinus Nijhoff Publishers

Veron (2008)

J. E. N. Veron (2008)

Mass extinctions and ocean acidification: biological constraints on geological dilemmas

Coral Reef Research, vol. 27, pp. 459-472

Veron et al. (2009)

J. E. N. Veron, O. Hoegh-Guldberg , T.M. Lenton, J.M. Lough, D.O. Obura, P. Pearce-Kelly,

C.R.C. Sheppard, M. Spalding, M.G. Stafford-Smith, and A.D. Rogers (2009)

The coral reef crisis: The critical importance of <350 ppm CO2

Marine Pollution Bulletin, vol. 58, pp. 1428–1436.

Verstraete et al. (2009).

Michel M Verstraete, Robert J Scholes, and Mark Stafford Smith (2009)

Climate and desertification: looking at an old problem through new lenses

Frontiers in Ecology and the Environment, vol. 7, pp. 421–428

Vietnam MONRE (2008)

Vietnam Ministry Of Natural Resources and Environment (2008)

National Target Program to Respond to Climate Change. Draft. (Unofficial Translation of Vietnamese Draft Version of 27/7/2008)

Hanoi, Vietnam

Retrieved:http://www.isgmard.org.vn/VHDocs/NationalPrograms/NTP%20RespondtoClimateChange.pDF

Vietnam MONRE (2010)

Vietnam Ministry Of Natural Resources and Environment (2010)

Vietnam's Second National Communication to the United Nations Framework Convention on Climate Change.

Hanoi , Vietnam

Vietnam NCCS (2011)

Vietnam National Climate Change Strategy (2011)

National Climate Change Strategy

Retrieved:http://www.dwf.org/sites/lauratest.drupalgardens.com/files/Vietnam%20Climate%20Change%20Strategy.en_.pdf.pdf

Vilà et al. (2007)

M. Vilà, J. D. Corbin, J. S. Dukes, J. Pino, S. D. Smith (2007)

Linking Plant Invasions to Global Environmental Change

in Canadell JG, Pataki D, Pitelka L (eds) : *Terrestrial Ecosystems in a Changing World* (chapter 8)

Berlin Heidelberg, The IGBP Series, Springer-Verlag

Vörösmarty et al. (2000)

C.J. Vörösmarty P. Green, J. Salisbury and R. B. Lammers (2000)

Global Water Resources: Vulnerability from Climate Change and Population Growth

Science, vol. 289,

Vörösmarty et al. (2010)

C.J. Vörösmarty, P.B. McIntyre, M.O. Gessner, D.Dudgeon, A.Prusevich, P.Green, S.Glidden, S.E. Bunn, C.A. Sullivan, C.Reidy Liermann, and P.M. Davies (2010)

Global threats to human water security and river biodiversity

Nature, vol. 467, pp. 555-561.

Wacker et al. (2006)

John G. Wacker, Chen-Lung Yang, Chwen Sheu (2006)

Productivity of production labor, non-production labor, and capital: An international study

International Journal of Production Economics, vol. 103, no. 2, pp. 863-872.

Wall (1998)

Geoffrey Wall (1998)

Implications of Global Climate Change for Tourism and Recreation in Wetland Areas

Climatic Change, vol. 40, no. 2, pp. 371-389

Wallace (2000)

J.S. Wallace (2000)

Increasing agricultural water use efficiency to meet future food production

Agriculture, Ecosystems and Environment, vol. 82, pp. 105–119

Wang et al. (2009)

Bin Wang et al. (2009)

The Effect of Acid Rain on Vegetation by Using Remote Sensing Monitoring in Zhejiang Province

Journal of Anhui Agricultural Sciences, vol. 23

Wang et al. (2010)

Hai-qiao Wang, Zu-yun Zou, Shi-qiang Chen and Yi-qun Li (2010)

Improving thermal comfort of high-temperature environment of heading face

through dehumidification

Journal Of Coal Science And Engineering (China), vol. 16, no. 4,pp. 389-393

Ward (2009)

Peter L. Ward (2009)

Sulfur dioxide initiates global climate change in four ways

Thin Solid Films, vol. 517, pp. 3188–3203

Ward et al. (2010)

Philip J Ward, Kenneth M Strzepek, W Pieter Pauw, Luke M Brander, Gordon A Hughes and Jeroen C J H Aerts (2010)

Partial costs of global climate change adaptation for the supply of raw industrial and municipal water: a methodology and application

Environmental Research Letters, vol. 5, no. 4

Warner et al. (2009)

Warner, K.; Ehrhart, C.; Sherbinin, A. de; Adamo, S.; Chai-Onn, T.(2009)

In search of shelter: mapping the effects of climate change on human migration and displacement

London, UK, Climate Change CARE International

Watson et al. (2012)

Reg A Watson, William W L Cheung, Jonathan A Anticamara, Rashid U Sumaila, Dirk Zeller and Daniel Pauly (2012)

Global marine yield halved as fishing intensity redoubles

Fish and Fisheries, vol. 10, pp. 235-251

Waugh et al. (2009)

D. W. Waugh, L. Oman, S. R. Kawa, R. S. Stolarski, S. Pawson, A. R. Douglass, P. A. Newman, J. E. Nielsen (2009)

Impacts of climate change on stratospheric ozone recovery

Geophysical Research Letters, vol. 36

Weart (2011)

Spencer Weart (2011)

The Discovery of Global Warming (website)

Retrieved: http://www.aip.org/history/climate/index.htm

Welch et al. (2010)

Jarrod R. Welch, Jeffrey R. Vincent, Maximilian Auffhammer, Piedad F. Moya, Achim Dobermann, and David Dawe (2010)

Rice yields in tropical/subtropical Asia exhibit large but opposing sensitivities to minimum and maximum temperatures

PNAS, vol. 107 , no. 33, pp. 14562–14567

Wei et al. (2009)

Ma Wei, Cheng Guodong, Wu Qingbai (2009)

Construction on permafrost foundations: Lessons learned from the Qinghai–Tibet railroad

Cold Regions Science and Technology, vol.59, Iss. 1, pp. 3-11

Weitzman (2007)

Martin L. Weitzman (2007)

A Review of The Stern Review on the Economics of Climate Change

Journal of Economic Literature, vol. XLV, pp. 703–724

Weitzman (2009)

M. L. Weitzman (2009)

On modeling and interpreting the economics of catastrophic climate change

The Review of Economics and Statistics .vol. XCI , No. 1

Wentzel (1982)

Ursachen des Waldsterbens in Mitteleuropa

Allgemeine Forst Zeitschrift, Vol. 43, pp. 1365-1368.

Werner and Simmons (2009)

Adrian D. Werner and Craig T. Simmons (2009)

Impact of Sea-Level Rise on Sea Water Intrusion in Coastal Aquifers

Ground Water, vol. 47, no. 2, pp. 197–204

WFLC (2004)

Wildland Fire Leadership Council (2004)

Large Fire Suppression Costs, Strategies for Cost Management. A report to the Wildland Fire Leadership Council from the Strategic Issues Panel on Fire Suppression Costs

USDA Forest Service

Retrieved: http://www.fs.fed.us/fire/ibp/cost_accounting/costmanagement_aug_04.pdf

Wheeler (2011)

Wheeler David (2011)

Quantifying Vulnerability to Climate Change: Implications for Adaptation Assistance

CGD Working Paper 240

Washington, D.C.: Center for Global Development

http://www.cgdev.org/content/publications/detail/1424759

WHO (1997)

World Health Organisation (1997)

Health and Environment in Sustainable Development: Five Years after the Earth Summit

WHO (1999)

WHO (1999)

WHO Infectious Diseases Report

Geneva, Switzerland: World Health Organization

WHO (2002)

WHO (2002)

The World Health Report 2002. Reducing Risks, Promoting Healthy Life

Geneva, Switzerland: World Health Organization

WHO (2002a)

WHO (2002a)

Global Solar UV Index: A Practical Guide

Geneva, Switzerland: World Health Organization

Retrieved: http://www.who.int/uv/

WHO (2003)

D. Campbell-Lendrum, A. Pruss-Ustun, C. Corvalan (2003)

How much disease could climate change cause?

In: AJ McMichael, D. Campbell-Lendrum, C. Corvalan, K.L. Ebi, Ak. Githeko, JS. Scheraga (eds.) *Climate Change and health: risks and responses* (pp. 133-155)

Geneva, Switzerland: World Health Organization

WHO (2004)

Majid Ezzati, Alan D. Lopez, Anthony Rodgers and Christopher J.L. Murray (eds) (2004)

Comparative Quantification of Health Risks: Global and Regional Burden of Disease Attributable to Selected Major Risk Factors

Geneva, Switzerland: World Health Organization

WHO (2006)

WHO (2006)

WHO Air quality guidelines for particulate matter, ozone, nitrogen dioxide and sulfur dioxide: Global update 2005. Summary of risk assessment

Geneva, Switzerland: World Health Organization

WHO (2009)

WHO (2009)

Global health risks: mortality and burden of disease attributable to selected major risks.

Geneva, Switzerland: World Health Organization

WHO (2010)

Lucien Manga, Magaran Bagayoko, Tim Meredith and Maria Neira (eds) (2010)

Overview of health considerations within National Adaptation Programmes of Action for climate change in least developed countries and small island states.

Geneva, Switzerland: World Health Organization

WHO (2011)

WHO (2011)

Meningococcal Meningitis

Fact sheet N° 141, December 2011

Retrieved: http://www.who.int/mediacentre/factsheets/fs141/en/#

WHO BDD (2000)

WHO Burden of Diseases Database (2000)

Global Burden of Disease Data, 2000

WHO BDD (2011)

WHO Burden of Diseases Database (2011)

Global Burden of Disease Data, 2011

The Global Health Observatory (GHO)

Retrieved: http://apps.who.int/ghodata/#

WHO Website (2012)

WHO Website

Global Health Atlas

Retrieved: http://apps.who.int/globalatlas/dataQuery/default.asp

WHO and RBMP (2010)

WHO and Roll Back Malaria Partnership (2010)

Malaria Funding & Resource Utilization: The First Decade of Roll Back Malaria

RBM Progress & Impact Series, vol. 1

Wiafe (2010)

George Wiafe (2010)

Coastal and Continental Shelf Processes in Ghana

Department of Oceanography and Fisheries, University of Ghana

Retrieved: http://www.onr.navy.mil/reports/FY10/cgwiafe.pdf

Wilby and Dessai (2010)

Robert L. Wilby and Suraje Dessai (2010)

Robust adaptation to climate change

Weather, vol. 65, no. 7

Wilkinson et al. (2012)

Sally Wilkinson, Gina Mills, Rosemary Illidge and William J. Davies (2012)

How is ozone pollution reducing our food supply?

Journal of Experimental Botany, vol. 63, no. 2, pp. 527-536

Wilkinson and Salvat (2012)

Clive Wilkinson and Bernard Salvat (2012)

Coastal resource degradation in the tropics: Does the tragedy of the commons apply for coral reefs, mangrove forests and seagrass beds?

Marine Pollution Bulletin, vol. 64, Iss. 6, pp. 1096 1106

Williams (2011)

James Bryan Williams (2011)

Strengthening Climate Cooperation, Compliance & Coherence

Social Science Research Network (SSRN)

Retrieved: http://ssrn.com/abstract=1740585 or http://dx.doi.org/10.2139/ssrn.1740585

Wittig et al. (2009)

V.E. Wittig, E.A . Ainsworth, S. L. Naidu, D. F. Karnosky and S. P. Long (2009)

Quantifying the impact of current and future tropospheric ozone on tree biomass, growth, physiology and biochemistry: a quantitative meta-analysis

Global Change Biology, vol. 15, pp. 396–424

WMO (2012)

World Meteorological Organization (2012)

Emission Scenarios

Retrieved:http://www.wmo.int/pages/themes/climate/emission_scenarios.php

Wolf (2009)

B.O. Wolf (2009)

Catastrophic avian mortality during heat waves and drought: the role of climate change and extreme events

Presentation COS 101-7

Paper presented in The 94th ESA (Ecological Society of America) Annual Meeting held in August 2-7, 2009

World Bank (2012)

World Bank (2012)

Various resources: World DataBank

http://data.worldbank.org/indicator

World Bank (2005)

World Bank (2005)

Bolivia Urban Infrastructure for the Poor Project Concept Sheet submitted 2006

http://www.worldbank.org/projects/P083979/bolivia-urban-infrastructure-project?lang=en

World Bank (2010)

World Bank (2010)

World Development Report 2010: Climate and Development.

Washington D.C., US: The International Bank for Reconstruction and Development/ The World Bank

http://go.worldbank.org/ZXULQ9SCCO

World Economic Forum (2011)

World Economic Forum (2011)

The Global Economic Burden of Non-communicable Diseases

A report by the World Economic Forum and the Harvard School of Public Health

Geneva: World Economic Forum

World Energy Council (2010)

World Energy Council (2010)

2010 Survey of Energy Resources

London, United Kingdom: World Energy Council

World Population Prospects (2011)

World Population Prospects (2011)

Various resources

Population Division, UN-DESA

http://esa.un.org/unpd/wpp/unpp/panel_population.htm

World Resources Institute Website(2012)

World Resources Institute Website

Reefs at Risk base GIS data

Retrieved: http://www.wri.org/publication/content/7911

WRI (2009)

World Resources Institute (2009)

World Greenhouse Gas Emissions: 2005

World Resources Institute

Retrieved: http://www.wri.org/chart/world-greenhouse-gas-emissions-2005

WTTC Website (2012)

World Travel and Tourism Council Website

Economic Data Search Tool

Retrieved : http://www.wttc.org/research/economic-data-search-tool/

WWAP (2009)

World Water Assessment Programme (2009)

The United Nations World Water Development Report 3: Water in a Changing World. Paris: UNESCO, and London: Earthscan.

WWF (2012)

WWF International (2012)

Living Planet Report 2012: Biodiversity, biocapacity and better choices

WWF, Zoological Society of London, Global Footprint Network and Global Footprint Network

Wu et al. (2010)

Temporary acceleration of the hydrological cycle in response to a CO2 rampdown

Peili Wu, Richard Wood, Jeff Ridley, and Jason Lowe

Geophysical Research Letters, vol. 37, L12705

Xu et al. (2010)

Jianfeng Xu, Ayman Eltaher, Paul Jukes (2010)

Warm Pipeline in Permafrost: A Sensitivity Study of the Major Thermal Properties

Paper presented in the ASME 2010 29th International Conference on Ocean, Offshore and Arctic Engineering (OMAE2010) June 6-11, 2010 , Shanghai, China

Paper no. OMAE2010-20495 pp. 793-799

Yang et al. (2005)

S. L. Yang , J. Zhang, J. Zhu , J. P. Smith, S. B. Dai, A. Gao and P. Li (2005)

Impact of dams on Yangtze River sediment supply to the sea and delta intertidal wetland response

Journal of Geophysical Research, vol. 110

Yamamoto et al. (2012)

T. Yamamoto, N. Hanasaki, K. Takahashi, Y. Hijioka (2012)

An Impact Assessment of Climate Change on Global Water Resources by Using a Water Scarcity Index Considering Seasonal Water Variability

Journal of Japan Society of Civil Engineers, Ser. B1 (Hydraulic Engineering), vol. 67, Iss. 4, pp. I-259- I-264

Yang and Zhu (2011)

Rang-Hong Yang and Ben-Zhen Zhu (2011)

Stability analysis of Qinghai-Tibet railway slope embankment in permafrost regions-

Rock and Soil Mechanics, vol. 7

Yardley et al. (2011)

Jane Yardley, Ronald J. Sigal and Glen P. Kenny (2011)

Heat health planning: The importance of social and community factors

Global Environmental Change, vol. 21, iss. 2, pp. 670-679

Yohe et al (2006)

G. Yohe, M. E. Schlesinger and N. G. Andronova (2006)

Reducing the risk of a collapse of the Atlantic thermohaline circulation

The Integrated Assessment Journal, Vol. 6, Iss. 1 Pp. 57–73

Zanobetti and Schwartz (2009)

Antonella Zanobetti and Joel Schwartz (2009)

The Effect of Fine and Coarse Particulate Air Pollution on Mortality: A National Analysis

Environmental Health Perspectives, vol. 117, no. 6 , pp. 897-903

NAVIGATOR

SEVERITY

Severity shows the scale of the overall or absolute global impact of a given indicator and the breadth of effects internationally. "Major" impacts might involve, for example, tens of billions of dollars of economic damage or over 100,000 deaths on average per year. Other indicators estimate much lower levels of damage or even positive net impacts, in which case the severity may be assessed as "Minimal".

SCALE (FROM MOST TO LEAST)

- Major
- Serious
- Select Concern
- Minimal

AFFECTED GROUPS

Affected Groups indicates the specific population segments or communities particularly affected or susceptible to the impacts of a given indicator. The groups may be socially, economically, geographically or otherwise defined depending on the impacts under examination.

- River basins
- Small islands
- Mountainous communities
- Arid forested zones
- Cities
- Subsistence farmers
- Humid tropical countries
- Outdoor occupations
- Middle income countries
- Pregnant women
- Elderly
- Farmers
- Indigenous groups
- Deforestation zones
- Heavily labouring workers
- Tropical countries
- Dryland communities
- Water-Intensive industries
- Arid regions
- Infants
- Small children/infants
- Children
- Cyclone belt countries
- Africa
- Arctic communities
- Low-elevation coastal communities
- Coastal cities
- Lower income communities
- Chronic disease sufferers
- Outdoor workers
- Fishermen
- Rural populations with poor energy access
- Remote communities
- Sahel meningitis belt
- Young adults
- Livelihoods derived from fishing
- Energy companies
- Beach resorts
- Low-elevation winter resorts
- Densely populated river ways
- Women
- Oil sand host communities
- Coastal communities
- Tropical forest communities/zones
- Newly-industrialized countries
- Transition economies
- Industrialized countries
- Lower-income groups
- Coal miners
- Vehicle drivers
- Coal and gas power plant workers
- Fair-skinned
- Developed countries
- China
- Subsistence fisherfolk
- SIDSs

CONFIDENCE

Confidence shows the level of confidence that the research team attributes to the indicator, based on a multi-point assessment. Judgements are made in relation to the set of indicators that make up the Monitor assessment only; so, for example, the research team has more confidence in indicators labelled "Robust" than in indicators labelled "Speculative". Some experts may however consider the robust indicators to still possess inadequate confidence, or speculative indicators to exceed simple speculation. A 3-point scale is used to evaluate whether each criterion reviewed contributes or detracts from the overall level of confidence.

CONFIDENCE LEVEL SCALE (FROM MOST TO LEAST)

- Robust
- Indicative
- Speculative

CRITERIA PER INDICATOR

- Science – Level of certainty/agreement in science on the basic parameters involved
- Architecture – Strength of the underlying model, with preference for global/multi-country and higher resolution studies
- Climate (Only applies to the Climate section) – Level of certainty/agreement in science on the magnitude of change in key climate change variables, such as rainfall or temperature
- Data – Quality of the socio-economic data sets used, with preference for accurate, updated, comprehensive and comparable data

CONFIDENCE SPECULATIVE

SEVERITY
AFFECTED
INJUSTICE
PRIORITY
MDG EFFECT

MDG EFFECT

The Millennium Development Goals (MDGs) represent the international community's eight primary objectives for poverty reduction to be achieved by 2015. The MDG Effect indicates an impact for specific MDGs. One of the eight goals relates to an international partnership for development and is not relevant to the Monitor's impact analysis. Any of the other seven goals are highlighted whenever an indicator assesses a Climate or Carbon effect that is understood to specifically undermine one or another of these goals.
(For more information on the MDGs visit: www.un.org/millenniumgoals)

- End Poverty and Hunger
- Achieve Universal Primary Education
- Promote Gender Equality
- Reduce Child Mortality
- Improve Maternal Health
- Combat HIV/AIDS & Infectious Diseases
- Ensure Environmental Sustainability

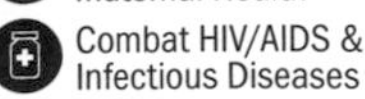

PRIORITY

(Only applies to Climate section)

Priority shows the amount of support a specific effect area has received through international climate funding. It denotes the level of priority that the effect or set of effects assessed by one Monitor indicator has, as reflected in international climate finance expenditures for adaptation. "High priority" denotes higher levels of funding from developed countries, targeting the issue in affected developing countries. "Low" or "no priority" is given to concerns for which financial support has been marginal or virtually absent. The OECD Creditor Reporting System sub-sector flows for 2010 have been used as the basis for the analysis (OECD CRS, 2012).

PRIORITY OF EFFECTS IN INTERNATIONAL CLIMATECHANGE FINANCE FLOWS
SCALE (FROM MOST TO LEAST)

- High priority
- Low priority
- Not a priority

INJUSTICE

(Only applies to Climate section)

Injustice shows how unjust or not a given effect is on the global scale. It denotes the level of injustice of a specific effect or set of effects as they are assessed by one of the Monitor's indicators. Injustice is highest when the affected countries have least responsibility for climate change and at its lowest when impacts are shared the most among countries with high responsibility. The four-point score is defined by statistical quartiles, so the level of injustice is also relative only to the Monitor's Climate section indicators themselves. Responsibility for climate change is based on total country GHG emissions from 1990-2005 (Mueller et al, 2007).

DISTRIBUTION OF CLIMATE CHANGE IMPACTS VERSUS RESPONSIBILITY FOR CLIMATE CHANGE

SCALE (FROM LEAST TO MOST)

Least unjust — Most unjust